Mid Term
Apr 6   TO P 83 Note

introduction to

MODERN NETWORK SYNTHESIS

Otto Brune   Wilhelm Cauer   Ronald Foster   Sidney Darlington

Ernst Guillemin   Hendrik Bode

introduction to

MODERN NETWORK SYNTHESIS

M. E. VAN VALKENBURG

Professor of Electrical Engineering
University of Illinois

NEW YORK · LONDON · SYDNEY

John Wiley & Sons, Inc.

Third Printing, October, 1964

Library of Congress Catalog Card Number: 60–10328

Printed in the United States of America

Preface

It is said that design is primarily the concern of the engineer just as analysis is primarily the concern of the scientist. Design has traditionally implied the use of handbooks, the know-how from experience, and the use of cut-and-try methods. It was not until after World War II that a scientific basis for design fully emerged, distinguished by the name *synthesis* and applied first to passive networks and later to automatic control systems and active networks. Synthesis has since become one of the important subjects in modern electrical engineering along with information theory, automatic control theory, and automatic computation, and no electrical engineering graduate is equipped to understand the literature or advanced practice without a knowledge of modern synthesis methods.

This book is written for use in a first course in network synthesis at the advanced undergraduate or beginning graduate level. The philosophy that has guided its preparation will be explained in terms of two characteristics of the field: (1) Network synthesis encompasses a spectrum of subjects ranging from the most abstract to the most practical. To some, network synthesis is strictly applied mathematics; to others, it is a means for solving day-by-day problems. (2) There are few subjects for which the literature is so vast and the number of methods so great.

With respect to the first point, I have tried to follow a middle path between rigor and completeness on one hand and applications to practical situations on the other. Because of the second point, it has been necessary to limit the number of subjects covered so that enough detail for understanding could be provided for each topic. In selecting the topics to be treated, I have been guided by the question, "What should a student learn in a course in network synthesis if he will never again be exposed to formal instruction in the subject?" Students who specialize in synthesis will be guided to advanced treatises by the footnotes and bibliography. It has been particularly gratifying in teaching from preliminary notes to find that the study of these topics has led some students to become skillful in the application of the subject to practical situations and others to make theoretical contributions to the field.

The reader of this book should have the usual undergraduate knowledge of network analysis and the Laplace transformation. Some of this assumed background is reviewed in the first two chapters. Other material of these chapters, network function definitions and frequency and magnitude scaling, for example, may be new to the reader and in this case should be mastered for later use.

The order in which the remaining topics appear is that found most successful in several experiments in teaching the subject from preliminary notes. Positive real functions are the foundation of network synthesis and are studied first. Elementary synthesis procedures are covered for the LC, RC and RL, and RLC cases. The related topics of approximation and the relationship of the parts of network functions help complete a study of one terminal-pair network synthesis by Chapter 9. It should be noted that the approximation methods of Chapter 9 are suited for "rough" approximation as in automatic control applications. Precision approximation procedures, often identified with telephone industry applications, are postponed until Chapter 13.

Chapter 10 introduces the subject of two terminal-pair synthesis with the Cauer ladder development. This chapter and the four that follow describe the major modern methods of two terminal-pair synthesis and also enumerate the important properties of the network functions that describe these networks. The last chapter of the book covers synthesis from image parameters. Although this topic is often excluded from "modern" methods, I strongly recommend that it be studied and understood in relationship to the other competitive methods of Chapters 14 and 15.

Depending upon the approach followed by the instructor, the book may be used for a one-semester course at the graduate level or may be expanded into a two-semester treatment by supplementing with collateral reading assignments. At the undergraduate level, our typical one-semester coverage has included Chapters 1, 2, 3, 5, 6, 9, 10, 13, and 16, and parts of 4, 8, 14, and 15.

Authors of books on network synthesis owe a special indebtedness to Professor Ernst A. Guillemin of Massachusetts Institute of Technology, which I acknowledge with pleasure. One of Professor Guillemin's contributions to this field has been to devise explanations for the subjects of synthesis in a form especially suited for student understanding and textbook presentation. He has also endowed a generation of teachers and engineers with an enthusiasm for his subject. I am personally indebted to one of his former students, Professor D. F. Tuttle, Jr., of Stanford University, who was my teacher.

I must also express my thanks to a number of associates at the University of Illinois who have assisted in many ways. These include Professors S. L. Hakimi, John Warfield, Nelson Wax, Richard Pantell, and especially Professor J. B. Cruz, Jr., who made numerous constructive criticisms for the improvement of the presentation resulting from his teaching of the course at the undergraduate level. Former students who have helped mold this work include Drs. Wan Hee Kim, Wataru Mayeda, Franklin F. Kuo, Roland E. Thomas, Basil R. Myers, Gene Leichner, K. S. Fu, Ray Basham, and Christopher Pottle. Don L. Epley and James R. Young assisted with the proofreading. Finally, I express my special thanks to my wife Evelyn for typing the manuscript and for her patience and encouragement during the writing of the book.

M. E. VAN VALKENBURG

Urbana, Ill.
February, 1960

Contents

Introduction

. . . . *1*

1.1   Identification of the network synthesis problem

Two important topics within the domain of electric network theory
are *network analysis* and *network synthesis*.   We assume that the reader
is familiar with the elementary methods of network analysis.   How
does network synthesis differ from network analysis?   To answer this
question will require definitions using words that invoke an immediate
recognition on the part of the reader.   Three such words which are
used extensively in describing the behavior of electric networks are
the *network*, the *excitation*, and the *response*.   An example of the identification of the network, excitation, and response is given in Fig. 1-1.

The word *network* is used to describe a collection of *elements* connected or coupled together.   The three passive elements are the
resistor, the capacitor, and the inductor (including the transformer).
These elements are idealized elements in that they are assumed to be
lumped, linear, finite, passive, and *bilateral* (sometimes abbreviated
LLFPB networks) and obey well-recognized laws.   The word *excitation*
is used to describe a source of electrical energy to be connected to the
network.   Two energy source idealizations (or active elements) we
shall deal with are the *constant-voltage source* and the *constant-current
source*.   Several other terms are used interchangeably with excitation,
such as driving force, applied voltage, and current source.   The
response of a network can be a particular current, a charge, a voltage
across some element or combination of elements, the energy dissipated
in a resistor, a ratio of voltage magnitudes for sinusoidal excitation,
etc.   Two *forms* of response of importance are the *time* response or
time-domain response (meaning the variation of some response with
time) and the *sinusoidal frequency* response or *frequency-domain*
response.

1

These words we have just used to describe electric networks have counterparts in practically all areas of scientific study. A wide variety of physical and biological phenomena may be described in terms of an action called a *stimulus* and a resultant reaction called a *response*. When a stimulus is applied to an organism, the response may be physical movement, chemical change, or both. The stimulus of an electric current in the leg of a frog causes muscular movement—a twitch—as discovered in Galvani's classic experiment in 1792. Ultraviolet light causes certain minerals to become fluorescent. In each example, we recognize the pattern of a stimulus (or excitation) and a corresponding response.

Having briefly reviewed definitions, let us now turn to an answer to our question about synthesis and analysis. If any two of the three quantities—the network, the excitation, and the response—are given,

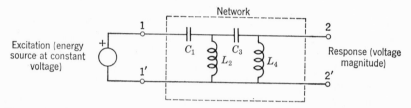

Fig. 1-1. An example of the identification of the network, excitation, and response.

the third may be found for linear networks. If the network and the excitation are given and the response is to be determined, the problem is defined as *analysis*. When the excitation and the response are given and it is required to determine a network, the problem is defined as *synthesis*. The third possibility, given the network and the response and required to find the excitation, has no generally accepted name and is not common. In some ways, analysis and synthesis are opposites. The word analysis comes from the Greek *lysis*, a loosening, and *ana*, up; hence a loosening up of a complex. Synthesis, on the other hand, means the building up of a complex from parts or elements. In network synthesis, we are concerned with the "building up" or design of networks to meet prescribed excitation-response characteristics.

There is another important difference between analysis and synthesis. In analysis there is a unique solution although it may be difficult to find. In synthesis, however, solutions are not unique and there may exist no solution at all. If there is any solution to a given problem, there are an indefinite number of other solutions from which a choice may be made (a general characteristic of engineering design).

How is the synthesis of a network accomplished? An example will point out typical steps and introduce some of the important features of synthesis procedures.* A certain generator may be represented with good accuracy as a constant-voltage source, as shown in Fig. 1-2. A network is to be designed to couple this source to the input of a vacuum-tube amplifier. For a sinusoidal input, it is required that the magnitude of the ratio of output to input voltage decrease linearly with frequency, as shown in Fig. 1-3(a). For the model we have identified, the function $|G_{12}(j\omega)| = |V_2(j\omega)/V_1(j\omega)|$ is an appropriate specification. What combination of elements for the network of Fig. 1-2 will give the prescribed performance? The selection of the kinds of elements, their connections, and their numerical values constitutes the solution to the synthesis problem.

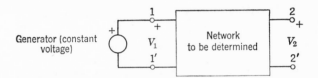

Fig. 1-2. A network of this general form is to be found to meet given excitation-response specifications.

As the specifications now stand, the answer to the synthesis problem is simple. With a finite number of elements, the characteristics of Fig. 1-3(a) *cannot* be realized at all. Functions having a prescribed variation over a band of frequencies and zero value for all other frequencies cannot be represented by a rational function of the form of a quotient of polynomials.† Our requirements must be altered in some manner to circumvent this limitation.

The first step then involves the changing of the requirements to include a permissible *tolerance*. We ask these questions: Do we really require the absolutely linear characteristic specified? Can we relax this requirement over part of the frequency range? The answers to such questions involve judgment. Someone must decide how closely the actual results attained must approximate the initial specification; someone must decide on allowable tolerance. The shaded area of Fig. 1-3(b) represents a compromise. The tolerance allowed from

---

* This example follows closely a description given by D. F. Tuttle, Jr., in "A problem in synthesis," *IRE Trans.*, **CT-2**, 6–18 (1953).

† An alternative explanation may be given in terms of the Payley-Weiner criterion; see, for example, G. E. Valley and H. Wallman, *Vacuum Tube Amplifiers*, McGraw-Hill Book Co., New York, 1948, p. 723.

ω_a to ω_b is small. Outside this frequency range greater deviation is permitted.

The next step is the determination of an equation for the curve shown in Fig. 1-3(c). We will show in a later chapter that the magnitude squared of the voltage ratio must be the quotient of rational and

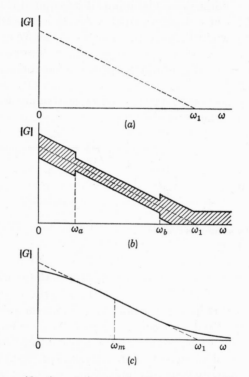

Fig. 1-3. The specifications to be met by the network of Fig. 1-2 are shown in (a). In (b) is shown the allowed tolerance; in (c) a realizable response function within the tolerances of (b).

even polynomials in ω. Such a quotient of polynomials is

$$|G(\omega)|^2 = \frac{a_0\omega^6 + a_2\omega^4 + a_4\omega^2 + a_6}{b_0\omega^6 + b_2\omega^4 + b_4\omega^2 + b_6} \tag{1.1}$$

There are any number of other polynomial ratios of lower or higher degrees that may be used. In general, the higher the degree of the assumed polynomials, the better the required curve can be approximated. However, every a and b coefficient in Eq. 1.1 is determined by the solution of a set of simultaneous linear equations, as many simultaneous equations as there are unknown coefficients. The limit of the number of simultaneous equations that can be conveniently solved limits the degree of the polynomials in equations like Eq. 1.1.

The most direct approach to the formation of the simultaneous algebraic equations is to select as many points as are needed from the curve of Fig. 1-3(c) and force the curve to pass through these points. For a somewhat more sophisticated approach, we can match the required slope at the frequency ω_m midway between ω_a and ω_b and require that other higher derivatives be zero at this frequency. In general, the two methods will result in different *approximations* to the required curve.

We will show later that not all functions we might find by the approximation methods just described correspond to networks with passive elements. A comparison of the approximation function with a list of requirements or necessary and sufficient conditions is known as *testing*.

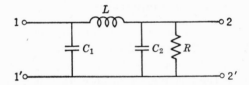

Fig. 1-4. The form of a network realization having the response of Fig. 1-3(c).

The last step is realization. We must find a network having a voltage-ratio response like Eq. 1.1. There are a number of methods by which this network may be found which we will study in later chapters. By one of these methods, we determine the network shown in Fig. 1-4 complete with element values in ohms, henrys, and farads (or microfarads). This network meets our specifications and is therefore a solution. There are many other possible solutions with different network structures and different element values. Have we found the best possible network? To answer this question, we frequently find other equivalent networks for comparison. We then select what appears to be the best solution based on criteria involving costs, convenience, engineering judgment. The selection of one solution from a number of alternatives is an important part of engineering which manifests itself much more clearly in synthesis than analysis.

While there exist an interesting variety of approaches to the solution of the synthesis problem, the steps will frequently follow those just outlined. These steps are: (1) determination of a suitable model to represent the system and the setting of specifications, (2) decisions on allowable tolerances from the specifications, (3) approximation, (4) testing, (5) realization as physical networks, and (6) a final choice from a number of alternatives.

Network synthesis had its beginnings in 1917 with the discovery of the electric filter by George Campbell in America and by Karl Wagner in Germany.* Significant contributions followed in the years from 1924 to 1931 by Zobel, Foster, Cauer, Brune, and Bode, and in 1939 by Darlington. World War II seems to have been a turning point in interest in the subject. Before that time, progress was slow, as the dates just given testify, and applications were mostly in the telephone industry. Since 1945, network synthesis has found wide application in diverse fields like vacuum-tube and transistor circuits, information transmission systems, automatic control systems, etc. The study of the synthesis of networks has become prerequisite to the understanding of modern electrical engineering.

1.2   Network equilibrium equations

The preceding section provided an introduction to the subject of network synthesis. The remainder of this chapter is devoted to a review of topics to be used later. We begin by considering the Kirchhoff laws for the formulation of network equations.

In formulating equilibrium equations for LLFPB networks, the Kirchhoff voltage law gives a summation of terms of the following three kinds:

$$R\,i(t), \qquad L\frac{di(t)}{dt}, \qquad \text{and} \qquad \frac{1}{C}\int i(t)\,dt \qquad (1.2)$$

Similarly, the Kirchhoff current law gives a summation of terms of the forms:

$$G\,v(t), \qquad C\frac{dv(t)}{dt}, \qquad \text{and} \qquad \frac{1}{L}\int v(t)\,dt \qquad (1.3)$$

The Laplace transforms of these terms are found using the following identities:

$$\mathscr{L}\,i(t) = \int_0^\infty i(t)e^{-st}\,dt \equiv I(s) \qquad (1.4)$$

$$\mathscr{L}\,\frac{di(t)}{dt} = s\,I(s) - i(0+) \qquad (1.5)$$

---

* For a detailed account of the development of network theory, see R. L. Dietzold, "Network theory comes of age," *Elec. Eng.*, **67**, 895–899 (Sept. 1948).

and $\qquad \mathcal{L} \int i(t)\, dt = \dfrac{I(s)}{s} + \dfrac{1}{s} \int i(t)\, dt \Bigg|_{t=0^+}$ $\qquad\qquad$ (1.6)

In network synthesis, it is conventional to neglect initial condition terms. Specifications are often given in terms of the sinusoidal steady state for which network functions are independent of initial conditions, leading to this convention. Neglecting initial conditions, terms in expressions 1.2 have the following transforms:

$$R\,I(s), \qquad Ls\,I(s), \qquad \text{and} \qquad \frac{1}{Cs}\,I(s) \qquad (1.7)$$

Here the multipliers of the transform current are *impedance functions*. Similarly, for expressions 1.3, the transform terms are

$$G\,V(s), \qquad Cs\,V(s), \qquad \text{and} \qquad \frac{1}{Ls}\,V(s) \qquad (1.8)$$

and the multipliers of $V(s)$ are *admittance functions*. These equations for R, L, and C are summarized in Table 1-1.

TABLE 1-1

	R	L	C
Symbol	○—◟◞◟◞◟◞—○ R	○—◠◠◠—○ L	○—┤├—○ C
Relationship of $v(t)$ and $i(t)$, instantaneous voltage and current	$v = Ri$	$v = L\dfrac{di}{dt}$	$v = \dfrac{1}{C} \int i\, dt$
Transform equations, initial conditions set equal to zero	$V = RI$	$V = LsI$	$V = \dfrac{1}{Cs}\,I$
Impedance, $Z(s)$	R	Ls	$\dfrac{1}{Cs}$
Admittance, $Y(s)$	$G = \dfrac{1}{R}$	$\dfrac{1}{Ls}$	Cs

To illustrate the use of impedance functions in loop-basis analysis, consider the network of Fig. 1-5. If all currents and voltages in the network are zero before the voltage source is connected, then the equilibrium equations are:

$$\left(L_1 s + R_1 + \frac{1}{C_1 s}\right) I_1 - \left(\frac{1}{C_1 s}\right) I_2 - (R_1 + L_1 s) I_3 = V_1 \quad (1.9)$$

$$-\left(\frac{1}{C_1 s}\right) I_1 + \left(L_4 s + R_2 + R_4 + \frac{1}{C_1 s}\right) I_2$$

$$- (L_4 s + R_4) I_3 = 0 \quad (1.10)$$

$$-(R_1 + L_1 s) I_1 - (L_4 s + R_4) I_2$$

$$+ \left(L_1 s + L_4 s + R_1 + R_4 + \frac{1}{C_3 s}\right) I_3 = 0 \quad (1.11)$$

In these equations, the coefficients of the current transforms are either the impedance of a loop or the impedance common to two loops.

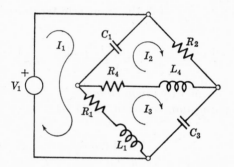

Fig. 1-5.   Network analyzed on the loop basis as an example.

Let these terms be distinguished as

$$\mathcal{Z}_{jj} = L_{jj} s + R_{jj} + \frac{1}{C_{jj} s} \quad (1.12)$$

for the coefficients for loop j, and

$$\mathcal{Z}_{jk} = L_{jk} s + R_{jk} + \frac{1}{C_{jk} s} \quad (1.13)$$

for the coefficients applying to loops j and k (the impedance of elements common to the two loops).   In terms of the example of Fig. 1-5, several terms may be identified like

$$L_{33} = L_1 + L_4, \qquad R_{23} = -R_4, \qquad C_{12} = -C_1, \; \cdots \quad (1.14)$$

Observe that the $\mathcal{Z}$ coefficients written in Eqs. 1.12 and 1.13 describe the general RLC network, or with one of the coefficients set equal to zero they describe LC, RC, or RL networks (to be considered in Chapters 5 and 6).

Consider a general network consisting of l loops. Let I_1, I_2, $\cdots$, I_l be the transforms of the l loop currents and V_1, V_2, $\cdots$, V_l be the sums of the transforms of the driving voltage in each of the loops. The application of Kirchhoff's voltage law to this network results in l simultaneous equations

$$
\begin{aligned}
Z_{11}I_1 + Z_{12}I_2 + \cdots + Z_{1l}I_l &= V_1 \\
Z_{21}I_1 + Z_{22}I_2 + \cdots + Z_{2l}I_l &= V_2 \\
\cdots\cdots\cdots\cdots\cdots\cdots\cdots\cdots\cdots \\
Z_{l1}I_1 + Z_{l2}I_2 + \cdots + Z_{ll}I_l &= V_l
\end{aligned}
\tag{1.15}
$$

where Z_{jj} is the self-impedance of loop j and Z_{jk} is the impedance common to loops j and k, j and k being any numbers from 1 to l. The sign of Z_{jk} is positive when I_j and I_k have the same reference direction but otherwise negative. These equations may be solved for the currents by the use of determinants. We define the determinant

$$
\Delta =
\begin{vmatrix}
Z_{11} & Z_{12} & Z_{13} & \cdots & Z_{1l} \\
Z_{21} & Z_{22} & Z_{23} & \cdots & Z_{2l} \\
\cdots & \cdots & \cdots & \cdots & \cdots \\
Z_{l1} & Z_{l2} & Z_{l3} & \cdots & Z_{ll}
\end{vmatrix}
\tag{1.16}
$$

to be the loop-basis system determinant. The minor M_{jk} is formed from the determinant Δ by removing the j row and the k column, and Δ_{jk} is the corresponding cofactor which is $(-1)^{j+k}M_{jk}$. The solution for the current I_1 in Eqs. 1.15 is given by Cramer's rule

$$
I_1 = \frac{M_{11}}{\Delta} V_1 - \frac{M_{21}}{\Delta} V_2 + \frac{M_{31}}{\Delta} V_3 - \cdots \pm \frac{M_{l1}}{\Delta} V_l \tag{1.17}
$$

or, in terms of the corresponding cofactors,

$$
I_1 = \frac{\Delta_{11}}{\Delta} V_1 + \frac{\Delta_{21}}{\Delta} V_2 + \frac{\Delta_{31}}{\Delta} V_3 + \cdots + \frac{\Delta_{l1}}{\Delta} V_l \tag{1.18}
$$

Any other current, I_k, is found by the expansion

$$
I_k = \frac{\Delta_{1k}}{\Delta} V_1 + \frac{\Delta_{2k}}{\Delta} V_2 + \frac{\Delta_{3k}}{\Delta} V_3 + \cdots + \frac{\Delta_{lk}}{\Delta} V_l \tag{1.19}
$$

Node equations are formulated using Kirchhoff's current law. As an example, consider the network of Fig. 1-6. If all initial conditions are zero, and V_1, V_2, and V_3 are the transforms of the three node-to-datum voltages, application of the current law gives three equations:

$$\left(C_1 s + G_1 + \frac{1}{L_1 s}\right) V_1 - (C_1 s + G_1) V_2 - \left(\frac{1}{L_1 s}\right) V_3 = I_0$$

$$-(C_1 s + G_1) V_1 + [(C_1 + C_2 + C_3) s + G_1] V_2 - (C_2 s) V_3 = 0 \quad (1.20)$$

$$-\left(\frac{1}{L_1 s}\right) V_1 - (C_2 s) V_2 + \left(C_2 s + G_2 + \frac{1}{L_1 s} + \frac{1}{L_2 s}\right) V_3 = 0$$

The coefficients of the voltage transforms in these equations are either the self-admittance for a given node (the summation of all

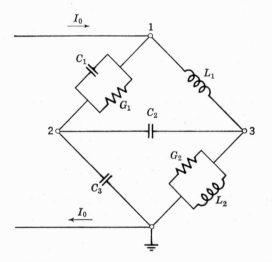

Fig. 1-6. Network driven by a current source, I_0, analyzed on the node basis.

admittance from node to datum with all other nodes grounded to the datum) or admittances common to two nodes. These admittance coefficients have the general form

$$\mathcal{Y}_{jk} = C_{jk} s + G_{jk} + \frac{1}{L_{jk} s} \quad (1.21)$$

as in Eqs. 1.12 and 1.13.

For a network of n nodes and a datum (or reference) node with current sources whose sums at each of the nodes have transforms $I_1, I_2, \cdots, I_n$, a set of equilibrium equations may be written on the node basis. Let the transforms of the voltages of the various nodes with respect to the datum node be $V_1, V_2, \cdots, V_n$. Then the application of Kirchhoff's current law to the network results in the following simultaneous equations

$$\mathcal{Y}_{11}V_1 + \mathcal{Y}_{12}V_2 + \mathcal{Y}_{13}V_3 + \cdots + \mathcal{Y}_{1n}V_n = I_1$$
$$\mathcal{Y}_{21}V_1 + \mathcal{Y}_{22}V_2 + \mathcal{Y}_{23}V_3 + \cdots + \mathcal{Y}_{2n}V_n = I_2$$
$$\cdots\cdots\cdots\cdots\cdots\cdots\cdots\cdots\cdots\cdots\cdots\cdots$$
$$\mathcal{Y}_{n1}V_1 + \mathcal{Y}_{n2}V_2 + \mathcal{Y}_{n3}V_3 + \cdots + \mathcal{Y}_{nn}V_n = I_n$$

(1.22)

where the admittance terms of the form $\mathcal{Y}_{jj}$ represent the admittance of all elements connected to node j with all other nodes grounded (to the datum), and the $\mathcal{Y}_{jk}$ terms represent the negative of admittance common to nodes j and k, j and k being any numbers from 1 to n. The node-basis equations may be solved for the voltages by means of determinants by defining the node-basis system determinant:

$$\Delta' = \begin{vmatrix} \mathcal{Y}_{11} & \mathcal{Y}_{12} & \mathcal{Y}_{13} & \cdots & \mathcal{Y}_{1n} \\ \mathcal{Y}_{22} & \mathcal{Y}_{22} & \mathcal{Y}_{23} & \cdots & \mathcal{Y}_{2n} \\ \cdots & \cdots & \cdots & \cdots & \cdots \\ \mathcal{Y}_{n1} & \mathcal{Y}_{n2} & \mathcal{Y}_{n3} & \cdots & \mathcal{Y}_{nn} \end{vmatrix}$$

(1.23)

As before, Δ_{jk}' is the cofactor formed from Δ'.

1.3   Network functions and the models they describe

Several of the most common ways networks are used in engineering applications are pictured in Fig. 1-7.   In (a) of this figure, a network is used as the load of a vacuum tube.   Networks for this application are selected because of the relationship of the current into the network and the voltage at its terminals.   The network of (b) is different:

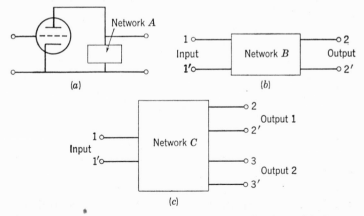

Fig. 1-7.   Various classes of engineering network applications with the networks identified by the number of terminal pairs.

input terminals and output terminals are identified. Such a network is called a *transmission* network; typical transmission networks are the filter, the equalizer, and the amplifier of the type shown in (*a*). The network of (*c*) is more complicated, representing such a system as a single-input coaxial transmission line or a microwave system from which several outputs are taken as identified in the figure. Comparing the three networks, we see that the feature that distinguishes one from another is the number of terminals, external connections to nodes of the network, that are identified. Now terminals are commonly associated together in pairs, two terminals being required to make an electrical connection. Two associated terminals constitute one *terminal pair*. Thus, the network of (*a*) is one terminal-pair

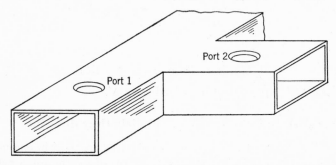

Fig. 1-8. Part of a microwave waveguide system showing typical locations of ports for input and output.

network, that of (*b*) is a two terminal-pair network, and a generalization of that of (*c*) is an *n* terminal-pair network.

It would be fortunate indeed if the terms we have introduced were universally accepted and so standardized. But there are synonyms, the most common of which are *pole* for terminal, and *port* for terminal pair. The word pole was first employed in the German network literature. Using it, we refer to networks as two poles, four poles, or possibly a three-pole network for the case of a common input and output terminal. The word port had its origin in microwave systems where, as pictured in Fig. 1-8, a port or round hole is cut into the waveguide to couple energy in or out of the system. Depending on the number of ports we identify, a system may be a one-port, a two-port, or an *n*-port one.

Network functions relate the transform of the excitation to the transform of the response. Network functions are computed by the following procedure:

(1) A system of equations of equilibrium formulated on either the loop or node basis are written in terms of the various voltages and currents in a network.

(2) The corresponding Laplace transform equations are determined with all initial conditions set equal to zero. (The setting of the initial conditions to zero is part of the definition of the network function.)

(3) The network function is found by algebraically solving for the ratio of the response transform to the excitation transform.

For one terminal-pair networks, only one voltage and one current are identified and so only one network function (and its reciprocal) can be defined. The driving-point impedance function or simply the

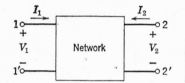

Fig. 1-9. A two terminal-pair network with input and output voltages and currents identified.

impedance of a network (so called because the terminals are connected to the driving force or energy source) is defined as

$$Z(s) = \frac{V(s)}{I(s)} \tag{1.24}$$

and is computed according to the procedure outlined above. The reciprocal of the impedance function is the *driving-point* admittance function or the admittance, $Y(s)$.

For the two terminal-pair network of Fig. 1-9, two currents and two voltages must be identified. A larger number of network functions are possible in this case: four different quantities taken two at a time gives six possible network functions (and the reciprocal of each of these six, of course). The pattern in which these four quantities, $V_1(s)$, $I_1(s)$, $V_2(s)$, and $I_2(s)$, are associated together is shown in Fig. 1-10, together with the symbol to be used to identify each of the network functions.*

For the two-port network of Fig. 1-9, the driving-point impedance at terminals 1-1' (port 1) is

$$Z_{11}(s) = \frac{V_1(s)}{I_1(s)} \tag{1.25}$$

* In later chapters, lower case letters, e.g., z_{11}, y_{22}, distinguish network functions describing models with open- or short-circuited terminations.

for a specified passive termination at terminals 2-2' (port 2). Similarly, the driving-point impedance at terminal pair 2-2' is

$$Z_{22}(s) = \frac{V_2(s)}{I_2(s)} \tag{1.26}$$

for a passive termination at 1-1'. The four other network functions are defined as transfer functions (or "trans-port" functions, if you like). Such functions are transfer in the sense that they relate a voltage or current at one terminal pair to the voltage or current at another terminal pair, for a given driving source and termination

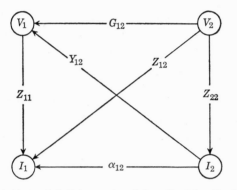

Fig. 1-10. The pattern of defining network functions for the two terminal-pair network in terms of V_1, I_1, V_2, and I_2. The arrow is directed toward the denominator quantity of the network function. Lower case z's are used to denote open-circuited termination networks, and lower case y's are for networks with short-circuited terminations.

condition. In writing these transfer functions, we will adopt the convention that the subscripts be in the order input, output—the direction of energy transfer. These functions are also defined as the ratio of a response transform to an excitation transform. Then the voltage-ratio transfer function is defined by the equation

$$\frac{V_2(s)}{V_1(s)} = G_{12}(s) \tag{1.27}$$

The current-ratio transfer function is

$$\frac{-I_2(s)}{I_1(s)} = \alpha_{12}(s) \tag{1.28}$$

The transfer impedance function is

$$\frac{V_2(s)}{I_1(s)} = Z_{12}(s) \qquad (1.29)$$

Finally, the transfer admittance function is

$$\frac{-I_2(s)}{V_1(s)} = Y_{12}(s) \qquad (1.30)$$

These relationships are summarized in Table 1-2.

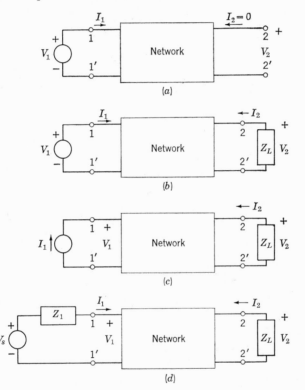

Fig. 1-11. Four models of networks which approximate physical systems. Classification is made according to the nature of the energy source, source impedance, and output termination.

These network functions are important in synthesis because they may be used to describe *models* which approximate actual systems. For the models shown in Fig. 1-11(a) and (b), the driving source has constant voltage and negligible internal impedance. For the model of (a), there is also negligible loading at the output terminals, as would be the case if the output voltage excited an electronic amplifier. In model (b), however, the output is loaded and the magnitude of current in the load is important. For the system of (a), a suitable specification function is G_{12}, while for (b) the function Y_{12} has more meaning. The model of Fig. 1-11(c) has as its physical counterpart a driving source such as a pentode which may be approximated as current source and a loaded output. For this model, the network function $Z_{12} = V_2/I_1$ or $\alpha_{12} = -I_2/I_1$ is a suitable specification in that it relates important voltage or current transforms of the model. A more general model is shown in (d) for which other network functions, say V_2/V_s, must be written. This network is known as a double-terminated network.

TABLE 1-2

Network	Ratio	Nature of Function	Symbol Used
	$\dfrac{V(s)}{I(s)}$	driving-point	$Z(s)$
	$\dfrac{I(s)}{V(s)}$	driving-point	$Y(s)$
	$\dfrac{V_1(s)}{I_1(s)}$	driving-point	$Z_{11}(s)$
	$\dfrac{V_2(s)}{I_2(s)}$	driving-point	$Z_{22}(s)$
	$\dfrac{V_2(s)}{I_1(s)}$	transfer	$Z_{12}(s)$
Terminals 1-1' are the driving terminals; 2-2' the load terminals	$\dfrac{-I_2(s)}{V_1(s)}$	transfer	$Y_{12}(s)$
	$\dfrac{V_2(s)}{V_1(s)}$	transfer	$G_{12}(s)$
	$\dfrac{-I_2(s)}{I_1(s)}$	transfer	$\alpha_{12}(s)$

1.4 Poles and zeros of network functions

The various voltage and current transforms in a given network are related to each other by network functions which are quotients of rational polynomials in the complex frequency variable s. This statement is illustrated by the network of Fig. 1-12. The differential equation describing the current in this network is

$$L\frac{di}{dt} + Ri + \frac{1}{C}\int i\,dt = v(t) \qquad (1.31)$$

Since $v(t) = e^{-2t}$, the transform is $V(s) = 1/(s + 2)$, and for the numerical values for R, L, and C shown in the figure, we have

$$\left(s + 2 + \frac{1}{s}\right)I(s) = \frac{1}{s + 2} \qquad (1.32)$$

or

$$I(s) = \frac{s}{(s^2 + 2s + 1)(s + 2)} \qquad (1.33)$$

A general transform function of this form of this equation may be written

$$\frac{p(s)}{q(s)} = \frac{a_0 s^n + a_1 s^{n-1} + \cdots + a_{n-1}s + a_n}{b_0 s^m + b_1 s^{m-1} + \cdots + b_{m-1}s + b_m} \qquad (1.34)$$

where the a and b coefficients are real constants, n is the degree of $p(s)$ if $a_0 \neq 0$, and m is the degree of $q(s)$ if $b_0 \neq 0$. If both polynomials are factored, then the network function $p(s)/q(s)$ may be written

$$\frac{p(s)}{q(s)} = \frac{a_0}{b_0}\frac{(s - z_1)(s - z_2)\cdots(s - z_n)}{(s - p_1)(s - p_2)\cdots(s - p_m)} \qquad (1.35)$$

where the roots of $p(s) = 0$, $z_1, z_2, \cdots, z_n$ are the *zeros* of the transform function, and the roots of $q(s) = 0$, $p_1, p_2, \cdots, p_m$ are the *poles* of the transform function. We make extensive use of plots of the poles and zeros of network functions and transform quantities in the complex frequency plane where the positions of the poles are designated by $\times$ and those of the zeros by $\bigcirc$.

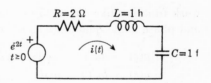

Fig. 1-12. The free and forced frequencies are computed for this network.

The geometrical interpretation of factors of the form $(s - z_1)$ is the basis of a method for visualizing the change in the value of a network function with changing frequency. Since both s and z_1 are complex in general, their difference is also complex which may be interpreted in terms of a magnitude and a phase. This is illustrated in Fig. 1-13 for $z_1 = -2 + j1$, and for an arbitrary value for s. To construct $s - z_1$ in the s plane, we carry out these steps: (1) From the given z_1, construct $-z_1$. (2) Add s and $-z_1$ to give $s - z_1$ as the phasor OA in Fig. 1-13(a). (3) Observe that the phasor OA has the same magnitude and phase as a phasor drawn *from z_1 to s*, as shown in Fig. 1-13(b). This equivalence of a rectangular and polar form for $s - z_1$ is expressed in the equation

$$s - z_1 = M_1 e^{j\theta_1} \qquad (1.36)$$

We may similarly represent pole factors, $s - p_1$, using a lower case m and the angle ϕ to distinguish the pole and zero factors. Then a net-

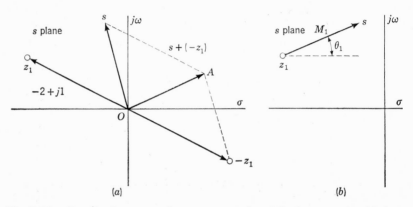

Fig. 1-13. Complex frequency plane representation of the factor $s - z_1$: (a) showing method of construction, and (b) identifying magnitude and phase.

work function like Eq. 1.35 may be expressed in terms of magnitude and phase angle quantities as follows:

$$\frac{p(s)}{q(s)} = \frac{a_0}{b_0} \frac{(s - z_1)(s - z_2) \cdots (s - z_n)}{(s - p_1)(s - p_2) \cdots (s - p_m)}$$

$$= \frac{a_0}{b_0} \frac{M_1 M_2 \cdots M_n}{m_1 m_2 \cdots m_m} e^{j(\theta_1 + \theta_2 + \cdots + \theta_n - \phi_1 - \phi_2 - \cdots - \phi_m)} \qquad (1.37)$$

From this relationship, the magnitude and phase angle of a function for a given value of s may be found. The phase angle is known as the *argument* of the function and is written as Arg $p(s)/q(s)$.

To illustrate, suppose that we are concerned with a network function of the form

$$\frac{p(s)}{q(s)} = K_1 \frac{s^3}{(s^2 + 2\alpha s + \alpha^2 + \omega_1{}^2)(s^2 + 2\alpha s + \alpha^2 + \omega_2{}^2)} \qquad (1.38)$$

having the pole and zero locations shown in Fig. 1-14. We wish to determine the variation of the magnitude of this function for $s = 0 + j\omega$ with increasing ω. Phasors are first drawn from each of

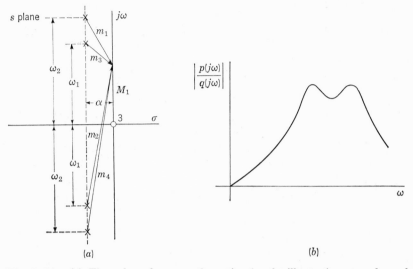

Fig. 1-14. (a) The pole and zero configuration for the illustrative example, and (b) the corresponding frequency-domain response found by the phasor construction shown in (a) and in Eq. 1.39.

the poles and zeros to a point on the imaginary axis. The computation of the magnitude function

$$\left| \frac{p(j\omega)}{q(j\omega)} \right| = \frac{K_1 M_1{}^3}{m_1 m_2 m_3 m_4} \tag{1.39}$$

for several values of ω, particularly in the region close to the poles, shows that this function is a double-humped resonance curve of the type encountered in the study of double-tuned circuits.

1.5   Complex frequency

Equations of the time-domain response of networks with loss contain terms of the form

$$2K_1 e^{-\sigma_1 t} \cos \omega_1 t \tag{1.40}$$

which are described as *damped sinusoids*. This term may be expanded in terms of exponentials as

$$2K_1 e^{-\sigma_1 t} \cos \omega_1 t = K_1 e^{-\sigma_1 t}(e^{-j\omega_1 t} + e^{j\omega_1 t}) = K_1[e^{-(\sigma_1 + j\omega_1)t}$$
$$+ e^{-(\sigma_1 - j\omega_1)t}] \quad (1.41)$$

The quantities

$$\sigma_1 \pm j\omega_1 = s_1 \text{ and } \bar{s}_1 \quad (1.42)$$

which appear in Eq. 1.41 are defined as *complex frequencies*, a phrase used by such early contributors to circuit theory as Heaviside (about 1900), Kennelly (1915), and Vannevar Bush (1917).* When $\sigma = 0$, and $s = j\omega$, Eq. 1.40 becomes $2K_1 \cos \omega_1 t$. In this equation, the quantity ω is seen to be the usual frequency† associated with sinusoidal generators and electronic oscillators. The frequency ω has come to be known as *real* frequency, perhaps real in the sense that it is identified with physical equipment. Now since every complex number is made up of a real and imaginary part, the only name left for σ is *imaginary* frequency. This term, misleading as it may be, was in general use before 1930. Another convention is to name ω *radian* frequency and σ *neper* frequency, thus avoiding the near-metaphysical names. But, however we identify the terms, the two components of frequency add together to give complex frequency. These frequency terms are readily interpreted in terms of their associated time-domain responses, as shown in Fig. 1-15.

The variable s, which we have named complex frequency, is identical with the Laplace transform variable. Transforms of voltages and currents, $V(s)$ and $I(s)$, are thus functions of the complex frequency variable just described.

For a one terminal-pair network transform, $I(s)$ is related to the excitation transform $V(s)$ by the network function $Y(s)$ in the equation,

$$I(s) = Y(s) V(s) \quad (1.43)$$

Since both $Y(s)$ and $V(s)$ are in general quotients of polynomials in s, we see that there are two distinct sources for the poles of the response function. And since the poles are the frequencies of the response modes, there are two kinds of frequencies in the response to a given

---

* See, for example, V. Bush, "The coupled circuit by the method of generalized angular velocities," *Proc. I.R.E.*, **5**, 363–382 (1917). Complex frequency is variously denoted by p and λ as well as s in the network theory literature.

† The use of ω as angular velocity in rotating mechanical systems is not to be confused with the use here of ω as frequency in radians per second. Another frequency unit is the cycle per second, denoted by the symbol f and related to ω by a 2π scale factor, $\omega = 2\pi f$.

excitation. Poles of $I(s)$ coming from $V(s)$ are distinguished as *forced* frequencies; poles from the network function $Y(s)$ are known as *free* or *natural* frequencies.

Frequency Classification	Form of Response
Real (or radian) $\sigma = 0,\ s = j\omega$	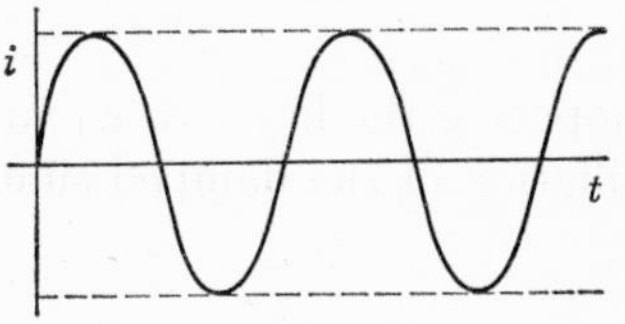
Imaginary (or neper) $\omega = 0,\ s = \sigma,\ \sigma < 0$ shown	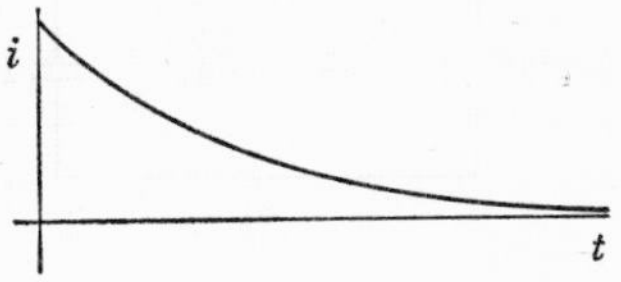
Complex $s = \sigma + j\omega,\ \sigma < 0$ shown	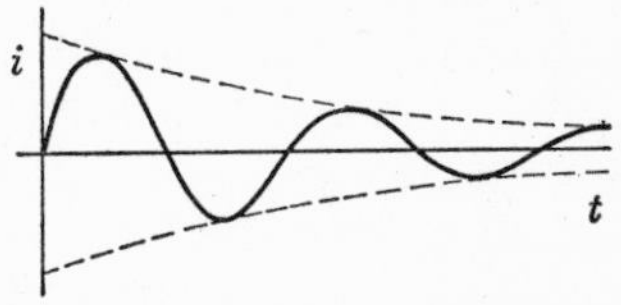

Fig. 1-15

Figure 1-16 shows two networks. For the element values and excitation forms chosen, the current response of both networks is identical and is

$$I(s) = \frac{s}{(s^2 + 1)(s + 1)} \tag{1.44}$$

if the energy sources are connected to unenergized systems at $t = 0$. For the network of Fig. 1-16(a), the poles at $\pm j1$ are free frequencies and the pole at -1 is a forced frequency. For the network of Fig. 1-16(b), however, the classifications are reversed and the pole at -1 is a free frequency and the poles at $\pm j1$ are forced frequencies.

The free-frequency response of any linear network having only nonmultiple poles may be written as a summation of response modes of the form

$$i_1(t) = 2K_1 e^{-\sigma_1 t} \cos \omega_1 t \tag{1.45}$$

where σ_1 and ω_1 may be zero as required.   The constant $2K_1$ is the magnitude of this particular response mode which is determined from a partial fraction expansion of the response transform.   The Laplace transform of Eq. 1.45 is

$$I_1(s) = \frac{2K_1(s + \sigma_1)}{(s + \sigma_1)^2 + \omega_1{}^2} \tag{1.46}$$

Comparing the last two equations, we see that ω_1 is the frequency of oscillation of the damped sinusoid and it is also the distance the pole

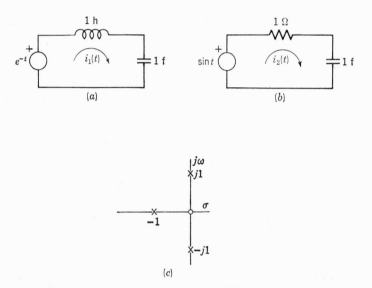

(a)   (b)

(c)

Fig. 1-16.   Two networks are shown in (a) and (b) which if energized at $t = 0$ have identical responses, $i_1 = i_2$ for $t \geq 0$.   (c) Poles and zeros of the common response.

is located from the real axis in the s plane.   Similarly, σ_1 is the damping factor or the reciprocal of the time constant of the envelope of the damped sinusoid, and is also the distance of the pole from the imaginary axis in the s plane.   Then poles with greater displacement from the real axis will correspond to modes with higher frequencies of oscillation.   And poles with greater displacement from the imaginary axis will be associated with response modes decaying more rapidly with time.*   These statements are illustrated in Fig. 1-17.   The total

* J. H. Mulligan, Jr., "The effect of pole and zero locations on the transient response of linear dynamic systems," *Proc. I.R.E.*, **37**, 516–529 (1949).

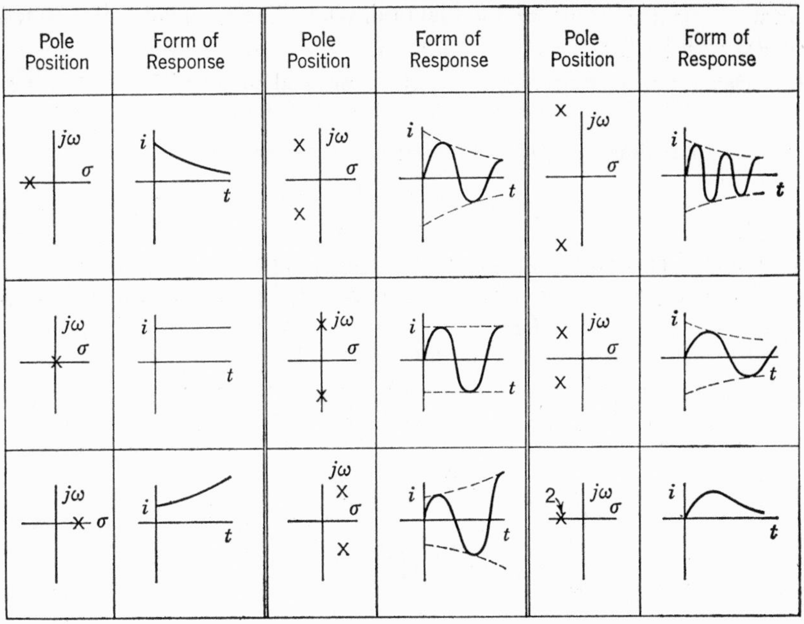

Pole Position	Form of Response	Pole Position	Form of Response	Pole Position	Form of Response

Fig. 1-17. An illustration of the various forms of the time-domain response as a function of the position of poles of network functions.

response is formed by the summation of the various response modes shown in the figure and other response forms associated with multiple poles (such as that shown in the lower right-hand corner of the figure).

FURTHER READING

For a more detailed study of the topics reviewed in this chapter, the reader is referred to the author's *Network Analysis*,* to Guillemin's *Introductory Circuit Theory*, to Skilling's *Electrical Engineering Circuits*, or to Brenner and Javid's *Analysis of Electric Circuits*.

PROBLEMS

1-1. Give one or more examples of devices excluded from consideration because of our assuming only LLFPB elements for the following reasons, taken

* Complete descriptions for the textbooks listed under Further Reading in this chapter and those to follow will be found in the Selected Bibliography at the end of the book.

one at a time: (*a*) the device is not lumped, (*b*) not linear, (*c*) not finite, (*d*) not passive, and (*e*) not bilateral.

1-2. Define a *rational* function. What is a rational polynomial? Give examples of functions that are not rational (preferably for several different reasons).

1-3. To approximate a given characteristic, the function

$$R(\omega) = \frac{1}{a_0\omega^4 + a_2\omega^2 + a_4}$$

is selected. This function is required to have the following values: at $\omega = 0$, $R = 1$; at $\omega = 1/\sqrt{2}$, $R = \frac{4}{3}$; at $\omega = 1$, $R = 1$. Determine the values for a_0, a_2, and a_4. Plot $R(\omega)$ for $0 \leq \omega \leq 2$; superimpose the desired $R(\omega)$ characteristic which has a value of unity for $0 \leq \omega \leq 1$ and zero for $\omega > 1$.

1-4. For the network shown in Fig. P1-4, write the loop-basis transform equations that describe the system when all initial conditions are zero.

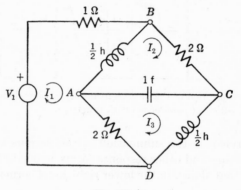

Fig. P1-4

1-5. In the network given in Fig. P1-5, three loop currents are identified. Using these currents, formulate a set of linear simultaneous transform equations on the loop basis, assuming all initial conditions to be zero.

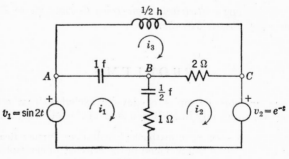

Fig. P1-5

1-6. Analyze the network of Fig. P1-4 on the node basis using node D as the datum.

1-7. Write the node-basis equations for the network of Fig. P1-5 using transform quantities and assuming initial conditions are zero. Use the smallest possible number of unknown transform voltages in your formulation.

1-8. In the network of Fig. P1-5, place a 1-ohm resistor in series with both voltage sources. Then repeat Prob. 1-7.

1-9. Using a ruler and protractor to determine the value of the quantities in Eq. 1.37, plot the magnitude and phase of the following network functions for $s = j\omega$, $0 \leq \omega \leq 5$:

(a) $\dfrac{1}{(s + 1)(s + 2)}$ (b) $\dfrac{s}{(s + 1)(s + 2)}$

(c) $5\dfrac{(s - 1)}{(s + 1)}$ (d) $5\dfrac{s^2 - s + 1}{s^2 + s + 1}$

1-10. Repeat Prob. 1-9 for the following network functions:

(a) $G_{12} = (s + \frac{17}{16})/(s + 1)$ and compare the magnitude and phase variation with $G_{12}' = 1$; this pole-zero combination is sometimes called a "dipole."

(b) $G_{12} = (s + 1)/(s + 20)$ and compare magnitude and phase variation with $G_{12}' = (s + 1)/20$. Comment on the effect of the pole at $s = -20$.

1-11. The pole-zero configurations of Fig. P1-11 are for voltage-ratio transfer functions, $G_{12} = V_2/V_1$. For each of the three plots, determine $|G_{12}(j\omega)|$ for several values of ω. Classify each of the response curves thus determined as "low-pass" or "band-pass" response.

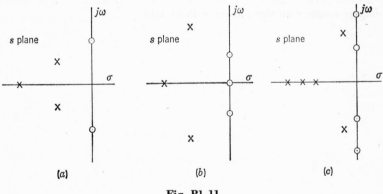

Fig. P1-11

1-12. Find and classify as either forced or free all frequencies in the network of Fig. P1-12.

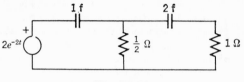

Fig. P1-12

1-13. In the network of Fig. P1-13, switch K is opened at $t = 0$, a steady state having previously been attained. Find the expression for the voltage of node a with respect to the datum, $v_a(t)$, for $t \geq 0$. Explain your result in terms of the free and forced frequencies in the system.

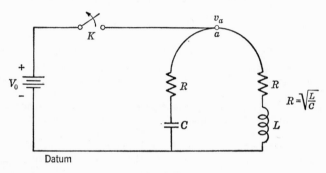

Fig. P1-13

1-14. Repeat Prob. 1-13 with the resistor in series with the capacitor replaced by a short circuit, such that C is in parallel with the RL series combination. Compare results with those found in Prob. 1-13.

Network Analysis

. . . . *2*

This chapter serves to review a number of topics in linear network analysis which are basic to synthesis methods to be studied in later chapters.

2.1 Network functions for series-parallel structures

Figure 2-1(a) shows a series connection of n one terminal-pair networks with each network identified in terms of its driving-point impedance. The total impedance of the combined networks is the sum of the impedances of the individual networks; thus

$$Z(s) = Z_1(s) + Z_2(s) + \cdots + Z_n(s) \qquad (2.1)$$

For the parallel connection of networks shown in Fig. 2-1(b), the total admittance is the sum of the admittances of the individual networks, and

$$Y(s) = Y_1(s) + Y_2(s) + \cdots + Y_n(s) \qquad (2.2)$$

For networks made up with subnetworks both in series and in parallel, the rules just given can be. applied successively to find the total impedance or admittance. For the network of Fig. 2-2, for example,

$$Z(s) = \frac{1}{Cs + 1/R_1} + Ls + R_2$$

$$= L \frac{s^2 + \left(\dfrac{R_2}{L} + \dfrac{1}{R_1 C}\right) s + \dfrac{R_1 + R_2}{R_1 L C}}{s + \dfrac{1}{R_1 C}} \qquad (2.3)$$

A very important form of series-parallel network, the *ladder* network, is represented in Fig. 2-3. If each block represents a single element, the network is identified as a *simple ladder*. In the general ladder, each of the series or parallel networks may be any one terminal-pair

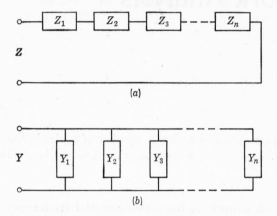

Fig. 2-1.   (a) Series connection and (b) parallel connection of subnetworks.

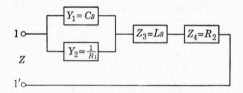

Fig. 2-2.   An example of a series-parallel network.

network of any complexity. The driving-point impedance for the network of the figure is, with no mutual inductance,

$$Z(s) = Z_1(s)$$
$$+ \cfrac{1}{Y_2(s) + \cfrac{1}{Z_3(s) + \cfrac{1}{Y_4(s) + \cfrac{1}{Z_5(s) + \cfrac{1}{Y_6(s) + \cfrac{1}{Z_7(s)} + \cdot}}}}} \qquad (2.4)$$

In other words, we find the driving-point impedance by starting at the "far" (nondriving-point) end of the network. The reciprocal of Z_7 is added to Y_6, the reciprocal of this sum is added to Z_5, and this procedure is repeated over and over until we have the driving-point impedance of the ladder network. The last equation is known as a *continued fraction*. We make extensive use of continued fractions, both in analysis and in synthesis. The driving-point impedance of a

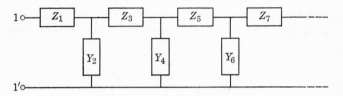

Fig. 2-3. Ladder network.

four-element ladder made up of inductors in the series arms and capacitors in the shunt arms is

$$Z(s) = L_1 s + \cfrac{1}{C_2 s + \cfrac{1}{L_3 s + \cfrac{1}{C_4 s}}} \qquad (2.5)$$

If $L_1 = L_3 = 1$ henry, and $C_2 = C_4 = 1$ farad, then

$$Z(s) = s + \cfrac{1}{s + \cfrac{1}{s + \cfrac{1}{s}}} = \frac{s^4 + 3s^2 + 1}{s^3 + 2s} \qquad (2.6)$$

In the computation of transfer functions for ladder networks, a method in which *unit output* is assumed and the corresponding input then found is used to advantage. In this method, the following steps are carried out.

(1) Unit output is assumed: $V_2 = 1$ volt or $I_2 = 1$ ampere.

(2) The input, V_1 or I_1, is then found by a step-by-step procedure involving the successive use of Kirchhoff's current law and Kirchhoff's voltage law.

(3) Because the elements of the network are linear, the input to give unit output is proportional to the input required to give any other

output:

$$\frac{\text{unit output}}{\text{input for unit output}} = \frac{\text{general output}}{\text{input to give general output}} \quad (2.7)$$

Having found V_1 or I_1 for a unit V_2 or I_2, we use this ratio to find V_2/V_1, I_2/I_1, V_2/I_1, I_2/V_1, etc.

We will illustrate these steps in terms of the ladder network of Fig. 2-4. Suppose that we wish to compute the voltage-ratio transfer function V_2/V_1 for this ladder network. We first assume that

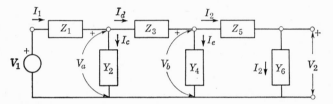

Fig. 2-4. Ladder network used to develop the unit output method for computing transfer functions.

$V_2 = 1$ volt and then write the following equations, starting at the output and working toward the input:

$$I_2 = Y_6 V_2 = Y_6 \text{ (since } V_2 = 1) \quad (2.8)$$

$$V_b = Z_5 I_2 + V_2 = Z_5 I_2 + 1 \quad (2.9)$$

$$I_e = Y_4 V_b \quad (2.10)$$

$$I_d = I_2 + I_e \quad (2.11)$$

$$V_a = Z_3 I_d + V_b \quad (2.12)$$

$$I_c = Y_2 V_a \quad (2.13)$$

$$I_1 = I_c + I_d \quad (2.14)$$

Finally $\qquad V_1 = Z_1 I_1 + V_a \qquad\qquad (2.15)$

Now we substitute the first of this set of equations into the second, the second into the third, etc., until we have an expression for V_1 in terms of only impedances and admittances. The reciprocal of this function multiplied by V_2 is the required voltage-ratio transfer function, V_2/V_1.

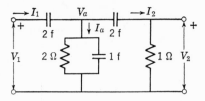

Fig. 2-5.   Network for Example 1.

Example 1.   Using the unit output method, we will compute the voltage-ratio function for the network shown in Fig. 2-5.   We first assume that $V_2 = 1$ volt.   Then

$$I_2 = Y_4 V_2 = 1 \text{ ampere} \tag{2.16}$$

$$V_a = Z_3 I_2 + V_2 = \frac{1}{2s} + 1 = \frac{2s + 1}{2s} \tag{2.17}$$

$$I_a = Y_2 V_a = (\tfrac{1}{2} + s)V_a = \frac{4s^2 + 4s + 1}{4s} \tag{2.18}$$

$$I_1 = I_a + I_2 = \frac{4s^2 + 4s + 1}{4s} + 1 = \frac{4s^2 + 8s + 1}{4s} \tag{2.19}$$

Finally $$V_1 = Z_1 I_1 + V_a = \frac{12s^2 + 12s + 1}{8s^2} \tag{2.20}$$

This is the necessary input for the unit output.   Then in general,

$$\frac{V_2}{V_1} = \frac{2}{3} \frac{s^2}{s^2 + s + \frac{1}{12}} \tag{2.21}$$

2.2   Network functions for general structures

The series- and shunt-connected networks that make up a ladder network may be arbitrarily complicated so long as each one is a one terminal-pair network without mutual inductance coupling one sub-network to another.   The addition of another element or combination of elements between adjacent nodes in the ladder does not impair the classification of the network as a ladder.   However, if we add a network which *bridges* nodes of a ladder—i.e., if two nonadjacent nodes are connected together by a new network—then the network so created is not a ladder.   This point is illustrated in Fig. 2-6.   Connecting new elements or combinations of elements between adjacent nodes such as a to b, b to c, etc., does not destroy the ladder nature of the network.   But the bridging of nodes a to c, b to d, etc., does.   Another familiar

bridged-node network is the bridge network shown in Fig. 2-7. Here
the removal of any one subnetwork restores the series-parallel nature
of the network.

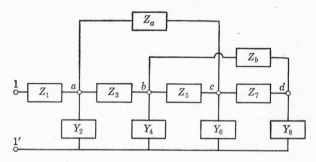

Fig. 2-6. A general network made from a ladder network with two nonadjacent
nodes bridged.

For the general nonseries-parallel network, the simple methods for
the computation of driving-point impedance described earlier in the

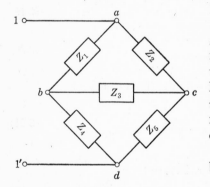

Fig. 2-7. A bridge network. If
the bridging network Z_3 is removed,
the network becomes a simple series-
parallel network.

preceding section no longer apply.
Resort must be made to a more
general approach. The determination of driving-point functions
then requires the writing of equilibrium equations on the *loop* (or
mesh) basis or the *node* basis by
means of Kirchhoff's laws, as was
done in Chapter 1.

Starting from the general loop-
basis system equations of Eqs.
1.15, we assume that there is a
single voltage source in loop 1, as
in Fig. 2-8(a), and that there are
no other voltage sources so that
$V_2 = V_3 = \cdots = V_l = 0$. For
this case, the transform current is, from Eq. 1.19,

$$I_1 = \frac{\Delta_{11}}{\Delta} V_1 \qquad (2.22)$$

and dividing by V_1 gives the driving-point admittance

$$Y(s) = \frac{I_1}{V_1} = \frac{\Delta_{11}}{\Delta} \qquad (2.23)$$

A similar result may be found by applying the node analysis method to the same network driven by a current source as shown in Fig. 2-8(b). We assume that there are no other current sources within the

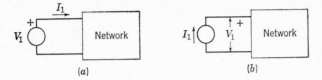

(a)   (b)

Fig. 2-8. One terminal-pair network used for deriving admittance and impedance in terms of determinants.

network so that $I_2 = I_3 = \cdots = I_n = 0$. Then the voltage transform V_1 is found from Eq. 1.24 in terms of node-basis determinants and cofactors as

$$V_1 = \frac{\Delta_{11}'}{\Delta'} I_1 \tag{2.24}$$

so that

$$\frac{V_1}{I_1} = Z = \frac{\Delta_{11}'}{\Delta'} \tag{2.25}$$

where Z is the driving-point impedance computed from the node-basis system determinant Δ'. This driving-point impedance is, of course, the reciprocal of the driving-point admittance found in Eq. 2.23:

$$\frac{\Delta}{\Delta_{11}} = \frac{\Delta_{11}'}{\Delta'} \quad \text{or} \quad \Delta\Delta' = \Delta_{11}\Delta_{11}' \tag{2.26}$$

Example 2. It is required to find the driving-point impedance of the bridge network shown in Fig. 2-9(a) with driving terminals 1-1' identified. Loop 1 is chosen to be the current in the driving terminal and node 1 is similarly selected. Node 1' is designated as the datum node, again required so that the voltage with respect to the datum node at 1 corresponds to the driving voltage. From the figure,

$$\Delta = \begin{vmatrix} 3 & -1 & -2 \\ -1 & 6 & -3 \\ -2 & -3 & 8 \end{vmatrix} = 73, \qquad \Delta_{11} = \begin{vmatrix} 6 & -3 \\ -3 & 8 \end{vmatrix} = 39 \tag{2.27}$$

$$\Delta' = \begin{vmatrix} \frac{3}{2} & -1 & -\frac{1}{2} \\ -1 & \frac{11}{6} & -\frac{1}{3} \\ -\frac{1}{2} & -\frac{1}{3} & \frac{7}{6} \end{vmatrix} = \frac{39}{36}, \qquad \Delta_{11}' = \begin{vmatrix} \frac{11}{6} & -\frac{1}{3} \\ -\frac{1}{3} & \frac{7}{6} \end{vmatrix} = \frac{73}{36} \tag{2.28}$$

Then

$$Z = \frac{\Delta}{\Delta_{11}} = \frac{\Delta_{11}'}{\Delta'} = \frac{73}{39} \text{ ohms} \tag{2.29}$$

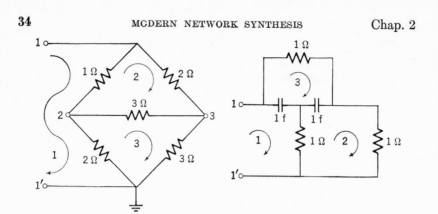

Fig. 2-9. (a) Bridge network for Example 2 with loops and nodes identified. (b) Ladder with bridged nodes of Example 3.

Example 3. When the network is other than purely resistive, the driving-point impedance or admittance will be a quotient of polynomials in s. The driving-point admittance, $Y(s)$, for the network of Fig. 2-9(b) is found by selecting loop 1 to include a voltage source at terminals 1-1'. The loop-basis system determinant is seen to be

$$\Delta = \begin{vmatrix} 1 + 1/s & -1 & -1/s \\ -1 & 2 + 1/s & -1/s \\ -1/s & -1/s & 1 + 2/s \end{vmatrix} \tag{2.30}$$

From this determinant and from Δ_{11} we find that

$$Y(s) = \frac{\Delta_{11}}{\Delta} = \frac{2s^2 + 5s + 1}{s^2 + 5s + 2} \tag{2.31}$$

The same approach may be used to compute transfer functions if other voltages or currents are identified. For example, if we break into a one terminal-pair network and find a branch carrying loop current I_j, as shown in Fig. 2-10(a), then this current is found from the equation

$$I_j = \frac{\Delta_{1j}}{\Delta} V_1 \tag{2.32}$$

so that

$$\frac{I_j}{V_1} = Y_{1j} = \frac{\Delta_{1j}}{\Delta} \tag{2.33}$$

where Y_{1j} is a transfer admittance function relating current I_j to V_1. If the loop carrying I_j is taken to be the output terminal with $j = 2$, then $Y_{12} = \Delta_{12}/\Delta$.

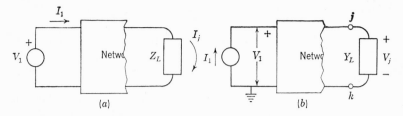

Fig. 2-10. Networks with (a) single internal loop exposed, and (b) two internal nodes exposed.

An entry into the network of Fig. 2-10(b) has identified nodes j and k and the node-to-node transform voltage V_j. This voltage is, from Eq. 1.24,

$$V_j = \frac{\Delta_{1j}' - \Delta_{1k}'}{\Delta'} I_1 \qquad (2.34)$$

where $\Delta_{1j}' I_1 / \Delta'$ is the voltage of node j with respect to the same reference. When node k is connected directly to the reference (grounded), an important practical case, then Eq. 2.34 simplifies to

$$\frac{V_j}{I_1} = Z_{1j} = \frac{\Delta_{1j}'}{\Delta'} \qquad (2.35)$$

where Z_{1j} is the transfer impedance relating V_j to I_1. Note that in general $Z_{1j} \neq 1/Y_{1j}$.

Example 4. For the network shown in Fig. 2-11, we see that

$$\Delta = \begin{vmatrix} 1/s & -1/s \\ -1/s & 2/s + 2s \end{vmatrix} = \frac{2s^2 + 1}{s^2}, \qquad \Delta_{12} = 1/s \qquad (2.36)$$

$$\Delta' = \begin{vmatrix} s + 1/2s & -1/2s \\ -1/2s & s + 1/2s \end{vmatrix} = s^2 + 1, \qquad \Delta_{12}' = 1/2s \qquad (2.37)$$

Making use of these determinants and cofactors, the following transfer functions are found:

$$Y_{12} = \frac{\Delta_{12}}{\Delta} = \frac{s}{2s^2 + 1}, \qquad Z_{12} = \frac{\frac{1}{2}}{s(s^2 + 1)} \qquad (2.38)$$

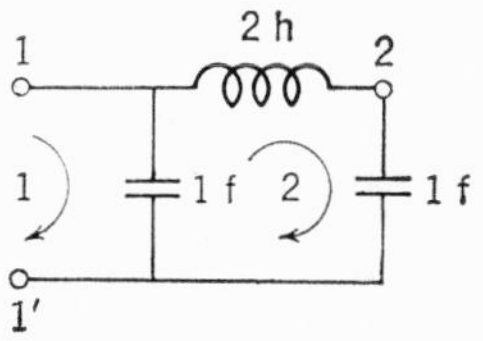

Fig. 2-11. Network for Example 4.

2.3   The open-circuit impedance and short-circuit admittance functions

A special class of impedance and admittance functions find wide use in network synthesis: the *open-circuit impedance* and *short-circuit admittance* functions. The definitions of these functions have their origin in a specialization of Eqs. 1.19 and 1.24. In the first of these, we identify voltage transforms V_1 and V_2 and in terms of these determine I_1 and I_2. Then

$$I_1 = \frac{\Delta_{11}}{\Delta} V_1 + \frac{\Delta_{21}}{\Delta} V_2 \qquad (2.39)$$

and

$$I_2 = \frac{\Delta_{12}}{\Delta} V_1 + \frac{\Delta_{22}}{\Delta} V_2 \qquad (2.40)$$

where, as before, Δ is the loop-basis system determinant and Δ_{11}, Δ_{12}, Δ_{21}, and Δ_{22} are cofactors. We next define each of the cofactor to Δ ratios to be admittance functions, since they are dimensionally admittance, by the pattern

$$y_{jk} = \frac{\Delta_{kj}}{\Delta} \qquad (2.41)$$

giving

$$I_1 = y_{11}V_1 + y_{12}V_2 \qquad (2.42)$$

and

$$I_2 = y_{21}V_1 + y_{22}V_2 \qquad (2.43)$$

From the last two equations, we see that the y functions may be defined in terms of voltage and current transforms by the following equations:

$$y_{11} = \left.\frac{I_1}{V_1}\right|_{V_2=0} \qquad (2.44)$$

$$y_{21} = \left.\frac{I_2}{V_1}\right|_{V_2=0} \qquad (2.45)$$

$$y_{12} = \left.\frac{I_1}{V_2}\right|_{V_1=0} \qquad (2.46)$$

and

$$y_{22} = \left.\frac{I_2}{V_2}\right|_{V_1=0} \qquad (2.47)$$

These four equations specify evaluation with either V_1 or V_2 equal to zero, implying that the terminals associated with these voltages be *short-circuited.* An arrangement by which these functions might be computed (or measured) is that shown in Fig. 2-12(a) and (b). In each case, computations (or measurements) are made under short-circuit conditions. For this reason, these admittance functions are known as *short-circuit admittance functions.*

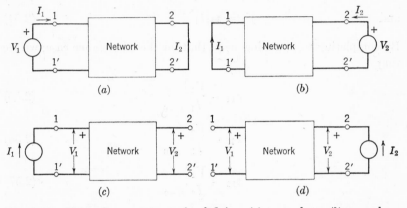

Fig. 2-12. Network arrangements for defining: (a) y_{11} and y_{21}, (b) y_{22} and y_{12}, (c) z_{11} and z_{21}, and (d) z_{22} and z_{12}.

The two networks of Fig. 2-12(a) and (b) may be used to arrive at another conclusion about these admittance functions. If we set V_1 equal to V_2 in the two networks, then by the *reciprocity theorem* I_1 will be equal to I_2. Then, it follows that

$$\frac{I_1}{V_2}\bigg|_{V_1=0} = \frac{I_2}{V_1}\bigg|_{V_2=0} \tag{2.48}$$

or
$$y_{12} = y_{21} \tag{2.49}$$

A similar analysis may be made starting from Eq. 1.24, which is the node-basis formulation of the network equations. Again identifying two voltages and two currents, we have for terminals $1'$ and $2'$ connected together

$$V_1 = \frac{\Delta_{11}'}{\Delta'} I_1 + \frac{\Delta_{21}'}{\Delta'} I_2 \tag{2.50}$$

and
$$V_2 = \frac{\Delta_{12}'}{\Delta'} I_1 + \frac{\Delta_{22}'}{\Delta'} I_2 \tag{2.51}$$

These quotients of a cofactor to a determinant are dimensionally impedance, and are defined as impedance functions by the pattern

$$z_{jk} = \frac{\Delta'_{kj}}{\Delta'} \tag{2.52}$$

Then

$$V_1 = z_{11}I_1 + z_{12}I_2 \tag{2.53}$$

and

$$V_2 = z_{21}I_1 + z_{22}I_2 \tag{2.54}$$

By completing steps analogous to that for the admittance case, we see that

$$z_{11} = \left. \frac{V_1}{I_1} \right|_{I_2=0} \tag{2.55}$$

$$z_{21} = \left. \frac{V_2}{I_1} \right|_{I_2=0} \tag{2.56}$$

$$z_{12} = \left. \frac{V_1}{I_2} \right|_{I_1=0} \tag{2.57}$$

and

$$z_{22} = \left. \frac{V_2}{I_2} \right|_{I_1=0} \tag{2.58}$$

In each case, the impedance function is defined with one of the currents set equal to zero, implying that they are to be computed (or

TABLE 2-1

Symbol	Name	Definition
y_{11}	short-circuit driving-point admittance	$\left. \dfrac{I_1}{V_1} \right\|_{V_2=0}$
y_{22}	short-circuit driving-point admittance	$\left. \dfrac{I_2}{V_2} \right\|_{V_1=0}$
y_{12} $(= y_{21})$	short-circuit transfer admittance	$\left. \dfrac{I_2}{V_1} \right\|_{V_2=0} = \left. \dfrac{I_1}{V_2} \right\|_{V_1=0}$
z_{11}	open-circuit driving-point impedance	$\left. \dfrac{V_1}{I_1} \right\|_{I_2=0}$
z_{22}	open-circuit driving-point impedance	$\left. \dfrac{V_2}{I_2} \right\|_{I_1=0}$
z_{12} $(= z_{21})$	open-circuit transfer impedance	$\left. \dfrac{V_2}{I_1} \right\|_{I_2=0} = \left. \dfrac{V_1}{I_2} \right\|_{I_1=0}$

measured) under open-circuit conditions.   Suitable conditions for this computation are shown in (c) and (d) of Fig. 2-12.   These functions are the *open-circuit impedance functions*.   Again the reciprocity theorem may be invoked to show that $z_{12} = z_{21}$.   The results of this discussion are summarized in Table 2-1.

The equations involving the y functions and those involving the z functions represent two different ways of relating two voltages to two currents for a given network.   It is evident that one set of functions may be expressed in terms of the other.   Solving Eqs. 2.42 and 2.43 for V_1 and V_2 gives

$$V_1 = \frac{y_{22}}{\Delta_y} I_1 + \frac{-y_{12}}{\Delta_y} I_2 \tag{2.59}$$

and

$$V_2 = \frac{-y_{21}}{\Delta_y} I_1 + \frac{y_{11}}{\Delta_y} I_2 \tag{2.60}$$

where

$$\Delta_y = y_{11} y_{22} - y_{12}{}^2 \tag{2.61}$$

Then

$$z_{11} = \frac{y_{22}}{\Delta_y}, \qquad z_{22} = \frac{y_{11}}{\Delta_y}$$

and

$$z_{12} = z_{21} = \frac{-y_{12}}{\Delta_y} = \frac{-y_{21}}{\Delta_y} \tag{2.62}$$

By the dual procedure, we find that

$$y_{11} = \frac{z_{22}}{\Delta_z}, \qquad y_{22} = \frac{z_{11}}{\Delta_z}$$

and

$$y_{12} = y_{21} = \frac{-z_{12}}{\Delta_z} = \frac{-z_{21}}{\Delta_z} \tag{2.63}$$

where

$$\Delta_z = z_{11} z_{22} - z_{12}{}^2 \tag{2.64}$$

Observe that Δ_z and Δ_y are related by the equation

$$\Delta_y \Delta_z = 1 \tag{2.65}$$

and also that

$$z_{11} y_{11} = z_{22} y_{22} \tag{2.66}$$

The various equations of equivalence between the y and z functions are summarized in Table 2-2.

TABLE 2-2

Admittance	Impedance	Determinants (Grounded Case)
y_{11}	$\dfrac{z_{22}}{\Delta_z}$	$\dfrac{\Delta_{11}}{\Delta}$
y_{22}	$\dfrac{z_{11}}{\Delta_z}$	$\dfrac{\Delta_{22}}{\Delta}$
y_{12}	$\dfrac{-z_{12}}{\Delta_z}$	$\dfrac{\Delta_{12}}{\Delta}$
$\dfrac{y_{22}}{\Delta_y}$	z_{11}	$\dfrac{\Delta_{11}'}{\Delta'}$
$\dfrac{y_{11}}{\Delta_y}$	z_{22}	$\dfrac{\Delta_{22}'}{\Delta'}$
$\dfrac{-y_{12}}{\Delta_y}$	z_{12}	$\dfrac{\Delta_{12}'}{\Delta'}$

Figure 2-13 shows a representation of a two terminal-pair network with the two currents and two voltages of the preceding discussion identified. It is conventional in network theory that both I_1 and I_2 are chosen with reference directions into the network and the positive reference terminal for each voltage is the upper one as shown. This convention has bearing on the sign of y_{12}, as will next be shown.

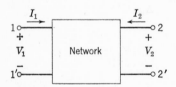

Fig. 2-13. Network representation showing the conventional current directions and voltage references for the general two terminal-pair network.

The impedance of the arms of the T network and the π network shown in Figs 2-14 and 2-15 are easily expressed in terms of the z and the y functions respectively. For the network of Fig. 2-14(a) using conventional references, we see that

$$z_{11} = Z_a + Z_c \tag{2.67}$$

$$z_{22} = Z_b + Z_c \tag{2.68}$$

and $$z_{12} = Z_c \tag{2.69}$$

The last equation is found by letting $I_2 = 1$ ampere and then computing V_1 with $I_1 = 0$. Then

$$V_1 = Z_c I_2 \qquad \text{or} \qquad z_{12} = Z_c \qquad (2.70)$$

Solving the three equations for Z_a, Z_b, and Z_c gives

$$Z_a = z_{11} - z_{12} \qquad (2.71)$$

$$Z_b = z_{22} - z_{12} \qquad (2.72)$$

and $$Z_c = z_{12} \qquad (2.73)$$

These expressions for the arms of the T network are shown in Fig. 2-14(b).

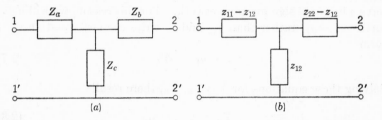

Fig. 2-14. T network expressed in terms of the open-circuit impedance functions.

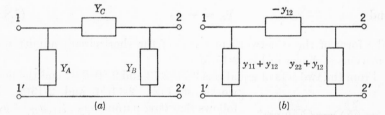

Fig. 2-15. π network expressed in terms of the short-circuit admittance functions.

The arms of the π network are most readily expressed in terms of the short-circuit admittance functions. For the network of Fig. 2-15(a), we find the driving-point admittances with appropriate terminal pairs short-circuited. Thus

$$y_{11} = Y_A + Y_C \qquad (2.74)$$

and $$y_{22} = Y_B + Y_C \qquad (2.75)$$

To determine y_{12}, we start from the defining equation

$$y_{12} = \frac{I_1}{V_2}\bigg|_{V_1=0} \qquad (2.76)$$

and let the output be $I_1 = 1$ ampere and $V_1 = 0$ (short circuit). Then

$$y_{12} = \frac{1}{V_2} \tag{2.77}$$

For the convention shown in Fig. 2-13, however, we see that the current reference direction and the voltage reference direction are not compatible and that y_{12} will have a negative sign. Thus

$$y_{12} = -Y_C \tag{2.78}$$

The reference direction convention we have adopted causes y_{12} to have a negative sign for any network. For this reason, we will henceforth use $-y_{12}$ rather than y_{12} and so write the last equation in the form

$$-y_{12} = Y_C \tag{2.79}$$

Solving these equations for Y_A, Y_B, Y_C, there results

$$Y_A = y_{11} + y_{12} \tag{2.80}$$

$$Y_B = y_{22} + y_{12} \tag{2.81}$$

and $\qquad\qquad Y_C = -y_{12} \tag{2.82}$

The form of the π network in terms of the short-circuit admittance functions is shown in Fig. 2-15(b).

From the two sets of equations 2.71–2.73 and 2.80–2.82 and the networks of Figs. 2-14(b) and 2-15(b), it follows that *three* parameters ($y_{11}, y_{22}, -y_{12}$ or z_{11}, z_{22}, z_{12}) are sufficient to completely describe a network for which an equivalent T or π network exists. For a one terminal-pair network, a single driving-point function (impedance or admittance) describes the network. But for the two terminal-pair network, two driving-point functions and one transfer function are required.

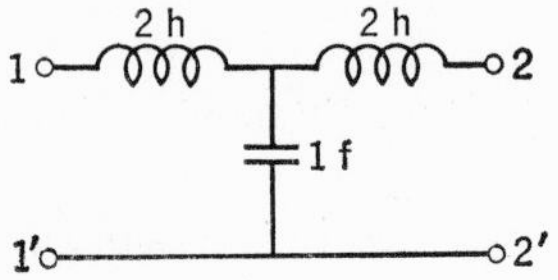

Fig. 2-16. Network for Example 5.

Example 5. For the network shown in Fig. 2-16, we see that

$$z_{11} = z_{22} = 2s + 1/s = \frac{2s^2 + 1}{s} \tag{2.83}$$

$$z_{12} = z_{21} = 1/s \tag{2.84}$$

$$y_{11} = y_{22} = \cfrac{1}{2s + \cfrac{1}{s + 1/2s}} = \frac{2s^2 + 1}{4s(s^2 + 1)} \qquad (2.85)$$

$$-y_{12} = -y_{21} = \frac{1}{4s(s^2 + 1)} \qquad (2.86)$$

From these results, the impedances of the arms of equivalent T and π networks may be found.

2.4   Transfer functions in terms of the y and z functions

In synthesis, specifications are often given in terms of such functions as G_{12}, Z_{12}, Y_{12}, or α_{12} as defined in Chapter 1. However, synthesis is usually accomplished in terms of the y or z functions, pointing to a need to express one set of functions in terms of the other. Figure 2-17

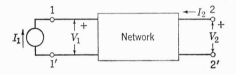

Fig. 2-17.   Network employed in deriving Eq. 2.88.

shows a network driven by a current source with open-circuit output terminals. This network is identical with that shown in Fig. 2-12(c) and is used to define z_{11} and z_{12}. The equations

$$\left.\frac{V_1}{I_1}\right|_{I_2=0} = z_{11} \quad \text{and} \quad \left.\frac{V_2}{I_1}\right|_{I_2=0} = z_{12} \qquad (2.87)$$

have a ratio which is the open-circuit voltage-ratio transfer function:

$$\left.\frac{V_2}{V_1}\right|_{I_2=0} = \left.G_{12}\right|_{I_2=0} = \frac{z_{12}}{z_{11}} \qquad (2.88)$$

This equation expresses G_{12} for open-circuit output terminals in terms of open-circuit impedance functions. An expression for the same G_{12} in terms of short-circuit admittance functions might be obtained by using the equalities in Table 2-2. Alternatively, we can derive this relationship by the application of Norton's theorem to the network shown in Fig. 2-18(a). The equivalent current source of Norton's theorem is found by short-circuiting the output terminals. By the definition of y_{12}, this current is

$$I_{2sc} = -y_{12}V_1 \qquad (2.89)$$

where the minus sign indicates that the current is opposite to the indicated positive direction. The Norton's theorem equivalent admittance is found by making V_1 zero. With terminals 1-1' short-circuited,

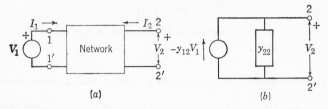

(a)   (b)

Fig. 2-18. (a) Network pertaining to Eq. 2.90, and (b) Norton's equivalent network.

the admittance at terminals 2-2' is y_{22}. The Norton's equivalent network is therefore that shown in Fig. 2-18(b). From this network, we see that the voltage V_2 is

$$V_2 = \frac{-y_{12}V_1}{y_{22}}$$

so that

$$\frac{V_2}{V_1} = -\frac{y_{12}}{y_{22}} \qquad (2.90)$$

The equation applies only to the case of open-circuited output terminals.

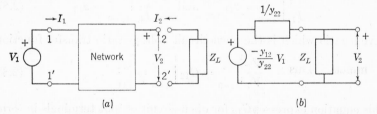

(a)   (b)

Fig. 2-19. (a) Network employed in deriving Eq. 2.93, and (b) Thévenin's equivalent network.

With a load connected to the output terminals, a new equation may be found by considering the network of Fig. 2-19(a). Analysis for this case will be in the terms of Thévenin's theorem. The Thévenin theorem equivalent voltage source is found by disconnecting the load Z_L and determining the open-circuit voltage at terminals 2-2'. With the load disconnected, the network is precisely that considered in Fig. 2-18(a). We have just determined this open-circuit output voltage,

Eq. 2.90, which is written in terms of V_1 as

$$V_{2oc} = \frac{-y_{12}}{y_{22}} V_1 \qquad (2.91)$$

The impedance at the open-circuited terminals 2-2' with $V_1 = 0$ (a short circuit) is $1/y_{22}$. The Thévenin's theorem equivalent network is therefore that shown in Fig. 2-19(b). From this network,

$$V_2 = Z_L \frac{-y_{12}/y_{22}}{1/y_{22} + Z_L} V_1 \qquad (2.92)$$

so that $\qquad \dfrac{V_2}{V_1} = \dfrac{-y_{12}/Y_L y_{22}}{1/y_{22} + 1/Y_L} = \dfrac{-y_{12}}{y_{22} + Y_L} = G_{12} \qquad (2.93)$

Observe that for $Y_L = 0$, corresponding to open-circuited output terminals, this equation reduces to that of Eq. 2.90.

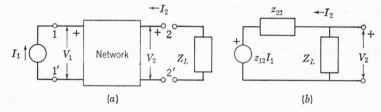

Fig. 2-20. (a) Network pertaining to Eq. 2.95, and (b) Thévenin's equivalent network.

In Fig. 2-20(a), the network first considered as Fig. 2-17 has been terminated in a load impedance Z_L. For this network, we will compute Z_{12} in terms of the open-circuit impedance functions, again making use of Thévenin's theorem. If the load is removed, the open-circuit output voltage is, from the definition of z_{12},

$$V_{2oc} = z_{12} I_1 \qquad (2.94)$$

The Thévenin's equivalent impedance at terminals 2-2' is found by replacing the current source by an open circuit. This input impedance is z_{22} by definition, and the Thévenin equivalent network is that shown in Fig. 2-20(b). From this network,

$$\frac{V_2}{I_1} = Z_{12} = \frac{z_{12} Z_L}{z_{22} + Z_L} \qquad (2.95)$$

From this equation, we can find the current-ratio transfer function by noting that for the network of Fig. 2-19(a), $V_2 = -Z_L I_2$ so that

$$\frac{-I_2}{I_1} = \alpha_{12} = \frac{z_{12}}{z_{22} + Z_L} \qquad (2.96)$$

The expression relating Y_{12} for the network of Fig. 2-19(a) may be found by noting that $I_2 = -Y_L V_2$ in Eq. 2.93 so that

$$\frac{I_2}{V_1} = -Y_{12} = \frac{-y_{12}Y_L}{y_{22} + Y_L} \tag{2.97}$$

Alternatively, this last equation may be derived by making use of the Norton's equivalent network of Fig. 2-21(b).

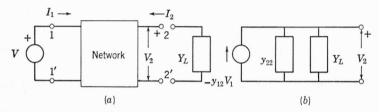

(a)   (b)

Fig. 2-21. (a) Network and (b) Norton's equivalent network which may be used in deriving Eq. 2.97.

These relationships are summarized in Table 2-3.

TABLE 2-3

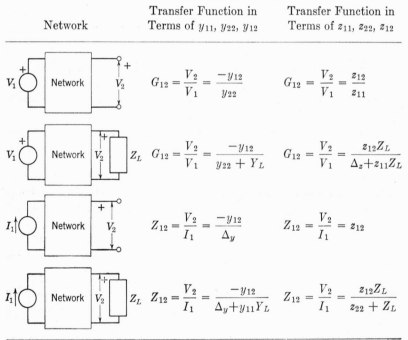

Network	Transfer Function in Terms of y_{11}, y_{22}, y_{12}	Transfer Function in Terms of z_{11}, z_{22}, z_{12}
V_1 — Network — V_2	$G_{12} = \dfrac{V_2}{V_1} = \dfrac{-y_{12}}{y_{22}}$	$G_{12} = \dfrac{V_2}{V_1} = \dfrac{z_{12}}{z_{11}}$
V_1 — Network V_2 — Z_L	$G_{12} = \dfrac{V_2}{V_1} = \dfrac{-y_{12}}{y_{22} + Y_L}$	$G_{12} = \dfrac{V_2}{V_1} = \dfrac{z_{12}Z_L}{\Delta_z + z_{11}Z_L}$
I_1 — Network — V_2	$Z_{12} = \dfrac{V_2}{I_1} = \dfrac{-y_{12}}{\Delta_y}$	$Z_{12} = \dfrac{V_2}{I_1} = z_{12}$
I_1 — Network V_2 — Z_L	$Z_{12} = \dfrac{V_2}{I_1} = \dfrac{-y_{12}}{\Delta_y + y_{11}Y_L}$	$Z_{12} = \dfrac{V_2}{I_1} = \dfrac{z_{12}Z_L}{z_{22} + Z_L}$

The arrangement of networks shown in Fig. 2-22 is described by the words cascade or tandem. For this combination of networks, a useful equation expressing the function $-y_{12}$ in the terms of the functions $-y_{12a}$ and $-y_{12b}$ of the component networks may be given. This relationship is derived by using the equivalent π networks of Fig.

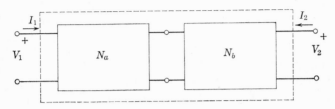

Fig. 2-22. Cascade or tandem connection of networks N_a and N_b. See Eq. 2.100.

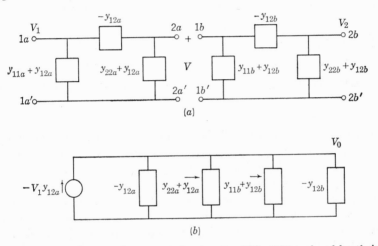

Fig. 2-23. (a) The cascade-connected networks of Fig. 2-22 replaced by their π equivalents. (b) Norton's equivalent network appropriate for the computation of $-y_{12}$.

2-23(a). Let the voltage at terminals $1a$-$1a'$ be V_1 and the current in the short-circuit connecting terminals $2b$-$2b'$ be I_2. From the Norton's equivalent network of Fig. 2-23(b), we see that the voltage V_0 is

$$V_0 = V_1 \frac{-y_{12a}}{y_{22a} + y_{11b}} \tag{2.98}$$

Since

$$I_2 = y_{12b} V_0 \tag{2.99}$$

then

$$\frac{I_2}{V_1} = -y_{12} = \frac{-y_{12a} y_{12b}}{y_{22a} + y_{11b}} \tag{2.100}$$

This equation, and its counterpart in terms of z_{12}, is important in a number of synthesis procedures where it is often called the partitioning theorem.*

2.5   Scaling network functions

The network of Example 5 contained a 1-farad capacitor. Why, you might ask, use such obviously impractical element sizes? The answer to this question may be given in terms of *scaling:* scaling in magnitude and scaling in frequency of network functions. Such multiple scaling as we intend to use is already familiar in relief maps constructed with a horizontal scale such as 1 inch represents 1 mile,

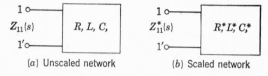

(a) Unscaled network   (b) Scaled network

Fig. 2-24. The two networks with identifications used in deriving the scaling relationships.

but with elevation characteristics exaggerated by the choice of a different vertical scale, say 1 inch represents 100 ft. Such maps make it easier to study geological features of a terrain, to locate ore bodies, or to place dams. Similarly, the scaling of frequency such that 10^6 cycles/sec becomes 1 radian/sec, and the scaling of magnitude such that 10^4 ohms becomes 1 ohm, eliminates unwieldy factors of 2π and powers of 10 from calculations and makes it possible to work with numbers in the range 1 to 10.

Consider the two network representations of Fig. 2-24. One is marked *unscaled* (the network from which we begin) and the other marked *scaled* has its features identified by an asterisk superscript. Suppose that we are given the driving-point impedance of the unscaled network, $Z_{11}(s)$, and we wish to change the frequency scale by replacing s by s/a and also to scale the magnitude by an amount b, where a and b are dimensionless, real, positive constants. The new impedance function resulting from such scaling will be

$$Z_{11}{}^*(s) = b\, Z_{11}(s/a) \qquad (2.101)$$

---

* Credited by Guillemin to H. Adler in an MIT M.S. thesis in 1948. See *Synthesis of Passive Networks*, p. 576.

If the two networks of Fig. 2-24 are identical in structure (topology) there is a simple relationship of element values in the two networks.

The impedance function $Z_{11}(s)$ is given by Eq. 2.25 in terms of the node-basis system determinant Δ' and the cofactor Δ_{11}',

$$Z_{11}(s) = \frac{\Delta_{11}'(s)}{\Delta'(s)} \qquad (2.102)$$

Now every element of Δ' and Δ_{11}' has the form

$$\mathcal{Y}_{jk} = \frac{1}{R_{jk}} + \frac{1}{L_{jk}s} + C_{jk}s \qquad (2.103)$$

as used in Eq. 2.102. If we replace s by s/a and multiply $\mathcal{Y}_{jk}$ by $1/b$ (since impedance is to be multiplied by b), then

$$\mathcal{Y}_{jk}{}^*(s) = \frac{1}{b}\,\mathcal{Y}_{jk}\left(\frac{s}{a}\right) = \frac{1}{bR_{jk}} + \frac{1}{bL_{jk}(s/a)} + \frac{1}{b}\,C_{jk}\frac{s}{a} \qquad (2.104)$$

Similarly, if every element in Δ' and Δ_{11}' is multiplied by $1/b$ and s is everywhere replaced by s/a, then the scaled impedance function is

$$Z_{11}{}^*(s) = \frac{1/b^{n-1}\Delta_{11}'(s/a)}{1/b^n\Delta'(s/a)} \qquad (2.105)$$

where n is the number of elements in the principal diagonal of the system determinant. This equation has the form of Eq. 2.101,

$$Z_{11}{}^*(s) = b\,Z_{11}(s/a) \qquad (2.106)$$

as required. Comparing terms in $\mathcal{Y}_{jk}$ and $\mathcal{Y}_{jk}{}^*$, we see that the last equation, Eq. 2.106, is satisfied when for each element

$$R^* = bR$$

$$L^* = \frac{b}{a}\,L \qquad (2.107)$$

$$C^* = \frac{1}{ab}\,C$$

This set of equations also provides an alternative definition of impedance scaling. If each inductance and each capacitance is multiplied by $1/a$, then the network is said to be frequency-scaled by a factor a. If every resistance and inductance is multiplied by b and every capacitance is divided by the same b, then the network is said to be magnitude-scaled by a factor b.

To illustrate magnitude scaling, suppose that we wish to scale the network of Fig. 2-25(a) by letting $b = \frac{1}{2}$.   Using Eqs. 2.107 with $a = 1$ (no frequency scaling) and $b = \frac{1}{2}$ gives the element values of Fig.

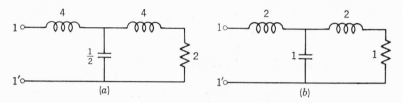

Fig. 2-25.   (a) An unscaled network, and (b) the magnitude-scaled network with $b = \frac{1}{2}$.

2-25(b).   The impedance of the unscaled network is

$$Z_{11}(s) = 2 \frac{4s^3 + 2s^2 + 4s + 1}{2s^2 + s + 1} \tag{2.108}$$

while the impedance for the scaled network is identical to Eq. 2.108 except that the scale factor 2 becomes 1.   Pole and zero locations are unaffected by magnitude scaling, as this example indicates.

Example 6.   The network of Fig. 2-26(a) is a symmetrical lattice terminated in a 1-ohm resistor.   The elements of the lattice are 1-farad capacitors

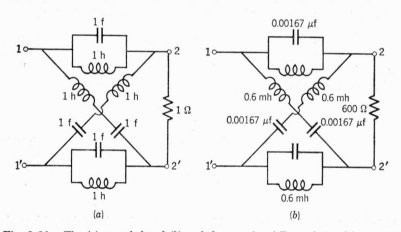

Fig. 2-26.   The (a) unscaled and (b) scaled networks of Example 6, with $a = 10^6$ and $b = 600$.

and 1-henry inductors.   Suppose that we wish to increase the impedance level by 600 (so that the network will be terminated in a 600-ohm resistive load), and at the same time scale the frequency such that the behavior of the unscaled network at 1 radian/sec takes place at 10^6 radians/sec in the scaled network. (This amounts to looking at the s plane with a magnifying glass.) Making use of Eqs. 2.107 with $b = 600$ and $a = 10^6$ gives the values in Table 2-4. The scaled network is shown in Fig. 2-26(b).

TABLE 2-4
Value

Element	Unscaled	Scaled
R	1	600 Ω
L	1	0.6 mh
C	1	0.00167 μf

The same procedure as used in Example 6 applies in "reducing" the scale of a network such as that of Fig. 2-26(b) to that of Fig. 2-26(a), say for analysis. The semantic difficulty in the words "scaled" and "unscaled" can be avoided if we always start with (a) of Fig. 2-24 and find (b). If we are scaling "up," then a and b are greater than 1; in scaling "down," they are less than 1.

It is also interesting to observe the effect of frequency scaling in the time domain, particularly with respect to the impulse response of networks. Since

$$I(s) = Y_{11}(s)\, V(s) \quad (2.109)$$

for a one terminal-pair network, then when $v(t)$ is a unit impulse (or Dirac delta function), $V(s) = 1$ and $I(s) = Y_{11}(s)$. For the network of Fig. 2-27(a),

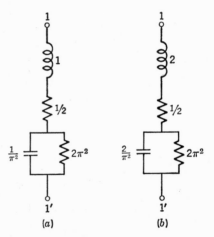

Fig. 2-27. (a) The unscaled network, and (b) the corresponding frequency-scaled network with $a = \frac{1}{2}$, used in studying the time-domain effects of scaling.

$$Y_{11}(s) = \frac{s + \frac{1}{2}}{(s + \frac{1}{2})^2 + \pi^2} \quad (2.110)$$

If we frequency-scale the network by letting $a = \frac{1}{2}$ (thus scaling "down" in frequency), the result is shown in Fig. 2-27(b) for which

$$Y_{11}{}^*(s) = Y_{11}(2s) = \frac{1}{2} \frac{s + \frac{1}{4}}{(s + \frac{1}{4})^2 + (\pi/2)^2} \qquad (2.111)$$

The corresponding impulse responses are

$$i(t) = e^{-\frac{1}{2}t} \cos \pi t \qquad (2.112)$$

$$i^*(t) = \tfrac{1}{2} e^{-\frac{1}{4}t} \cos \tfrac{1}{2}\pi t \qquad (2.113)$$

This result is an application of the Laplace transform pair,

$$\mathcal{L}^{-1} F(s/a) = a\, f(at) \qquad (2.114)$$

Figure 2-28 shows the frequency scaling in terms of pole and zero locations in the s plane, and also shows the corresponding time responses

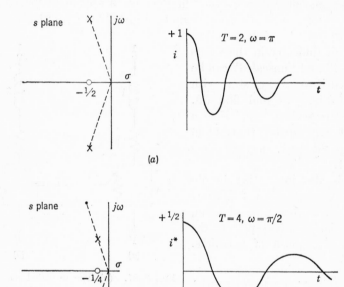

Fig. 2-28. Impulse response for (a) the unscaled network, and (b) the scaled network ($a = \frac{1}{2}$). T is the time constant of the envelope of the damped sinusoid.

given by Eqs. 2.112 and 2.113. Time scaling and its relationship to frequency scaling is especially important in analog studies (e.g., in using the electronic analog computer).

The scaling methods given for driving-point functions do not apply to transfer functions such as the voltage- and current-ratio transfer functions. The open-circuit voltage-ratio transfer function is, by Eq. 2.90,

$$G_{12} = \frac{V_2}{V_1}\bigg|_{I_2=0} = \frac{-y_{12}}{y_{22}} \qquad (2.115)$$

But by Eq. 2.41, $y_{12} = \Delta_{21}/\Delta$ and $y_{22} = \Delta_{22}/\Delta$ so that

$$G_{12} = \frac{-\Delta_{21}}{\Delta_{22}} \qquad (2.116)$$

and G_{12} is seen to be a quotient of cofactors. Making the same scaling substitutions as in Eq. 2.105 by replacing s by s/a and each element of the cofactors by $1/b$ gives

$$G_{12}{}^* = -\frac{1/b^{n-1}}{1/b^{n-1}}\frac{\Delta_{12}(s/a)}{\Delta_{22}(s/a)} \qquad (2.117)$$

and, finally

$$G_{12}{}^*(s) = G_{12}(s/a) \qquad (2.118)$$

Thus the voltage-ratio transfer function is *unaffected* by magnitude scaling. In summary:

(1) All network functions are affected by frequency scaling; s is everywhere replaced by s/a.

(2) Network functions expressible as a ratio of determinants of different orders are affected by magnitude scaling; network functions which may be written as the quotient of determinants of the same orders are not affected by magnitude scaling.

FURTHER READING

For supplementary reading on the topics of this chapter, the following three textbooks are especially recommended: Balabanian, *Network Synthesis*, Chapter 1; Guillemin, *Synthesis of Passive Networks*, Chapter 6; and Bode, *Network Analysis and Feedback Amplifier Design*, Chapter 1. For an excellent exposition of the relationship of network functions to the y and z functions, see Truxal's *Automatic Feedback Control System Synthesis*, Chapter 3. The subject of scaling is treated in Guillemin's *Introductory Circuit Theory*, pp. 309–311 and 436–437, and a chapter on frequency scaling is given by Storer in *Passive Network Synthesis*, Chapter 14. See also Tuttle's *Network Synthesis*, Vol. I, pp. 20–22.

PROBLEMS

2-1. (*a*) Find the driving-point impedance, $Z(s)$, for the two networks illustrated in Fig. P2-1, and show that the two impedances are identical.

(*b*) Find the poles and zeros of $Z(s)$ found in part (*a*).

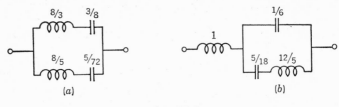

Fig. P2-1

2-2. The three RC networks of Fig. P2-2 have the same driving-point impedance. Verify this statement by showing that

$$Z(s) = \frac{(s+1)(s+3)}{s(s+2)}$$

for each of the three networks. If only the two driving-point terminals are accessible for each of the networks (the elements being encased in a black box), is there any way one of the networks could be distinguished from the other two? Explain your answer.

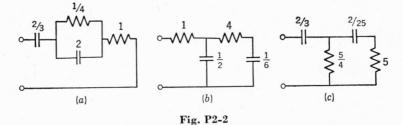

Fig. P2-2

2-3. Find the driving-point impedance of the network shown in Fig. P2-3 with the switch K open (thereby disconnecting R). Repeat this computation with the switch closed and with $R = 1$ ohm. Compare the number of terms present in the numerator and denominator polynomials of $Z(s)$ under the two conditions.

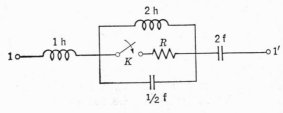

Fig. P2-3

2-4. Determine the driving-point impedance, $Z(s)$, for the resistive bridge network of Fig. P2-4.

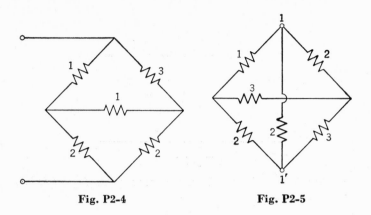

Fig. P2-4   **Fig. P2-5**

2-5. Terminals 1-1' are to be considered the driving-point terminals of the network shown in Fig. P2-5.

(a) How many loop equations must be written in describing this network completely?

(b) How many node equations must be written?

(c) Find Z_{11}'.

2-6. Figure P2-6 is a bridge network, similar to Fig. P2-4 but containing two inductors and one capacitor.

(a) Is this bridge balanced?

(b) Show that the driving-point impedance is

$$Z(s) = \frac{s^2 + \frac{1}{2}s + \frac{1}{2}}{s^2 + s + 2}$$

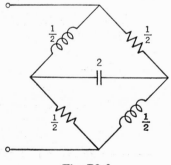

Fig. P2-6

2-7. Figure P2-7 is a bridged ladder network. For this network, find the two system determinants, Δ and Δ'. Using one of these determinants, and the appropriate cofactor, find the driving-point admittance function, $Y(s)$.

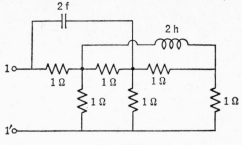

Fig. P2-7

2-8. Show that the impedance $Z(s)$ of the network with mutual inductance as illustrated in Fig. P2-8 is

$$Z(s) = \frac{s^2 + s + 2}{2s^2 + s + 1}$$

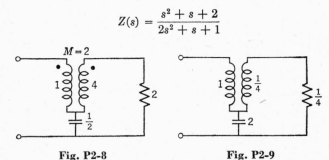

Fig. P2-8   **Fig. P2-9**

2-9. It is known that the driving-point impedance of the network given in Fig. P2-9 is

$$Z(s) = \frac{s^2 + \frac{1}{2}s + \frac{1}{2}}{s^2 + s + 2}$$

   (a) What must be the value of the coefficient of mutual inductance, M?
   (b) What must be the polarity markings on the coils?

2-10. For the resistive bridged-T network of Fig. P2-10, determine numerical values for Z_{12}, Y_{12}, G_{12}, and α_{12}.

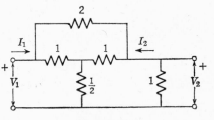

Fig. P2-10

2-11. A particular network has five nodes with a 1-ohm resistor connected between each of the five nodes (ten resistors in the network). If V_1 is applied from node 1 to node 2, and V_2 is measured from node 3 to node 4, find $G_{12} = V_2/V_1$.

2-12. For the resistive ladder network shown in Fig. P2-12, find I_2/V_1 by the unit output method.

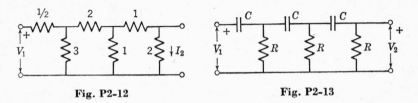

Fig. P2-12 Fig. P2-13

2-13. The network illustrated in Fig. P2-13 is part of the equivalent network of the phase-shift oscillator. Determine $G_{12} = V_2/V_1$ for this network by the unit output method.

2-14. For the network of Fig. P2-14, show that

$$\frac{V_2}{V_1} = \frac{(4s^2 + 1)(s^2 + 1)}{16s^4 + 9s^2 + 1}$$

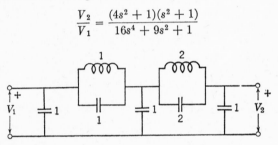

Fig. P2-14

2-15. Draw the schematic of a network whose short-circuit transfer admittance, y_{12}, has a pole at infinity.

2-16. For the ladder network of Fig. P2-16, compute $z_{12}(s)$ as a quotient of polynomials in s.

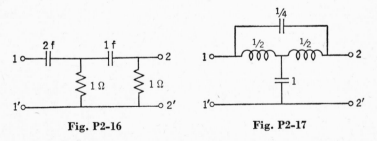

Fig. P2-16 Fig. P2-17

2-17. Figure P2-17 shows a bridged-T network. For this network, find z_{11}, z_{22}, and z_{12}.

2-18. For the network of Fig. P2-18, show that

$$y_{11} = \frac{(s+1)(s+3)}{(s+2)(s+4)} \quad \text{and} \quad -y_{12} = \frac{K(s+1)}{(s+2)(s+4)}$$

Determine the value for K.

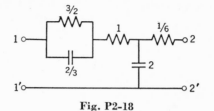

Fig. P2-18

2-19. Figure P2-19 shows two resistive paralleled ladder networks.

(a) Find the equivalent T network and the equivalent π network by first finding z_{11}, z_{22}, and z_{12}, and y_{11}, y_{22}, and y_{12}.

(b) Determine a value for G_{12} with the output terminals open.

(c) Find G_{12} with the network terminated in a 1-ohm resistor.

(d) Find Z_{12} with the network terminated in a 1-ohm resistor.

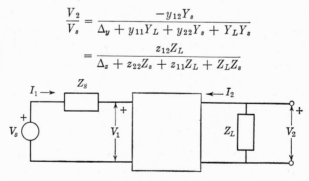

Fig. P2-19

2-20. Figure P2-20 shows a two terminal-pair network driven by a voltage source of impedance Z_s terminated in an impedance Z_L.

(a) For this network, show that

$$\frac{V_2}{V_s} = \frac{-y_{12}Y_s}{\Delta_y + y_{11}Y_L + y_{22}Y_s + Y_LY_s}$$

$$= \frac{z_{12}Z_L}{\Delta_z + z_{22}Z_s + z_{11}Z_L + Z_LZ_s}$$

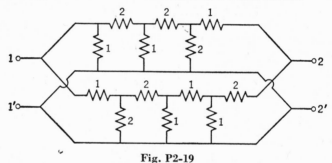

Fig. P2-20

(b) Simplify these equations for the case $Z_L = \infty$.

(c) Simplify these equations for the case $Z_s = 0$, $Z_L \neq 0$, and compare with corresponding expressions in Table 2-3.

(d) Simplify these equations for the case $Z_s = 0$, $Z_L = \infty$, and compare with corresponding expressions in Table 2-3.

2-21. For the cascade-connected networks illustrated in Fig. 2-22, show that

(a) $z_{12} = \dfrac{z_{12a}z_{12b}}{z_{22a} + z_{11b}}$ (b) $G_{12} = \dfrac{V_2}{V_1} = \dfrac{-y_{12a}z_{12b}}{1 + y_{22a}z_{11b}}$

(c) $\alpha_{12} = \dfrac{I_2}{I_1} = \dfrac{y_{12b}z_{12a}}{1 + y_{11b}z_{22a}}$

2-22. The networks of Fig. P2-1 are to be scaled by increasing the level of impedance by 100 and scaling the frequency such that 1 radian/sec becomes 100,000 radians/sec. Find the element values in the scaled network.

2-23. Repeat Prob. 2-22, but with $a = 100$, and $b = 10^5$. Are the resulting element values practical?

2-24. The network shown in Fig. P2-24 is an m-derived composite low-pass filter (designed on the image parameter basis) with a cutoff frequency of 1200 cycles/sec, and frequencies of infinite attenuation of 1500 and 1700 cycles/sec. (This is interesting but unessential information as far as working the problem is concerned.) You are required to scale this network so that all elements have values in ohms, farads, or henrys in the range 1 to 5. Give the values of a and b that meet this specification, and also give all element values in the scaled network (the one with element values ranging from 1 to 5).

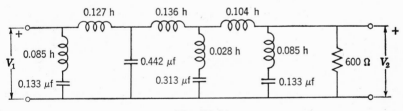

Fig. P2-24

2-25. For the bridged-T network of Fig. P2-25 with $Z_a Z_b = R_0{}^2$, show that

$$\frac{V_1}{V_2} = 1 + \frac{Z_a}{R_0}$$

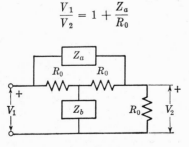

Fig. P2-25

2-26. Figure P2-26 shows three networks synthesized by methods to be discussed in later chapters. That shown in (*a*) of the figure is due to Kim, that of (*b*) due to Bott and Duffin, and that of (*c*) due to Pantell. Show that the networks have the same driving-point impedance:

$$Z(s) = 2\frac{s^2 + \frac{1}{2}s + \frac{1}{2}}{s^2 + s + 2}$$

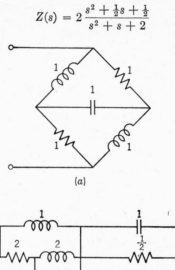

(*a*)

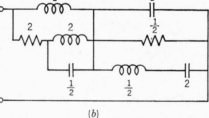

(*b*)

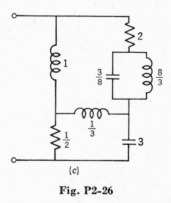

(*c*)

Fig. P2-26

2-27. Figure P2-27 represents a resistive network made up of 1-ohm resistors which is infinite in extent in every direction. Determine the value of the driving-point impedance at terminals *a* and *b* of the figures. Explain your method. (*Hint:* Make use of current sources and the superposition theorem.)

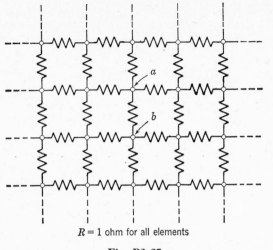

$R = 1$ ohm for all elements

Fig. P2-27

2-28. (a) The following algorithm is proposed:

For a network of n nodes, compute (or measure) the admittance Y_1 at a chosen node pair and then coalesce (solder together) the two nodes. Compute (or measure) Y_2 at another node pair and then coalesce that node pair. Continue to Y_{n-1}. The node-basis system determinant is equal to the product

$$\Delta' = Y_1 Y_2 Y_3 \cdots Y_{n-1}$$

1. By considering a number of successively more complex networks and computing Δ' by conventional means and by the algorithm, show that the algorithm is reasonable.

2. Prove that the algorithm is valid. Or outline how you think such a proof may be constructed.

(b) Consider the dual of the algorithm of part (a):

Cut into a branch and measure the impedance Z_1 at the cut (including of course the impedance of the cut branch). Cut into another branch (leaving the first cut open) and measure the impedance Z_2 at the second cut. Continue until all loops (or circuits) in the network are interrupted by cuts. The mesh-basis system determinant is equal to the product

$$\Delta = Z_1 Z_2 Z_3 \cdots Z_m$$

Repeat items 1 and 2 of part (a). (This result is due to Professor Samuel Mason of MIT.)

Positive Real
Functions

· · · · · · · · · · · · · · · · 3

3.1 Driving-point functions

It was shown in the last chapter that the driving-point impedance
and admittance functions for all networks made up of elements con-
forming to the LLFPB restrictions are rational* and have the form of
a quotient of polynomials in s, the complex frequency variable. As a
first step in studying synthesis, we must inquire into the converse
proposition: Do all quotients of polynomials describe some network?
The answer to this is a definite no, as we shall see. The requirements
imposed on driving-point functions are numerous and were first given
in complete form by Otto Brune† in his MIT doctoral thesis in 1931.
Brune's work culminates earlier pioneer work of Cauer, Foster, Fry,
and others, and marks the true beginning of the systematic study of
network synthesis.

The Brune requirements we are about to study are important
because they offer criteria by which we may determine whether a given
function having a form resulting from an approximation procedure or
some other means can possibly represent a network. If the trial
function fails to meet the criteria in every respect, we are spared the
task of looking for a network representation. We know then that
none exists.

---

* A *rational function* has a finite number of poles and no other singularities.
Thus a function like $1/(s + \sqrt{s^2 + 1})$ is not rational.

† "Synthesis of a finite two terminal network whose driving-point impedance is
a prescribed function of frequency," *J. Math. and Phys.*, **10**, 191–236 (1931).
Brune has lived in Southern Africa most of his life where he is now Principal
Research Officer of the National Physical Research Laboratories, Pretoria.

To start with, we know that the driving-point impedance may be expressed as a quotient of polynomials written in the form

$$Z(s) = \frac{p(s)}{q(s)} = \frac{a_0 s^n + a_1 s^{n-1} + \cdots + a_{n-1}s + a_n}{b_0 s^m + b_1 s^{m-1} + \cdots + b_{m-1}s + b_m} \qquad (3.1)$$

where n is the degree of the numerator polynomial and m the degree of the denominator polynomial. These polynomials may be factored to identify the poles and zeros of $Z(s)$:

$$Z(s) = \frac{a_0}{b_0} \frac{(s - z_1)(s - z_2) \cdots (s - z_n)}{(s - p_1)(s - p_2) \cdots (s - p_m)} \qquad (3.2)$$

Suppose that we have access to the elements within a one terminal-pair network and that energy is supplied internally by charging one or more capacitors. (We shall invent a switching scheme that will charge the capacitors and then insert them in the otherwise passive network at a given instant of time.) What will be the form of the response of the network to this excitation?

If we short-circuit terminals 1 and 1′ and designate the current transform in this short circuit as $I_1(s)$ from Eq. 1.18, this current is

$$I_1 = \frac{1}{\Delta}[\Delta_{11} V_1(s) + \Delta_{21} V_2(s) + \cdots + \Delta_{l1} V_l(s)] \qquad (3.3)$$

where Δ is the loop-basis system determinant and $V_j(s)$ is, for the problem being considered, the transform of the summation of initial capacitor voltages around loop j.

In Chapter 2, we found that the driving-point admittance of the passive network at terminals 1-1′ is

$$\frac{1}{Z(s)} = \frac{\Delta_{11}}{\Delta} \qquad (3.4)$$

Observe that $I_1(s)$ for the short-circuited terminals and $1/Z(s)$ appear to have the same denominator, the loop-basis system determinant Δ. But before we can make such an identification, we must compare the numerators of the two quantities. We do this by first examining the character of Δ. A typical element in the determinant Δ has the form

$$R_{jk} + L_{jk}s + \frac{1}{C_{jk}s} \qquad (3.5)$$

When Δ is expanded, there results a product of terms of this form which may be reduced to the form

$$\Delta = a_c s^c + a_{c-1} s^{c-1} + \cdots + a_{-d}s^{-d} \qquad (3.6)$$

which is equivalent to

$$\Delta = \frac{a_c s^{c+d} + a_{c-1} s^{c+d-1} + \cdots + a_{-d}}{s^d} \tag{3.7}$$

For example, a two-loop network has the system determinant

$$\begin{vmatrix} s + 1 + \dfrac{1}{s} & -1 \\ & \\ -1 & 2s + 1 + \dfrac{2}{s} \end{vmatrix} = 2s^2 + 3s + 4 + \frac{3}{s} + \frac{2}{s^2} \tag{3.8}$$

or

$$\Delta = \frac{2s^4 + 3s^3 + 4s^2 + 3s + 2}{s^2} \tag{3.9}$$

Since the cofactor Δ_{11} is formed in the same way as Δ, it will be reducible to the same general form as Eq. 3.7.

Turning next to the numerator of Eq. 3.3, we recall that the transform voltages, $V_j(s)$, in the numerator of this equation are loop summations of terms like V_0/s, where V_0 is the initial capacitor voltage.* The multiplication of cofactors by terms like V_0/s results in an expression like Eq. 3.7 for the numerator of $I_1(s)$. From this discussion, we conclude that the poles of $I_1(s)$ and $1/Z(s)$ are the zeros of $\Delta(s)$ and in the case of incomplete cancellation of denominator factors of the form s^d in Eq. 3.7, a factor s^r may also appear in the denominator of $I_1(s)$. Since the poles of $I_1(s)$ and $1/Z(s)$ are thus identical except at the origin, the poles of $I_1(s)$ are the zeros of $Z(s)$, and

$$I_1(s) = \frac{p_1(s)}{s^r(s - z_1)(s - z_2) \cdots (s - z_m)} \tag{3.10}$$

If $r = 0$ and $I_1(s)$ has no repeated poles, then the partial fraction expansion of $I_1(s)$ is

$$I_1(s) = \frac{K_{z_1}}{s - z_1} + \frac{K_{z_2}}{s - z_2} + \cdots + \frac{K_{z_m}}{s - z_m} \tag{3.11}$$

where the constants $K_{z_1}, K_{z_2}, \cdots$ are the residues of $I_1(s)$ evaluated at $z_1, z_2, \cdots$. If, however, $r \neq 0$, there will be added to this expan-

---

* This is the initial condition transform corresponding to a charged capacitor. See the author's *Network Analysis*, p. 200.

sion terms like

$$\frac{K_{0,r}}{s^r} + \frac{K_{0,r-1}}{s^{r-1}} + \cdots + \frac{K_{0,1}}{s} \qquad (3.12)$$

Similarly, if there are repeated poles in $I_1(s)$, then the term in Eq. 3.11 for the repeated pole will be replaced by the expansion

$$\frac{K_{zj,m}}{(s - z_j)^m} + \frac{K_{zj,m-1}}{(s - z_j)^{m-1}} + \cdots + \frac{K_{zj,1}}{s - z_j} \qquad (3.13)$$

The current response in the short-circuited terminals, $i_1(t)$, is now found from the inverse transform of terms in the last three equations

$$i_1(t) = K_{z_1}e^{z_1 t} + K_{z_2}e^{z_2 t} + \cdots + K_{z_n}e^{z_n t} \qquad (3.14)$$

plus the possibility of terms like

$$\mathcal{L}^{-1}\frac{K_{0,r}}{s^r} = \frac{K_{0,r}t^{r-1}}{(r - 1)!} \quad \text{or} \quad \mathcal{L}^{-1}\frac{K_{zj,m}}{(s - z_j)^m} = K'_{zj,m}t^{m-1}e^{z_j t} \quad (3.15)$$

Mention should be made of the possibility that a factor in $p_1(s)$ in Eq. 3.10 will cancel with a denominator factor, thereby giving a zero value for the corresponding residue in Eq. 3.11.

Fundamental laws, exemplified by Maxwell's and Kirchhoff's equations, are mathematical idealizations of laws of Nature observed by measurement. The next step in this discussion requires that we consider a possible laboratory measurement on the network being considered. Suppose that we insert charged capacitors into the network at various points at a reference instant of time and observe the current in short-circuited terminals 1-1'. This current has never been observed to continue to increase in magnitude as time increases. Instead, the following possibilities exist: (1) It exponentially reduces to zero, (2) it oscillates with ever decreasing amplitude, or (3) it oscillates and the amplitude decreases so slowly that we describe the response as sustained oscillation (see Fig. 3-1). Since this is the behavior which Nature requires, we must adjust the mathematical representation to conform. First, we require that $r = 0$ in Eq. 3.10 for otherwise $i_1(t)$ would increase with time or (for $r = 1$) remain constant with time. Next, we require that the real part of poles of $I_1(s)$ be negative. Finally, we admit the possibility that the real part of simple poles of $I_1(s)$ can be zero to correspond to the approximation of a sustained oscillation. Multiple poles of $I_1(s)$ with negative real parts are permitted since terms like that of the second part of Eq. 3.15 have the limit,

$$\lim_{t \to \infty} t^{m-1}e^{z_j t} = 0 \text{ if } \operatorname{Re} z_j < 0 \qquad (3.16)$$

The conclusion that r in Eq. 3.10 must be zero implies that the poles of $I_1(s)$ are always among the zeros of $Z(s)$, although the possibility of factor cancellation in $I_1(s)$ mentioned earlier does not permit us to conclude that poles of $I_1(s)$ will be identical with the zeros of $Z(s)$. Thus some zeros of the impedance function of a one terminal-pair network are the free frequencies of the short-circuited driving-point terminals with the network excited by charged capacitors.

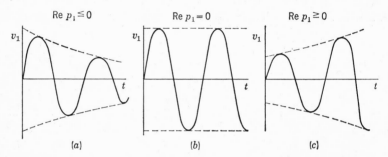

Fig. 3-1. For a response of the form $v_1 = K_{p_1}e^{p_1 t} + K_{p_2}e^{p_2 t}$, where p_1, $p_2 = \sigma \pm j\omega$, three response possibilities are given: (a) damped oscillation for $\sigma \le 0$, (b) sustained oscillation for $\sigma = 0$, and (c) unstable oscillation for $\sigma \ge 0$.

All conclusions given thus far apply to the zeros of $Z(s)$. Identical properties for the poles are found by considering the voltage at the open-circuit terminals 1-1' which, from Eq. 1.22, is

$$V_1(s) = \frac{1}{\Delta'}[\Delta_{11}' I_1(s) + \Delta_{21}' I_2(s) + \cdots + \Delta_{n1}' I_n(s)] \quad (3.17)$$

where Δ' is the node-basis system determinant, in comparison with the expression for driving-point impedance,

$$Z(s) = \frac{\Delta_{11}'}{\Delta'} \qquad (3.18)$$

A parallel derivation to that just given for the short-circuit current leads to the conclusion that when a network is internally excited by charged capacitors, the free frequencies of the open-circuit voltage response are among the poles of $Z(s)$.

We conclude, therefore, that a *necessary condition* for both poles and zeros of driving-point functions is that its real part must be negative (or zero); poles and zeros must be in the *left* half of the s plane (or on the imaginary axis). Furthermore, the a and b coefficients of $p(s)$ and $q(s)$ in Eq. 3.1 are all positive since the product of terms like

$$s + \sigma_1 \quad \text{and} \quad s^2 + \alpha_1 s + \beta_1 \tag{3.19}$$

always results in a polynomial with positive coefficients.

3.2 Brune's positive real functions

What other law of Nature can we make use of in deducing further properties of driving-point functions? Following Brune's work in

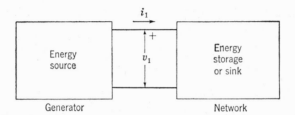

Fig. 3-2. Representation of an energy source connected to a one terminal-pair network, used in the definition of positive real functions.

1931, we consider the energy delivered to a network from a source of constant voltage, as represented in Fig. 3-2. The energy delivered from the source to the network is chosen to be positive, and that returned from the network to the source to be negative. (This choice of sign is arbitrary and is made to conform with convention.) If the network is initially relaxed (made up of elements fresh from the stockroom without charge on capacitors or current in inductors), then the energy in the passive network is always positive, $w(t) \geq 0$. The power, being the time rate of change of energy, $dw(t)/dt$, may be positive, zero, or negative, but the network can return at most the energy it receives from the source so that $w(t)$ is always greater than or equal to 0.

The Brune derivation assumes as the form of the driving voltage of the energy source:

$$v(t) = e^{\sigma_1 t} \sin \omega_1 t \tag{3.20}$$

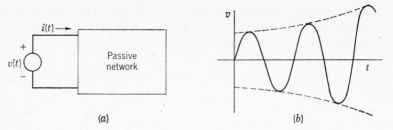

Fig. 3-3. (a) The same network as used in Fig. 3-2 with (b) an exponentially increasing, oscillatory applied voltage.

as shown in Fig. 3-3.   The transform of this function is

$$V(s) = \mathcal{L}\, v(t) = \frac{\omega_1}{(s - \sigma_1)^2 + \omega_1{}^2} \tag{3.21}$$

from which we see that the forced frequencies of the system are

$$s_1,\; \bar{s}_1 = \sigma_1 \pm j\omega_1 \equiv |s_1| e^{\pm j\theta} \tag{3.22}$$

identified in Fig. 3-4(a).   The current transform $I(s)$ is

$$I(s) = Y(s)\, V(s) = \frac{\omega_1 Y(s)}{(s - \sigma_1)^2 + \omega_1{}^2} \tag{3.23}$$

This current transform may be expanded by partial fractions, giving

$$\frac{\omega_1 Y(s)}{(s - \sigma_1)^2 + \omega_1{}^2} = \frac{K_{\sigma_1 - j\omega_1}}{s - \sigma_1 + j\omega_1} + \frac{K_{\sigma_1 + j\omega_1}}{s - \sigma_1 - j\omega_1} + \frac{K_{p_1}}{s - p_1}$$

$$+ \frac{K_{p_2}}{s - p_2} + \cdots + \frac{K_{p_m}}{s - p_m} \tag{3.24}$$

where $p_1, p_2, \cdots, p_m$ are the m simple* poles of $Y(s)$, which are different from $\sigma_1 \pm j\omega_1$ since $Y(s)$ has no poles in the right half plane. The residue $K_{\sigma_1 - j\omega}$ has the value

$$K_{\sigma_1 - j\omega_1} = \frac{\omega_1 Y(\sigma_1 - j\omega_1)}{-2j\omega_1} = \frac{|Y_1| e^{-j\phi}}{-2j} \tag{3.25}$$

and the residue of the conjugate of this pole has the conjugate residue

$$K_{\sigma_1 + j\omega_1} = \frac{\omega_1 Y(\sigma_1 + j\omega_1)}{2j\omega_1} = \frac{|Y_1| e^{j\phi}}{2j} \tag{3.26}$$

* For this derivation, it is not necessary that the poles be simple; the same conclusions may be reached for multiple poles.

as illustrated in polar form in Fig. 3-4(b). Let that portion of the current transform equal to the first two terms of Eq. 3.24 be $I_1(s)$. Then the corresponding time-domain current is $i_1(t) = \mathcal{L}^{-1} I_1(s)$ or

$$i_1(t) = \frac{|Y_1|}{2j} [e^{j\phi} e^{(\sigma_1 + j\omega_1)t} - e^{-j\phi} e^{(\sigma_1 - j\omega_1)t}] \qquad (3.27)$$

$$= |Y_1| e^{\sigma_1 t} \left[\frac{e^{j(\omega_1 t + \phi)} - e^{-j(\omega_1 t + \phi)}}{2j} \right] \qquad (3.28)$$

$$= |Y_1| e^{\sigma_1 t} \sin (\omega_1 t + \phi) \qquad (3.29)$$

This part of the solution is called the particular integral. The remaining terms in Eq. 3.24 are designated as $I_2(s)$, and the cor-

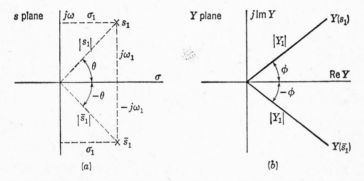

Fig. 3-4. (a) The identification of complex frequencies in the s plane and (b) the corresponding admittance functions shown in the complex Y plane.

responding time-domain function, called the complementary function, is

$$i_2(t) = K_{p_1} e^{p_1 t} + K_{p_2} e^{p_2 t} + \cdots + K_{p_m} e^{p_m t} \qquad (3.30)$$

where the real parts of the poles $p_1, p_2 \cdots , p_m$ are negative as discussed in the preceding section. The total current at the driving-point terminals is the sum of i_1 and i_2 given by Eqs. 3.29 and 3.30.

Consider the power to have two parts, that due to i_1 and that due to i_2. Then

$$P_1(t) = v(t)\, i_1(t) = e^{\sigma_1 t} \sin \omega_1 t [|Y_1| e^{\sigma_1 t} \sin (\omega_1 + \phi)] \qquad (3.31)$$

$$= e^{2\sigma_1 t} |Y_1| \sin \omega_1 t \sin (\omega_1 t + \phi)$$

Similarly,

$$P_2(t) = v(t)\, i_2(t) = e^{\sigma_1 t} \sin \omega_1 t (K_{p_1} e^{p_1 t} + \cdots + K_{p_m} e^{p_m t}) \qquad (3.32)$$

The equation for P_1 may be written in a form better suited to our needs by using the familiar identity

$$\sin x \sin y = \tfrac{1}{2}[\cos (x - y) - \cos (x + y)] \tag{3.33}$$

so that

$$P_1(t) = \tfrac{1}{2}e^{2\sigma_1 t}|Y_1|[\cos \phi - \cos (2\omega_1 t + \phi)] \tag{3.34}$$

We next modify the form of this equation by observing that

$$\operatorname{Re} Y_1 e^{2\sigma_1 t} = |Y_1| e^{2\sigma_1 t} \cos \phi \tag{3.35}$$

is the first term in Eq. 3.34 when expanded, and

$$\operatorname{Re} Y_1 e^{2s_1 t} = \operatorname{Re} Y_1 e^{2(\sigma_1 + j\omega_1)t}$$
$$= \operatorname{Re} \left[|Y_1| e^{j\phi} e^{2(\sigma_1 + j\omega_1)t} \right] \tag{3.36}$$

or $\qquad \operatorname{Re} Y_1 e^{2s_1 t} = |Y_1| e^{2\sigma_1 t} \cos (2\omega_1 t + \phi) \tag{3.37}$

which is recognized to be the second term in Eq. 3.34 when expanded. Then the power is

$$P_1(t) = \tfrac{1}{2} \operatorname{Re} [Y_1(e^{2\sigma_1 t} - e^{2s_1 t})] \tag{3.38}$$

The energy in the network is expressed in terms of the power by the integral,

$$w(t) = \int_0^t P(t) \, dt \tag{3.39}$$

so that the energy w_1 is, for large values of t,

$$w_1(t) = \tfrac{1}{2} \operatorname{Re} Y_1 \left(\frac{e^{2\sigma_1 t}}{2\sigma_1} - \frac{e^{2s_1 t}}{2s_1} \right) + C_1 \tag{3.40}$$

where C_1 is introduced so that $w_1(0) = 0$. Carrying out the same operations to find w_2, we substitute Eq. 3.32 into Eq. 3.39 giving

$$w_2(t) = \sum_j K_{pj} \int_0^t e^{\sigma_1 t} e^{p_i t} \sin \omega_1 t \, dt \tag{3.41}$$

For large t, we see that the envelope of w_2 increases as $e^{(\sigma_1 + \operatorname{Re} p_j)t}$, where $\operatorname{Re} p_j < 0$, whereas w_1 is bounded by $e^{2\sigma_1 t}$. Thus $w_2 \ll w_1$ for large t and w_2 may be neglected. By factoring out the common real and positive $e^{2\sigma_1 t}$ of Eq. 3.40, we have

$$w(t) \approx w_1(t) = \tfrac{1}{4} e^{2\sigma_1 t} \operatorname{Re} \left(\frac{Y_1}{\sigma_1} - \frac{Y_1 e^{j2\omega_1 t}}{s_1} \right) + C_1 \tag{3.42}$$

For the energy to be positive for large t, it is necessary that

$$\text{Re} \left(\frac{Y_1}{\sigma_1} - \frac{Y_1 e^{j2\omega_1 t}}{s_1} \right) \geq 0 \tag{3.43}$$

This equation may be expanded by finding the real part of each term, after substituting $|s_1| e^{j\theta}$ for s_1, giving

$$\left[\frac{\text{Re } Y_1}{\sigma_1} - \frac{|Y_1|}{|s_1|} \cos (2\omega_1 t + \phi - \theta) \right] \geq 0 \tag{3.44}$$

What are the requirements that this condition be fulfilled? There are two requirements:

(1) The first term must be positive. Since $\sigma = \text{Re } s_1$ has been taken to be positive in the derivation, we require that the corresponding $\text{Re } Y_1$ be positive. We may drop the subscript 1, which implies a right half s plane location, if we specify the restriction, $\text{Re } s \geq 0$. Then we require that

$$\text{Re } Y(s) \geq 0 \text{ for } \text{Re } s \geq 0 \tag{3.45}$$

(2) In order that Eq. 3.44 be positive, it is necessary that the positive first term be greater than the maximum value of the second term. Since the maximum value of the cosine function is $+1$, we require that

$$\frac{\text{Re } Y_1}{\sigma_1} \geq \frac{|Y_1|}{|s_1|} \tag{3.46}$$

This equation may be rearranged in the form

$$\frac{\text{Re } Y_1}{|Y_1|} \geq \frac{\text{Re } s_1}{|s_1|} \tag{3.47}$$

To interpret this requirement in terms of s plane and Y plane geometry, refer to Fig. 3-4. From the figure, we see that $\text{Re } Y_1/|Y_1|$ is the cosine of the angle ϕ; similarly, $\text{Re } s_1/|s_1|$ is the cosine of θ. Then Eq. 3.47 may be written

$$\cos \phi \geq \cos \theta \quad \text{or} \quad |\phi| \leq |\theta| \tag{3.48}$$

which must hold for the range of θ covering the right half of the s plane, $\theta \leq \pi/2$. This inequality of angles is illustrated in Fig. 3-5. Now ϕ is the argument of $Y(s)$ and θ is the argument of s. Hence the second requirement may be written

$$|\text{Arg } Y(s)| \leq |\text{Arg } s| \text{ for } |\text{Arg } s| \leq \pi/2 \tag{3.49}$$

This is the second requirement. Are these two requirements in conflict? Is one stronger than the other?

A cursory examination of the two requirements we have been discussing indicates some duplication. The second requirement clearly implies the first. But since the converse is not apparent by inspection, it appears that the second requirement is stronger than the first. Proof that the two requirements are *identical* is given by Brune* using Pick's theorem, and by Guillemin† using Schwarz's lemma. Thus the requirements

$$\text{Re } Y(s) \geq 0 \text{ for Re } s \geq 0 \tag{3.50}$$

and
$$\left| \text{Arg } Y(s) \right| \leq \left| \text{Arg } s \right| \text{ for } \left| \text{Arg } s \right| \leq \pi/2 \tag{3.51}$$

are equivalent and so may be used interchangeably. The functions $Y(s)$ so defined were given the name *positive real* functions by Brune. Functions satisfying the requirement that $Y(s)$ be real when s is real

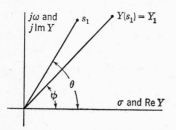

are called *real* functions. If, in addition, $Y(s)$ satisfies Eq. 3.50, then it is a positive real function (usually abbreviated as a p.r. function) and is sometimes called a Brune function. Positive real functions are then defined as functions satisfying the two requirements

Fig. 3-5. An illustration of the requirement that the admittance angle ϕ be less than the frequency angle θ.

$$\text{Re } Y(s) \geq 0 \text{ for Re } s \geq 0$$

and
$$Y(s) \text{ real when } s \text{ is real} \tag{3.52}$$

This definition is the keystone of the theory of network synthesis, and will be encountered often in the pages that follow.

If $Y(s)$ is expressed in polar form, we have

$$Y(s) = H \frac{M_1 M_2 \cdots M_n}{m_1 m_2 \cdots m_m} e^{j(\alpha_1 + \alpha_2 + \cdots - \beta_1 - \beta_2 - \cdots)} \tag{3.53}$$

where we have used α as the angle of a zero factor

$$s - z_k = M_k e^{j\alpha_k} \tag{3.54}$$

and β as a pole factor angle

$$s - p_k = m_k e^{j\beta_k} \tag{3.55}$$

* *Loc. cit.*
† *The Mathematics of Circuit Analysis*, pp. 420 ff.

rather than ϕ and θ because we have already used ϕ and θ in this derivation.   The real part of $Y(s)$ is

$$\text{Re } Y(s) = H \frac{M_1 M_2 \cdots M_n}{m_1 m_2 \cdots m_m} \cos (\alpha_1 + \alpha_2 + \cdots - \beta_1 - \cdots)$$

$$(3.56)$$

In order that the real part of $Y(s)$ be positive as required by Eq. 3.45, it is necessary that

$$|\phi| = |\alpha_1 + \alpha_2 + \cdots + \alpha_n - \beta_1 - \beta_2 - \cdots - \beta_m| \leq \pi/2 \quad (3.57)$$

for all values of s in the right half of the s plane, i.e., for $\text{Re } s \geq 0$. This requirement is illustrated by Fig. 3-6.   In that figure, θ, the

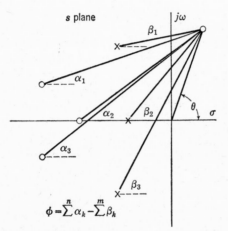

$$\phi = \sum_{}^{n} \alpha_k - \sum_{}^{m} \beta_k$$

Fig. 3-6.   The angle θ is required to be greater than the angle ϕ, defined in the figure, for all right half plane locations.

argument of s, is identified.   The second requirement, Eq. 3.49, states that the summation of zero factor and pole factor angles given in Eq. 3.57 must be less than or equal to θ.   This is a rigid restriction on pole and zero locations, far stronger than anything we have previously found.   It is not enough that the poles and zeros be in the left half plane, and occur in conjugate pairs if complex.   It is also required that the conditions of Eqs. 3.45 and 3.49 be satisfied.

3.3   Properties of positive real functions

All of our conclusions thus far have been for the admittance function $Y(s)$.   What about the impedance function $Z(s)$, the reciprocal of the admittance function? If the numerator and denominator polynomials of $Y(s)$ are separated into their real and imaginary parts,

$$Y(s) = \frac{p(s)}{q(s)} = \frac{u_1(\sigma, \omega) + jv_1(\sigma, \omega)}{u_2(\sigma, \omega) + jv_2(\sigma, \omega)} \qquad (3.58)$$

then the real part of $Y(s)$ may be found by multiplying $Y(s)$ by the conjugate of the denominator

$$\text{Re } Y(s) = \text{Re}\left(\frac{u_1 + jv_1}{u_2 + jv_2} \frac{u_2 - jv_2}{u_2 - jv_2}\right) = \frac{u_1u_2 + v_1v_2}{u_2{}^2 + v_2{}^2} \qquad (3.59)$$

Now if $Y(s)$ is positive real, then

$$\frac{u_1u_2 + v_1v_2}{u_2{}^2 + v_2{}^2} \geq 0 \text{ for Re } s \geq 0 \qquad (3.60)$$

by the first of Eqs. 3.52. By the same procedure, the real part of $1/Y(s)$ is

$$\text{Re } \frac{1}{Y(s)} = \frac{u_1u_2 + v_1v_2}{u_1{}^2 + v_1{}^2} \qquad (3.61)$$

The numerator of this equation is identical with the numerator of Re $Y(s)$ in Eq. 3.60 and the denominator is always positive. Hence

$$\text{Re } [1/Y(s)] = \text{Re } Z(s) \geq 0 \text{ for Re } s \geq 0 \qquad (3.62)$$

and $Z(s)$ is positive real, and all statements made about admittance apply to impedance.

The conditions just given are the necessary conditions for $Y(s)$ or $Z(s)$ to represent a physical network made up of passive elements. The conditions are necessary but are they sufficient? Brune, in his 1931 paper, showed that the requirement that a driving-point function be positive real was sufficient by demonstrating that a network could always be found to correspond to the positive real driving-point function. His sufficiency condition proof, a general method for synthesis, will be studied in a later chapter.

Let us reconsider our conclusion in Section 3.1 that the poles and zeros of $Y(s)$ cannot have positive real parts. Suppose that $Y(s)$ contains a pole of p_k of multiplicity r such that

$$Y(s) = \frac{p(s)}{q_1(s)(s - p_k)^r} = \frac{H(s - z_1) \cdots (s - z_n)}{(s - p_1) \cdots (s - p_k)^r \cdots (s - p_m)}$$

$$(3.63)$$

The partial fraction expansion of $Y(s)$ is

$$Y(s) = \frac{K_{p_k,r}}{(s - p_k)^r} + \frac{K_{p_k,r-1}}{(s - p_k)^{r-1}} + \cdots + \frac{K_{p_k,1}}{s - p_k}$$
$$+ \frac{K_{p_1}}{s - p_1} + \frac{K_{p_2}}{s - p_2} + \cdots + \frac{K_{p_m}}{s - p_m} \qquad (3.64)$$

Consider $Y(s)$ at points in the s plane very near to p_k. If we select points sufficiently near to p_k that the value of the first term in the partial fraction expansion of Eq. 3.64 is very large compared to all other terms, then*

$$Y(s) \cong \frac{K_{p_k,r}}{(s - p_k)^r}, \qquad s \to p_k$$
$$(3.65)$$

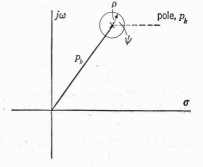

Fig. 3-7.   The location of a neighborhood near the pole p_k in the s plane.

Such a region is shown in Fig. 3-7. For convenience, assume that all points of interest near p_k are on a circle of radius ρ as shown. The equation for this circle is

$$s = p_k + \rho e^{j\psi} \qquad (3.66)$$

where, as shown in Fig. 3-7, p_k is a phasor which is added to the phasor expressed in polar form, $\rho e^{j\psi}$. Equation 3.66 may also be written

$$s - p_k = \rho e^{j\psi} \qquad (3.67)$$

Let $K_{p_k,r}$ be written in the polar form

$$K_{p_k,r} = |K| e^{j\beta} \qquad (3.68)$$

Substituting Eqs. 3.67 and 3.68 into Eq. 3.65 gives

$$Y(s) = \frac{K_{p_k,r}}{(s - p_k)^r} = \frac{|K| e^{j\beta}}{\rho^r e^{jr\psi}} = \frac{|K|}{\rho^r} e^{j(\beta - r\psi)} \qquad (3.69)$$

Then the real part of $Y(s)$ is

$$\text{Re } Y(s) = \frac{|K|}{\rho^r} \cos (\beta - r\psi) \qquad (3.70)$$

This equation is displayed in Fig. 3-8 with Re $Y(s)$ plotted as a function of ψ, showing the variation of the real part of $Y(s)$ for values of s

* If in doubt about this result, let $|s - p_k|$ be 10^{-6} and $r = 3$, and compare several terms of Eq. 3.64.

around the small circle of Fig. 3-7.   When we have traced the complete
path around the circle, the angle ψ will have ranged from 0 to 2π
radians.   And as ψ changes from 0 to 2π, Re $Y(s)$ will change sign
$2r$ times.   This means that in a neighborhood of the pole p_k, on a

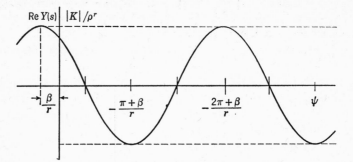

Fig. 3-8.   The variation of the real part of $Y(s)$ with the angle ψ defined in Fig. 3-7
for points in the neighborhood of the pole p_k.

circle of radius as small as we like, we can find places where Re $Y(s)$
is negative.   And this is true whether the pole p_k is in the left half or
right half of the s plane.   Now such behavior is not allowed in the
right half plane for positive real functions.   In the left half plane,
there are no restrictions on the real part of $Y(s)$, but in the right half
plane we insist that Re $Y(s) \geq 0$.
The only way this can be accomplished is to exclude poles from
the right half plane.   Since
$1/Y(s) = Z(s)$ is also a positive
real function, the same statement can be made about the
zeros of $Y(s)$.

There remains the boundary of
the right half plane, the imaginary axis, to take into account.
Can poles be located on the
imaginary axis and the function
be positive real?   Figure 3-9
shows such a pole with a circle

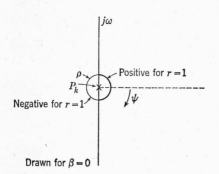

Fig. 3-9.   Pole located on the $j\omega$ axis
used to show that such poles must be
simple and their residues real and
positive.

of radius ρ around the pole.   From Eq. 3.70, we see that there
is but one possibility for Re $Y(s)$ to remain positive for values of s on
the circle and in the right half plane.   The possibility is $\beta = 0$ and
$r = 1$ so that Re $Y(s)$ is positive for Re $s \geq 0$.   The condition $r = 1$

implies that the pole on the imaginary axis must be simple; the condition $\beta = 0$ in Eq. 2.68 which expresses the residue as $|K|e^{j\beta}$ implies that the residue must be real and positive. We thus permit poles on the imaginary axis if they are simple and if their residues are real and positive. Zeros on the imaginary axis are similarly required to be simple, and as a dual of the residue requirement it is necessary that $dY(s)/ds$ be real and positive at each zero.

An interesting property is evident from Fig. 3-6 with the point s_1 chosen so that θ is nearly $\pi/2$ and ω very large. Since ϕ is limited in magnitude to be less than $\pi/2$, there cannot be an excess of finite poles or zeros greater than 1. Another approach to the same problem makes use of the argument condition. We first rearrange $Y(s)$ written in polynomial form as follows:

$$Y(s) = \frac{a_0 s^n + a_1 s^{n-1} + \cdots + a_{n-1}s + a_n}{b_0 s^m + b_1 s^{m-1} + \cdots + b_{m-1}s + b_m} \tag{3.71}$$

$$= H \frac{s^n \left(1 + \frac{a_1}{a_0}\frac{1}{s} + \cdots + \frac{a^n}{a_0}\frac{1}{s^n}\right)}{s^m \left(1 + \frac{b_1}{b_0}\frac{1}{s} + \cdots + \frac{b_m}{b_0}\frac{1}{s^m}\right)} \tag{3.72}$$

where $H = a_0/b_0$. For large values of s, the admittance function is approximately

$$Y(s) \cong Hs^{n-m} \tag{3.73}$$

Now we have written $Y(s)$ and s in the polar forms $Y(s) = |Y(s)|e^{j\phi}$ and $s = |s|e^{j\theta}$. We may evaluate ϕ in terms of θ from Eq. 3.73, since

$$\phi = \text{Arg } Hs^{n-m} = \text{Arg } H |s|^{n-m}e^{j(n-m)\theta} = (n-m)\theta \tag{3.74}$$

For values of s in the right half plane, $\text{Re } s \geq 0$, Eq. 3.48 requires that $|\phi| \leq |\theta|$. Substituting the value we have just found for ϕ into this equation gives

$$|(n-m)\theta| \leq |\theta| \qquad \text{or} \qquad |n-m| \leq 1 \tag{3.75}$$

Clearly, this equation can be satisfied only for $n - m = 1$, 0, or -1. And since $Y(s)$ has n zeros and m poles, it follows that the number of finite poles can differ from the number of finite zeros by 1 at most for positive real functions.*

A similar approach may be followed to show that the terms of lowest degree of the numerator and denominator polynomials of $Y(s)$ can

---

* If poles or zeros at infinity are counted, the total number of poles always equals the total number of zeros for any rational function.

differ in degree at most by unity. For small values of s, the lower degree terms become important and $Y(s)$ may be approximated as

$$Y(s) \cong \frac{\cdots + a_{n-2}s^2 + a_{n-1}s + a_n}{\cdots + b_{m-2}s^2 + b_{m-1}s + b_m} \qquad (3.76)$$

If $a_n \neq 0$ and $b_m \neq 0$, then $Y(0) = a_n/b_m$, which is a positive and real constant consistent with the requirements for positive real functions. Let $a_n = 0$ and $b_m \neq 0$. Then

$$\lim_{s \to 0} Y(s) = \lim_{s \to 0} \frac{a_{n-1}s}{b_m} \qquad (3.77)$$

which is a positive real function. However, if $a_n = 0$ and in addition $a_{n-1} = 0$, $b_m \neq 0$, then

$$\lim_{s \to 0} Y(s) = \lim_{s \to 0} \frac{a_{n-2}s^2}{b_m} \qquad (3.78)$$

and there is a zero of multiplicity 2 at $s = 0$. But $s = 0$, the origin, is part of the imaginary axis, and zeros on this axis must be simple. Hence, if $a_n = 0$, and $b_m \neq 0$, then a_{n-1} cannot be zero if $Y(s)$ is to be positive real. If $b_m = 0$, then by similar arguments b_{m-1} cannot be zero without there being a pole of multiplicity 2 at the origin, again not permitted for positive real functions.

TABLE 3-1
Properties of Positive Real Functions

1. The coefficients of the numerator and denominator polynomials in $Y(s) = p(s)/q(s)$ are real and positive. As a consequence:

(a) $Y(s)$ is real when s is real.

(b) Complex poles and zeros of $Y(s)$ occur in conjugate pairs.

(c) The scale factor, $H = a_0/b_0$, is real and positive.

2. The poles and zeros of $Y(s)$ have either negative or zero real parts.

3. Poles of $Y(s)$ on the imaginary axis must be simple and their residues must be real and positive. The same statement applies to the poles of $1/Y(s)$.

4. The degrees of the numerator and denominator polynomials in $Y(s)$ differ at most by 1. Thus the number of finite poles and finite zeros of $Y(s)$ differ at most by 1.

5. The terms of lowest degree in the numerator and denominator polynomials of $Y(s)$ differ in degree at most by 1. So $Y(s)$ has neither multiple poles nor zeros at the origin.

A number of the important properties of positive real functions are summarized in Table 3-1. They are necessary but not sufficient conditions for a function to be positive real.

Example 1. The function

$$Y_1(s) = 5 \frac{s^2 + 2s + 1}{s^3 + 2s^2 + 2s + 40} = 5 \frac{(s+1)(s+1)}{(s+4)(s^2 - 2s + 10)} \tag{3.79}$$

is not positive real because it has two poles in the right half plane.

$$Y_2(s) = \frac{s^3 + 5s}{s^4 + 2s^2 + 1} = \frac{s(s^2 + 5)}{(s^2 + 1)^2} \tag{3.80}$$

is not positive real because of the multiple poles on the imaginary axis.

FURTHER READING

For a clear and concise treatment of the material of this chapter, there is no better source than the original work of Otto Brune, cited at the beginning of the chapter. In addition, see Tuttle's *Network Synthesis*, Vol. I, pp. 163–220; Chapter 2 of Storer's *Passive Network Synthesis*; or Chapter 2 of Stewart's *Circuit Theory and Design*.

PROBLEMS

3-1. In the network shown in Fig. P3-1, the two switches are simultaneously closed at $t = 0$, connecting a capacitor with 1 coulomb of charge into the relaxed passive network.

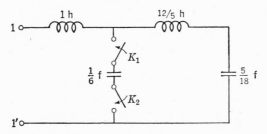

Fig. P3-1

(*a*) Show that the open-circuit voltage response at terminals 1-1' contains only pole frequencies of $Z(s)$.

(*b*) Show that the short-circuit current response at terminals 1-1' contains only zero frequencies of $Z(s)$.

3-2. Repeat Prob. 3-1 with the network modified by moving the two switches, K_1 and K_2, so that they are on either side of the $\frac{5}{18}$-farad capacitor.

3-3. To a passive network with driving-point admittance $Y(s)$ is applied a unit step voltage at $t = 0$. Assuming that the generator-network system is stable, as defined in the chapter, show that the real part of the poles of $Y(s)$ must be negative or zero. Under what condition(s) will the real part be zero? Explain.

3-4. Repeat the Brune derivation of Section 3.2 if the applied voltage is written in the form $v(t) = e^{\sigma_1 t} \cos \omega_1 t$, the form actually used by Brune in his 1931 paper.

(a) Find $i_1(t)$ in a form similar to Eq. 3.29.

(b) Continue the derivation started in part (a) until you arrive at a form equivalent to Eq. 3.44.

3-5. Consider the following function:

$$F(s) = \frac{1}{[(s - 1)^2 + 4]^3 (s + 1)}$$

(a) Expand $F(s)$ by partial fractions in the form of Eq. 3.64.

(b) Consider a region very near the multiple pole, $p_1 = 1 + j2$. In a circular disk around p_1 (say 10^{-6} units from p_1 but you may enlarge the radius to be an inch or so), crosshatch regions in which $\mathrm{Re}\,F(s)$ is negative, leaving blank the regions in which $\mathrm{Re}\,F(s)$ is positive.

3-6. An admittance function has its only finite zero at $s = -1$ and two poles at $-\alpha \pm j\beta$. Find the range of allowable values for α and β such that $Y(s)$ is positive real. Show the boundaries of allowed locations in the s plane.

3-7. $Y_1(s)$ and $Y_2(s)$ are two positive real functions. Consider the six combinations of these functions given below. Are these combinations of themselves positive real, or conditionally positive real? If conditionally positive real, what are the conditions?

(a) $Y_1 + Y_2$ (b) $Y_1 - Y_2$
(c) $Y_1 Y_2$ (d) Y_1/Y_2
(e) $(Y_1 Y_2)^{1/2}$ (f) $(Y_1/Y_2)^{1/2}$

3-8. The following functions are not positive real. Which of the various reasons in Table 3-1 may be cited in showing this?

(a) $\dfrac{(s^2 + 1)(s^2 + 2)}{s(s^2 + 3)}$ (b) $\dfrac{s^3 + 6s^2 + 2s + 1}{s + 4}$

(c) $\dfrac{s^2 + 2s + 1}{s^2}$ (d) $\dfrac{s^3 + 7s^2 + 15s + 9}{s^4 + 6s^2 + 9}$

3-9. Is the function $F(s) = s + \sqrt{s^2 + 1}$ positive real? Justify your answer.

3-10. Given the positive real admittance function

$$Y(s) = K \frac{(s + \alpha_1)(s + \alpha_2)}{(s + \beta_1)(s + \beta_2)}$$

show that if Re $Y(j\omega) = 0$ the frequency at which this occurs is

$$\omega = (\alpha_1\alpha_2\beta_1\beta_2)^{\frac{1}{4}}$$

3-11. Let $F(s)$ be a positive real function with zeros at $s = \pm j\omega_0$. Show that $F_1(s) = F(s)/(s^2 + \omega_0{}^2)$ is not positive real unless Re $F(j\omega)$ is zero for all ω.

3-12. The current response of a one terminal-pair LLFPB network due to the application of a unit step of voltage is

$$i(t) = a_1e^{-t} + a_2e^{-2t} + a_3$$

If the same network is excited at its driving terminals by a unit step of current, the voltage response is

$$v(t) = b_1e^{-4t} + b_2e^{-5t} + b_3$$

where the a and b coefficients are constants but their values are not known. The steady-state current due to a direct voltage of 50 volts is 1 ampere.

(a) Find $Z(s)$, the driving-point impedance of the network.
(b) Is this $Z(s)$ positive real? Give reasons.

Testing Driving-Point Functions

. . . . *4*

The conclusions of Chapter 3 will now be applied in establishing a testing procedure for driving-point functions. The procedure will be based on a study of the maximum modulus theorem, the Routh-Hurwitz criterion, and the Sturm test.

4.1 An application of the maximum modulus theorem

When one or more of the properties in Table 3-1 are not satisfied by a function under test, then that function is not positive real. But a function can satisfy all five requirements and yet not be positive real, these requirements being necessary but not sufficient. A complete test to establish the positive real character of a function apparently requires a demonstration that Re $Y(s) \geq 0$ for all right half plane values of s. This is a formidable task, especially when $Y(s)$ is made up of polynomials of degree higher than 2. Fortunately, equivalent sets of conditions better suited to the routine testing of functions may be found by making use of the maximum modulus theorem of complex variable theory.

The maximum modulus theorem tells us that a *rational* function with no singularities within and on the boundary of a region attains its maximum magnitude (modulus) in that region on the boundary and that this maximum is bounded.* If $|Y(s)|$ attains its maximum value on a boundary, then the theorem may be applied to $|1/Y(s)|$ to show that $|Y(s)|$ also attains its minimum value in the region on the boundary providing there are no zeros within or on the boundary of the

* See Guillemin, *The Mathematics of Circuit Analysis*, pp. 327–330; Tuttle, *Network Synthesis*, Vol. I, pp. 24–88; or any textbook on complex variable theory.

region. The meaning of the theorem with respect to maximum and minimum magnitudes is illustrated by Fig. 4-1. There the poles and zeros of an admittance function $Y(s)$ are identified together with a region containing no poles or zeros. The magnitude of $Y(s)$ at any point s_1 may be expressed as a quotient of phasor magnitude products, as in Eq. 3-53:

$$|Y(s)| = H \frac{M_1 M_2 \cdots M_n}{m_1 m_2 \cdots m_m} \tag{4.1}$$

At a point on the boundary of the region near to the pole p_1, the magnitude $|Y(s)|$ is larger because m_1, the distance from p_1 to s_1, is small.

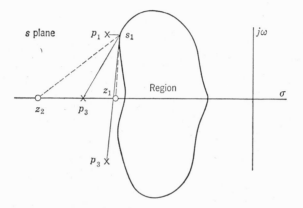

Fig. 4-1. Poles and zeros of $Y(s)$ and a region in which the maximum modulus theorem may be applied.

Moving the point s_1 to any other point inside the region will decrease $|Y(s)|$ since m_1 will change more rapidly than any other of the phasor distances in Eq. 4.1. At another point near to a zero, such as that shown on the negative real axis in Fig. 4-1, the distance M_1, from zero z_1 to a point on the boundary of the region, is small and $|Y(s)|$ is small. Again, moving the point to the interior of the region causes M_1 to increase more rapidly than other phasor distances change. From this discussion, we see that it is plausible that maximum and minimum magnitudes occur on the boundaries of the region, provided of course that the region contains no poles or zeros. (See Prob. 4-1.)

The maximum modulus theorem has a corollary for the minimum value of the real part of a function. Consider two functions, $F(s)$ and $Y(s)$, related by the equation,

$$F(s) = e^{-Y(s)} \tag{4.2}$$

Suppose that $Y(s)$ has no poles in a region. Then $F(s)$ has no singularities in that region and the maximum modulus theorem is applicable. If $Y(s) = U + jV$, then

$$\left|F(s)\right| = e^{-U} = e^{-\text{Re } Y(s)} \tag{4.3}$$

and the maximum value of $\left|F(s)\right|$ corresponds to the minimum value attained by Re $Y(s)$. Since the maximum value of $\left|F(s)\right|$ occurs on the boundary of the region enclosed, the minimum value of Re $Y(s)$ occurs on the boundary of a region without singularities.

Now the region in the complex frequency plane of particular interest to us is the right half plane, a region bounded by the imaginary axis

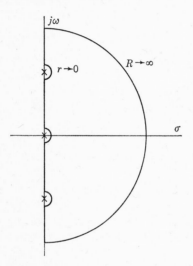

as shown in Fig. 4-2. In order that the real part corollary of the maximum modulus theorem may be applied, it is necessary that there be no poles within the region or *on the boundary* of the region. What about the boundary? Positive real functions are permitted to have simple poles on the boundary so long as the residues evaluated at the poles have real, positive values. This conflict is resolved by excluding consideration of the imaginary axis poles in applying the theorem. The exclusion is represented in Fig. 4-2 by drawing semicircles of infinitesimal radius around them, giving the distorted boundary shown. Application of the theorem to the region so defined tells us that the

Fig. 4-2. A contour enclosing the right half plane but avoiding poles on the imaginary axis.

minimum value of Re $Y(s)$ will be found on the imaginary axis boundary, and similarly that the minimum value of Re $Z(s) = \text{Re } [1/Y(s)]$ will also occur on this boundary. By this maneuver, the region of our concern is reduced from the vastness of the right half of the s plane to simply the imaginary axis. If we find the minimum value that Re $Y(j\omega)$ has for all values of ω, then, provided other conditions are satisfied so that the maximum modulus theorem may be applied, we are assured that this is the minimum value of Re $Y(s)$ for the entire right half plane, i.e., for Re $s \geq 0$.

In summary, the positive real character of a rational function may be tested by carrying out the following three steps:

(1) We first test to see that there are no poles or zeros* in the right half plane to be sure that the real part corollary of the maximum modulus theorem applies there.

(2) Poles of $Y(s)$ on the imaginary axis, excluded from the region to which the maximum modulus theorem is applied by a boundary distortion, must be simple and the residues evaluated at these poles must be real and positive.

(3) It is required that

$$\text{Re } Y(j\omega) \geq 0 \text{ for } 0 \leq \omega \leq \infty \tag{4.4}$$

[Testing in the complete range, $-\infty < \omega < +\infty$, is not necessary since Re $Y(j\omega)$ is an even function, as we will show later in this section.]

If a function satisfies these three requirements, then it is positive real. Thus these requirements are equivalent to the conditions:

and
$$\begin{aligned} \text{Re } Y(s) &\geq 0 \text{ for Re } s \geq 0 \\ Y(s) &\text{ real for } s \text{ real} \end{aligned} \tag{4.5}$$

The two sets of conditions may be used interchangeably to show that $Y(s)$ is a positive real function.

4.2   Properties of Hurwitz polynomials

In carrying out step (1) of the preceding section, a number of testing procedures are available to determine the sign of the real part of the roots of a polynomial without the necessity of finding numerical values for the roots. Two of these are the Routh rule and the Hurwitz criterion, sometimes grouped together as the Routh-Hurwitz criterion. We will now outline the method of use of the Hurwitz criterion which we will find is particularly suited to our needs.

Let the polynomial $p(s)$ be either the numerator or denominator of a positive real function. From our studies in the preceding section, we know that the zeros of $p(s)$ must fall into two classifications: (1) zeros with negative real parts, and (2) zeros with no real parts. This being the case, $p(s)$ may be written in the form

$$p(s) = s\, W(s)\, p_1(s) \tag{4.6}$$

---

* In the procedure given in some textbooks, the zeros are not so tested. If the function has right half plane zeros, it will fail the third test since it cannot be positive real. Since the third test is more difficult to complete than the first, testing of the zeros is recommended.

Here the multiplier s is present to account for the possibility of a zero at the origin, $W(s)$ is an *even* polynomial whose zeros may be conjugate imaginary or conjugate complex, and $p_1(s)$ is a polynomial whose zeros all have negative real parts. The polynomial $p_1(s)$ is known as a *Hurwitz polynomial* after the German mathematician who first studied the properties of these polynomials in 1896. The polynomial $p(s)$ of Eq. 4.6 is called a *modified* Hurwitz polynomial if $W(s)$ has simple zeros on the imaginary axis only.

Two properties of modified Hurwitz polynomials are immediately evident. Since $p(s)$ is formed from but three kinds of factors, namely,

$$(s + a), \ a \text{ real and positive or zero}$$
$$(s^2 + b^2), \ b \text{ real} \tag{4.7}$$
$$\text{and} \qquad (s^2 + 2cs + c^2 + d^2), \ c \text{ real and positive, } d \text{ real}$$

corresponding to real, imaginary, and complex zeros as shown in Fig.

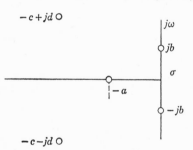

4-3, and no negative signs occur: (1) all of the coefficients of a Hurwitz polynomial must be real and positive, and (2) no powers of s can be absent between the term of highest degree and that of lowest degree, since without negative signs the possibility of term cancellation does not exist. An important exception to the second statement occurs with only

Fig. 4-3. Possible locations of the zeros of the modified Hurwitz polynomials, $p(s) = s \ W(s) \ p_1(s)$.

$(s^2 + b^2)$ factors present giving a polynomial with even power terms only, or $(s^2 + b^2)$ factors with an s multiplier giving odd power terms only in the polynomial.

We may separate the polynomial $p(s)$ into its even part $m(s)$ and its odd part $n(s)$ with m containing only even power terms and n only odd power terms of $p(s)$. For example, if

$$p(s) = s^6 + 3s^5 + 8s^4 + 15s^3 + 17s^2 + 12s + 4 \tag{4.8}$$

then
$$m(s) = s^6 + 8s^4 + 17s^2 + 4s^0 \tag{4.9}$$

and
$$n(s) = 3s^5 + 15s^3 + 12s \tag{4.10}$$

Note that the letters m and n are appropriately chosen since M is even with respect to its mid-point and N is odd with respect to its mid-point. The even and odd parts of $p(s)$ are defined by the equations

$$m(s) = \tfrac{1}{2}[p(s) + p(-s)] \qquad (4.11)$$

and
$$n(s) = \tfrac{1}{2}[p(s) - p(-s)] \qquad (4.12)$$

At this point we define a new function, which is the quotient of m to n (or n to m)

$$\psi(s) = \frac{m(s)}{n(s)} = \frac{p(s) + p(-s)}{p(s) - p(-s)} \qquad (4.13)$$

or
$$\psi(s) = \frac{\dfrac{p(s)}{p(-s)} + 1}{\dfrac{p(s)}{p(-s)} - 1} \qquad (4.14)$$

In the next few steps, we will show that $\psi(s)$ is positive real as an intermediate step in the derivation of the Hurwitz criterion. To do

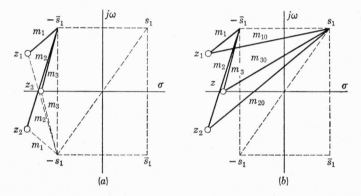

Fig. 4-4. Figures used to show by geometry that (a) $|p(-\bar{s}_1)| = |p(-s_1)|$, and (b) $|p(s_1)| > |p(-s_1)|$ providing s_1 has a right half plane location.

this requires that we examine the nature of the quotient $p(s)/p(-s)$ which appears in Eq. 4.14. In Fig. 4-4 is shown a point s_1 in the right half of the s plane. This point and points $\bar{s}_1$, $-s_1$, and $-\bar{s}_1$ form a *quad* of points with the same magnitude for real and imaginary parts. In the same figure are shown three zeros of $p(s)$ with left half plane locations as required of Hurwitz polynomials. We first observe that $|p(-\bar{s}_1)| = |p(-s_1)|$ since m_1, m_2, and m_3 as identified in Fig. 4-4(a) are the same phasor magnitudes, and

$$|p(-\bar{s}_1)| = |p(-s_1)| = m_1 m_2 m_3 \qquad (4.15)$$

In Fig. 4-4(b), we compare $|p(-\bar{s}_1)|$ with $|p(s_1)|$. Observe that m_1 and m_{10}, m_2 and m_{20}, m_3 and m_{30} have the same imaginary component.

but that the real component of m_{10} is greater than the real component of m_1, m_{20} greater than m_2, and m_{30} greater than m_3.   Then

$$m_{10} > m_1, \qquad m_{20} > m_2, \qquad m_{30} > m_3 \qquad (4.16)$$

and since

$$|p(s_1)| = m_{10}m_{20}m_{30} > m_1 m_2 m_3 \qquad (4.17)$$

we have, making use of Eq. 4.15,

$$|p(s_1)| > |p(-s_1)| \qquad (4.18)$$

or

$$\left| \frac{p(s)}{p(-s)} \right| > 1 \text{ for Re } s > 0 \qquad (4.19)$$

By similar reasoning, we show that

$$\left| \frac{p(s)}{p(-s)} \right| = 1 \text{ for Re } s = 0 \qquad (4.20)$$

and

$$\left| \frac{p(s)}{p(-s)} \right| < 1 \text{ for Re } s < 0 \qquad (4.21)$$

Let $p(s)/p(-s) = U + jV$ so that for Re $s \geq 0$,

$$\left| \frac{p(s)}{p(-s)} \right| = \sqrt{U^2 + V^2} \geq 1 \qquad (4.22)$$

Now

$$\text{Re } \psi(s) = \text{Re } \frac{U + jV + 1}{U + jV - 1} = \frac{U^2 + V^2 - 1}{(U - 1)^2 + V^2} \qquad (4.23)$$

The denominator of this equation is always nonnegative, and Eq. 4.22 compared with the numerator of this equation tells us that

$$\text{Re } \psi(s) \geq 0 \text{ for Re } s \geq 0 \qquad (4.24)$$

This conclusion together with the observation from Eq. 4.13 that $\psi(s)$ is real when s is real tells us that $\psi(s)$ is a positive real function and $1/\psi(s) = n(s)/m(s)$ is also positive real.

If $\psi(s)$ is formed to have a pole at infinity by selecting the function $m(s)$ or $n(s)$ of higher degree to be its numerator polynomial, then it can be expanded by partial fractions as

$$\psi(s) = \alpha_1 s + \frac{1}{\psi_1(s)} \qquad (4.25)$$

where

$$\alpha_1 = \lim_{s \to \infty} \frac{\psi(s)}{s} \qquad (4.26)$$

Then the function $\psi_1(s)$ has three important properties.   If the degrees of numerator and denominator of $\psi(s)$ are $n + 1$ and n, then those of $\psi_1(s)$ are n and $n - 1$.   Thus:

(1) $\psi_1(s)$ has a simpler form than $\psi(s)$.

(2) It follows directly that $\psi_1(s)$ has a pole at infinity.

(3) $\psi_1(s)$ is positive real as is established from the following observations:

(a) $\psi_1(s)$ is real when s is real since this property applies to the positive real $\psi(s)$ and to $\alpha_1 s$.

(b) $1/\psi_1(s)$ has the same poles as $\psi(s)$ except for the one at infinity, and therefore none are in the right half plane.

(c) The poles of $1/\psi_1(s)$ on the imaginary axis are the same as those of positive real $\psi(s)$ which are simple.   The residues of $1/\psi_1(s)$ evaluated at these simple poles are real and positive, the residues being unaffected by completing one step of a partial fraction expansion.

(d) Since $\mathrm{Re}\ \alpha_1 j\omega = 0$, it follows that

$$\mathrm{Re}\ \psi(j\omega) = \mathrm{Re}\ \frac{1}{\psi_1(j\omega)} \geq 0 \tag{4.27}$$

for all ω.

(e) Finally, since $1/\psi_1(s)$ is positive real, so is $\psi_1(s)$.

The expansion of Eq. 4.25 is next repeated for $\psi_1(s)$, then for $\psi_2(s)$, etc.   Each time, the degree of the numerator and denominator polynomials is reduced by 1 so that the expansion terminates in $\psi_{n-1} = \alpha_n s$, giving the finite *Stieltjes continued fraction*:

$$\psi(s) = \alpha_1 s + \cfrac{1}{\alpha_2 s + \cfrac{1}{\alpha_3 s + \cfrac{1}{\ddots + \cfrac{1}{\alpha_n s}}}} \tag{4.28}$$

The Hurwitz criterion states that it is necessary that the α coefficients be positive and real for $p(s)$ to be Hurwitz.   The sufficiency of the test requires that we examine the expansion in more detail by returning to the equation $p(s) = s\, W(s)\, p_1(s)$.   The presence or absence of the s multiplier is evident by inspection of $p(s)$ and so may be removed before testing. The product $W(s)\, p_1(s)$, however, must be tested by determining $W(s)$ to insure that its roots are imaginary and simple. This is accomplished by the procedure we describe next. Letting $p_1(s) = m_1(s) + n_1(s)$, we have

$$p_1 W = m_1 W + n_1 W \qquad (4.29)$$

Now $W(s)$ is an even function and the product of two even functions, $W(s)$ and $m_1(s)$, is also even, just as the product $W(s)\, n_1(s)$ is an odd function. From Eq. 4.29 the function $\psi(s)$ is next formed. We will consider the case in which the part of $p(s)$ of higher degree is in the numerator. Then if m_1 is of higher degree than n_1,

$$\psi(s) = \frac{m_1 W}{n_1 W} \qquad (4.30)$$

This function is next expanded as a Stieltjes continued fraction.

The first step in the expansion of $\psi(s)$ is accomplished by simple long division:

$$\psi(s) = \frac{m_1 W}{n_1 W} = \alpha_1 s + \frac{1}{\psi_1(s)} \qquad (4.31)$$

where $\qquad \dfrac{1}{\psi_1(s)} = \dfrac{m_1 W}{n_1 W} - \alpha_1 s = \dfrac{(m_1 - \alpha_1 n_1 s)W}{n_1 W} = \dfrac{m_2 W}{n_1 W} \qquad (4.32)$

Observe from this equation that W emerges unscathed in the same positions as in Eq. 4.30. Also, in this equation, $n_1 W$ is now of higher degree than $m_2 W$. If this quotient if first inverted, the long division may be repeated for $\psi_1(s)$ to give

$$\psi_1(s) = \frac{n_1 W}{m_2 W} = \alpha_2 s + \frac{1}{\psi_2(s)} \qquad (4.33)$$

where, as before,

$$\psi_2(s) = \frac{m_2 W}{(n_1 - \alpha_2 m_2 s)W} = \frac{m_2 W}{n_2 W} = \alpha_3 s + \frac{1}{\psi_3(s)} \qquad (4.34)$$

The pattern of the expansion is thus seen to be one of invert and divide one step, again invert and divide one step. If this procedure is continued, the next to last step is

$$\psi_{n-2}(s) = \frac{(As^2 + B)W}{CsW} = \alpha_{n-1} s + \frac{BW}{CsW} \qquad (4.35)$$

where $\alpha_{n-1} = A/C$, and A, B, and C are real constants. The last step in the expansion is

$$\psi_{n-1}(s) = \frac{CsW}{BW} = \alpha_n s \qquad (4.36)$$

At this point, $W(s)$ is recognized as the function that cancels. The expansion not only tells us whether $p(s)$ is Hurwitz, but also determines the function $W(s)$ which is needed in the testing procedure!

Two possible forms of even factors in $W(s)$ are recognized as (1) $(s^2 + \omega_j^2)$ and (2)

$$(s^2 + \alpha s + \beta)(s^2 - \alpha s + \beta) = s^4 + (2\beta - \alpha^2)s^2 + \beta^2 \qquad (4.37)$$

which has real positive coefficients providing that $2\beta \geq \alpha^2$. The first form is acceptable for $p(s)$ to be modified Hurwitz, but the second is not since it has two zeros in the right half plane. Thus it is necessary that the zeros of $W(s)$ be determined before conclusions can be reached concerning $p(s)$.

The procedure by which this examination of the zeros of $W(s)$ may be accomplished is derived by assuming that $W(s)$ has a zero of multiplicity α at $j\omega_1$. Then

$$W(s) = (s - j\omega_1)^\alpha Q(s) \qquad (4.38)$$

We next form the derivative of $W(s)$ with respect to s,

$$W'(s) = \alpha(s - j\omega_1)^{\alpha-1} Q(s) + (s - j\omega_1)^\alpha Q'(s) \qquad (4.39)$$

The quotient of $W'(s)$ to $W(s)$ is

$$\frac{W'(s)}{W(s)} = \frac{\alpha}{s - j\omega_1} + \frac{Q'(s)}{Q(s)}$$

$$= \frac{\alpha}{s - j\omega_1} + \frac{\alpha}{s + j\omega_1} + \frac{\beta}{s - j\omega_2} + \cdots \qquad (4.40)$$

where the last equation is found by repeatedly expanding factors like Q'/Q. In this equation, α, β, and all other residues are positive. If W'/W is a summation of terms like those in Eq. 4.40 with positive residues, this quotient is positive real with poles and zeros which alternate on the imaginary axis, and $W(s)$ is composed of factors like $s^2 + \omega_j^2$. In this case, the function under test $p(s)$ is modified Hurwitz providing zeros on the imaginary axis are simple (required by our definition of modified Hurwitz polynomials). We can determine the multiplicity of imaginary axis zeros of $W(s)$ by expanding W'/W as a continued fraction. If W has a zero of multiplicity n, W' will contain this zero with multiplicity $n - 1$. These multiple zeros will be common factors in the quotient W'/W but their presence will be detected by the premature termination of the continued fraction expansion.

If W'/W is not positive real, then the only possibility remaining is that W contain a quad of zeros of the form of Eq. 4.37. In this case $p(s)$ is *not* Hurwitz. Thus we see that a necessary and sufficient condition for $W(s)$ to have simple zeros on the imaginary axis is for W'/W to be positive real and its continued fraction expansion not to terminate prematurely.*

Example 1. Consider a polynomial of known zeros,

$$p(s) = s(s^2 + 2s + 1)(s^2 + s + 1)(s^2 + 4)$$
$$= s^7 + 3s^6 + 8s^5 + 15s^4 + 17s^3 + 12s^2 + 4s \qquad (4.41)$$

Note that all of the coefficients are real and positive as required and that no powers of s in the polynomial are missing. Polynomial $p(s)$ has a zero at $s = 0$ which may be removed by forming $p(s)/s$ before the testing starts. Then

$$\psi(s) = \frac{s^6 + 8s^4 + 17s^2 + 4}{3s^5 + 15s^3 + 12s} \qquad (4.42)$$

The formation of the continued fraction from $\psi(s)$ is done by synthetic division, a procedure also known as *Euclid's algorithm*. This algorithm is carried out in the following steps:

$$3s^5 + 15s^3 + 12s)s^6 + 8s^4 + 17s^2 + 4(\tfrac{1}{3}s \leftarrow \text{first division}$$
$$\underline{s^6 + 5s^4 + \ 4s^2}$$
$$3s^4 + 13s^2 + 4)3s^5 + 15s^3 + 12s(s \leftarrow \text{second division}$$
$$\underline{3s^5 + 13s^3 + \ 4s}$$
$$2s^3 + \ 8s)3s^4 + 13s^2 + 4(\tfrac{3}{2}s \leftarrow \text{third}$$
$$\underline{3s^4 + 12s^2}$$
$$s^2 + 4)2s^3 + 8s(2s \leftarrow \text{fourth}$$
$$\underline{2s^3 + 8s}$$
$$0$$

$$(4.43)$$

The continued fraction expansion is

$$\psi(s) = \tfrac{1}{3}s + \cfrac{1}{s + \cfrac{1}{\tfrac{3}{2}s + \cfrac{1}{2s}}} \qquad (4.44)$$

The coefficients of the continued fraction expansion ($\alpha_1 = \tfrac{1}{3}$, $\alpha_2 = 1$, $\alpha_3 = \tfrac{3}{2}$, and $\alpha_4 = 2$) are all real and positive so that the polynomial under test is Hurwitz and the zeros are in the left half plane, in agreement with the known zeros in Eq. 4.41. Also the polynomial $W(s)$ is recognized from the fourth division in the Euclid algorithm of Eq. 4.43 and is $W(s) = s^2 + 4$, again in

---

* Cf. E. J. Routh, *Dynamics of a System of Rigid Bodies*, originally published in 1860; reprinted by Dover Publications, New York, 1955, pp. 223–231.

agreement with Eq. 4.41.   This $W(s)$ would have been canceled in Eq. 4.42 had it been known, i.e.,

$$\psi(s) = \frac{s^6 + 8s^4 + 17s^2 + 4}{3s^5 + 15s^3 + 12s} = \frac{(s^4 + 4s^2 + 1)(s^2 + 4)}{(3s^3 + 3s)(s^2 + 4)} \qquad (4.45)$$

Example 2.   Consider

$$p(s) = 2s^6 + s^5 + 13s^4 + 6s^3 + 56s^2 + 25s + 25 \qquad (4.46)$$

$$\psi(s) = \frac{2s^6 + 13s^4 + 56s^2 + 25}{s^5 + 6s^3 + 25s} \qquad (4.47)$$

$$= 2s + \frac{1}{s\dfrac{s^4 + 6s^2 + 25}{s^4 + 6s^2 + 25}} \qquad (4.48)$$

Since $s^4 + 6s^2 + 25 = (s + 1 + j2)(s + 1 - j2)(s - 1 + j2)(s - 1 - j2)$, it follows that $p(s)$ is not Hurwitz.

Now we start at the other end of the partial fraction expansion and examine the consequences of each linear combination of terms.   As the continued fraction is *collapsed*, each combination like

$$\psi_{n-1}(s) + \frac{1}{\psi_n(s)\dfrac{W(s)}{W(s)}} = \frac{p_1(s)}{q_1(s)} \qquad (4.49)$$

is an odd function which is positive real providing that $W(s)$ has no right half plane zeros, and all α's are positive.   These properties apply to each step in collapsing the partial fraction and so apply to $\psi(s)$.

The Hurwitz criterion is applied to $p = Wp_1 = m + n$ by forming $\psi = (m/n)^{\pm 1}$ having a pole at infinity.   Providing $W(s)$ has simple, conjugate imaginary zeros only, p is Hurwitz if all of the α coefficients in the continued fraction expansion of $\psi(s)$ are real and positive.   These conditions are both necessary and sufficient.

4.3   The computation of residues

The second step of our testing procedure requires that we examine the poles and their residues for both $Y(s)$ and $1/Y(s)$ along the imaginary axis.   Such poles and zeros will have been detected in step (1) of Section 4.1 as a by-product of the Hurwitz test in the form of $W(s)$. The required residues are found by partial fraction expansion, a routine operation though sometimes tedious.   To amplify the meaning of the requirement that the residues of imaginary axis poles be real and positive, we next turn to an interpretation of residues in terms of phasors in the s plane.

Let $Y(s)$ be written in factored form,

$$Y(s) = H \frac{(s - z_1)(s - z_2) \cdots (s - z_n)}{(s - p_1)(s - p_2) \cdots (s - p_m)} \qquad (4.50)$$

If there are no multiple poles in $Y(s)$, then the partial fraction expansion is

$$Y(s) = \frac{K_{p_1}}{s - p_1} + \frac{K_{p_2}}{s - p_2} + \cdots + \frac{K_{p_m}}{s - p_m} \qquad (4.51)$$

where the coefficients $K_{p_1}, K_{p_2}, \cdots, K_{p_m}$ are the residues associated with the poles. The residues may be evaluated by use of Heaviside's expansion theorem in two steps: (1) multiply $Y(s)$ by $(s - p_k)$, and (2) let $s = p_k$, giving the residue K_{p_k}. Solving for K_{p_2}, for example, gives

$$K_{p_2} = H \frac{(s - z_1)(s - z_2) \cdots (s - z_n)}{(s - p_1)(s - p_3) \cdots (s - p_m)} \bigg|_{s = p_2} \qquad (4.52)$$

or

$$K_{p_2} = H \frac{(p_2 - z_1)(p_2 - z_2) \cdots (p_2 - z_n)}{(p_2 - p_1)(p_2 - p_3) \cdots (p_2 - p_m)} \qquad (4.53)$$

Any other residue may be evaluated in the same way. In Chapter 1, we interpreted factors like $p_2 - z_1$ as phasors directed from z_1 to p_2, as

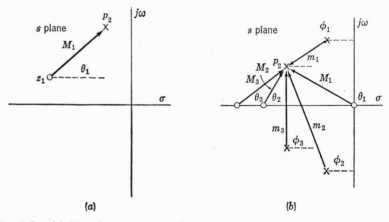

(a)   (b)

Fig. 4-5. (a) The phasor representation of the factor $p_2 - z_1$, and (b) the various phasors involved in the computation of the residue for a complex p_2.

shown in Fig. 4-5(a). When each factor in Eq. 4.53 is interpreted this way, there results an array of phasors each directed *toward* the pole associated with the desired residue as in Fig. 4-5(b). To evaluate the residue, each factor in Eq. 4.53 is written in polar form, with zero factors

$$p_2 - z_k = M_k e^{j\theta_k} \tag{4.54}$$

and pole factors

$$p_2 - p_k = m_k e^{j\phi_k} \tag{4.55}$$

Then the residue is, for pole p_2,

$$K_{p_2} = H \frac{M_1 M_2 M_3 \cdots M_n}{m_1 m_3 m_4 \cdots m_m} e^{j(\theta_1 + \theta_2 + \cdots - \phi_1 - \phi_3 - \cdots)} \tag{4.56}$$

where m_2 and ϕ_2 are missing here, and in the evaluation of any residue K_{p_k}, m_k and ϕ_k will be similarly missing. The use of this phasor representation aids in interpreting the meaning of the residue of a pole,

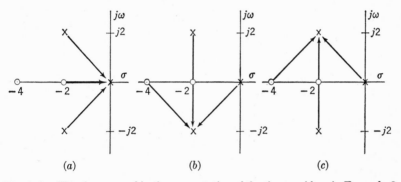

(a)   (b)   (c)

Fig. 4-6. The phasors used in the computation of the three residues in Example 3: (a) for K_0, (b) for K_{-2-j2}, (c) for K_{-2+j2}.

although computation with ruler and protractor is usually too inaccurate for use in synthesis.

Example 3. In the partial fraction expansion

$$Y(s) = \frac{(s+2)(s+4)}{s[(s+2)^2 + 2^2]} = \frac{K_0}{s} + \frac{K_{-2-j2}}{s+2+j2} + \frac{K_{-2+j2}}{s+2-j2} \tag{4.57}$$

the residues may be evaluated using Eq. 4.56 by referring to the phasors represented in Fig. 4-6. From the three figures, we see that

$$K_0 = \frac{2 \times 4}{2\sqrt{2} \times 2\sqrt{2}} e^{j(0° + 0° + 45° - 45°)} = 1 \tag{4.58}$$

$$K_{-2-j2} = \frac{2 \times 2\sqrt{2}}{4 \times 2\sqrt{2}} e^{j(-90° - 45° + 90° + 135°)} = j\tfrac{1}{2} \tag{4.59}$$

and

$$K_{-2+j2} = \frac{2 \times 2\sqrt{2}}{4 \times 2\sqrt{2}} e^{j(90° + 45° - 90° - 135°)} = -j\tfrac{1}{2} \tag{4.60}$$

The last equation tells us that the residues of conjugate poles are themselves conjugate.

A word of caution: This graphical method applies only for simple poles. For a pole of multiplicity r, the partial fraction expansion is

$$\frac{p(s)}{(s - p_1)^r q_1(s)} = \frac{K_{p_1,r}}{(s - p_1)^r} + \frac{K_{p_1,r-1}}{(s - p_1)^{r-1}} + \cdots + \frac{K_{p_1,1}}{s - p_1} + \cdots \tag{4.61}$$

and the method just described applies to the evaluation of $K_{p_1,r}$ only. (See Prob. 4-11 for an equation that applies to the evaluation of other coefficients.) However, we need not be concerned about multiple poles in this chapter because we intend to use this method in the evaluation of residues of simple imaginary axis poles only. Such a pole is shown in Fig. 4-7. For the residue to be real at this pole, Eq. 4.56 tells us that it is necessary that

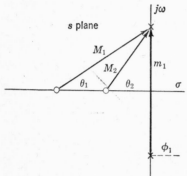

$$\theta_1 + \theta_2 + \theta_3 + \cdots - \phi_1 - \phi_2 - \phi_3 - \phi_4 - \cdots = 0 \tag{4.62}$$

Fig. 4-7. At imaginary axis poles, it is necessary that the summation of θ's just equal the summation of ϕ's if the function is to be positive real.

i.e., the summation of the zero factor angles must just exactly equal the summation of the pole factor angles. This is a very exacting requirement we make of these residues and a very exacting requirement made of functions to be positive real. It is surprising that any functions ever make the grade.

Another expression for the residue of a network function evaluated at one of its poles finds application in our study. Let $Z(s)$ be written as a quotient of $m(s)$ and $q(s)$, and let p_i be a simple pole of $Z(s)$. The residue is evaluated as follows:

$$K_{p_i} = \lim_{s \to p_i} (s - p_i) \frac{m(s)}{q(s)} \tag{4.63}$$

Now $q(p_i) = 0$ since p_i is a zero of $q(s)$ and this quantity may be subtracted from $q(s)$ without changing its value. Then

$$K_{p_i} = \lim_{s \to p_i} \frac{m(s)}{\dfrac{q(s) - q(p_i)}{s - p_i}} \tag{4.64}$$

or
$$K_{p_i} = \frac{\lim\limits_{s \to p_i} m(s)}{\lim\limits_{s \to p_i} \dfrac{q(s) - q(p_i)}{s - p_i}} \tag{4.65}$$

Finally, we recognize the denominator as the definition of the derivative evaluated at the pole p_i so that

$$K_{p_i} = \frac{m(p_i)}{\left.\dfrac{d}{ds} q(s)\right|_{p_i}} \tag{4.66}$$

4.4 Even and odd functions

We come next to the third step, the last hurdle $Y(s)$ must clear before it is a full-fledged positive real function. It is necessary that Re $Y(j\omega)$ be positive or zero for all values of ω. To compute Re $Y(j\omega)$ from $Y(s) = p(s)/q(s)$, we first separate $p(s)$ and $q(s)$ into even and odd parts,

$$Y(s) = \frac{p(s)}{q(s)} = \frac{m_1(s) + n_1(s)}{m_2(s) + n_2(s)} \tag{4.67}$$

If we multiply $Y(s)$ by $q(-s)/q(-s)$ or $(m_2 - n_2)/(m_2 - n_2)$, there results

$$Y(s) = \frac{p(s) \, q(-s)}{q(s) \, q(-s)} = \frac{(m_1 m_2 - n_1 n_2) + (m_2 n_1 - m_1 n_2)}{m_2{}^2 - n_2{}^2} \tag{4.68}$$

Now since the product of two even functions or two odd functions is itself an even function, while the product of an even and an odd function is odd, we see that

$$\text{even part of } Y(s) = \text{Ev } Y(s) = \frac{m_1 m_2 - n_1 n_2}{m_2{}^2 - n_2{}^2} \tag{4.69}$$

$$\text{odd part of } Y(s) = \text{Od } Y(s) = \frac{m_2 n_1 - m_1 n_2}{m_2{}^2 - n_2{}^2} \tag{4.70}$$

The substitution of $s = j\omega$ into an even polynomial gives a real number, and the substitution of $s = j\omega$ into an odd polynomial gives an imaginary number. Hence

$$\text{Ev } Y(s) \Big|_{s = j\omega} = \text{Re } Y(j\omega) \tag{4.71}$$

and
$$\text{Od } Y(s) \Big|_{s = j\omega} = j \text{ Im } Y(j\omega) \tag{4.72}$$

From these equations, we see that Re $Y(j\omega)$ is an *even* function in ω and Im $Y(s)$ is *odd* in ω.

The denominator of Eq. 4.68 is $q(s) \, q(-s)$. When $s = j\omega$, $q(j\omega)$ and $q(-j\omega)$ are conjugates and their product is a magnitude squared which is always positive, i.e.,

$$(m_2 + n_2)(m_2 - n_2) \Big|_{s=j\omega} = q(j\omega) \, q(-j\omega) = |q(j\omega)|^2 > 0 \quad (4.73)$$

Because the denominator of Re $Y(j\omega)$ is always positive, it need not be considered in testing the sign of Re $Y(j\omega)$. We need only consider the numerator, which is

$$m_1 m_2 - n_1 n_2 \Big|_{s=j\omega} \equiv A(\omega^2) \quad (4.74)$$

This even polynomial may be written as

$$A(\omega^2) = A_0\omega^{2r} + A_2\omega^{2r-2} + \cdots + A_{2r-2}\omega^2 + A_{2r} \quad (4.75)$$

or $\quad A(\omega^2) = A_0(\omega^2 + \delta_1{}^2)(\omega^2 + \delta_2{}^2) \cdots (\omega^2 + \delta_r{}^2) \quad (4.76)$

where $2r$ is equal to or less than the sum of the degrees of $p(s)$ and $q(s)$, depending on which terms cancel in forming $m_1 m_2 - n_1 n_2$ with $s = j\omega$. What conditions can we give that are sufficient to insure that $A(\omega^2)$ will be positive or zero, but never negative? From Eq. 4.75, we see that if all of the A coefficients are positive, then there is no doubt that $A(\omega^2) \geq 0$. But can some coefficients be negative and $A(\omega^2)$ still be positive for all ω? The answer to this question is that some coefficients can be negative, as we shall see. But at least it is necessary that the first and last coefficients, A_0 and A_{2r}, be positive, for otherwise $A(\omega^2)$ would be negative for very large ω or very small ω.

Turning next to the second form of $A(\omega^2)$, Eq. 4.76, observe that the roots may be (1) real and positive, (2) real and negative, or (3) complex if conjugate. For these three possibilities, the requirement that $A(\omega^2) \geq 0$ leads to the conclusions that:

(1) Terms like $\omega^2 + \delta_1{}^2$ for $\delta_1{}^2$ real and positive are always positive and so are permitted.

(2) Terms like $\omega^2 + \delta_2{}^2$ for $\delta_2{}^2$ real and negative are only conditionally positive and so must be of even multiplicity to be permitted, i.e., $\omega^2 + \delta_2{}^2$ must be raised to some even power.

(3) Complex terms occurring in conjugate pairs like $(\omega^2 + \delta_3{}^2) \times (\omega^2 + \overline{\delta_3{}^2})$ are themselves conjugate complex and hence have a prod-

uct which is the square of an absolute value and so positive. Hence these terms are permitted.

Thus, the sole restriction for $A(\omega^2) \geq 0$ is that there be no positive real zeros of $A(\omega^2)$ of odd multiplicity!

To insure that this condition is fulfilled, we may do one of the following:

(1) Factor $A(\omega^2)$. This may be difficult if the degree of the polynomial in ω^2 is high.

(2) Plot $A(\omega^2)$ over a sufficiently large range of ω to insure that it is never negative.*

(3) Make use of Sturm's theorem to determine the presence of real zeros within any interval of ω, including 0 to ∞.

An example will illustrate the first possibility, after which we will turn to a study of Sturm's theorem.

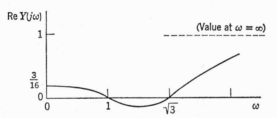

Fig. 4-8.   The real part of $Y(j\omega)$ for Example 4.   The function is not positive real.

Example 4.   Consider the admittance function given by the equation

$$Y(s) = \frac{s^2 + \frac{3}{4}s + \frac{3}{4}}{s^2 + s + 4} \tag{4.77}$$

From Eq. 4.69

$$\text{Ev } Y(s) = \frac{(s^2 + \frac{3}{4})(s^2 + 4) - (\frac{3}{4}s)s}{(s^2 + 4)^2 - s^2} \tag{4.78}$$

$$= \frac{s^4 + 4s^2 + 3}{s^4 + 7s^2 + 16} \tag{4.79}$$

From Eq. 4.75,

$$A(\omega^2) = \omega^4 - 4\omega^2 + 3 = (\omega^2 - 3)(\omega^2 - 1) \tag{4.80}$$

Then Re $Y(j\omega)$ has zeros of odd multiplicity with real positive values and is negative from $\omega = 1$ to $\omega = \sqrt{3}$, as shown in Fig. 4-8. The function being considered is *not* positive real. But then, most functions are not.

---

* This may be done by digital computer. See G. H. Leichner, "Network synthesis using a digital computer," *Proc. N.E.C.*, **12**, 830–838 (1956).

4.5 Sturm's theorem

In describing Sturm's theorem,* we first introduce a new variable $x = \omega^2$ and relabel our $A(\omega^2)$ function to be $P_0(x)$. Then since the $A_0, A_2, \cdots, A_{2r}$ coefficients in the series for $A(\omega^2)$ are no longer suitable because of their subscripts, we use a coefficients so that $A(\omega^2)$ is transformed to

$$P_0(x) = a_0 x^r + a_1 x^{r-1} + \cdots + a_{r-1} x + a_r \qquad (4.81)$$

In this form, the function is the first of a set of functions known as Sturm functions. The second is found from the first by differentiation, which gives

$$P_1(x) = r a_0 x^{r-1} + \cdots + 2 a_{r-2} x + a_{r-1} \qquad (4.82)$$

The remaining Sturm functions are found by a variation of the Euclid algorithm used earlier in the Hurwitz test. If $P_0(x)$ is divided by $P_1(x)$ to give a two-term quotient, the remainder is the negative of the next Sturm function, $P_2(x)$, i.e.,

$$\frac{P_0}{P_1} = \beta_1 x + \beta_2 + \frac{-P_2}{P_1} \qquad (4.83)$$

and $P_2(x)$ is 1 degree lower than $P_1(x)$. The division is repeated to give the next Sturm function,

$$\frac{P_1}{P_2} = \beta_3 x + \beta_4 + \frac{-P_3}{P_2} \qquad (4.84)$$

The algorithm may be continued until (1) the last Sturm function P_r of degree 0 is found, or (2) the remainder is identically zero. We will postpone consideration of the second possibility and assume that we form all of the Sturm functions, $P_0, P_1, P_2, \cdots, P_r$. The use of these functions will be explained in terms of Table 4-1. In the table, v_a and v_b are the number of changes in sign as we scan across the table from P_0 to P_r. Sturm's theorem tells us that the number of real zeros

---

* For more detail, see such textbooks as W. V. Lovitt, *Elementary Theory of Equations*, Prentice-Hall, New York, 1939, pp. 121–128, or L. E. Dickson, *New First Course in the Theory of Equations*, John Wiley & Sons, New York, 1939, pp. 75 ff.

of $P_0(x)$ in the interval $x = a$ to $x = b$ is $|v_a - v_b|$. By using as limits $x = 0$ and $x = \infty$, the total number of real zeros of $P_0(x)$ is found. By the repeated use of the theorem for various values of x, the values

TABLE 4-1

Limits	P_0	P_1	P_2	P_3	$\cdots$	P_r	Variations in Sign
$x = a$	$+$	$-$	$-$	$+$	$\cdots$	$+$	v_a
$x = b$	$+$	$+$	$-$	$-$	$\cdots$	$+$	v_b

of the zeros may be found with any desired accuracy. Observe incidentally that the β's of Eqs. 4.83 and 4.84 are not used in the actual testing, but are by-products determined in finding the next Sturm function.

Example 5. For this example, let us study the $A(\omega^2)$ of Example 4, given by Eq. 4.80. For $A(\omega^2) = \omega^4 - 4\omega^2 + 3$, the corresponding first Sturm functions

$$P_0(x) = x^2 - 4x + 3 \tag{4.85}$$

and

$$P_1(x) = 2x - 4 \tag{4.86}$$

Dividing P_0 by P_1,

$$\begin{array}{r} 2x - 4)\overline{x^2 - 4x + 3}(\tfrac{1}{2}x - 1 \\ \underline{x^2 - 2x} \\ -2x + 3 \\ \underline{-2x + 4} \\ -1(= -P_2) \end{array} \tag{4.87}$$

From P_0, P_1, and $P_2 = +1$, as just determined, we construct Table 4-2. This

TABLE 4-2

Sign of:

Limits	P_0	P_1	P_2	Sign Changes
$x = 0$	$+$	$-$	$+$	2
$x = \infty$	$+$	$+$	$+$	0

table shows that there are two real zeros from $x = 0$ to $x = \infty$, as we already know by factoring $P_0(x)$. The manner in which the zeros can be located in a more difficult problem is shown in Table 4-3. From this table, we see that the first zero is bounded by $x = \tfrac{1}{2}$ and $x = \tfrac{3}{2}$, and the second zero by $x = \tfrac{3}{2}$ and $x = 4$.

TABLE 4-3

Sign of:

Limits	P_0	P_1	P_2	Sign Changes
0	$+$	$-$	$+$	2
$\frac{1}{2}$	$+$	$-$	$+$	2
$\frac{3}{2}$	$-$	$-$	$+$	1
4	$+$	$+$	$+$	0

Example 6. Consider a function of degree 4,

$$P_0(x) = x^4 - 8x^3 + 23x^2 - 28x + 12 \tag{4.88}$$

from which the next Sturm function is found by differentiation,

$$P_1(x) = 4x^3 - 24x^2 + 46x - 28 \tag{4.89}$$

The first division gives

$$
\begin{array}{r}
4x^3 - 24x^2 + 46x - 28)\overline{x^4 - 8x^3 + 23x^2 - 28x + 12}(\tfrac{1}{4}x - \tfrac{1}{2} \\
\underline{x^4 - 6x^3 + \tfrac{23}{2}x^2 - \tfrac{28}{4}x} \\
- 2x^3 + \tfrac{23}{2}x^2 - 21x + 12 \\
\underline{- 2x^3 + 12x^2 - 23x + 14} \\
- \tfrac{1}{2}x^2 + 2x - 2[= -P_2(x)]
\end{array}
\tag{4.90}
$$

Before going through the next cycle to find $P_3(x)$, observe that if Eq. 4.84 is multiplied by $1/k_1$, where k_1 is a positive constant, there results

$$\frac{P_1}{k_1 P_2} = \frac{\beta_3}{k_1} x + \frac{\beta_4}{k_1} + \frac{-P_3}{k_1 P_2} \tag{4.91}$$

showing that if P_1 is divided by $k_1 P_2$ rather than P_2, the β's are changed but the value of P_3 *is not.* Hence, to simplify the next step numerically, let us multiply $P_2(x)$ in Eq. 4.90 by 2. Then the next division is

$$
\begin{array}{r}
x^2 - 4x + 4)\overline{4x^3 - 24x^2 + 46x - 28}(4x - 8 \\
\underline{4x^3 - 16x^2 + 16x} \\
- 8x^2 + 30x - 28 \\
\underline{- 8x^2 + 32x - 32} \\
- 2x + 4[= -P_3(x)]
\end{array}
\tag{4.92}
$$

and $P_3(x) = 2x - 4$. Multiplying P_3 by $\tfrac{1}{2}$ and dividing into $k_1 P_2$ gives

$$
\begin{array}{r}
x - 2)\overline{x^2 - 4x + 4}(x - 2 \\
\underline{x^2 - 2x} \\
- 2x + 4 \\
\underline{- 2x + 4} \\
0
\end{array}
\tag{4.93}
$$

The expansion has terminated prematurely by there being a zero remainder, a possibility mentioned earlier. What has happend? If P_0 has a multiple zero, its derivative P_1 has this zero also. Then in the first division of P_0 by P_1 there was a common factor in P_0 and P_1, just as there was a common factor $W(s)$ in the division of m_1 by n_1 in the Hurwitz test (cf. Eq. 4.30). And just as in the Hurwitz test the common factor was revealed in the last step, so in the expansion for the Sturm test the Sturm function *before* the zero remainder is the common factor in P_0 and P_1. This common factor for this example is $P_3 = 2x - 4 = 2(x - 2)$, meaning that $(x - 2)^2$ must be in $P_0(x)$. Then by division of $(x - 2)^2$ into P_0,

$$\begin{aligned} P_0(x) &= (x^2 - 4x + 4)(x^2 - 4x + 3) \\ &= (x - 2)^2(x - 1)(x - 3) \end{aligned} \tag{4.94}$$

and our testing need continue no further, since $x = 1$ and $x = 3$ are zeros of odd multiplicity. This example has shown how the use of Sturm's theorem need not always proceed to the construction of a table, because the formation of the Sturm functions will reveal the presence of multiple zeros in $P_0(x)$.

Suppose that the Sturm function before the occurrence of the zero remainder is of degree 3:

$$P_g(x) = b_0 x^3 + b_1 x^2 + b_2 x + b_3 \tag{4.95}$$

What do we know about the $P_0(x)$ from which this $P_g(x)$ was generated? By using the Sturm test on $P_g(x)$, we can tell whether it contains positive, real zeros. Further, these zeros can be found by repeated use of Sturm's theorem, or in some other way.* If the Sturm test does reveal real positive zeros in $P_g(x)$, then there are three possibilities for zeros of $P_0(x)$:

(1) There may be three zeros of $P_0(x)$ of multiplicity 2, e.g., $(x - 1)^2(x - 2)^2(x - 3)^2$.

(2) There may be one zero of multiplicity 2 and one of multiplicity 3, e.g., $(x - 1)^3(x - 2)^2$.

(3) Finally, there may be one zero of $P_0(x)$ of multiplicity 4, e.g., $(x - 1)^4$.

For the first and last cases, we must then examine the remaining zeros of $P_0(x)$; for the second case, the search for positive, real zeros of odd multiplicity has ended and the function under test is not positive real. But if a function has satisfied all previous tests outlined in this section, and it can be shown with the Sturm test that the zeros of $P_0(x)$ are

---

* A useful fact to remember in factoring polynomials like

$$a_0 x^n + a_1 x^{n-1} + \cdots + a_{n-1} x + a_n$$

is that with $a_0 = 1$, a_1 is the sum of the negative of the zeros while a_n is the product of the negative of the zeros of the polynomial.

negative real, complex, or positive real and of even multiplicity, then the function under test *is* positive real.

4.6 An alternative test for positive real character

An alternative testing procedure that avoids the necessity of computing residues has been given by Talbot* and is derived from the properties of the bilinear transformation,

$$W = \frac{Y-1}{Y+1} \quad \text{or} \quad Y = \frac{1+W}{1-W} \tag{4.96}$$

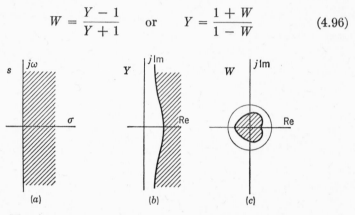

Fig. 4-9. Mapping properties of the bilinear transformation $W = (Y-1)/(Y+1)$ in the s, Y, and W planes.

The specific property to be used is illustrated by Fig. 4-9, which shows that

$$\text{Re } Y(s) \gtreqless 0 \text{ implies } |W(s)| \lesseqgtr 1 \tag{4.97}$$

and conversely. We are searching for requirements to be imposed on $W(s)$ in order that $Y(s)$ be positive real. From the last equation, we see that

$$|W(s)| \leq 1 \text{ for Re } s \geq 0 \tag{4.98}$$

is completely equivalent to

$$\text{Re } Y(s) \geq 0 \text{ for Re } s \geq 0 \tag{4.99}$$

Also, when $W(s)$ is real in Eq. 4.96, $Y(s)$ is also real. Then if $Y(s)$ is real when s is real, $W(s)$ is also real when s is real. Comparing these

---

* "A new method of synthesis of reactance networks," Monograph No. 77, *Proc. I.E.E. (London), Part IV*, **101**, 73–90 (1954). See his theorem 4.

observations with the defining equations for positive real functions, Eqs. 3.52, we see that an alternative set of necessary and sufficient conditions for a positive real function are contained in the following statement:

$Y(s) = [1 + W(s)]/[1 - W(s)]$ is positive real if (a) $W(s)$ is real when s is real, and (b) $|W(s)| \leq 1$ when Re $s \geq 0$.

The second part of the requirement may be stated in terms of equivalent conditions better suited for use in testing. If $W(s)$ has no poles in the right half plane or on the imaginary axis, then by the maximum modulus theorem it is necessary only that

$$|W(j\omega)| \leq 1, \qquad 0 \leq \omega \leq \infty \tag{4.100}$$

To insure that the maximum modulus theorem applies, we observe that if $Y(s) = p(s)/q(s)$, then

$$W(s) = \frac{p(s) - q(s)}{p(s) + q(s)} \tag{4.101}$$

and, in terms of this equation, it is required that $p(s) + q(s)$ be strictly Hurwitz* (not *modified* Hurwitz). This is insured if the associated continued fraction expansion results in positive α coefficients only, and the expansion does *not* terminate prematurely (since this would indicate imaginary axis roots). Finally, we observe that from the transformation of Eq. 4.97, $|W(j\omega)| \leq 1$ for all ω implies Re $Y(j\omega) \geq 0$ for all ω. Thus:

$Y(s) = p(s)/q(s)$ is positive real if (a) $Y(s)$ is real when s is real, (b) $p(s) + q(s)$ is Hurwitz, and (c) Re $Y(j\omega) \geq 0$ for all ω.

With this simplification, a complete testing procedure may be written as given in Table 4-4. It is not at all necessary that the testing be done in the order given in the table. Experience will show, however, that the steps are generally in the order of increasing difficulty. If a function is not positive real, it is better that it fail the requirement demanding the minimum expenditure of your effort. If it is positive real, then it is necessary to carry out *every* step in the table to show it. These conclusions are summarized in Tables 4-4 and 4-5.

---

* We assume that all factors common to $p(s)$ and $q(s)$ are removed before the polynomial $p + q$ is formed.

TABLE 4-4
A Procedure for Testing for Positive Real Character
of Rational Polynomial Quotients*

1. *Inspection test for necessary conditions.* It is required that:

(a) All polynomial coefficients be real and positive.

(b) Degrees of numerator and denominator polynomials differ at most by 1.

(c) Numerator and denominator terms of lowest degree differ at most by 1.

(d) Imaginary axis poles and zeros be simple.

(e) There be no missing terms in numerator and denominator polynomials unless all even or all odd terms are missing.

2. *Test for necessary and sufficient conditions:*

(a) $Y(s)$ must be real when s is real.

(b) If $Y(s) = p(s)/q(s)$, then $p(s) + q(s)$ must be Hurwitz.
This requires that:

      i. the continued fraction expansion of the Hurwitz test give only real and positive α's, and

      ii. the continued fraction not end prematurely.

(c) In order that Re $Y(j\omega) \geq 0$ for all ω, it is necessary and sufficient that

$$A(\omega^2) = m_1 m_2 - n_1 n_2 \Big|_{s=j\omega}$$

have no real positive roots of odd multiplicity. This may be determined by factoring $A(\omega^2)$ or by the use of Sturm's theorem.

---

* These requirements assume that all common factors in numerator and denominator polynomials have been removed.

Example 7. Consider the function

$$Y(s) = \frac{2s^2 + s + 1}{s^2 + s + 2} \tag{4.102}$$

The inspection test, step 1 in Table 4-4, reveals no obvious defects. Poles and zeros are clearly in the left half plane (from the quadratic formula), so that the residue test need not be carried out. It is only necessary to carry out step 2(c).

$$m_1 m_2 - n_1 n_2 \Big|_{s=j\omega} = 2(\omega^4 - 2\omega^2 + 1) = 2(\omega^2 - 1)^2 \tag{4.103}$$

This function is always positive or zero and the function is positive real. Note that $Y(j1) = 0 + j1$.

Example 8. The function

$$Y(s) = \frac{2s^3 + 2s^2 + 3s + 2}{s^2 + 1} \tag{4.104}$$

TABLE 4-5
Positive Real Function Equivalent Requirements

1. For $Y(s)$ to be a *real function*, $Y(s)$ must be real when s is real.   Equivalent statements:

  (a) Arg $Y(s) = 0$ or π when Arg $s = 0$.

  (b) $W = (Y - 1)/(Y + 1)$ is real when s is real.

2. For $Y(s)$ to be a *positive real function*, condition 1 and any of the following six equivalent conditions are required:

  (a) Re $Y(s) \geq 0$ for Re $s \geq 0$.

  (b) $\big|$Arg $Y(s)\big| \leq \big|$Arg $s\big|$ for $\big|$Arg $s\big| \leq \pi/2$.

  (c) i. $Y(s)$ has no poles in the right half plane.

   ii. Imaginary axis poles of $Y(s)$ are simple; residues evaluated at these poles are real and positive.

   iii. Re $Y(j\omega) \geq 0$, $0 \leq \omega \leq \infty$.

  (d) $W(s) = (Y - 1)/(Y + 1) \leq 1$, for Re $s \geq 0$.

  (e) i. $W(s)$ has no poles on the imaginary axis or in the right half plane.

   ii. $\big|W(j\omega)\big| \leq 1$, $0 \leq \omega \leq \infty$.

  (f) i. If $Y = p/q$, $p + q$ must be Hurwitz.

   ii. Re $Y(j\omega) \geq 0$, $0 \leq \omega \leq \infty$.

---

is slightly more complicated than the function in Example 7, but still passes the requirements of step 1 in Table 4-4.   The poles are seen to be at $s = \pm j1$. The Hurwitz test is successful.

$$3s^2 + 3)2s^3 + 3s(\tfrac{2}{3}s$$
$$\underline{2s^3 + 2s}$$
$$s)3s^2 + 3(3s$$
$$\underline{3s^2} \qquad\qquad (4.105)$$
$$3)s(\tfrac{1}{3}s$$
$$\underline{s}$$
$$0$$

The real part test of step 2(c) shows that

$$m_1 m_2 - n_1 n_2 \Big|_{s=j\omega} = (2s^2 + 2)(s^2 + 1) \Big|_{s=j\omega} = 2(\omega^2 - 1)^2 \quad (4.106)$$

which is always positive or zero as required.   All of the tests are successful and the function $Y(s)$ of Eq. 4.104 is positive real.

FURTHER READING

The properties of positive real functions are discussed in Guillemin's *The Mathematics of Circuit Analysis*, pp. 409–422, and *Synthesis of Passive Networks*, pp. 6–37.   A clear discussion is given by Tuttle in *Network Synthesis*,

Vol. I, pp. 143–219. See also Bayard, *Théorie des réseaux de Kirchhoff*, Chapter 17. Regarding the graphical interpretation of residues, see the author's *Network Analysis*, pp. 225–230, Truxal's *Automatic Feedback Control System Synthesis*, pp. 26–29, or Stewart's *Circuit Theory and Design*, Chapter 2. A concise summary of the topics covered in the chapter is given in Chapter 2 in Storer's *Passive Network Synthesis*.

"A thing is obvious mathematically after you see it."

Dean R. D. Carmichael
Quoted in the *Pi Mu Epsilon Journal*

PROBLEMS

4-1. Figure P4-1 shows the poles and zeros of a function $Y(s)$ and also identifies a region in the s plane (crosshatched). Where in or on the boundary of this region do the following occur: (a) the maximum magnitude of $Y(s)$, (b)

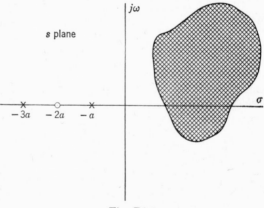

Fig. P4-1

the maximum real part of $Y(s)$, (c) the maximum imaginary part of $Y(s)$, (d) the maximum phase of $Y(s)$, and (e) the minimum value of the four quantities just described? Answer the question by duplicating the figure, upon which you may superimpose the required identifications.

4-2. Repeat Prob. 4-1 for the same crosshatched s plane region, but with poles at $s = -a$, and $s = -a \pm ja$.

4-3. Show that for a rational polynomial $F(s)$ with real coefficients,

$$F(\bar{s}_1) = \overline{F(s_1)}$$

where the bars indicate the conjugate value. Does the same conclusion hold for a quotient of rational polynomials?

4-4. Consider a 3rd-degree equation in s,

$$a_0s^3 + a_1s^2 + a_2s + a_3 = 0$$

Using the Hurwitz criterion, show that in addition to all of the coefficients being real and positive there is an additional relationship of the coefficients that must be fulfilled in order that all roots have negative real parts. Find this condition.

4-5. Which of the following polynomials are Hurwitz polynomials?

(a) $s^5 + 8s^4 + 24s^3 + 28s^2 + 23s + 6$
(b) $s^5 + 6.5s^4 + 16s^3 + 18.5s^2 + 10s + 2$

In addition to determining which of the following polynomials are Hurwitz, find all the imaginary roots of these polynomials.

(c) $s^7 + 6s^6 + 14s^5 + 18s^4 + 17s^3 + 12s^2 + 4s$
(d) $s^6 + 5s^4 + 5s^3 + 2s^2 + 7s + 13$
(e) $s^6 + 7s^4 + 14s^2 + 8$
(f) $s^6 - 5s^5 + 4s^4 - 3s^3 + 2s^2 + s + 1$
(g) $s^8 + 6.5s^7 + 17s^6 + 25s^5 + 26s^4 + 20.5s^3 + 10s^2 + 2s$

4-6. Repeat Prob. 4-5(c) for the following polynomials:

(a) $s^4 + 2s^3 + 3s^2 + 4s + 3$
(b) $s^5 + 6s^4 + 12s^3 + 12s^2 + 11s + 6$
(c) $s^5 + 4s^4 + 4s^3 + 4s^2 + 3s + 3$
(d) $s^7 + 2s^6 + 5s^5 + 10s^4 + 7s^3 + 14s^2 + 3s + 6$
(e) $s^6 + 1$

4-7. It is explained in the text that the Hurwitz criterion is equivalent in objective to the Routh criterion (sometimes called the Routh rule). This problem requires that you compare the two criteria.

(a) Prepare a statement of the Routh criterion.*
(b) Apply the criterion to Eq. 4.41 of Example 1.
(c) What in the Routh procedure corresponds to "premature termination" in the Hurwitz test?
(d) Can you see any advantages of one procedure as compared to the other?

4-8. Determine the residues at the poles of the following admittance function by a graphical construction and by the use of Eq. 4.53.

$$Y(s) = 10 \frac{(s + 1)(s + 4)}{s(s + 3)(s + 6)}$$

4-9. Repeat the last problem for the admittance function

$$Y(s) = 17 \frac{(s + 1)(s + 2)(s + 5)}{s(s^2 + 2s + 2)(s + 4)}$$

---

* See any textbook on servomechanisms, or Gardner and Barnes, *Transients in Linear Systems*, Vol. I, pp. 197–201, or the author's *Network Analysis*, Chapter 16.

4-10. Given the driving-point function

$$Y(s) = \frac{2s^3 + 2s^2 + 3s + 2}{s^2 + 1}$$

which is positive real, show that the residues at the poles are real and positive by a graphical determination and by using Eq. 4.53.

4-11. Suppose that $Y(s)$ contains a double pole at $-p_l$.

(a) Show that the residue at this pole is

$$K_{-p_l,1} = (s + p_l)^2 \, Y(s) \left(\sum_{k=1}^{n} \frac{1}{s + z_k} - \sum_{k=1}^{m \neq l} \frac{1}{s + p_k} \right) \Bigg|_{s = -p_l}$$

(b) Consider a network function (not driving-point)

$$G(s) = \frac{s}{(s + 1)^2(s^2 + 2s + 2)}$$

Show that $K_{-1,2} = -1$, $K_{-1,1} = 1$, $K_{-1+j} = \frac{1}{2}(1 + j)$.

Draw a phasor diagram to illustrate the quantities involved in each computation of a coefficient. Can Eq. 4.53 be used to find these coefficients?

4-12. Which of the following polynomials remain positive for all real values of ω?

(a) $\omega^{10} + 6\omega^8 + 4\omega^6 + 7\omega^4 + 9\omega^2 + 1$
(b) $\omega^6 - 3\omega^4 - \omega^2 + 3$
(c) $\omega^8 + 2\omega^6 - 3\omega^4 - 4\omega^2 + 2$
(d) $\omega^8 - \omega^4 - 2\omega^2 + 2$

4-13. Which of the following polynomials remain positive or zero for all real values of ω?

(a) $\omega^8 + 3$
(b) $\omega^6 - 3\omega^2 + 2$
(c) $\omega^8 + 2\omega^6 - 3\omega^4 - 4\omega^2 + 2$
(d) $\omega^{10} + \omega^8 + 3\omega^6 - 3\omega^4 + 4\omega^2 + 10$

4-14. In working a given problem, it is found that the Sturm test does not terminate prematurely and $P_0(x)$ does have roots in the interval $x = 0$ to $x = \infty$. What can you then conclude about the corresponding $A(\omega^2)$ without further test?

4-15. Consider the admittance function

$$Y(s) = \frac{s^2 + \frac{1}{2}s + 1}{(s + \frac{1}{2})(s + a_1)}$$

where a_1 is real and positive.

(a) Determine one value of a_1 such that $Y(s)$ is not positive real.
(b) Determine a_1 and ω_1 such that Re $Y(j\omega_1) = 0$.

A graphical analysis will suffice.

4-16. Show that

$$Y(s) = \frac{s^3 - 1}{4s^3 - 3s^2 - 1}$$

is a positive real function.   In view of this example, how should property 1 of Table 3-1 be modified?

4-17. Determine by inspection which of the pole-zero configurations shown in Fig. P4-17 represent positive real functions.   Give reasons for your answers.

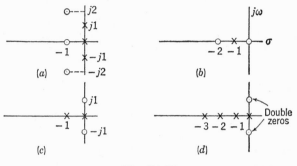

Fig. P4-17

4-18. Show that the admittance function

$$Y(s) = H\frac{s^2 + a_1s + a_0}{s^2 + b_1s + b_0}$$

is positive real if

$$a_1b_1 \geq (\sqrt{a_0} - \sqrt{b_0})^2$$

4-19. Test each of the following functions to see if it is positive real function. Show each step in your testing carefully.

(a) $\dfrac{s^3 + 6s^2 + 7s + 3}{s^2 + 2s + 1}$

(b) $\dfrac{s(s + 3)(s + 5)}{(s + 1)(s + 4)}$

(c) $\dfrac{s^3 + s^2 + s + 1}{s^3 + 2s^2 + s + 2}$

(d) $\dfrac{s^5 + 5s^3 + 4s}{s^4 + 8s^2 + 15}$

(e) $\dfrac{3s^4 - 4s^3 + 8s^2 - 16s + 9}{3s^4 - 3s^3 - s^2 - s + 2}$

(f) $\dfrac{s^4 + 2s^3 + 3s^2 + s + 1}{s^4 + s^3 + 3s^2 + 2s + 1}$

(g) $\dfrac{2s^3 + s^2 + 4s + 1}{s^3 + 3s^2 + 3s + 1}$

(h) $\dfrac{8s^4 + 6s^3 + 10s^2 + 3s + 2}{4s^4 + 12s^3 + 5s^2 + 6s + 1}$

(i) $\dfrac{6s^3 + 10s^2 + 10s + 1}{6s^3 + 6s^2 + 9s + 2}$

4-20. A network is made up of three series two-element networks connected in parallel. The first network consists of an inductor L and a capacitor C in series; the second of a capacitor C_1 in series with a resistor R_1; the third of an inductor L_2 in series with a resistor R_3. Show that the real part of the impedance function for $s = j\omega$, Re $Z(j\omega)$, has a zero of 2nd degree at the frequency $\omega_1 = 1/\sqrt{LC}$. What will be the degree of the zero at ω_1 in Im $Z(j\omega)$?

4-21. Consider an admittance function $Y(s)$ which has no poles or zeros in the right half plane nor on the imaginary axis. But the minimum value of Re $Y(j\omega)$ is negative, being equal to -1. Is the new function $Y(s) + 1$ positive real?

4-22. The function $Y(s)$ has poles in the left half plane only but its zeros are in the right half plane and on the imaginary axis. Show that the function $Y(s) + K$ may be made to have all of its zeros in the left half plane by a suitable choice of the real positive constant K.

4-23. Show that if $Z(s)$ and $W(s)$ are positive real functions, then $Z(W)$ is again a positive real function.

4-24. Show that if $Y(s)$ is positive real, then $Y(1/s)$ is positive real.

4-25. Show that if the polynomial $P(s)$ is Hurwitz then the quotient $P'(s)/P(s)$ is positive real.

4-26. Determine whether the following function is positive real:

$$Z(s) = \left(\frac{s + 10}{s + 11}\right)^{10}$$

Driving-Point Synthesis
with *LC* Elements

. . . . *5*

From our study of the conditions necessary for a driving-point function to characterize a network of passive elements, we turn next to a study of procedures for the synthesis of one terminal-pair networks. Our study in this chapter will be limited to networks containing only *LC* kinds of elements. The *RC* and *RL* cases will be considered in the next chapter.

5.1 Elementary synthesis operations

The discussion in this first section applies to *all* one terminal-pair networks. Two one terminal-pair networks are said to be *equivalent* when they have the same driving-point impedance or admittance. The two networks shown in (*a*) and (*b*) of Fig. 5-1 are equivalent when

$$Z(s) = Z_1(s) + Z_2(s) \tag{5.1}$$

Similarly, the two networks shown in (*c*) and (*d*) of Fig. 5-1 are equivalent under the condition

$$Y(s) = Y_1(s) + Y_2(s) \tag{5.2}$$

Suppose that we are given a positive real function, $Z(s)$ or $Y(s)$, and desire to select appropriate forms for Z_1 and Z_2 or for Y_1 and Y_2. We require that each function in the sum be positive real. In addition, we will select functions in the sum that are of reduced degree in numerator and/or denominator compared to the original function. When one of the functions in the sum is so simple that it can be recognized as the impedance or admittance of some network (a single element or two kinds of elements in series or in parallel), then we know we are making progress. If this expansion process is repeated until all of the functions in the sum are so identified, synthesis is complete.

There is a special terminology we shall use in describing the synthesis procedure. If we solve Eq. 5.1 for $Z_2(s)$, then

$$Z_2(s) = Z(s) - Z_1(s) \tag{5.3}$$

and Z_1 is said to have been *removed* from Z in forming the new function Z_2. Similarly, the network corresponding to Z_1, represented in Fig. 5-1(b), is said to have been removed from the remaining network described by the impedance Z_2. Further, if the network that has been removed is associated with a given pole or zero of the original network impedance, that pole or zero of the function is also said to have been

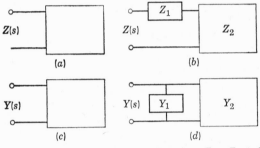

Fig. 5-1. (a) and (b) are equivalent networks when $Z = Z_1 + Z_2$, (c) and (d) are equivalent networks when $Y = Y_1 + Y_2$.

removed. Then the expression "remove a pole at infinity" means that the pole at infinity of $Z(s)$ does not appear in $Z_2(s)$, having been removed in forming $Z_1(s)$. When the pole of impedance at infinity is associated with an inductor, the inductor has been removed from the network represented by $Z(s)$ in forming the new impedance $Z_2(s)$. There are five important *removal operations*, which we next describe.

The removal of a pole at infinity. Consider an impedance function $Z(s)$ with a pole at infinity. For there to be such a pole, it is required that the numerator polynomial of $Z(s)$ be of degree 1 larger than the degree of the denominator polynomial, as in the function

$$Z(s) = \frac{a_{n+1}s^{n+1} + a_n s^n + \cdots + a_1 s + a_0}{b_n s^n + b_{n-1}s^{n-1} + \cdots + b_1 s + b_0} \tag{5.4}$$

By ordinary long division of the numerator by the denominator, we have

$$Z(s) = Hs + \frac{c_n s^n + c_{n-1}s^{n-1} + \cdots + c_1 s + c_0}{b_n s^n + b_{n-1}s^{n-1} + \cdots + b_1 s + b_0} \tag{5.5}$$

where $H = a_{n+1}/b_n$. Let Hs be Z_1 and the second term be Z_2 such that

$$Z_2(s) = \frac{c_n s^n + c_{n-1} s^{n-1} + \cdots + c_1 s + c_0}{b_n s^n + b_{n-1} s^{n-1} + \cdots + b_1 s + b_0} = Z(s) - Hs \quad (5.6)$$

Now the difference of two positive real functions is not necessarily positive real. Is $Z_2(s)$ positive real? This question is answered in terms of the criteria of the Chapter 4, namely:

(1) $Z_2(s)$ must have no poles in the right half plane.

(2) Poles of $Z_2(s)$ on the imaginary axis must be simple, and the residues of $Z_2(s)$ at these poles must be real and positive.

(3) Re $Z_2(j\omega) \geq 0$ for all ω.

(1) Comparing Eqs. 5.4 and 5.6, we see that $Z(s)$ and $Z_2(s)$ have the same poles. Since $Z(s)$ is positive real (premise), all poles of $Z_2(s)$

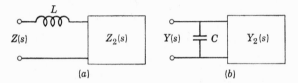

Fig. 5-2. Network interpretation of the removal of a pole at infinity ($s = \infty$).

are in the left half plane or on the imaginary axis. (2) Also, all poles of $Z_2(s)$ on the imaginary axis are simple. The residues of $Z_2(s)$ at the imaginary poles are unaffected by what amounts to one step in the partial fraction expansion of the positive real $Z(s)$. (3) The real part of $Z_1(s) = Hs$ for $s = j\omega$ is zero. Hence

$$\text{Re } Z_2(j\omega) = \text{Re } Z(j\omega) \geq 0 \quad (5.7)$$

for all ω as required. Since all three conditions are satisfied, $Z_2(s)$ is positive real. What is the network represented by the term $Z_1(s) = Hs$? By comparison with the impedance of an inductor, $Z_L(s) = Ls$, the network is an inductor of value $L = H = a_{n+1}/b_n$. We see that the removal of a pole at infinity corresponds to the removal of an inductor from the network as in Fig. 5-2(a).

When the function originally considered is admittance rather than impedance, the function $Y_1(s) = Hs$ corresponds to the admittance of a capacitor, $Y_C(s) = Cs$, and the network for $Y_1(s)$ is a capacitor having the value $C = H = a_{n+1}/b_n$ as illustrated in Fig. 5-2(b).

The removal of a pole at zero. If $Z(s)$ has a pole at the origin, then it may be written in the form

$$Z(s) = \frac{a_0 + a_1 s + \cdots + a_{n-1} s^{n-1} + a_n s^n}{b_1 s + b_2 s^2 + \cdots + b_m s^m} \tag{5.8}$$

Once again by long division, we have

$$Z(s) = \frac{K_0}{s} + \frac{d_1 + d_2 s + \cdots + d_n s^{n-1}}{b_1 + b_2 s + \cdots + b_m s^{m-1}} \tag{5.9}$$

$$= Z_1(s) + Z_2(s) \tag{5.10}$$

where $K_0 = a_0/b_1$. Once again we must answer two questions: Is $Z_2(s)$ positive real? What network has the impedance of the form of $Z_1(s)$? The answer to the first question is that $Z_2(s)$ is positive real

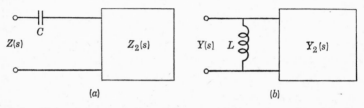

(a)   (b)

Fig. 5-3. Network interpretation of the removal of a pole at the origin ($s = 0$).

for the same three reasons just outlined for the case of removing a pole at infinity. By comparison with the equations $Z_C = 1/Cs$ and $Y_L = 1/Ls$, we see that the removal of the term K_0/s as impedance corresponds to the removal of a capacitor of value $C = 1/K_0$ and that the removal of K_0/s as admittance corresponds to the removal of an inductor of value $L = 1/K_0$. This interpretation of the removal of a pole at the origin in terms of the removal of elements from a network is illustrated in Fig. 5-3.

The removal of conjugate imaginary poles. If $Z(s)$ contains poles on the imaginary axis, say poles at $s = \pm j\omega_1$, then $Z(s)$ will have the factors $(s + j\omega_1)(s - j\omega_1) = s^2 + \omega_1^2$ in the denominator polynomial which may be written

$$Z(s) = \frac{p(s)}{(s^2 + \omega_1^2) q_1(s)} \tag{5.11}$$

A part of the partial fraction expansion of $Z(s)$ gives

$$Z(s) = \frac{K_{j\omega_1}}{s - j\omega_1} + \frac{K_{-j\omega_1}}{s + j\omega_1} + Z_2(s) \tag{5.12}$$

Now the residues of $Z(s)$ at the conjugate poles must themselves be conjugate, and since $K_{j\omega_1}$ and $K_{-j\omega_1}$ are residues at the imaginary poles of the positive real function, $Z(s)$, and therefore real and positive,

$$K_{j\omega_1} = K_{-j\omega_1} \equiv K_1 \qquad (5.13)$$

Then our expression for $Z(s)$ in Eq. 5.12 may be written in the form

$$Z(s) = \frac{2K_1 s}{s^2 + \omega_1^2} + Z_2(s) \qquad (5.14)$$

where the first term in this equation is identified as $Z_1(s)$. We now face the same problems considered in the removal of the poles at infinity and zero: Is $Z_2(s)$ a positive real function? What network has the impedance of $Z_1(s)$? $Z_2(s)$ is positive real for reasons parallel to those given in justification for the removal of a pole at infinity and because

$$\operatorname{Re} Z_1(j\omega) = \operatorname{Re} \frac{j\omega 2K_1}{-\omega^2 + \omega_1^2} = 0 \qquad (5.15)$$

so that $\operatorname{Re} Z_2(j\omega) = \operatorname{Re} Z(j\omega) \geq 0$ for all ω as required. The network corresponding to $Z_1(s)$ is recognized by dividing numerator and denominator by $2K_1 s$ to give

$$Z_1(s) = \frac{2K_1 s}{s^2 + \omega_1^2} = \frac{1}{\dfrac{s}{2K_1} + \dfrac{\omega_1^2}{2K_1 s}} = \frac{1}{Y_a + Y_b} \qquad (5.16)$$

Here $Y_a = s/2K_1$ is the admittance of a capacitor with $C = 1/2K_1$ and $Y_b = \omega_1^2/2K_1 s$ is the admittance of an inductor of value $L =$

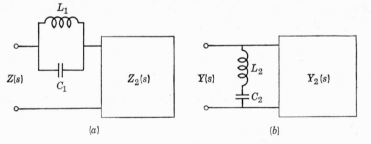

(a)   (b)

Fig. 5-4. Network interpretation of the removal of conjugate poles at $s = \pm j\omega_1$. In (a), $L_1 = 2K_1/\omega_1^2$ and $C_1 = 1/2K_1$; in (b), $L_2 = 1/2K_1$ and $C_2 = 2K_1/\omega_1^2$.

$2K_1/\omega_1^2$. Since the two admittances are added to give the reciprocal of the network impedance, the inductor and capacitor are connected in parallel as shown in Fig. 5-4(a).

If the positive real function is an admittance function rather than impedance, then Eq. 5.16 becomes

$$Y_1(s) = \frac{1}{Z_a + Z_b} \tag{5.17}$$

and $Z_a = s/2K_1$ is the impedance of an inductor having the value $L = 1/2K_1$ and $Z_b = \omega_1^2/2K_1 s$ is the impedance of a capacitor with $C = 2K_1/\omega_1^2$. And since Eq. 5.17 requires that the impedance be added to give the reciprocal of the network admittance, the network evidently has the form of a series connection of L and C as shown in Fig. 5-4(b). These operations are summarized in Table 5-1.

TABLE 5-1
Removal of Poles on the Imaginary Axis

Location of Pole(s)	If Pole of Impedance Series Element is:	If Pole of Admittance, Parallel Element is:
0	C	L
∞	L	C
$\pm j\omega_k$	LC in parallel	LC in series

The partial removal of poles. The removal of poles from impedance or admittance functions discussed thus far has been accomplished by the formation of a new impedance function $Z_2 = Z - Z_1$, where Z_1 may be either Hs, K_0/s, or $2K_1s/(s^2 + \omega_1^2)$. If a *fraction* of Z_1 subtracted from $Z(s)$, then the resultant function is

$$Z_2'(s) = Z(s) - k Z_1(s), \qquad 0 \le k \le 1 \tag{5.18}$$

For example, if $Z(s) = p(s)/q(s)$ is positive real and if K_1 is the residue of $Z(s)$ at the poles $s = \pm j\omega_1$, then the new function

$$Z_2'(s) = Z(s) - k \frac{2K_1 s}{s^2 + \omega_1^2}, \qquad 0 \le k \le 1 \tag{5.19}$$

$$= \frac{p(s)}{q_1(s)(s^2 + \omega_1^2)} - k \frac{2K_1 s}{s^2 + \omega_1^2} \tag{5.20}$$

$$= \frac{p_1(s)}{q(s)}$$

is positive real, has the same poles as $Z(s)$, but has *different* zeros. Because of this change of zeros, the partial removal of poles is known as *"zero shifting."* Zero shifting is an important operation in synthesis procedures and will be studied in a later chapter.

The removal of a constant. If a real number R_1 is subtracted from $Z(s)$ such that

$$Z_2(s) = Z(s) - R_1 \tag{5.21}$$

or
$$Z(s) = R_1 + Z_2(s) \tag{5.22}$$

then $Z_2(s)$ is positive real if R_1 is equal to or less than the minimum value of the real part of $Z(j\omega)$. This follows from the definition of positive real functions and applies to admittance functions as well as impedance functions. If we are dealing with impedance functions, then the constant R_1 represents the impedance of a resistor; for admittance functions, R_1 is the admittance (or conductance) of a resistor.

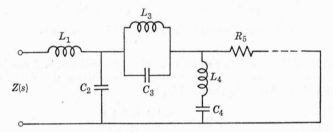

Fig. 5-5. Illustrating synthesis by the successive removal of poles of impedance or admittance and the removal of constants.

The operations just described can be applied repeatedly to an impedance function. If a positive real function $Z(s)$ has poles at $s = \pm j\omega_1$, $\pm j\omega_2, \cdots, \infty$, then these poles can be removed to give

$$Z(s) = Hs + \sum_{i=0}^{n} \frac{2K_i s}{s^2 + \omega_i^2} + Z_2(s) \tag{5.23}$$

and $Z_2(s)$, as well as all other terms in the expansion, is positive real. And if $Z(s)$ has zeros at $s = 0, \pm j\omega_a, \pm j\omega_b, \cdots, \pm j\omega_m$, then these zeros of $Z(s)$ may be removed as poles of $Y(s) = 1/Z(s)$ as

$$\frac{1}{Z(s)} = H's + \sum_{i=0}^{m} \frac{2K_i s}{s^2 + \omega_i^2} + \frac{1}{Z_2(s)} \tag{5.24}$$

where, again, each term in the expansion is positive real. It is possible that a real constant can be removed from $Z_2(s)$ or $1/Z_2(s)$ to represent a resistor. Repeated application of a pole removal or a constant removal is the basis of the philosophy of network synthesis of one terminal-pair networks. See Fig. 5-5.

Example 1.   Consider the driving-point admittance function

$$Y(s) = \frac{6s^2 + 6s + 9}{s^2 + s + 1} \tag{5.25}$$

An inspection of this function shows that there are no poles or zeros on the imaginary axis, including zero and infinity.   Can a real positive constant be removed from $Y(s)$?   To answer this question, we must find the minimum

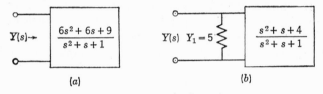

(a)   (b)

Fig. 5-6.   Two equivalent networks for Example 1.

value of Re $Y(j\omega)$.   If it is greater than 0, then a real constant can be subtracted from $Y(s)$ and the resultant will still be positive real.   We first compute Re $Y(j\omega)$.   The even part of $Y(s)$ is

$$\text{Ev } Y(s) = \frac{6s^4 + 9s^2 + 9}{s^4 + s^2 + 1} \tag{5.26}$$

Setting s to $j\omega$, we see that

$$\text{Re } Y(j\omega) = \frac{6\omega^4 - 9\omega^2 + 9}{\omega^4 - \omega^2 + 1} \tag{5.27}$$

To find the minimum value of this function, we differentiate the quotient and set the resulting equation equal to 0 as

$$\frac{d}{d\omega^2} \text{Re } Y(j\omega) = \frac{3\omega^4 - 6\omega^2}{D(\omega^2)} = 0 \tag{5.28}$$

and the desired minimum occurs at $\omega^2 = 2$.   Then

$$\text{Re } Y(j\sqrt{2}) = \frac{(6 \times 4) - (9 \times 2) + 9}{4 - 2 + 1} = 5 \tag{5.29}$$

Subtracting 5 from $Y(s)$ given in Eq. 5.25 gives

$$Y_2(s) = Y(s) - 5 = \frac{6s^2 + 6s + 9}{s^2 + s + 1} - 5 = \frac{s^2 + s + 4}{s^2 + s + 1} \tag{5.30}$$

which is a positive real function.   Since there are no poles on the imaginary axis (including $s = 0$ and $s = \infty$), this admittance function cannot be further reduced by pole removal.   The synthesis of such functions will be considered in Chapter 7.   The network interpretation of the removal of a constant is illustrated in Fig. 5-6.

5.2   *LC* network synthesis

Consider an impedance function $Z(s)$ which is positive real and, in addition, has the property that Re $Z(j\omega) = 0$ for all ω.* If $Z(s)$ is written in the form

$$Z(s) = \frac{m_1 + n_1}{m_2 + n_2} \tag{5.31}$$

then, from Eq. 4.69,

$$\text{Ev } Z(s) = \frac{m_1 m_2 - n_1 n_2}{m_2{}^2 - n_2{}^2} \tag{5.32}$$

and the real part of $Z(j\omega)$ is

$$\text{Re } Z(j\omega) = \text{Ev } Z(s) \Big|_{s=j\omega} \tag{5.33}$$

In terms of these equations, how can we insure that Re $Z(j\omega)$ is indeed equal to 0? There are but three nontrivial ways: (1) We can make $m_1 = 0$ and $n_2 = 0$. (2) We can make $m_2 = 0$ and $n_1 = 0$. (3) Or we can make $m_1 m_2 - n_1 n_2 = 0$. The first possibility leads to $Z(s)$ in the form n_1/m_2, the second to m_1/n_2, and the third after algebraic reduction also to n_1/m_2. Then the only two forms in which $Z(s)$ may appear are

$$Z(s) = \frac{m_1(s)}{n_2(s)} \quad \text{or} \quad Z(s) = \frac{n_1(s)}{m_2(s)} \tag{5.34}$$

and $Z(s)$ is always the quotient of even to odd or odd to even polynomials. Now if the odd function is in the numerator of $Z(s)$, then $Z(s)$ will have a zero at $s = 0$, but if it is in the denominator, $Z(s)$ will have a pole at the origin. At infinity, either of the forms of $Z(s)$ given in Eqs. 5.34 may have either a pole or a zero, depending on whether the even or odd function is of higher degree. These statements are summarized in Table 5-2.

---

* A rigorous derivation of these properties may be made in terms of energy functions. By this method, it is shown that

$$Z(s) = F_0 + sT_0 + E_0/s$$

where F_0 is related to dissipated power, T_0 to magnetic stored energy, and E_0 to electrical stored energy, and each of these three functions is real and positive. Since $F_0 = 0$ for *LC* networks [just as Re $Z(j\omega) = 0$ in our derivation], it follows that the zeros of $Z(s)$ are located on the imaginary axis; dual arguments involving $Y(s)$ lead to the same conclusions for the poles of $Z(s)$. For a detailed treatment of energy functions, see Tuttle, *Network Synthesis*, Vol. I, pp. 125–145.

TABLE 5-2
Poles and Zeros of $Z(s)$ at Zero and Infinity

$Z(s)$	$s = 0$	$s = \infty$
m_1/n_2	pole	zero or pole
n_1/m_2	zero	zero or pole

Since $Z(s)$ is positive real, m_2 is Hurwitz. From the results of the last chapter, this means that since m_2 is an even polynomial in s, all of its zeros must be simple and pure imaginary. Similarly, n_2 is Hurwitz and equal to s times an even polynomial so that its zeros are also simple and pure imaginary. The same conclusions hold for m_1 and n_1. Thus $Z(s)$ can be written in the form

$$Z(s) = \frac{H(s^2 + \omega_{z_1}{}^2)(s^2 + \omega_{z_2}{}^2)(s^2 + \omega_{z_3}{}^2) \cdots}{s(s^2 + \omega_{p_1}{}^2)(s^2 + \omega_{p_2}{}^2) \cdots} \tag{5.35}$$

where ω_{z_1} can be zero or not depending upon whether $Z(s)$ has a zero or a pole at the origin. The partial fraction expansion of the last equation is

$$Z(s) = Hs + \frac{K_0}{s} + \frac{K_{j\omega_{p_1}}}{s - j\omega_{p_1}} + \frac{K_{-j\omega_{p_1}}}{s + j\omega_{p_1}} + \frac{K_{j\omega_{p_2}}}{s - j\omega_{p_2}} + \cdots \tag{5.36}$$

where Hs is present if there is a pole at infinity, and K_0/s is present if there is a pole at the origin.

Since $Z(s)$ is positive real, all residues at the imaginary axis poles are real and positive and $K_{j\omega_{p_r}} = K_{-j\omega_{p_r}} = K_{p_r} > 0$, and Eq. 5.36 becomes

$$Z(s) = Hs + \frac{K_0}{s} + \sum_{r=1}^{n} \frac{2K_{p_r}s}{s^2 + \omega_{p_r}{}^2} \tag{5.37}$$

With all of the poles and zeros of $Z(s)$ on the imaginary axis, we are especially interested in the behavior of $Z(s)$ when $s = j\omega$. Since

$$Z(j\omega) = \text{Re } Z(j\omega) + j \text{ Im } Z(j\omega) \tag{5.38}$$

and Re $Z(j\omega) = 0$, we have

$$Z(j\omega) = j \text{ Im } Z(j\omega) = j X(\omega) \tag{5.39}$$

where $X(\omega)$ is an odd function known as the *reactance function*. If we are concerned with admittance rather than impedance, then

$$Y(j\omega) = j \text{ Im } Y(j\omega) = j B(\omega) \tag{5.40}$$

where $B(\omega)$ is the *susceptance function*. The reactance function for Eq. 5.37 is

$$X(\omega) = \frac{-K_0}{\omega} + \sum_{r=1}^{n} \frac{2K_{p,\omega}}{-\omega^2 + \omega_r^2} + H\omega \tag{5.41}$$

From the slope of the reactance versus frequency curve, we can deduce another interesting property of the functions under study. This slope is

$$\frac{dX}{d\omega} = \frac{K_0}{\omega^2} + \sum_{r=1}^{n} \frac{2K_{p_r}(\omega^2 + \omega_r^2)}{(-\omega^2 + \omega_r^2)^2} + H \tag{5.42}$$

Now every factor in this equation is positive for all positive and negative values of ω. From this we see that

$$\frac{dX}{d\omega} > 0 \text{ for } -\infty < \omega < \infty \tag{5.43}$$

and the slope of the reactance versus frequency curve is always positive. (The same statement may be made for the slope of the susceptance versus frequency curve.) We have shown that there is always either a pole or a zero at $s = 0$ for the $Z(s)$ we are studying. If there is a zero at $s = 0$, the reactance curve must have the form shown in Fig. 5-7; for a pole at the origin, the reactance curve of Fig. 5-8 applies. Inspection of these two curves shows that since the slope must always be positive, it is necessary that the poles and zeros separate each other, that the poles and zeros alternate along the real frequency axis. This is known as the *separation property* for reactance functions and is due to Zobel and to Foster (1924).* Because of the separation property, we see that the pole and zero frequencies of Eq. 5.35 must be related by the equation,

$$0 < \omega_{z_1} < \omega_{p_1} < \omega_{z_2} < \omega_{p_2} < \cdots \tag{5.44}$$

What is the network representation of $Z(s)$? Comparing Eq. 5.37 with the equations for the impedance of the networks studied in Sec-

---

* R. M. Foster, "A reactance theorem," *Bell System Tech. J.*, **3**, 259–267 (1924). This paper by Ronald M. Foster (1896–   ) is often described as the first devoted to synthesis of networks in the modern sense. Many of Foster's derivations were introduced in an earlier paper by Zobel, but Foster first brought all of the ideas together in the form of a reactance theorem. Foster was with the Bell System from 1917 to 1943 and since 1943 has been head of the department of mathematics at the Polytechnic Institute of Brooklyn. Otto J. Zobel (1887–   ) was a member of the staff in the Bell System from 1916 to 1952.

tion 5.1, we see that synthesis is accomplished completely in terms of pole removal at the origin, infinity, and at finite real frequencies, all on the imaginary axis of the s plane. The network consists of a series connection of a capacitor, a number of parallel LC networks, and an

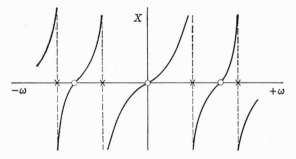

Fig. 5-7. Reactance plotted as a function of frequency to illustrate that $dX/d\omega > 0$, that poles and zeros alternate with ω, and that $X(\omega)$ is an odd function.

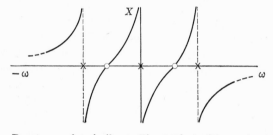

Fig. 5-8. Reactance plot similar to Fig. 5-7 but with a pole at the origin.

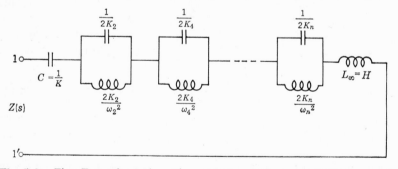

Fig. 5-9. First Foster form of reactive network. C_0 is present if $Z(s)$ has a pole at $s = 0$ and L_∞ is present if $Z(s)$ has a pole at infinity.

inductor, as shown in Fig. 5-9. This network configuration is due to Foster and is known as the *first Foster form* of reactive network. Since all elements in the network are inductors or capacitors, the networks described by the specifications of this section are LC networks.

The equation of $Z(s)$ was written so that there was a pole at the origin and a pole at infinity.   If $Z(s)$ has no pole at the origin (and so has a zero), the first term in the partial fraction expansion is missing, and the capacitor shown in Fig. 5-9 is not present in the network. Similarly, if there is a zero rather than a pole at infinity, then the first term in Eq. 5.37, Hs, is not present and the inductor shown in the network of Fig. 5-9 is replaced by a short circuit.   We see that the following pattern describes the network of the first Foster form in terms of $Z(s)$: (a) a pole at the origin corresponds to the series capacitor, C_0; (b) a pole at infinity corresponds to the series inductor, L_∞; and (c) every denominator factor of the form $s^2 + \omega_1{}^2$ corresponds to a series-connected network made up of a parallel inductor and capacitor, sometimes known as a "tank" circuit.

The first Foster form of LC network is found by expanding $Z(s)$ by partial fractions and identifying terms in the summation with impedances of simple networks.   The form of the equation

$$Z(s) = Z_1 + Z_2 + \cdots + Z_n \qquad (5.45)$$

implies a series connection of the simple networks.   An alternative method of realizing a network is accomplished in the following steps: (1) Form the admittance function, $Y = 1/Z$.   (2) Expand $Y(s)$ as a partial fraction.   (3) Identify the resulting terms in the expansion with the admittance of simple network structures.   The form of the equation

$$Y(s) = \frac{1}{Z(s)} = Y_1 + Y_2 + \cdots + Y_m \qquad (5.46)$$

implies a network of parallel-connected elements or combinations of elements.   Since $Y(s)$ has the same general form as $Z(s)$, this expansion will result in a summation containing any or all of the following terms:

$$Y(s) = \frac{K_0}{s} + \sum_{r=1}^{n} \frac{2K_r s}{s^2 + \omega_r{}^2} + Hs \qquad (5.47)$$

From Section 5.1, we know that the first term corresponds to the removal of a pole at the origin and has the network representation of an inductor since $Y_L = 1/Ls$.   Similarly, the last term represents the removal of a pole at infinity corresponding to the network element capacitor since $Y_C = Cs$.   The remaining terms corresponds to the removal of poles of admittance from the imaginary axis and are represented by a series LC networks.   The general form of network resulting from the partial fraction expansion of admittance is shown in Fig. 5-10.

This network is shown as the *second Foster form* of reactive network. A given impedance function $Z(s)$ may thus be represented by two forms of networks, one resulting from the partial fraction expansion about the poles of $Z(s)$, the other from the partial fraction expansion about the zeros of $Z(s)$ which are the poles of $Y(s) = 1/Z(s)$.

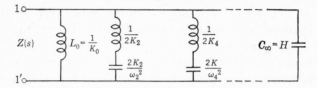

Fig. 5-10. Second Foster form of reactive network derived from the expansion of $Y(s) = 1/Z(s)$. L_0 is present if $Z(s)$ has a zero at $s = 0$ and C_∞ is present if $Z(s)$ has a zero at infinity.

The evaluation of the constants, K_0, K_r, and H, is accomplished by the usual procedure for expanding by partial fractions using the following equations [given for $Z(s)$ but applicable to the expansion of $Y(s)$ by substituting Y for Z]:

$$K_0 = s\, Z(s) \Big|_{s=0} \tag{5.48}$$

$$2K_r = \frac{(s^2 + \omega_r^2)\, Z(s)}{s} \Big|_{s^2 = -\omega_r^2} \tag{5.49}$$

and
$$H = \lim_{s \to \infty} \frac{Z(s)}{s} \tag{5.50}$$

Example 2. Consider the impedance function

$$Z(s) = \frac{(s^2 + 1^2)(s^2 + 3^2)}{s(s^2 + 2^2)} \tag{5.51}$$

The corresponding reactance function is found by letting $s = j\omega$ and is

$$X(\omega) = \frac{(\omega^2 - 1)(\omega^2 - 9)}{\omega(\omega^2 - 4)} \tag{5.52}$$

The reactance versus frequency plot for this equation is shown in Fig. 5-11(a). When $\omega = 0$, $X = -\infty$. As ω increases, the value of X increases toward a positive value, becoming equal to 0 at $\omega = 1$. When $\omega = 2$, X has increased to $+\infty$, but when ω exceeds the value of 2, the factor $(\omega^2 - 4)$ changes sign, and the reactance changes from positive to negative values. This changing of sign is repeated for all finite poles of $X(\omega)$. From the equation for $dX/d\omega$, Eq. 5.42, we see that

$$\lim_{\omega \to \infty} \frac{dX}{d\omega} = H \tag{5.53}$$

as shown on the figure.   Furthermore, this is the *minimum* slope of the reactance versus frequency plot since, by Eq. 5.42, the slope is the summation of
terms due to the capacitor alone, the inductor alone, and the parallel LC networks alone.

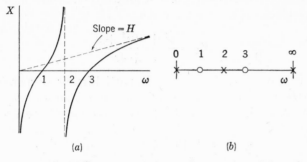

(a)   (b)

Fig. 5-11.   (a) A plot of Eq. 5.52 and (b) a representation of the pole and zero
locations.

Using Eqs. 5.48, 5.49, and 5.50, the partial expansion of $Z(s)$ is

$$Z(s) = \frac{\frac{9}{4}}{s} + \frac{\frac{15}{4}s}{s^2 + 4} + s$$

or

$$Z(s) = \frac{1}{\frac{4}{9}s} + \frac{1}{\frac{4}{15}s + 1/\frac{15}{16}s} + s \qquad (5.54)$$

The element values for the first Foster form of network are shown in Fig.
5-12(a).   Expanding the admittance function gives

$$Y(s) = \frac{\frac{3}{8}s}{s^2 + 1} + \frac{\frac{5}{8}s}{s^2 + 9}$$

$$= \frac{1}{\frac{8}{3}s + 1/\frac{3}{8}s} + \frac{1}{\frac{8}{5}s + 1/\frac{5}{72}s} \qquad (5.55)$$

From this equation, the element values for the second Foster form of network
are seen to be those shown in Fig. 5-12(b).   These networks have the same

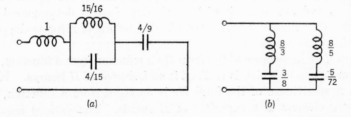

(a)   (b)

Fig. 5-12.   Two network realizations for Eq. 5.51: (a) the first Foster form, and
(b) the second Foster form.

driving-point impedance, $Z(s)$.   If the two networks were enclosed in black
boxes, it would be impossible to distinguish the two networks by testing at

the input terminals. Note also that the two networks have the same number of elements.

The impedance function of Example 2 will serve to introduce the LC ladder network structure first studied by Wilhelm Cauer in 1927. The impedance

$$Z_1 = \frac{s^4 + 10s^2 + 9}{s^3 + 4s} \tag{5.56}$$

has a pole at infinity, the term in the partial fraction expansion being Hs with $H = 1$. If the factor s is removed from Z_1, the resulting function will not have a pole at infinity and so must have a zero there. Thus

$$Z_2 = \frac{s^4 + 10s^2 + 9}{s^3 + 4s} - s = \frac{6s^2 + 9}{s^3 + 4s} \tag{5.57}$$

The reciprocal of this impedance, $Y_2 = 1/Z_2$, does have a pole at infinity which may be removed by subtracting $\frac{1}{6}s$ from Y_2:

$$Y_3 = \frac{s^3 + 4s}{6s^2 + 9} - \frac{1}{6}s = \frac{\frac{5}{2}s}{6s^2 + 9} \tag{5.58}$$

This process may be repeated by forming the reciprocal of Y_3 and removing from Y_3 the pole at infinity. Thus

$$Z_4 = \frac{6s^2 + 9}{\frac{5}{2}s} - \frac{12}{5}s = \frac{18}{5s} \tag{5.59}$$

This function has a zero at infinity, but the reciprocal has a pole at infinity,

$$Y_4 = \tfrac{5}{18}s \tag{5.60}$$

which may be removed. With this pole removal, the process ends with $Y_5 = 0$ (an open circuit). The steps in this development are illustrated in Fig. 5-13, which records the shifting of zeros as the poles at infinity are removed.

Now if an impedance of the form Hs is removed from a function, the network element which is realized is an inductor of H henrys. However, if admittance of the form Hs is removed from a function, the network element is a capacitor of H farads. The various removal steps of this development are seen to result in the network shown in the process of development in Fig. 5-14. The network formed by the removal of poles at infinity is known as the *first Cauer form* of reactive network. Synthesis of this form of network is accomplished in the

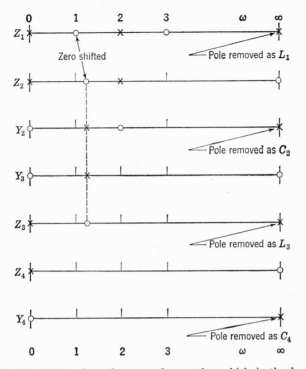

Fig. 5-13. Illustrating the pole removal operation which is the basis of the continued fraction expansion to find the first Cauer form of reactive network.

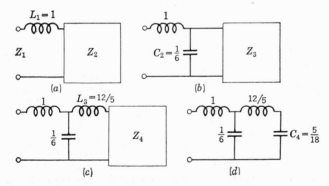

Fig. 5-14. Steps in the synthesis of the first Cauer form of reactive network by the successive removal of poles.

following steps. If $Z_1(s) = m/n$, where m is of higher degree than n, then the pole at infinity of Z_1 is removed to give Z_2 as

$$Z_2(s) = \frac{m_1(s)}{n(s)} = Z_1(s) - H_1 s \tag{5.61}$$

where Z_2 has a zero at infinity. We next form $Y_2 = 1/Z_2$ which has a pole at infinity which is removed as follows:

$$Y_3(s) = \frac{n_2(s)}{m_1(s)} = Y_2(s) - H_2 s \tag{5.62}$$

These two steps are equivalent to the equations

$$Z_1 = L_1 s + Z_2 \tag{5.63}$$

$$\frac{1}{Z_2} = C_1 s + Y_3 \tag{5.64}$$

This process may be repeated following the pattern, "remove a pole, invert and remove a pole," to give the following form to Z_1:

$$Z_1(s) = L_1 s + \cfrac{1}{C_2 s + \cfrac{1}{L_3 s + \cfrac{1}{C_4 s + \cdot}}} \tag{5.65}$$

which is recognized as the familiar continued fraction expansion studied earlier in connection with the Hurwitz criterion. This development follows the general pattern,

$$Z(s) = Z_1 + \cfrac{1}{Y_2 + \cfrac{1}{Z_3 + \cfrac{1}{Y_4 + \cfrac{1}{Z_5 + \cdot}}}} \tag{5.66}$$

which is the driving-point impedance of the ladder network shown in Fig. 5-15.

If the impedance function being expanded as a continued fraction has no pole at infinity, then it has a zero there. If this is the case, the function is first inverted and expansion proceeds as usual.   In terms of the network of Fig. 5-15(a), if $Z(s)$ has no pole at infinity, then L_1 is not present in the network realization and the first element is C_2.   Thus we see that the nature of the first element of the network is fixed by the nature of $Z(s)$ at infinity: if $Z(s)$ has a pole at infinity,

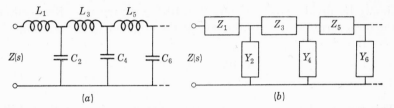

Fig. 5-15.   (a) *LC* ladder network of the first Cauer form, and (b) representation of the general ladder network.

the first element is an inductor; if it has a zero at infinity, the first element is a capacitor.

In a similar way, the nature of the *last* or *end* element is fixed by the nature of $Z(s)$ at the origin ($s = 0$).   The only two possible network endings are shown in Fig. 5-16.   These endings, when attached to the general first Cauer form of *LC* network shown in Fig. 5-15(a), form the complete network.   With the ending shown in Fig. 5-16(a), there is a short-circuit path at zero frequency around the periphery of the network through the inductors.   This short circuit corresponds to a zero

Fig. 5-16.   The two possible arrangements of the last (or end) elements for the first Cauer form of reactive network.

of impedance at $s = 0$.   However, with the network ending shown in Fig. 5-16(b), this short-circuit path through the inductors is broken by the capacitor to give a pole of impedance at $s = 0$.   Hence, if $Z(s)$ has a pole at the origin of the s plane, the last element is a capacitor; if it has a zero at $s = 0$, the last element is an inductor.

Another synthesis procedure which is similar to that just studied involves the *successive removal of poles at the origin*, and gives rise to networks known as the *second Cauer form* of reactive networks.   Let us once more use the same impedance function of Example 2 to introduce the method. The partial fraction expansion of the impedance function

$$Z_1(s) = \frac{s^4 + 10s^2 + 9}{s^3 + 4s} \tag{5.67}$$

has a term $\frac{9}{4}/s$ which has a pole at the origin. (This value is found simply by dividing $4s + s^3$ into $9 + 10s^2 + s^4$; try it.) Removal of the term corresponding to the pole at the origin gives the new impedance function,

$$Z_2(s) = \frac{s^4 + 10s^2 + 9}{s^3 + 4s} - \frac{9}{4s} = \frac{s(s^2 + \frac{31}{4})}{s^2 + 4} \tag{5.68}$$

This function has a zero at the origin, but its reciprocal $Y_2 = 1/Z_2$ has the necessary pole at the origin with a term $\frac{16}{31}/s$ in its partial fraction expansion. Removing this term from Y_2 gives Y_3:

$$Y_3(s) = \frac{s^2 + 4}{s(s^2 + \frac{31}{4})} - \frac{16}{31}\frac{1}{s} = \frac{\frac{15}{31}s}{s^2 + \frac{31}{4}} \tag{5.69}$$

The cycle is once again repeated by subtracting $\frac{961}{60}/s$ from $Z_3 = 1/Y_3$, giving

$$Z_4 = \frac{s^2 + \frac{31}{4}}{\frac{15}{31}s} - \frac{961}{60}\frac{1}{s} = \frac{31}{15}s \tag{5.70}$$

Finally,

$$Y_4 = \frac{1}{Z_4} = \frac{\frac{15}{31}}{s} \tag{5.71}$$

and this term corresponding to a pole at the origin is removed to terminate the procedure (the next admittance function has the value $Y_5 = 0$, an open circuit). These pole removal steps and the consequent zero shifting are illustrated in Fig. 5-17. The various steps of the actual network realization are shown in Fig. 5-18. An impedance function of the form K_0/s is seen to be a capacitor in the network, and an admittance of the same form represents an inductor. The two Cauer network realizations are shown in Fig. 5-19 for comparison.

A positive real impedance function for which Re $Z(j\omega) = 0$ for all ω,

$$Z(s) = \frac{a_0 + a_2s^2 + \cdots + a_{n-2}s^{n-2} + a_ns^n}{b_1s + b_3s^3 + \cdots + b_ms^m} \tag{5.72}$$

may be expanded in a continued fraction in terms of poles at the origin by the removal of the pole at the origin, inverting the resulting function

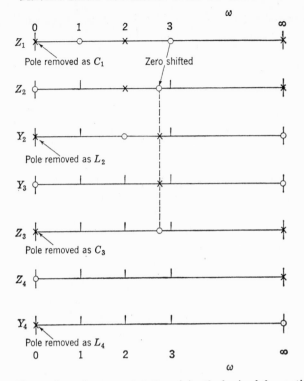

Fig. 5-17. Illustrating pole removal at the origin, the basis of the continued fraction expansion for the second Cauer form of reactive network.

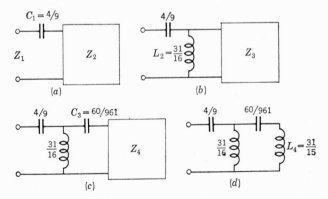

Fig. 5-18. Steps in the synthesis of the second Cauer form of reactive network by the successive removal of poles at the origin.

to create a pole at the origin which is removed, and continuing this process until the expansion is complete. Such an expansion gives

$$Z(s) = \cfrac{1}{C_1 s} + \cfrac{1}{\cfrac{1}{L_2 s} + \cfrac{1}{\cfrac{1}{C_3 s} + \cfrac{1}{\cfrac{1}{L_4 s} + \cdot}}} \tag{5.73}$$

Since the first term of the expansion is impedance, the second must be admittance, etc., alternating as impedance, admittance, impedance.

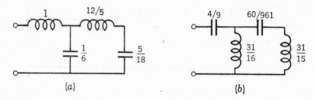

Fig. 5-19. Networks equivalent to those of Fig. 5-12: (a) the first Cauer form, and (b) the second Cauer form.

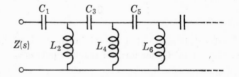

Fig. 5-20. The second Cauer form of reactive network.

Fig. 5-21. The two possible arrangements of the last (or end) elements for the second Cauer form of reactive network.

The corresponding network is seen to be composed of capacitors connected in series and inductors connected in shunt. The general form of the second Cauer reactive network is shown in Fig. 5-20. The only two possible endings for this network are shown in Fig. 5-21. By analysis similar to that given for the first Cauer form of LC network, we may conclude that the end elements are fixed by the poles or zeros at $s = 0$ and $s = \infty$.

The following three definitions in terms of the poles and zeros of Fig. 5-22 prove to be useful. Poles and zeros are lumped together into the inclusive phrase *critical frequencies*. Poles and zeros located at $s = 0$ and $s = \infty$ are classified as *external* critical frequencies. All other poles and zeros form the *internal* critical frequencies.

Because of the separation property for reactive networks and because there must be either a pole or a zero at $s = 0$ and

Fig. 5-22. Poles and zeros of Z located on the imaginary axis used to define internal and external critical frequencies.

$s = \infty$, it is evident that if the internal poles and zeros are specified, the external critical frequencies are determined. In terms of the general form for $Z(s)$,

$$Z(s) = H \frac{(s^2 + \omega_1^2)(s^2 + \omega_3^2) \cdots (s^2 + \omega_{n+1}^2)}{s(s^2 + \omega_2^2) \cdots (s^2 + \omega_n^2)} \tag{5.74}$$

we see that $\omega_1, \omega_2, \omega_3, \cdots, \omega_{n+1}$ are the internal critical frequencies. If these values are given, together with the information as to which values are poles and which zeros, then only one additional fact must be given in order to completely specify $Z(s)$. This fact must be the value of H or equivalent information, such as the value of reactance at some noncritical frequency or the slope of the reactance curve at some nonpole frequency.

Thus, we see that the number of pieces of information for an impedance function that must be specified to make that $Z(s)$ unique is equal to the number of internal critical frequencies plus 1. How many unknowns in the form of element values in a network are then determined by these specifications? From n simultaneous independent equations, we may determine n unknowns. If the specifications are in number 1 more than the number of internal critical frequencies, we may determine only this same number of element values assuming canonical forms.

This same conclusion is reached by another approach. Using the first Foster form for a model, we recognize that the number of elements in the network, E, just equals the total number of poles on the entire imaginary axis, and that the number of poles, N, equals the number of zeros. Since there are two external critical frequencies, the total number of internal critical frequencies is $2N - 2 = 2E - 2$. The number of internal critical frequencies in the interval 0 to $+\infty$, C, is half the total or $C = \frac{1}{2}(2E - 2)$ such that

$$E = C + 1 \tag{5.75}$$

Networks containing the minimum number of elements to meet given specifications, equal to the number of internal critical frequencies plus 1, are known as *canonical forms*. The four network structures studied thus far in this chapter, the two Foster and two Cauer forms of networks, are canonical forms. (See Prob. 5-14.) These networks are completely equivalent; if all were enclosed within black boxes, one could not be distinguished from another. Often one form is preferred over another because of practical considerations: element size, compensation for parasitic effects, etc. It therefore cannot be said that one canonical form is always the best. However, synthesis of the four forms is straightforward and permits the four forms (or other mixed forms) to be found for comparison.

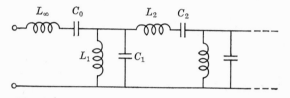

Fig. 5-23. The fifth canonical form of LC network.

A mixed form of importance (sometimes called the *fifth* canonical form) is that shown in Fig. 5-23. It results from a continued fraction expansion alternating about infinity and about zero, giving

$$Z(s) = L_\infty s + \frac{1}{C_0 s} + \cfrac{1}{C_1 s + \cfrac{1}{L_1 s} + \cfrac{1}{\cdot}}$$

(5.76)

This form finds application in the ladder development to be studied as a two terminal-pair synthesis method in Chapter 10.

FURTHER READING

A more detailed treatment of LC network synthesis from an elementary point of view is given in Van Valkenburg, *Network Analysis*, pp. 274–309. Comprehensive treatments from an advanced point of view are given by Tuttle, *Network Synthesis*, Vol. I, see also Guillemin, *Synthesis of Passive Networks*, pp. 107–134, and Storer, *Passive Network Synthesis*, pp. 24–28. In addition, an excellent summary is contained in Guillemin, *Communication Networks*, Vol. II, pp. 184–216. A short treatment is given by Stewart,

Circuit Theory and Design, pp. 177–190.   Source material is in papers of R. M. Foster, "A reactance theorem," *Bell System Tech J.*, **3**, 259–267 (1924), O. J. Zobel, "Transmission characteristics of electric wave filters," *Bell System Tech. J.*, **3**, 567 (1924), and Wilhelm Cauer, "The realization of impedances with prescribed frequency dependance," *Arch. Electrotech.*, **15**, 355–388 (1926).

PROBLEMS

5-1. Using a graphical construction of phasors in the s plane, find the sign of the residue at each pole ($\omega > 0$) of the following functions:

$$(a)\ \frac{s}{s^2 + 1} \qquad (b)\ \frac{s(s^2 + 4)}{s^2 + 1} \qquad (c)\ \frac{s(s^2 + 9)}{(s^2 + 1)(s^2 + 4)}$$

Use induction to generalize these results to cases with more poles and zeros to show that the poles and zeros of $Z(s)$ where Re $Z(j\omega) = 0$ are interlaced on the imaginary axis.

5-2. Find the first and second Foster forms of LC networks for the impedance

$$Z(s) = \frac{s(s^2 + 2)}{(s^2 + 1)(s^2 + 3)}$$

5-3. Repeat Prob. 5-2 for the impedance

$$Z(s) = 78 \frac{s(s^2 + 2)(s^2 + 4)}{(s^2 + 1)(s^2 + 3)}$$

The use of magnitude normalization is suggested.

5-4. Find the first and second Cauer forms of LC networks, including element values, for the impedance function of Prob. 5-2.

5-5. Repeat Prob. 5-4 for the impedance function of Prob. 5-3.

5-6. Figures 5-13 and 5-17 illustrate the shifting of zeros and removal of poles in the Cauer method of ladder network synthesis. Complete charts like Figs. 5-13 and 5-17 for the following impedance function:

$$Z(s) = \frac{(s^2 + 1)(s^2 + 9)(s^2 + 25)}{s(s^2 + 4)(s^2 + 16)}$$

Give the final ladder network realizations in a form similar to Fig. 5-19, complete with element values.

5-7. Repeat Prob. 5-6 for the impedance

$$Z(s) = \frac{s(s^2 + 4)(s^2 + 36)}{(s^2 + 1)(s^2 + 25)(s^2 + 81)}$$

5-8. An LC network is to be designed to meet the following specifications:

(a) It is to have infinite impedance at 1200 cycles/sec and at 5000 cycles/sec.

(*b*) It is to have zero impedance at 2400 cycles/sec.

(*c*) It is to have a reactance of 100 ohms at 3000 cycles/sec.

(1) Determine the impedance function from these specifications.

(2) Find the four canonical network realizations, including element values.

(3) Select the network you consider to be the best network from an engineering point of view, considering element size, cost, and other practical matters.

The use of frequency and magnitude scaling is suggested.

5-9. A reactance function has zeros at $\omega = 0$, 1, and 2 radians/sec. At these frequencies, the slope of reactance with frequency is unity. Determine the location of the poles of the reactance function and H, the scale factor, that meets these specifications.

5-10. Show that the slope of the reactance versus frequency curve for LC networks approaches its minimum value when frequency approaches an infinite value. (In other words, show that the limiting slope for large frequency is the minimum slope.)

5-11. Show that if the number of inductors differs from the number of capacitors by more than 1 in an LC network there are redundant elements, in the sense that a canonical network with fewer elements has the same driving-point impedance.

5-12. Find a network which is equivalent to the one shown in Fig. P5-12 but which contains a minimum number of elements.

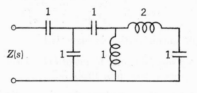

Fig. P5-12

5-13. Show that the two Foster forms and the two Cauer forms of reactive networks are canonical forms containing a number of elements equal to the number of internal critical frequencies plus 1. Is it possible for an LC network to have fewer elements than a canonical LC network and have the same impedance function?

5-14. From the four pole-zero configurations shown in Fig. P5-14, draw the schematic diagrams of the two Foster and the two Cauer networks. (Element values cannot be determined, of course.)

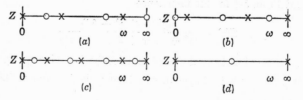

Fig. P5-14

5-15. The minimum number of elements required to synthesize an LC network is five capacitors and four inductors.

(a) Draw the pole-zero configuration in the form of Fig. P5-14.

(b) Repeat part (a) for five capacitors and six inductors.

5-16. Given the driving-point impedance function,

$$Z(s) = \frac{s(s^2 + 2)}{(s^2 + 1)(s^2 + 4)}$$

(a) Synthesize a ladder network of the first Cauer form for this impedance function.

(b) Synthesize another network by first removing a network corresponding to one-half of the residue of the poles at $\pm j1$ (the removal of part of a pole) and then synthesize the remaining impedance as a ladder network. Compare the network found with that of part (a).

5-17. The fifth canonical form of LC network, a combination of the two Cauer forms, is shown in Fig. 5-23.

(a) Show that this form results when poles at zero and infinity are simultaneously removed.

(b) Under what conditions with respect to the form of $Z(s)$ may this form of network be developed?

(c) Show that it is a canonical form.

5-18. Find element values for a network having the same driving-point impedance as the network shown in Fig. P5-18 but with only three elements. Generalize the results of this exercise to show that the number of L and C elements cannot differ by more than 1 if the network realization is to be canonical.

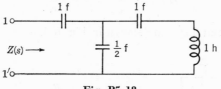

Fig. P5-18

5-19. Figure P5-19 illustrates a network consisting of capacitor C_1 and a box containing three inductors and two capacitors connected together.

(a) Draw a pole-zero configuration for $Z(s)$.

(b) Is the answer you gave for part (a) unique?

(c) If your answer to part (b) is yes, explain your reasoning, using basic properties of LC networks. If your answer to part (b) is no, outline the other possibilities.

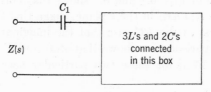

Fig. P5-19

RC and RL
Networks

· · · · · · · · · · · · · · · · · *6*

6.1   Properties of RC network functions

Figure 6-1 shows simple series RC and parallel RC networks.   The impedance of the parallel network of Fig. 6-1(a) is

$$Z_a(s) = \frac{1}{C_a} \frac{1}{s + 1/R_a C_a} \tag{6.1}$$

and the admittance of the network of Fig. 6-1(b) is

$$Y_b(s) = \frac{1}{R_b} \frac{s}{s + 1/R_b C_b} \tag{6.2}$$

Plots of $Z_a(\sigma)$ and $Y_b(\sigma)$ are shown in Fig. 6-2.

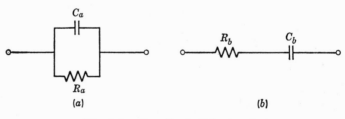

(a)   (b)

Fig. 6-1.   Two simple RC networks.

A comparison of Eqs. 6.1 and 6.2 shows that both have their poles on the negative real axis in the s plane, suggesting that this axis is of the same interest in the RC case that the imaginary axis was in the LC case.   Comparison also shows that $Z(s)$ and $Y(s)/s$—not $Y(s)$— have the same form for these two particular networks.   These are

140

observations from analysis.   When networks of the form of these two are connected together in some arbitrary fashion, what will be the properties of $Z(s)$ at the input terminals?

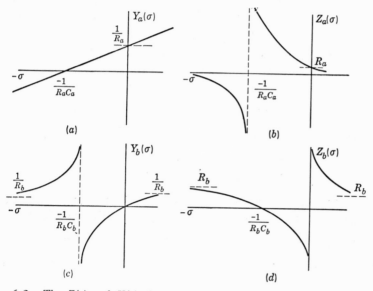

Fig. 6-2. The $Z(\sigma)$ and $Y(\sigma)$ characteristics of the two networks of Fig. 6-1.

A derivation to supply the answer to this question will stress the similarity of RC networks to the LC networks of the last chapter.   We begin with the equation

$$Z(s) = \frac{\Delta(s)}{\Delta_{11}(s)} \tag{6.3}$$

which is the reciprocal of Eq. 2.23.   For LC networks, each element in Δ and so in Δ_{11} is of the form

$$z_{jk} = L_{jk}s + \frac{1}{C_{jk}s} \tag{6.4}$$

and for RC networks the elements are

$$z_{jk} = R_{jk} + \frac{1}{C_{jk}s} \tag{6.5}$$

for loop-basis analysis.   To exploit known properties of LC networks, consider a transformation first used for this purpose by Cauer, $s = p^2$.

While this choice appears to be arbitrary,* its use is justified if it leads to useful results.   With this transformation, z_{jk} becomes

$$R_{jk} + \frac{1}{C_{jk}p^2} = \frac{1}{p}\left(R_{jk}p + \frac{1}{C_{jk}p}\right) \tag{6.6}$$

which now has the form of Eq. 6.4 for the LC networks multiplied by the factor $1/p$.   If $1/p$ is factored from each of the r rows of Δ and $r-1$ rows of Δ_{11}, and the resulting determinants are identified by an asterisk, then

$$Z_{RC} = \frac{\Delta(s)}{\Delta_{11}(s)} = \frac{(1/p^r)\,\Delta^*(p)}{(1/p^{r-1})\,\Delta_{11}{}^*(p)} = \frac{1}{p}\frac{\Delta^*(p)}{\Delta_{11}{}^*(p)} \tag{6.7}$$

or

$$Z_{RC}(s) = \left[\frac{1}{p}Z_{LC}(p)\right]_{p^2=s} \tag{6.8}$$

It is this relationship that will allow us to deduce the properties of RC networks from our knowledge of LC networks.   It specifies that we form $Z_{LC}(p)$ and then divide this expression by p.   If we then replace p^2 by s, the result is the impedance of the RC network, Z_{RC}. We carry out this operation for the most general form of Z_{LC} with a pole both at the origin and at infinity, namely,

$$Z_{LC}(s) = H\frac{(s^2+\omega_1{}^2)(s^2+\omega_3{}^2)(s^2+\omega_5{}^2)\,\cdots}{s(s^2+\omega_2{}^2)(s^2+\omega_4{}^2)\,\cdots} \tag{6.9}$$

having the partial fraction expansion,

$$Z_{LC}(s) = \frac{K_0{}'}{s} + \frac{2K_2{}'s}{s^2+\omega_2{}^2} + \cdots + K_\infty{}'s \tag{6.10}$$

where all of the residues, $K_j{}'$, are real and positive.   From Eq. 6.9,

$$\frac{1}{p}Z_{LC}(p) = H\frac{(p^2+\omega_1{}^2)(p^2+\omega_3{}^2)\,\cdots}{p^2(p^2+\omega_2{}^2)\,\cdots} \tag{6.11}$$

Replacing p^2 by s and letting $\omega_j{}^2 = \sigma_j$ (both being real, positive constants), we have

$$Z_{RC}(s) = H\frac{(s+\sigma_1)(s+\sigma_3)\,\cdots}{s(s+\sigma_2)\,\cdots} \tag{6.12}$$

---

* This choice is made because it transforms the imaginary axis into the real axis.

The same operation applied to Eq. 6.10 gives, letting $2K_j' = K_j$, $K_0' = K_0$, and $K_\infty' = K_\infty$,

$$Z_{RC}(s) = \frac{K_0}{s} + \frac{K_2}{s + \sigma_2} + \frac{K_4}{s + \sigma_4} + K_\infty \tag{6.13}$$

Now if instead $Z_{LC}(s)$ of Eq. 6.9 has a zero at $s = 0$, then Eq. 6.12 becomes (see Fig. 6-3)

$$Z_{RC}(s) = H \frac{(s + \sigma_2)(s + \sigma_4) \cdots}{(s + \sigma_1)(s + \sigma_3) \cdots} \tag{6.14}$$

which has the same form of partial fraction expansion as Eq. 6.13 but with $K_0 = 0$.

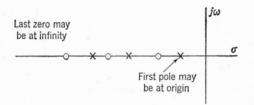

Fig. 6-3.   The pole and zero configuration of $Z_{RC}(s)$ in Eq. 6.14.

From these results we may state the following properties of RC impedance functions:

(1) All poles and zeros are simple and are located on the negative real axis of the s plane.

(2) Poles and zeros are interlaced.

(3) The lowest critical frequency (the one nearest the origin on the real axis) is a pole which is at the origin only if $K_0 \neq 0$.

(4) The highest critical frequency (the one the greatest distance from the origin on the real axis) is a zero which is at infinity only if $K_\infty = 0$.

(5) The residues evaluated at the poles of $Z_{RC}(s)$ are real and positive.

(6) Statement (2) suggests a slope property similar to that found for LC networks.   The slope $dZ(\sigma)/d\sigma$ is found by summing derivatives of Eq. 6.13, a typical term of which is

$$\frac{d}{d\sigma}\left(\frac{K_j}{\sigma + \sigma_j}\right) = \frac{-K_j}{(\sigma + \sigma_j)^2} \tag{6.15}$$

which is negative for all values of σ, both positive and negative, since K_j is positive. Thus

$$\frac{d\,Z_{RC}(\sigma)}{d\sigma} < 0 \qquad (6.16)$$

a conclusion illustrated in Fig. 6-4(a).

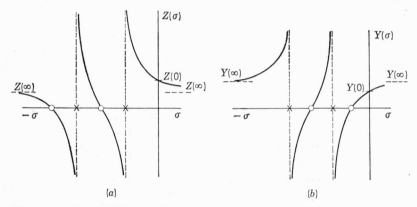

Fig. 6-4. Plots of $Z(\sigma)$ and $Y(\sigma)$ showing that the slope $dZ/d\sigma$ is negative and $dY/d\sigma$ is positive.

(7) From this same figure, we see that since there are no poles and zeros along the positive real axis, then

$$Z_{RC}(\infty) \leq Z_{RC}(0) \qquad (6.17)$$

In a similar investigation of RC admittance functions, we begin with the reciprocal of Eq. 6.8, which is

$$Y_{RC}(s) = [p\,Y_{LC}(p)]_{p^2=s} \qquad (6.18)$$

Assuming a form for $Y_{LC}(s)$ like that of Eq. 6.9, since impedances and admittances for LC networks have the same properties, we find that

$$p\,Y_{LC}(p) = p\left(\frac{K_0'}{p} + \frac{2K_1'p}{p^2 + \omega_1{}^2} + \cdots + K_\infty'p\right) \qquad (6.19)$$

Again letting $p^2 = s$, $\omega_j{}^2 = \sigma_j$, and $2K_j' = K_j$ except for $j = 0$ and ∞,

$$\frac{Y_{RC}(s)}{s} = \frac{K_0}{s} + \frac{K_1}{s + \sigma_1} + \cdots + K_\infty \qquad (6.20)$$

which has the same form as Eq. 6.13 for impedance.

If we examine the slope of a typical term in the partial fraction expansion of $Y_{RC}(\sigma)$, we see that

$$\frac{d}{d\sigma}\left(\frac{K_j\sigma}{\sigma + \sigma_j}\right) = K_j\frac{\sigma_j}{(\sigma + \sigma_j)^2} \qquad (6.21)$$

which is positive for all σ since K_j and all σ_j are positive, and

$$\frac{d\,Y_{RC}(\sigma)}{d\sigma} > 0 \qquad (6.22)$$

as illustrated in Fig. 6-4(b).   Again observe that as a consequence of the slope property,

$$Y_{RC}(0) \leq Y_{RC}(\infty) \qquad (6.23)$$

Table 6-1 compares the properties of Z_{RC} and Y_{RC} as well as Y_{RC}/s.

TABLE 6-1
Properties of RC Impedance and Admittance Functions

Impedance, $Z(s)$	Admittance, $Y(s)$
1. All poles and zeros are simple and are located on the negative real axis of the s plane.	1. All poles and zeros are simple and are located on the negative real axis of the s plane.
2. Poles and zeros interlace.	2. Poles and zeros interlace.
3. The lowest critical frequency is a pole which may be at $s = 0$.	3. The lowest critical frequency is a zero which may be at $s = 0$.
4. The highest critical frequency is a zero which may be at infinity.	4. The highest critical frequency is a pole which may be at infinity.
5. The residues at the poles of $Z(s)$ are real and positive.	5. The residues at the poles of $Y(s)$ are real and negative; the residues of $Y(s)/s$ are real and positive.
6. The slope $dZ/d\sigma$ is negative.	6. The slope $dY/d\sigma$ is positive.
7. $Z(\infty) < Z(0)$.	7. $Y(0) < Y(\infty)$.

6.2   Foster form of RC networks

With this catalog of properties of RC impedance and admittance functions, we turn next to synthesis procedures.   Suppose that we are given $Z_{RC}(s)$ in the form of Eq. 6.13.   This equation may be arranged to facilitate recognition of element values.   Thus

$$Z_{RC}(s) = \frac{1}{s/K_0} + \sum_{k=1}^{n}\frac{1}{s/K_k + \sigma_k/K_k} + K_\infty \qquad (6.24)$$

The first term of Eq. 6.24 represents the impedance of a capacitor having a value of $1/K_0$ farads. The second term is the impedance of the parallel-connected RC network studied earlier with $R_k = K_k/\sigma_k$ and $C_k = 1/K_k$. The last term represents the impedance of a resistor with $R = K_\infty$ ohms. The network structure is the series connection implied by the addition of impedances in Eq. 6.24 as shown in Fig. 6-5.

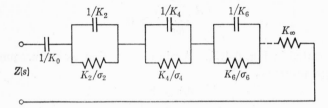

Fig. 6-5. The first Foster form of RC network.

By analogy to the LC case, this network structure is identified as the *first Foster form* of RC network, although all of the four canonical forms were first described by Cauer.*

Example 1. Let it be required to find a network for the impedance function

$$Z(s) = \frac{(s+1)(s+3)}{s(s+2)} \tag{6.25}$$

The partial fraction expansion of this $Z(s)$ is

$$Z(s) = \frac{\frac{3}{2}}{s} + \frac{\frac{1}{2}}{s+2} + 1 \tag{6.26}$$

The RC network of the first Foster form for this impedance is shown in Fig. 6-6. From this example, we see that the removal of a pole on the negative real axis of the s plane is equivalent to the removal of a parallel RC network from the impedance function.

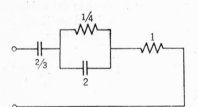

The role of the parallel RC network is analogous to the LC "tank" network of the last chapter. Figure 6-7 shows analogous "resonance" behavior in the two kinds of networks, and also shows the waveforms of voltages, when applied to the networks, result in zero current in the steady state. (See Prob. 6-2.)

Fig. 6-6. RC network realization of Example 1.

These equivalences are helpful in visualizing behavior in RC networks in terms of the more familiar LC resonance phenomena.

* Some authors call these RC networks, and the corresponding RL networks *Foster-like* forms.

At a point parallel to this in the study of LC networks, we found the second Foster form by a partial fraction expansion of $Y(s) = 1/Z(s)$. For RC networks, the proper function to expand is $Y_{RC}(s)/s$ given by

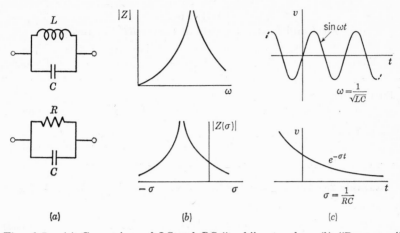

(a)   (b)   (c)

Fig. 6-7. (a) Comparison of LC and RC "tank" networks. (b) "Resonance" phenomena for the two structures. (c) Voltage waveforms that result in no current at the driving terminals.

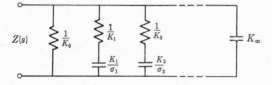

Fig. 6-8. Second Foster form of RC network with element values as determined by the partial fraction expansion.

Eq. 6.20. Multiplying this equation by s gives

$$Y(s) = K_0 + \sum_{i=1}^{n} \frac{K_i s}{s + \sigma_i} + K_\infty s \qquad (6.27)$$

or

$$Y(s) = K_0 + \sum_{i=1}^{n} \frac{1}{1/K_i + \sigma_i/K_i s} + K_\infty s \qquad (6.28)$$

The form of Eq. 6.28 tells us that three kinds of networks are connected in parallel. The first term clearly represents the conductance of a resistor. The second term is the admittance of a series-connected RC network, with $R_i = 1/K_i$ ohms, and $C_i = K_i/\sigma_i$ farads. The last term is the admittance of a capacitor with $C_\infty = K_\infty$ farads. The form of the network for this admittance expansion is known as the *second Foster form* and is shown in Fig. 6-8. These results are summarized in Table 6-2.

TABLE 6-2

First and Last Elements in Foster *RC* Networks

Form	Behavior of $Z(s)$ at Origin	First Element	Behavior of $Z(s)$ at Infinity	Last Element
First Foster	pole	C	constant	R
	constant	none	zero	none
Second Foster	constant	R	zero	C
	pole	none	constant	none

Example 2. The reciprocal of the impedance function of Example 1 is

$$Y(s) = \frac{s(s+2)}{(s+1)(s+3)} \tag{6.29}$$

If we expand $Y(s)$ directly by partial fractions, we get

$$Y(s) = \frac{-\frac{1}{2}}{s+1} + \frac{-\frac{3}{2}}{s+3} + 1 \tag{6.30}$$

illustrating the fact that the signs of the residues of $Y(s)$ at its poles are negative. The proper function to expand is $Y(s)/s$ giving

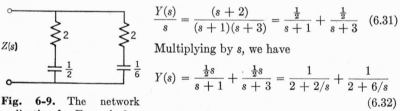

$$\frac{Y(s)}{s} = \frac{(s+2)}{(s+1)(s+3)} = \frac{\frac{1}{2}}{s+1} + \frac{\frac{1}{2}}{s+3} \tag{6.31}$$

Multiplying by s, we have

$$Y(s) = \frac{\frac{1}{2}s}{s+1} + \frac{\frac{1}{2}s}{s+3} = \frac{1}{2+2/s} + \frac{1}{2+6/s} \tag{6.32}$$

Fig. 6-9. The network realization for Example 2.

The network realization is that of Fig. 6-9.

6.3   Foster form of *RL* networks

We consider next *RL* networks and carry out an investigation that parallels that just completed for *RC* networks. A typical term in the loop-basis system determinant for *RL* networks is

$$z_{jk} = L_{jk}s + R_{jk} \tag{6.33}$$

Letting $s = p^2$ and rearranging in a form similar to that for LC networks:

$$Z_{jk} = p^2 L_{jk} + R_{jk} = p\left(pL_{jk} + \frac{R_{jk}}{p}\right) \qquad (6.34)$$

Carrying out the same operations as in Eqs. 6.4 through 6.8 gives

$$Z_{RL}(s) = p\,Z_{LC}(p) \qquad (6.35)$$

and

$$Y_{RL}(s) = \frac{1}{p}\,Y_{LC}(p) \qquad (6.36)$$

Comparing these expressions with the corresponding two for the RC case, Eqs. 6.8 and 6.18, we see that the impedance expression for the RL case has the same form as the admittance expression for the RC case, and RL admittance is similar to RC impedance. Then the conclusions reached for the RC case for impedance apply to the RL case for admittance and vice versa. The instructions needed for finding the properties of RL driving-point functions are given in Table 6-3.

TABLE 6-3
Properties of Foster RL Networks

Property	Instructions	Then Given in:
Plot of $Z(\sigma)$ and $Y(\sigma)$	Interchange Y and Z	Fig. 6-4
Poles and zeros, residues, slope, etc.	Interchange Y and Z	Table 6-1
First and last element values	Replace C by L, interchange zero and pole	Table 6-2

From the discussion of this section, we make the following summarizing statements about networks with RC or RL elements only:

(1) If $Z(s)$ is positive real, all of its poles and zeros are located on the negative real axis of the s plane, poles and zeros are interlaced, and the smallest and largest critical frequencies are of opposite kinds (one a pole and one a zero), then $Z(s)$ can be realized as an RL network or an RC network, but not both.

(2) If the smallest critical frequency of $Z(s)$ is a pole, $Z(s)$ can be realized as an RC network; if a zero, the network is RL.

(3) An RC impedance function is realizable as an RL admittance function, and an RC admittance function is realizable as an RL impedance function.

(4) The removal of a pole of $Z(s)$ on the negative real axis gives a parallel RC or RL network; the removal of a pole of $Y(s)$—which is a zero of $Z(s)$—on the negative real axis gives a series RC or RL network. In general, the function remaining after either removal operation will be positive real only if the $Z(s)$ satisfies the requirements of statement (1) above.

6.4 The Cauer form of RC and RL networks

For RC networks, we now know that $Z(0) > Z(\infty)$ and $Y(\infty) > Y(0)$; for RL networks, $Z(\infty) > Z(0)$ and $Y(0) > Y(\infty)$. These relations are basic in the synthesis method which results in ladder network structures which we will study next. Since both the impedance and the admittance functions for RC networks have real, positive values at zero and infinity, it follows that Re $Z(j0) >$ Re $Z(j\infty)$ and that Re $Y(j\infty) >$ Re $Y(j0)$ since $Z(\sigma)$ with $\sigma = 0$ is the same as $Z(j\omega)$ with $\omega = 0$, and $Z(\sigma)$ with $\sigma = \infty$ is the same as $Z(j\omega)$ with $\omega = \infty$, i.e., both zero and infinity are each one point in the s plane. Now, to remove a constant from $Z(s)$ and have the resulting impedance remain positive real, it is necessary that the constant be less than or equal to the minimum value that Re $Z(j\omega)$ attains for all positive ω. We can find the values for Re $Z(j0) = Z(0)$ and Re $Z(j\infty) = Z(\infty)$. But what about intermediate values of Re $Z(j\omega)$ between 0 and ∞?

To answer this question, we find Re $Z(j\omega)$ and Re $Y(j\omega)$ from Eqs. 6.13 and 6.20. Thus, using primes to distinguish residues for the two cases,

$$\text{Re } Z(j\omega) = \sum_{i=2}^{n} \frac{\sigma_i K_i}{\omega^2 + \sigma_i^2} + K_\infty \tag{6.37}$$

and

$$\text{Re } Y(j\omega) = \sum_{i=1}^{m} \frac{K_i'\omega^2}{\omega^2 + \sigma_i^2} + K_0 \tag{6.38}$$

The derivatives of these functions are

$$\frac{d}{d\omega}\text{Re } Z(j\omega) = \sum_{i=2}^{n} \frac{-2K_i\sigma_i\omega}{(\omega^2 + \sigma_i^2)^2} \tag{6.39}$$

and

$$\frac{d}{d\omega}\text{Re } Y(j\omega) = \sum_{i=1}^{m} \frac{2K_i'\sigma_i^2\omega}{(\omega^2 + \sigma_i^2)^2} \tag{6.40}$$

From these equations, we see that since K_i and K_i' are nonnegative, the slope of the Re $Z(j\omega)$ against ω curve is always nonpositive and the slope of Re $Y(j\omega)$ plotted against ω is always nonnegative. We see now that Re $Z(j\omega)$ is *always decreasing* or monotonically decreasing from its maximum value $Z(0)$ to its minimum value $Z(\infty)$. Similarly, Re $Y(j\omega)$ is *always increasing* from the minimum value $Y(0)$ to the maximum value $Y(\infty)$. Then $Z(s) - Z(\infty)$ and $Y(s) - Y(0)$ are both positive real functions. Similar statements may be made for the impedance function and admittance function for *RL* networks with Y and Z interchanged. Our conclusions for *RC* functions are illustrated in Fig. 6-10.

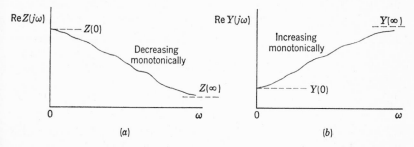

Fig. 6-10. The variation of Re $Z(j\omega)$ and Re $Y(j\omega)$ with ω for *RC* networks. For *RL* networks exchange Y and Z.

A specific impedance function will be used to show the application of these ideas to the Cauer ladder network development. Consider

$$Z(s) = \frac{(s + 1)(s + 3)}{s(s + 2)} \tag{6.41}$$

which is the impedance of an *RC* network. Figure 6-11 illustrates the steps in the development. Since $Z(\infty) = 1$ is the minimum value of Re $Z(j\omega)$, a constant of impedance is first removed, giving a resistor of 1 ohm. The removal of this constant shifts the zeros of $Z(s)$ in forming $Z_1(s)$ as follows:

$$Z_1(s) = \frac{s^2 + 4s + 3}{s^2 + 2s} - 1 = \frac{2s + 3}{s^2 + 2s} = \frac{1}{Y_1} \tag{6.42}$$

This shifting is shown in Fig. 6-11, the zero at -1 moving to -1.5 and the zero at -3 moving to $-\infty$. The admittance $Y_1 = 1/Z_1$ has a pole at infinity. This pole at infinity may be removed to give a capacitor element. The removal of this pole is equivalent to the removal of the term $\frac{1}{2}s$ so that $C_2 = \frac{1}{2}$ farad.

$$Y_2(s) = \frac{s^2 + 2s}{2s + 3} - \frac{s}{2} = \frac{\frac{1}{2}s}{2s + 3} = \frac{1}{Z_2} \qquad (6.43)$$

From Fig. 6-11, we see that Z_2 has a finite value at infinity and since this is the minimum value of Re $Z_2(j\omega)$, $Z_2(\infty) = 4$ ohms may be

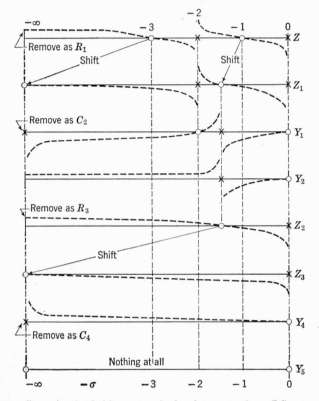

Fig. 6-11. Steps in the ladder network development of an RC network by a continued fraction expansion about infinity. The dashed lines show $Z(\sigma)$ and $Y(\sigma)$ for the various steps. The resulting network is known as the first Cauer form of RC network.

removed as R_3, resulting in a new impedance function,

$$Z_3 = \frac{2s + 3}{\frac{1}{2}s} - 4 = \frac{6}{s} = \frac{1}{Y_3} \qquad (6.44)$$

Now Y_3 has a pole at infinity which is removed by removing the term $s/6$ corresponding to a capacitor of value $C_4 = \frac{1}{6}$ farad. With the removal of this pole, nothing remains and the development is complete.

The steps shown in Fig. 6-11 are neatly summarized by a continued fraction expansion of $Z(s)$,

$$Z(s) = 1 + \cfrac{1}{\cfrac{s}{2} + \cfrac{1}{4 + \cfrac{1}{s/6}}} \tag{6.45}$$

This continued fraction expansion is easily found by the divide, invert, divide procedure with the detailed steps carried out as follows:

$$
\begin{array}{r}
s^2 + 2s \overline{)s^2 + 4s + 3} (1 \leftarrow R_1 \\
\underline{s^2 + 2s} \\
2s + 3 \overline{)s^2 + 2s} (s/2 \leftarrow C_2 s \\
\underline{s^2 + \tfrac{3}{2}s} \\
\tfrac{1}{2}s \overline{)2s + 3} (4 \leftarrow R_3 \\
\underline{2s} \\
3 \overline{)\tfrac{1}{2}s} (s/6 \leftarrow C_4 s \\
\underline{\tfrac{1}{2}s} \\
0
\end{array}
\tag{6.46}
$$

The resulting ladder network is shown in Fig. 6-12. By analogy to the LC case, this network is described as an RC network of the *first Cauer form.*

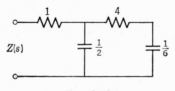

$Z(s)$ 1   4 $\tfrac{1}{2}$ $\tfrac{1}{6}$

Fig. 6-12

The same example may be expanded about the origin as a continued fraction to give the *second Cauer form* of RC network. In this development, poles of impedance at the origin are removed as capacitors in a series position in the ladder. Since $Y(0) < Y(\infty)$, the admittance at $s = 0$ may be removed as a resistor in a shunt position and the new admittance function thus formed will be positive real. The details of this particular operation are shown in Fig. 6-13. This figure and the arguments just outlined provide the justification of the continued frac-

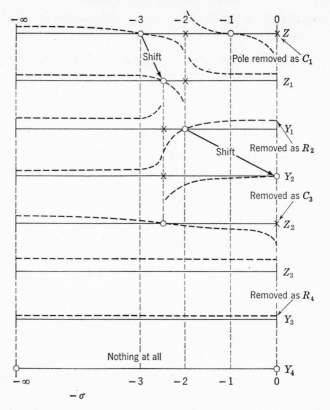

Fig. 6-13. Steps in the ladder network development of an RC network to give the second Cauer form. The dashed lines show $Z(\sigma)$ and $Y(\sigma)$ for the various steps.

tion expansion about the origin which is found by the following division pattern:

$$
2s + s^2 \overline{\smash{\big)}\, 3 + 4s + s^2} \left(\frac{3}{2}\frac{1}{s} \leftarrow 1/C_1 s\right.
$$
$$
\underline{3 + \tfrac{3}{2}s}
$$
$$
\tfrac{5}{2}s + s^2 \overline{\smash{\big)}\, 2s + s^2} \left(\tfrac{4}{5} \leftarrow 1/R_2\right.
$$
$$
\underline{2s + \tfrac{4}{5}s^2}
$$
$$
\tfrac{1}{5}s^2 \overline{\smash{\big)}\, \tfrac{5}{2}s + s^2} \left(\frac{25}{2}\frac{1}{s} \leftarrow 1/C_3 s\right.
$$
$$
\underline{\tfrac{5}{2}s}
$$
$$
s^2 \overline{\smash{\big)}\, \tfrac{1}{5}s^2} \left(\tfrac{1}{5} \leftarrow 1/R_4\right.
$$
$$
\underline{\tfrac{1}{5}s^2}
$$
$$
0
$$

$$(6.47)$$

From this, the continued fraction is seen to be

$$Z(s) = \frac{3}{2s} + \cfrac{1}{\frac{4}{5} + \cfrac{1}{\frac{25}{2s} + \cfrac{1}{\frac{1}{5}}}}$$ (6.48)

The second Cauer form of network for the $Z(s)$ of Eq. 6.41 is shown in Fig. 6-14. In these networks, the capacitor is always in the series position and the resistor in the shunt position. Just as in the LC case

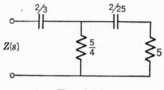

Fig. 6-14

the nature of the first and last elements in the ladder network was determined by the nature of $Z(s)$ at zero and infinity, so it is for RC networks as summarized in Table 6-4.

TABLE 6-4
The End Elements for Cauer RC Networks

Form	Kind of End Elements
First Cauer	If $Z(s)$ has a zero at $s = \infty$, the first element is C_2. If $Z(s)$ is a constant at $s = \infty$, the first element is R_1. If $Z(s)$ has a pole at $s = 0$, the last element is C_n. If $Z(s)$ is a constant at $s = 0$, the last element is R_n.
Second Cauer	If $Z(s)$ has a pole at $s = 0$, the first element is C_1. If $Z(s)$ is a constant at $s = 0$, the first element is R_2. If $Z(s)$ has a zero at $s = \infty$, the last element is C_n. If $Z(s)$ is a constant at $s = \infty$, the last element is R_n.

The similarities of the RL and RC cases were outlined in Section 6.1 for the Foster forms of networks. These same similarities apply for the Cauer forms of networks, and the results for the RC case may be applied to the RL case with the changes given in Table 6-5. Table 6-6 gives a summary of the procedures and networks for the Foster and Cauer forms.

TABLE 6-5
Properties of Cauer *RL* Networks

Property	Instructions	Then Given in:
Variation of Re $Z(j\omega)$ and Re $Y(j\omega)$	Interchange Z and Y	Fig. 6-10
End elements	Interchange zero and pole; substitute L for C	Table 6-4
Figures showing development of ladder network	Slopes opposite direction for Y and Z; expansion about ∞ gives first Cauer, about 0 second Cauer	Figs. 6-11 and 6-13

TABLE 6-6
Summary of Synthesis Procedures for Two-Element-Kind Networks

Network Form	Procedure	Resulting *LC* Network. For *RC* Case, Replace *L* by *R*; for *RL* Case, Replace *C* by *R*
First Foster	Partial fraction expansion of $Z(s)$*	
Second Foster	Partial fraction expansion of $Y(s)$†	
First Cauer	Continued fraction expansion of $Z(s)$ or $Y(s)$ about infinity	
Second Cauer	Continued fraction expansion of $Z(s)$ or $Y(s)$ about zero	

* For *RL* case, expand $Z(s)/s$ rather than $Z(s)$.

† For *RC* case, expand $Y(s)/s$ rather than $Y(s)$.

FURTHER READING

An excellent summary of *RC* network synthesis is given by Truxal in *Automatic Feedback Control System Synthesis*, pp. 169–187. Other reference material treating the *RC* as well as the *LC* case is given in the Further Reading section of Chapter 5.

PROBLEMS

6-1. The network shown in Fig. P6-1 is required to have poles at $s = -1$ and $s = -3$ and zeros at $s = -2$ and $s = -4$. The "first" element is a resistor of value $R = \frac{8}{3}$ ohms. Find the other elements of the network.

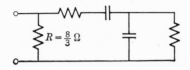

Fig. P6-1

6-2. Figure 6-7(*c*) shows waveforms which are applied to the networks of Fig. 6-7(*a*) to give zero current in the steady state. Let these voltages be applied to the networks at $t = 0$. Find the current that results in each case.

6-3. Synthesize the first and second forms of Foster networks for the impedance

$$Z(s) = \frac{(s + 2)(s + 5)}{(s + 1)(s + 3)}$$

6-4. Find the two Foster networks meeting the specification

$$Z(s) = \frac{(s + 2.5)(s + 10)}{(s + 1)(s + 7.5)}$$

6-5. Find the first and second forms of Cauer network for the impedance function

$$Z(s) = \frac{(s + 2)(s + 6)}{(s + 1)(s + 5)}$$

6-6. A four-element network is a ladder network with a minimum number of elements to realize a given $Z(s)$. The two resistors have the value of A ohms and the two capacitors have the value of A farads. What are the possible forms of the driving-point impedance, $Z(s)$?

6-7. Synthesize the first and second Foster networks for the impedance

$$Z(s) = \frac{(s + 1)(s + 4)}{(s + 3)(s + 5)}$$

6-8. Synthesize the first and second Cauer forms of networks for the impedance functions

$$\text{(a)} \;\; Z(s) = \frac{2s + s^2}{3 + 4s + s^2} \qquad\qquad \text{(b)} \;\; Z(s) = \frac{s^2 + 7s + 4}{3s^2 + 2s}$$

6-9. An impedance function has simple poles at -1 and -4 and simple zeros at -2 and -5. $Z(0) = 10$ ohms. Find the four canonical networks with element values.

6-10. You are required to synthesize a network from the impedance function

$$Z(s) = 2300 \frac{(s + 1350)(s + 6750)}{s(s + 4050)}$$

but to do it in a special order, namely:

(a) Scale $Z(s)$ such that all critical frequencies are small integers (or zero) and the scale factor is unity.

(b) Synthesize a network from the scaled $Z(s)$.

(c) Find the actual element values by inverse frequency scaling and magnitude scaling.

6-11. The network given in Fig. P6-11 is to be connected in parallel or in series with another network such that the total driving-point impedance is equal to 1 ohm for all frequencies. The given network has the impedance Z_1

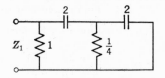

Fig. P6-11

and the desired network has the impedance Z_2 so that the requirements of the problem are that either

$$Z_1(s) + Z_2(s) = 1 \qquad \text{or} \qquad \frac{1}{Z_1(s)} + \frac{1}{Z_2(s)} = 1$$

(a) Can we use the series connection, the parallel connection, or either connection?

(b) Determine a network with element values for $Z_2(s)$ in the form of a ladder. (This problem will suggest one approach to "impedance matching.")

6-12. A network is made up of the series connection of an RL network and an RC network. Assuming that neither of the networks is a short circuit, investigate the following questions:

(a) Where are the poles located?

(b) Where are the zeros located?

(c) What is the behavior at the origin and at infinity?

6-13. A network containing two negative elements is shown in Fig. P6-13. Find the driving-point impedance for this network. Is the input impedance positive real? Under what conditions may a nonphysical network have a positive real driving-point impedance? Discuss.

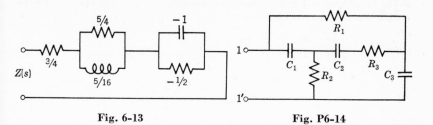

Fig. 6-13   Fig. P6-14

6-14. (*a*) Show that the *RC* network of Fig. P6-14 is a canonic form in the sense that it uses the minimum number of elements required to realize $Z_{11}(s)$, except for one special degenerate case. Give element relationships corresponding to the degenerate case.

(*b*) Give the pole-zero pattern for the driving-point impedance function for the regular and the degenerate cases of part (*a*).

6-15. Each of the networks of Fig. P6-15 is a bridged-T network of the special kind studied in Prob. 2-25.

(*a*) If *n* such networks are cascaded in the figure with the same R_0 throughout, show that

$$G = \frac{V_n}{V_0} = \frac{\text{constant}}{(1 + z_1)(1 + z_2) \cdots (1 + z_n)}$$

where $z_j = Z_j/R_0$ and Z_j is the Z_a of Prob. 2-25 for the *j*th network in cascade.

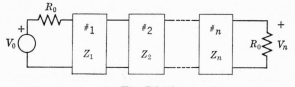

Fig. P6-15

(*b*) Given an appropriate *G* function, it is always possible to factor it in such a way that the $(1 + z_j)$ factors contain a z_j which is positive real.* Consider the following specification function

$$G(s) = \frac{s(s^2 + 5)(s^2 + 3s + 2)}{(s^2 + 2s + 5)(s^2 + 4s + 5)(s^2 + 4.4s + 4.2)}$$

* See Tuttle, *Network Synthesis,* Vol. I, Chapter 11.

with $R_0 = 1$ ohm; synthesize a chain of bridged-T networks to this specification. Use only L and C or only R and C or L in any one Z_1, and use the minimum number of sections possible. Give a complete schematic diagram showing all element values.

6-16. Determine if the following two functions are positive real. Give reasons to justify your conclusions.

$$(a) \quad Y(s) = \frac{(s + 2)(s + 3)}{(s + 1)(s + 4)} \qquad (b) \quad Y(s) = \frac{(s + 2)^2}{s^2 + 4}$$

RLC One Terminal-Pairs

For a given positive real function $Z(s)$, the poles at the origin, $\pm j\omega_i$, and infinity, as well as a constant equal at most to the minimum value of Re $Z(j\omega)$, can always be removed and the remainder function is positive real. In the special case that all of the poles and zeros are on the negative real axis and interlaced, these poles may be removed from either $Z(s)$ or $Z(s)/s$ and the remainder function is positive real. By repeated use of the pole removal and constant removal operations, a part of the network known as the _Foster preamble_ may be realized, or in some cases the network may be completely realized. But the impedance function may reduce to a form with no poles or zeros on the imaginary axis and with a real part of $Z(j\omega)$ equal to 0 at one or more frequencies. In this case, what next? The functions we describe are known as _minimum functions_, having been so named by Bode.[*] Brune was the first to describe a method of synthesizing minimum positive real functions in 1931. Before studying his method as well as more recent methods, we first outline important properties of these minimum functions.

7.1 Minimum positive real functions

An impedance function with no poles on the imaginary axis is known as a _minimum reactance function_. An admittance function having this property is a _minimum susceptance function_. Similarly, an impedance function whose real part vanishes at some real frequency is known as a _minimum resistance function_ and for admittance, a _minimum conductance function_. A function which is simultaneously minimum reactance, susceptance, resistance, and conductance is known simply as a _minimum function_. Minimum functions are a special class

[*] _Network Analysis and Feedback Amplifier Design_, p. 123.

of driving-point impedance or admittance functions that are positive real and in addition: (1) have no poles or zeros on the imaginary axis of the s plane, (2) have finite, real, positive values at $s = 0$ and $s = \infty$, and (3) have a real part that vanishes for at least one finite real frequency, ω_1, such that $Z(j\omega_1) = 0 \pm jX_1$ with $X_1 \neq 0$. To fulfill the second requirement, it is necessary that the degree of the numerator of $Z(s)$ just equal that of the denominator. The third requirement relates to the variation of the real part of $Z(j\omega)$ with frequency. The nature of the real part of $Z(j\omega)$ was considered in Section 4.4. It was shown that only the sign of

$$A(\omega^2) = m_1 m_2 - n_1 n_2 \Big|_{s=j\omega} \tag{7.1}$$

need be considered in testing the sign of Re $Z(j\omega)$. In factored form, $A(\omega^2)$ was written in Eq. 4.76:

$$A(\omega^2) = K_1(\omega^2 + \delta_1^2)(\omega^2 + \delta_2^2) \cdots (\omega^2 + \delta_n^2) \tag{7.2}$$

One or more of these δ^2's must be real and negative in order that Re $Z(j\omega)$ reduce to 0 as required of minimum functions. If these

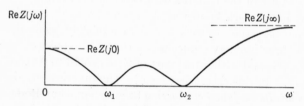

Fig. 7-1. Plot of Re $Z(j\omega)$ for a minimum function.

zeros in ω^2 are real and positive, it is necessary that they be of even multiplicity in order that $A(\omega^2)$ always be positive. If Re $Z(j\omega)$ is 0 at the frequencies ω_1 and ω_2, for example, then $A(\omega^2)$ must have the form

$$A(\omega^2) = (\omega^2 - \omega_1^2)^{k_1}(\omega^2 - \omega_2^2)^{k_2} A_1(\omega^2) \tag{7.3}$$

where k_1 and k_2 are positive even integers of value 2 or greater, and $A_1(\omega^2)$ is positive for all values of ω. A plot of Re $Z(j\omega)$ for this particular case of $A(\omega^2)$, Eq. 7.3, is shown in Fig. 7-1. Observe that the slope of curve is 0 at the frequencies ω_1 and ω_2.

Example 1. Consider the partially factored driving-point impedance function

$$Z_0(s) = \frac{2s^4 + 3s^3 + 5s^2 + 5s + 1}{(s^2 + 1)(2s^2 + 2s + 4)} \tag{7.4}$$

This $Z_0(s)$ is clearly not a minimum function since there are poles on the imaginary axis at $s = \pm j1$. Removal of these poles corresponds to the removal of a parallel LC network with $L = 1$ henry and $C = 1$ farad since

$$Z_0(s) = \frac{s}{s^2 + 1} + \frac{2s^2 + s + 1}{2s^2 + 2s + 4} \tag{7.5}$$

We must now examine the second term in this equation to see if it is a minimum function. There are neither poles nor zeros on the imaginary axis, and the value of the function at zero and infinite frequency is finite, real, and positive. The real part of $Z(j\omega)$ is

$$\text{Re } Z(j\omega) = \frac{\omega^4 - 2\omega^2 + 1}{\omega^4 - 3\omega^2 + 4} = \frac{(\omega^2 - 1)^2}{\omega^4 - 3\omega^2 + 4} \tag{7.6}$$

From this equation, we see that $\text{Re } Z(j\omega) = 0$ at $\omega = 1$ and that the function is therefore a minimum function. At the frequency $\omega = 1$, the impedance is $Z(j1) = j\frac{1}{2}$ ohm. The variation of $\text{Re } Z(j\omega)$ for this example is shown in Fig. 7-2.

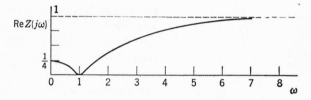

Fig. 7-2. Plot of Re $Z(j\omega)$ for Example 1.

Minimum functions may be studied in terms of the angle condition for positive real functions studied in Chapter 3. In Eq. 3.57 it was shown that the angle of a positive real $Z(s)$ must satisfy the condition,

$$\left| \text{Arg } Z(j\omega) \right| \leq 90° \tag{7.7}$$

This requirement for minimum functions is that the angle be exactly $\pm 90°$ when $\text{Re } Z(j\omega) = 0$, or that

$$\left| \sum_{i=1}^{n} \theta_i - \sum_{i=1}^{n} \phi_i \right| = 90° \tag{7.8}$$

where the θ angles are measured from the zeros to $j\omega_1$ and the ϕ angles are measured from the poles to the same point. When the real part of $Z(j\omega)$ vanishes at the frequency $j\omega_1$, then $Z(j\omega)$ is imaginary and has the magnitude

$$\left| Z(j\omega_1) \right| = \left| X_1 \right| = K \frac{M_1 M_2 M_3 \cdots}{m_1 m_2 m_3 \cdots} \Bigg|_{s=j\omega_1} \tag{7.9}$$

where M_1, M_2, $\cdots$, M_n are distances from the zeros to $j\omega_1$ and m_1, m_2, $\cdots$, m_n are the corresponding pole distances. The angle condition of Eq. 7.8 and the magnitude condition of Eq. 7.9 form the basis of a graphical procedure making use of ruler and protractor for rough testing of potentially minimum functions and for visualizing the meaning of the minimum function

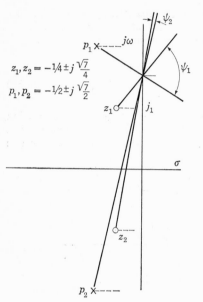

$$z_1, z_2 = -\tfrac{1}{4} \pm j \frac{\sqrt{7}}{4}$$

$$p_1, p_2 = -\tfrac{1}{2} \pm j \frac{\sqrt{7}}{2}$$

Fig. 7-3. Pole-zero configuration showing the angle condition for a minimum function.

requirements. This will be illustrated by an example.

The pole-zero configuration shown in Fig. 7-3 corresponds to the second factor in Eq. 7.5 of Example 1. In that example, it was shown that Re $Z(j\omega) = 0$ at $\omega = 1$. In testing such a function by the ruler-protractor method, it is sometimes helpful to pair off poles and zeros to form angles, identified as ψ in Fig. 7-3, which are the difference of zero and pole angles, $\theta - \phi = \psi$. Equation 7.8 in terms of ψ angles becomes, for this example, $\psi_1 + \psi_2 = 90°$. Inspection of Fig. 7-3 indicates that it is reasonable that this angle condition is fulfilled and that $X_1 = KM_1M_2/m_1m_2 = \tfrac{1}{2}$ ohm as found previously. When the frequency at which Re $Z(j\omega) = 0$ is not known, it can be found by a cut-and-try procedure employing the criteria of Eq. 7.8.

7.2 Brune's method of *RLC* synthesis

How shall we penetrate the impedance armor of the network represented by the positive real minimum function to remove the first element? We seem to require an entirely *new* approach. All previously studied techniques of pole removal and constant removal have already been fully exploited in arriving at the minimum function. The point chosen by Brune* for his attack on the problem is the frequency

* "Synthesis of a finite two terminal network whose driving-point impedance is a prescribed function of frequency," *Jour. Math. and Phys.*, **10**, 191 (1931). Same as his MIT Sc.D. thesis (1930).

$s = \pm j\omega_1$ at which the real part of the impedance function vanishes, as shown in Fig. 7-4. At this frequency, Re $Z(j\omega_1) = 0$ but $Z(j\omega_1)$ itself is nonzero and finite (otherwise there would be a pole or a zero on the imaginary axis which could be removed), is imaginary, and is either positive or negative. If X_1 in $Z(j\omega_1) = jX_1$ is positive, the network we seek is represented at the frequency ω_1 by the equivalent network of a single inductor; when X_1 is negative, the network is similarly represented by a negative inductor (or a single capacitor) equivalent network. At any other frequency, the simple equivalent networks fail, but this observation suggests the next step. Brune showed that the removal of the inductor, whether positive or negative, gives a network with elements equivalent to a transformer.

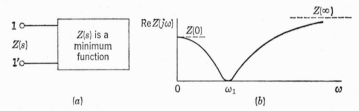

Fig. 7-4. Situation at the outset of the Brune procedure: (a) $Z(s)$ is a minimum function, (b) Re $Z(j\omega_1) = 0$, but $Z(j\omega_1) = jX_1$ where X_1 is real but either positive or negative.

The philosophy of the Brune method will be introduced from an elementary example, postponing consideration of the general case.

Example 2. The positive real function

$$Z(s) = \frac{s^2 + s + 2}{2s^2 + s + 1} \tag{7.10}$$

is a minimum function having a real part which vanishes at $\omega_1 = 1$. At that frequency, the impedance is $Z(j1) = -j1$ which we assume is due to a negative inductor of value $L_1 = X_1/\omega_1 = -1$ henry. When this inductor is removed, the impedance remaining is Z_1 where

$$Z(s) = -s + Z_1(s) \tag{7.11}$$

or $$Z_1(s) = Z(s) + s \tag{7.12}$$

Observe that Z_1 is a positive real function, being the sum of two other positive real functions. The realization of Z_1 is accomplished by recognizing that it must have a zero at $s = \pm j\omega_1$, for otherwise the negative inductor could not represent the network at this frequency. Then

$$Z_1(s) = \frac{s^2 + s + 2}{2s^2 + s + 1} + s = \frac{2s^3 + 2s^2 + 2s + 2}{2s^2 + s + 1} = \frac{2(s^2 + 1)(s + 1)}{2s^2 + s + 1} \tag{7.13}$$

and Z_1 has the anticipated zeros at $s = \pm j1$. These zeros of Z_1 are poles of $Y_1 = 1/Z_1$ which may be removed to give

$$Y_1(s) = \frac{\frac{1}{2}s}{s^2 + 1} + \frac{\frac{1}{2}}{s + 1} = \frac{1}{2s + 2/s} + \frac{1}{2s + 2} \qquad (7.14)$$

The network realization is that shown in Fig. 7-5(a) which terminates in a 2-ohm resistor. Now the three inductors of this figure, two positive and one

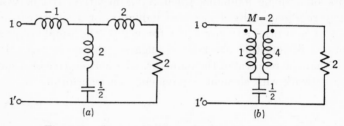

(a)   (b)

Fig. 7-5. Brune network realization for Example 2.

negative, are the equivalent of the ideal transformer shown in Fig. 7-5(b) having unity coupling coefficient. By recognizing the ideal transformer as a passive element, we have a realization!

To justify each step in the general case, we begin with a positive real minimum function, $Z(s)$. Our first step then is to remove an inductor having the value $L_1 = X_1/\omega_1$, a real number which may be either positive or negative. We consider the positive and negative possibilities as two separate cases.

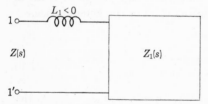 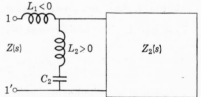

Fig. 7-6. Illustrating the first step in the Brune procedure for Case 1, the removal of a negative inductor.

Fig. 7-7. The second step in the Brune procedure is the removal of a shunt-connected series LC circuit which is resonant at frequency ω_1.

Case 1, L_1 is negative. From the network of Fig. 7-6, we see that if $L_1 < 0$, then the removal of the term corresponding to the pole at infinity gives a new impedance function,

$$Z_1(s) = Z(s) - L_1 s \qquad (7.15)$$

Now $L_1 s$ is not a positive real function for $L_1 < 0$, but $Z_1(s)$ is positive real. The impedance $Z_1(s)$ has a zero at $j\omega_1$ since

$$Z(j\omega_1) - j\omega_1 L_1 = 0 \qquad (7.16)$$

This means that $Y_1(s) = 1/Z_1(s)$ has a pole at the frequency $j\omega_1$ which can be removed as a series LC network connected in shunt, as shown in Fig. 7-7. Since $Z_1(s)$ is positive real, both L_2 and C_2 are positive. The figure provides us with a physical interpretation of the steps completed so far. At the frequency $j\omega_1$, the series-connected L_2C_2 network is in resonance and short-circuits the network with the impedance Z_2 with the result that the network is represented by the single inductor L_1 as required. The admittance of the network remaining is

$$Y_2(s) = Y_1(s) - \frac{2K_1s}{s^2 + \omega_1{}^2} \qquad (7.17)$$

and the network elements have the positive values

$$L_2 = 1/2K_1 \qquad \text{and} \qquad C_2 = 2K_1/\omega_1{}^2 \qquad (7.18)$$

since K_1 is positive. Furthermore, $Y_2(s)$ is a positive real function since the removal of conjugate imaginary poles from a positive real function leaves a positive real function.

What shall we remove next? We can see the answer to this question if we compute $Y_2(s)$ and $Z_2(s) = 1/Y_2(s)$ in terms of $Z(s)$, K_1, and L_1. Substituting Eq. 7.15 into Eq. 7.17 gives

$$Y_2(s) = \frac{1}{Z(s) - L_1s} - \frac{2K_1s}{s^2 + \omega_1{}^2} \qquad (7.19)$$

This equation simplifies to the following form:

$$Z_2(s) = \frac{-L_1s^3 + Z(s)s^2 - L_1\omega_1{}^2s + Z(s)\omega_1{}^2}{(1 + 2K_1L_1)s^2 - 2K_1 Z(s)s + \omega_1{}^2} \qquad (7.20)$$

Since $Z(s)$ is real, finite, and positive for infinite s, being a minimum function, we see that $Z_2(s)$ has a pole at infinity which may be removed as an inductor having the value

$$L_3 = \frac{-L_1}{1 + 2K_1L_1} \qquad (7.21)$$

Furthermore, L_3 must be positive since $Z_2(s)$ was shown to be a positive real function. It is interesting to trace the origin of this pole at infinity of $Z_2(s)$. The impedance $Z(s)$ has no pole at infinity, being a minimum function. However, the addition of the term $-L_1s$ to $Z(s)$ causes $Z_1(s)$ to have a pole at infinity, Eq. 7.15. By Eq. 7.17, $Y_2(s)$ has a zero at infinity since $Y_1(s)$ and $-2K_1s/(s^2 + \omega_1{}^2)$ both have zeros at infinity. Thus we see that $Z_2(s)$ has a pole at infinity as shown in Eq. 7.20. In effect, L_3 corresponds to the removal of a pole at infinity that was inserted into $Z(s)$ in removing L_1s from $Z(s)$. We first put a pole at infinity that we do not have and then we give it back again. What is the net gain from borrowing and then repaying? Since $Z_2(s)$ is positive real and

$$Z_3(s) = Z_2(s) - L_3 s \qquad (7.22)$$

we see that $Z_3(s)$ is also positive real. Any network function has the same number of poles as zeros if the poles or zeros at infinity are counted. In forming $Z_1(s)$, we increased the number of poles and zeros by 1 compared to the number in $Z(s)$. The removal of the series LC network in forming $Z_2(s)$ decreased the number by 2, and the last step, the removal of L_3 in forming $Z_3(s)$, effects a further reduction of 1. The net reduction of the number of poles and zeros in $Z_3(s)$ compared to $Z(s)$ is thus 2. The operations just described can be repeated until the final function has no poles or zeros and so is a positive constant corresponding to a terminating resistor. The changes in the degree of the numerator and denominator of $Z(s)$ are summarized in Table 7-1.

TABLE 7-1

Function	Degree of Numerator	Degree of Denominator
Z	n	n
Z_1	$n + 1$	n
Y_1	n	$n + 1$
Y_2	$n - 2$	$n - 1$
Z_2	$n - 1$	$n - 2$
Z_3	$n - 2$	$n - 2$

The network consisting of three inductors and one capacitor shown in Fig. 7-8 is known as a *Brune network*. The operations that result in the reduction of the number of poles and zeros of the minimum function $Z(s)$ by 2 are known as a *Brune cycle*. Figure 7-8 shows one Brune cycle. The positive real function $Z_3(s)$ may be realized by again reducing it to a minimum function by a constant removal operation followed by a second Brune cycle. Thus any positive real function can be synthesized. By this means, Brune first showed that the requirement that a driving-point function be positive real was not only necessary but also *sufficient* for a passive network realization to exist.

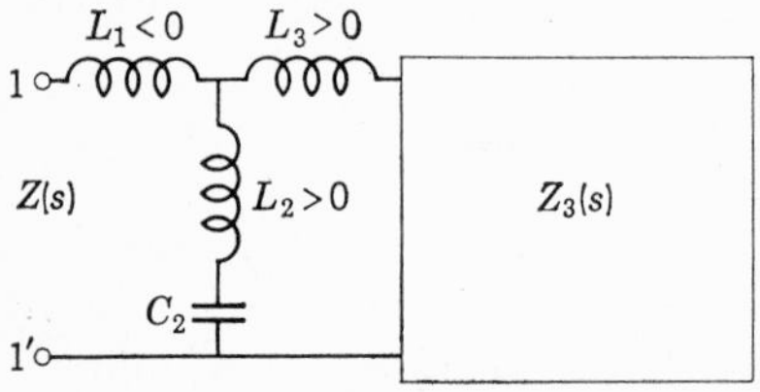

Fig. 7-8. The completed Brune cycle for Case 1, $L_1 < 0$. For Case 2, L_3 is negative and both L_1 and L_2 are positive. $Z_3(s)$ is positive real.

Our acceptance of this conclusion depends on a justification of the assertion that the three inductors of the Brune network, including one negative element, are equivalent to a transformer which is considered to be a realizable element. We begin by considering the equivalent T of the transformer shown in Fig. 7-9(a) with the polarity marks indicated. Writing loop equations for the two networks of the figure

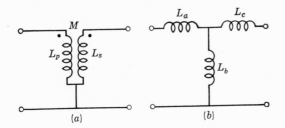

Fig. 7-9. The T equivalent of a transformer with a common terminal.

leads to the conclusion that for the networks to be equivalent it is necessary that

$$L_p = L_a + L_b$$
$$L_s = L_b + L_c \tag{7.23}$$

and

$$M = L_b$$

The coefficient of coupling of a transformer is defined by the equation

$$k = \frac{M}{\sqrt{L_p L_s}} \quad \text{or} \quad k^2 = \frac{M^2}{L_p L_s} \tag{7.24}$$

By substituting Eqs. 7.23 into the last expression, we see that

$$k^2 = \frac{M^2}{L_p L_s} = \frac{L_b{}^2}{(L_a + L_b)(L_b + L_c)} \tag{7.25}$$

Now the L_a in these equations is L_1 in the Brune network of Fig. 7-8, $L_b = L_2$ has the value $1/2K_1$ given in Eq. 7.18, and $L_c = L_3$ was found to be $-L_1/(1 + 2K_1L_1)$ in Eq. 7.21. Using these values we find that

$$L_p L_s = \left(L_1 + \frac{1}{2K_1}\right)\left(\frac{-L_1}{1 + 2K_1 L_1} + \frac{1}{2K_1}\right) = \left(\frac{1}{2K_1}\right)^2 \tag{7.26}$$

so that from Eq. 7.25 the coefficient of coupling is required to have *unit value.* Observe also that $L_s = L_b + L_c$ is always positive since

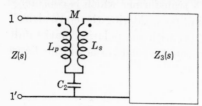

both L_b and L_c are positive. Then, since K_1 is both real and positive in the equation $L_p L_s = (1/2K_1)^2$, L_p is required to have the same sign as L_s and so is positive. Realization of networks using the Brune method thus depends on a transformer having positive primary and secondary inductance but having unity coefficient of coupling. The final

Fig. 7-10. A network which is equivalent to the Brune network shown in Fig. 7-8. For such networks, the coefficient of coupling is 1.

form of the Brune network which is equivalent to that of Fig. 7-8 is shown in Fig. 7-10.

Case 2, L_1 is positive. When $L_1 > 0$, the removal of L_1 as a network element gives

$$Z_1(s) = Z(s) - L_1 s \qquad (7.27)$$

which is not necessarily a positive real function.* In Case 1, we first removed a negative element which resulted in a positive real function that was synthesized. In contrast, we here remove a positive element

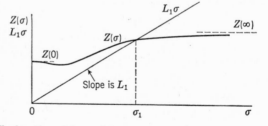

Fig. 7-11. The location of the positive real zero of $Z_1(s)$ for Case 2. σ_1 is the zero.

and a nonpositive real function results. Why is $Z_1(s)$ not positive real? Suppose that we plot $Z(\sigma)$ as a function of σ. Since $Z(s)$ is a minimum function, we know that both $Z(0)$ and $Z(\infty)$ are finite, real, and positive. We also know that $Z(s)$, being positive real, has no poles or zeros for positive σ. From these observations, we see that the plot of $Z(\sigma)$ versus σ must have the form shown in Fig. 7-11. On the same coordinates, let us plot the product $L_1\sigma$ as a function of σ. The intersection of these two curves satisfies the condition $Z(\sigma) - L_1\sigma = 0$, which by Eq. 7.27 is a zero of $Z_1(s)$. Since the two curves must intersect, $Z_1(s)$ must have a real zero in the right half plane and for this

---

* Tuttle calls this function a pseudo-positive-real function and discusses its properties. See his *Network Synthesis*, Vol. I, pp. 514–534.

reason is not a positive real function. Brune made use of a theorem in functions of a complex variable due to Pick to show that there is not more than one zero in the right half plane for $Z_1(s) = Z(s) - L_1 s$.

One additional pair of zeros of $Z_1(s)$ can be located, just as in Case 1, from the observation that $Z_1(s)$ has a zero at $s = \pm j\omega_1$. As in Case 1, this pole of $1/Z_1(s)$ is removed as a series $L_2 C_2$ network connected in shunt. The resulting admittance function

$$Y_2(s) = Y_1(s) - \frac{2K_1 s}{s^2 + \omega_1^2} \qquad (7.28)$$

is again not positive real. However, K_1, the residue of $Y_1(s)$ evaluated at the pole at $\pm j\omega_1$, is real and positive. (See Prob. 7-13.) There results

$$Z_2(s) = \frac{-L_1 s^3 + Z(s)s^2 - L_1 \omega_1^2 s + Z(s)\omega_1^2}{(1 + 2K_1 L_1)s^2 - 2K_1 Z(s)s + \omega_1^2} \qquad (7.29)$$

or $\qquad Z_2(s) = \dfrac{(s^2 + \omega_1^2)[Z(s) - L_1 s]}{(1 + 2K_1 L_1)s^2 - 2K_1 Z(s)s + \omega_1^2} \qquad (7.30)$

and since $Z(s) - L_1 s$ is 0 at $s = \sigma_1$, as shown in Fig. 7-11, $Z_2(s)$ has the same real right half plane zero as $Z_1(s)$. Following the steps of Case 1, we observe that $Z_2(s)$ has a pole at infinity which may be removed by subtracting

$$L_3 s = \frac{-L_1}{1 + 2K_1 L_1} s \qquad (7.31)$$

from $Z_2(s)$. From this equation, L_3 is negative since L_1 and K_1 are positive. Does the removal of a negative element from the nonpositive real $Z_2(s)$ make the impedance

$$Z_3(s) = Z_2(s) - L_3 s \qquad (7.32)$$

positive real? This is a crucial question, for if $Z_3(s)$ is not positive real, then the Brune cycle for Case 2 is unsuccessful. The impedance $Z_3(s)$ is shown to be positive real by using Eq. 7-29 together with Eq. 7.32 to show that

$$Z_3(s) = \frac{Z(s)s^2 - 2K_1 L_1^2 \omega_1^2 s + 2K_1 L_p Z(s)\omega_1^2}{(2K_1 L_p)^2 s^2 - [(1/L_s) Z(s)s] + \omega_1^2 2K_1 L_p} \qquad (7.33)$$

This equation has the same form as the corresponding equation for Case 1 (see Prob. 7-10) which was known to be positive real so that $Z_3(s)$ for Case 2 is positive real. And since the same cycle of operations was completed for Case 2 as for Case 1, $Z_3(s)$ has two fewer poles and two fewer zeros than $Z(s)$.

The completion of the Brune cycle for Case 2 starts by adding a pole at infinity to $Z(s)$. This addition results in a zero of $Z_1(s)$ in the right half plane. The last step amounts to the removal of this pole at infinity so that the right half plane zero is removed at the same time, leaving a positive real function. The cycle may be completed as many times as necessary to completely realize any driving-point function.

We have yet to compute the required value of the coefficient of coupling of the transformer equivalent of the Brune network and to assure ourselves that both L_p and L_s are positive. Since

$$L_p L_s = \left(L_1 + \frac{1}{2K_1}\right)\left(\frac{1}{2K_1} - \frac{L_1}{1 + 2K_1 L_1}\right) = \left(\frac{1}{2K_1}\right)^2 \quad (7.34)$$

and $M^2 = (1/2K_1)^2$, we see that $k^2 = M^2/L_p L_s = 1$ and a coefficient of coupling of unity is required once more. Also $L_p = L_1 + L_2$ is positive since both L_1 and L_2 are positive. Then by Eq. 7.34, $L_s = L_2 + L_3$ is always positive.

Example 3. The positive real function

$$Z(s) = \frac{s^2 + \frac{1}{2}s + \frac{1}{2}}{s^2 + s + 2} \quad (7.35)$$

is a minimum function and Re $Z(j\omega_1) = 0$ at $\omega_1 = 1$. At this frequency $Z(j1) = +j\frac{1}{2}$ ohm. The inductor L_1 has the value $X_1/\omega_1 = \frac{1}{2}$ henry. The

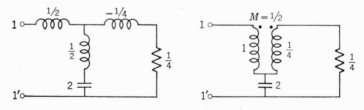

Fig. 7-12. Brune network realization for Example 3.

removal of this inductor gives

$$Z_1(s) = \frac{s^2 + \frac{1}{2}s + \frac{1}{2}}{s^2 + s + 2} - \frac{1}{2}s = \frac{-\frac{1}{2}s^3 + \frac{1}{2}s^2 - \frac{1}{2}s + \frac{1}{2}}{s^2 + s + 2} \quad (7.36)$$

Factoring the numerator polynomial,

$$Z_1(s) = \frac{\frac{1}{2}(s^2 + 1)(-s + 1)}{s^2 + s + 2} \quad (7.37)$$

Then

$$Y_1(s) = \frac{2s}{s^2 + 1} + \frac{4}{-s + 1} = \frac{1}{s/2 + 1/2s} + \frac{1}{-s/4 + \frac{1}{4}} \quad (7.38)$$

The final network realization is seen to be that shown in Fig. 7-12.

7.3   The method of Bott and Duffin

Brune was the first to provide a general method for the synthesis of one terminal-pair networks from positive real impedance functions. The Brune network, however, contains transformers requiring unity coefficient of coupling. Such transformers are not attractive as network elements for practical reasons. It was not until eighteen years after Brune's pioneer work that it was shown that the use of transformers is not necessary. In 1947, P. I. Richards,* then a graduate student at Harvard, showed that if $Z(s)$ is a positive real function, then the special function

$$R(s) = \frac{k\,Z(s) - s\,Z(k)}{k\,Z(k) - s\,Z(s)} \qquad (7.39)$$

is also positive real for real, positive values of k, and that the complexity of $R(s)$ is not greater than that of $Z(s)$. He made use of a multiple transformation of the type employed in Section 4.6 in studying positive real functions. Two years later, Bott and Duffin,† mathematicians at Carnegie Institute of Technology, made use of the Richards transformation to show that positive real functions can always be synthesized without ideal transformers.

Our explanation of the method of Bott and Duffin starts by solving for $Z(s)$ in Eq. 7.39. There results

$$Z(s) = \frac{k\,Z(k)\,R(s) + Z(k)s}{k + s\,R(s)} \qquad (7.40)$$

This equation may be written as the sum

$$Z(s) = \frac{k\,Z(k)\,R(s)}{k + s\,R(s)} + \frac{Z(k)s}{k + s\,R(s)} \qquad (7.41)$$

If we next divide the denominator by the numerator for each term, we have

$$Z(s) = \frac{1}{\dfrac{1}{Z(k)\,R(s)} + \dfrac{s}{k\,Z(k)}} + \frac{1}{\dfrac{k}{Z(k)s} + \dfrac{R(s)}{Z(k)}} \qquad (7.42)$$

---

* "A special class of functions with positive real part in half-plane," *Duke Math J.*, **14**, 777–786 (1947). Richards also discusses the problem of eliminating transformers in his paper, "Resistor-transmission-line circuits," *Proc. I.R.E.*, **36**, 217–220 (1948).

† R. Bott and R. J. Duffin, "Impedance synthesis without the use of transformers," *J. Appl. Phys.*, **20**, 816 (1949). The Bott and Duffin exposition requires but one-half page as a letter to the editor in contrast to forty-five pages in Brune's paper. Raoul Bott is now at Harvard University.

In order to associate this equation with a network, we observe that the equation is of the general form

$$Z(s) = \frac{1}{1/Z_1 + 1/Z_C} + \frac{1}{1/Z_L + 1/Z_2} \tag{7.43}$$

and that the network is connected as shown in Fig. 7-13. Comparing Eqs. 7.42 and 7.43, we see that the following identifications may be made:

$$Z_1 = Z(k)\,R(s); \qquad\qquad Z_2 = Z(k)/R(s) \tag{7.44}$$

and $\qquad Z_C = k\,Z(k)/s \equiv 1/C_1 s; \qquad Z_L = Z(k)s/k \equiv L_2 s \tag{7.45}$

From Eqs. 7.45:

$$C_1 = 1/k\,Z(k); \qquad L_2 = Z(k)/k \tag{7.46}$$

In Eqs. 7.44–7.46, $Z(k)$ is always positive if k is positive, $Z(s)$ being a positive real function. This being the case, we see that both Z_1 and

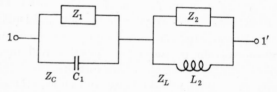

Fig. 7-13. The network structure suggested by the form of the Richards function in Eq. 7.43.

Z_2 are positive real functions since $R(s)$, the Richards function, is positive real.

The evaluation of Z_1, Z_2, C_1, and L_2 starts at the same point as in the Brune method of synthesis, namely, at the frequency ω_1 where

$$\text{Re } Z(j\omega_1) = 0 \qquad \text{and} \qquad Z(j\omega_1) = jX_1 \tag{7.47}$$

where X_1 may be either positive or negative. Let us consider the two sign possibilities as two separate cases.

Case A, X_1 is positive. From Eq. 7.43 with $s = j\omega_1$, we have

$$Z(j\omega_1) = jX_1 = \frac{1}{\dfrac{1}{Z_1(j\omega_1)} + j\omega_1 C_1} + \frac{1}{\dfrac{1}{j\omega_1 L_2} + \dfrac{1}{Z_2(j\omega_1)}} \tag{7.48}$$

One possibility in satisfying this equation occurs when $1/Z_1 = \infty$, and $1/Z_2 = 0$. This condition may be visualized from the network shown in Fig. 7-13. Since $Z_1 = Z(k)\,R(s)$ and $Z_2 = Z(k)/R(s)$, this requires that $R(s)$ have a zero at $s = j\omega_1$. This in turn requires that the numerator of Eq. 7.39 be equal to 0 at this frequency:

$$k\,Z(s) - s\,Z(k) = 0 \text{ at } s = j\omega_1 \qquad (7.49)$$

Rearranging this equation gives

$$\frac{Z(j\omega_1)}{j\omega_1} = \frac{jX_1}{j\omega_1} = L_2 = \frac{Z(k)}{k} \qquad (7.50)$$

where there is only one real and positive value of k available to be used here. Now $L_2 = X_1/\omega_1$ is found by the procedure of the Brune method so that k may be found by solving for the positive value of k satisfying the equation $Z(k) = kL_2$ and from this we may evaluate Z_1, Z_2, and C_1. The impedance Z_1 has a zero at $s = j\omega_1$ and Z_2 has

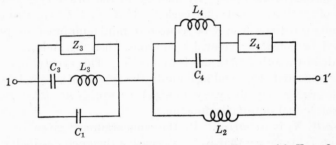

Fig. 7-14.　The Bott and Duffin network for Case A with $X_1 > 0$.

a pole at this frequency. The poles of $1/Z_1$ and Z_2 may be removed by the following expansions:

$$\frac{1}{Z_1} = \frac{2K_1's}{s^2 + \omega_1{}^2} + \frac{1}{Z_3} \qquad (7.51)$$

and

$$Z_2 = \frac{2K_1s}{s^2 + \omega_1{}^2} + Z_4 \qquad (7.52)$$

These pole removal operations leave Z_3 and Z_4 positive real. The residues K_1' and K_1 determine the values of the series-connected C_3 and L_3 and the parallel-connected L_4 and C_4 shown in Fig. 7-14 from the equations

$$C_3 = 2K_1'/\omega_1{}^2; \qquad L_3 = 1/2K_1' \qquad (7.53)$$

and

$$C_4 = 1/2K_1; \qquad L_4 = 2K_1/\omega_1{}^2 \qquad (7.54)$$

From Fig. 7-14 we see why L_2 represents the network at the frequency ω_1, for at that frequency the series LC network appears to be a short circuit whereas the parallel LC network behaves as an open circuit.

Elements represented by impedances Z_3 and Z_4 determine the behavior of the entire network at zero and infinite frequencies.

For the development described thus far to be represented as progress toward the synthesis of the minimum function $Z(s)$, it is necessary to show that the complexity of $Z_3(s)$ and $Z_4(s)$ is less than that of $Z(s)$. The impedances Z_1 and Z_2, shown in Fig. 7-13 and defined by Eqs. 7.44, are directly or inversely related to the Richards function $R(s)$. It was shown by Richards that $R(s)$ is of the same complexity as $Z(s)$. Hence both $Z_1(s)$ and $Z_2(s)$ have the same complexity as $Z(s)$. However, the removal of the conjugate imaginary poles from $1/Z_1$ and Z_2 in Eqs. 7.51 and 7.52 causes Z_3 and Z_4 to have two fewer poles and zeros than $Z(s)$. This is the same accomplishment as was found in one Brune cycle. By analogy to the Brune cycle, we may speak of a "Bott and Duffin cycle." If Z_3 and Z_4 are themselves minimum functions or may be reduced to minimum functions by pole removal or constant removal operations, then Z_3 and Z_4 may be expanded by another Bott and Duffin cycle. This cycle of operations may be repeated again and again until the synthesis is complete. By this means, we may always synthesize a network *without transformers* for positive real impedance functions.

Case B, X_1 is negative. By the same argument given for Case A and Fig. 7-13, we see that if X_1 is negative then one possibility is for Z_1 to have a pole and Z_2 a zero at the frequency $s = j\omega_1$ in order that the network may be represented by C_1 at the frequency ω_1. From the equations for Z_1 and Z_2 given in Eqs. 7.44, namely $Z_1 = Z(k) R(s)$ and $Z_2 = Z(k)/R(s)$, we see that $R(s)$ is required to have a pole at $s = j\omega_1$, which requires that the denominator in $R(s)$ in Eq. 7.39 be 0 at this frequency. Then

$$k Z(k) - s Z(s) = 0 \text{ at } s = j\omega_1 \tag{7.55}$$

or
$$k Z(k) - j\omega_1 j X_1 = 0 \tag{7.56}$$

and
$$k Z(k) = -\omega_1 X_1 \tag{7.57}$$

where $k Z(k)$ is a real, positive number since X_1 is negative. By Eqs. 7.46, we see that the value of C_1 is

$$C_1 = -1/\omega_1 X_1 \tag{7.58}$$

and that by solving the equation $k Z(k) = -\omega_1 X_1$ for the real positive value of k that L_2 is found as

$$L_2 = Z(k)/k \tag{7.59}$$

and that Z_1' and Z_2' may be evaluated.   Removal of the poles of Z_1' and $1/Z_2'$ at $s = \pm j\omega_1$ defines the impedance functions Z_3' and Z_4' as

$$Z_1' = \frac{2K_1 s}{s^2 + \omega_1{}^2} + Z_3' \qquad (7.60)$$

and
$$1/Z_2' = \frac{2K_1's}{s^2 + \omega_1{}^2} + \frac{1}{Z_4'} \qquad (7.61)$$

where Z_3' and Z_4' are positive real.   The network represented by the last two equations is an enlargement of the network shown in Fig. 7-13

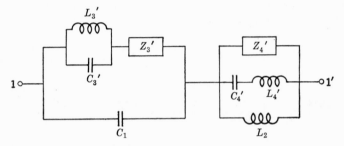

Fig. 7-15.   The Bott and Duffin network for Case B with $X_1 < 0$.

and is as shown in Fig. 7-15.   In this network,

$$C_3' = 1/2K_1; \qquad L_3' = 2K_1/\omega_1{}^2 \qquad (7.62)$$

and
$$C_4' = 2K_1'/\omega_1{}^2; \qquad L_4' = 1/2K_1' \qquad (7.63)$$

The conclusions made for Case A for the complexity of Z_3' and Z_4' compared to $Z(s)$ clearly apply for Case B.

Example 4.   Consider the positive real function of Example 3 given in Eq. 7-35:

$$Z(s) = \frac{s^2 + \frac{1}{2}s + \frac{1}{2}}{s^2 + s + 2} \qquad (7.64)$$

The real part of $Z(j\omega)$ vanishes at $\omega_1 = 1$ and $Z(j1) = +j\frac{1}{2}$.   Since X_1 is positive, we will follow the procedure outlined as Case A.   The inductor has the value $L_2 = X_1/\omega_1 = \frac{1}{2}$ henry and k is found from Eq. 7.50 by solving the equation

$$Z(k) = \tfrac{1}{2}k$$

or
$$k^3 - k^2 + k - 1 = (k - 1)(k^2 + 1) = 0 \qquad (7.65)$$

From this equation, we see that the only real value of k is $k = 1$ and from Eq. 7.64 for $Z(s)$ we find that $Z(1) = \frac{1}{2}$.   Then $C_1 = 1/k\,Z(k) = 2$ farads.

We next find the Richards function $R(s)$ from Eq. 7.39. It is

$$R(s) = \frac{1}{2} \frac{(-s + 1)(s^2 + 1)}{(-s + 1)(s^2 + s + 1)} \tag{7.66}$$

Knowing $R(s)$ we next find Z_1 and Z_2:

$$Z_1 = Z(k)\, R(s) = \frac{1}{4} \frac{s^2 + 1}{s^2 + s + 1} = \cfrac{1}{\cfrac{1}{s/4 + 1/4s} + 4} \tag{7.67}$$

and

$$Z_2 = Z(k)/R(s) = \frac{s^2 + s + 1}{s^2 + 1} = \frac{1}{s + 1/s} + 1 \tag{7.68}$$

Observe that the constants 4 and 1 in these two equations are the impedances Z_3 and Z_4 in Eqs. 7.51 and 7.52. The complete network is shown in Fig. 7-16.

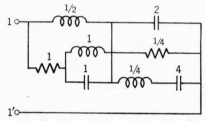
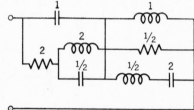

Fig. 7-16. Bott and Duffin network realization for the impedance of Eq. 7.64 in Example 4.

Fig. 7-17. Bott and Duffin network realization for the impedance of Eq. 7.69 in Example 5.

Example 5. For a Case B example, consider the positive real minimum function of Example 2:

$$Z(s) = \frac{s^2 + s + 2}{2s^2 + s + 1} \tag{7.69}$$

In Example 2 it was found that $\omega_1 = 1$ and $X_1 = -1$. From Eq. 7.58, we first find C_1 to be $-1/\omega_1 X_1 = 1$ farad. The constant k is the real root of the equation, from Eq. 7.57,

$$k\, Z(k) = 1; \qquad k^3 - k^2 + k - 1 = (k - 1)(k^2 + 1) = 0 \tag{7.70}$$

from which we conclude that $k = 1$ and $Z(1) = 1$. From Eq. 7.59 we compute L_2 to be $Z(k)/k = 1$ henry. The Richards function is

$$R(s) = 2\frac{s^2 + s + 1}{s^2 + 1} \tag{7.71}$$

Then

$$Z_1(s) = Z(k)\, R(s) = 2\frac{s^2 + s + 1}{s^2 + 1} = \frac{1}{s/2 + 1/2s} + 2 \tag{7.72}$$

and

$$Z_2(s) = Z(k)/R(s); \qquad Y_2(s) = \frac{1}{s/2 + 1/2s} + 2 \tag{7.73}$$

The Bott and Duffin network realization is shown in Fig. 7-17. The steps illustrated by these two examples are summarized in Table 7-2.

TABLE 7-2

Steps in the Bott and Duffin Cycle

	Re $Z(j\omega_1) = 0$	$Z(j\omega_1) = jX_1$
Step	Case A, $X_1 > 0$	Case B, $X_1 < 0$
1	Find $L_2 = X_1/\omega_1$	Find $C_1 = -1/\omega_1 X_1$
2	Find k from $Z(k) = kL_2$	Find k from $Z(k) = 1/kC_1$
3	Find C_1 from $C_1 = 1/k\,Z(k)$	Find L_2 from $L_2 = Z(k)/k$
4	Remove poles of $1/Z_1$ and Z_2 at $\pm j\omega_1$ with residues K_1' and K_1	Remove poles of Z_1' and $1/Z_2'$ at $\pm j\omega_1$ with residues K_1 and K_1'
5	$C_3 = 2K_1'/\omega_1^2$ $L_3 = 1/2K_1'$	$C_3' = 1/2K_1$ $L_3' = 2K_1/\omega_1^2$
6	$C_4 = 1/2K_1$ $L_4 = 2K_1/\omega_1^2$	$C_4' = 2K_1'/\omega_1^2$ $L_4' = 1/2K_1'$
7	Network is now as shown in Fig. 7-14	Network is now as shown in Fig. 7-15
8	Synthesize Z_3 and Z_4 by pole and constant removal or by another cycle	Synthesize Z_3' and Z_4' by pole and constant removal or by another cycle

Comparing the networks synthesized for the same impedance functions by the Brune method (Examples 2 and 3) and by the Bott and

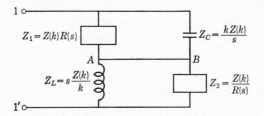

Fig. 7-18. The Bott and Duffin network arranged as a balanced bridge.

Duffin method (Examples 4 and 5), we see that there are more elements in the Bott and Duffin realization. Apparently the price we pay to avoid transformers is extra elements.

Other networks equivalent to those of Fig. 7-13 are found by arranging the elements in the form of a bridge as shown in Fig. 7-18. Now this bridge is balanced if

$$Z_1 Z_2 = Z_L Z_C \tag{7.74}$$

Computing these impedance products we see that

$$Z_1 Z_2 = R(s) \, Z(k) \, \frac{Z(k)}{R(s)} = [Z(k)]^2 \tag{7.75}$$

and

$$Z_L Z_C = \frac{Z(k)s}{k} \frac{k \, Z(k)}{s} = [Z(k)]^2 \tag{7.76}$$

The Bott and Duffin network is indeed a *balanced bridge*, as was first pointed out by F. M. Reza.* Being a balanced bridge, points A and B

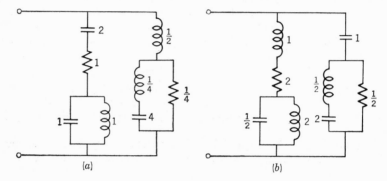

Fig. 7-19. Equivalent networks for (*a*) Fig. 7-16 and (*b*) Fig. 7-17, due to the balanced-bridge nature of the Bott-Duffin realization.

of Fig. 7-18 are at the same potential so that the short circuit now connecting these points can be removed and replaced by any network whatsoever† without changing the driving-point impedance $Z(s)$. When an open circuit is chosen in place of the short circuit from A to B, the equivalent networks shown in Fig. 7-19 result.

7.4 Actual realization difficulties

Both the Brune and the Bott and Duffin network realizations have limited practical application because of accuracy requirements made on their element values. This accuracy requirement, or sensitivity to

---

* "Conversion of a Brune cycle with an ideal transformer into a cycle without an ideal transformer," *IRE Trans.*, **CT-1**, 71 (1954).

† Using an inductor of appropriate value, Storer, Pantell, and others have shown that it is possible to reduce the number of elements in the realization by 1. See J. E. Storer, "Relationship between the Bott-Duffin and Pantell impedance synthesis," *Proc. I.R.E.*, **42**, 1451 (1954), and R. H. Pantell, "New methods of driving-point and transfer function synthesis," ERL Report No. 76, Stanford University (1954); summarized in *Proc. I.R.E.*, **42**, 861 (1954).

element changes, may be visualized in terms of pole and zero migrations resulting from element changes.*

TABLE 7-3

Coupling	Real Zero	Conjugate Zeros
$k = 1$		$-0.159 \pm j0.810$
$k = 0.99$	-11.2	$-0.166 \pm j0.821$
$k = 0.98$	-5.44	$-0.172 \pm j0.834$
$k = 0.95$	-1.99	$-0.179 \pm j0.879$

Consider the Brune network realization of

$$Z(s) = \frac{22s^2 + 7s + 15}{12s^2 + 2s + 12} \tag{7.77}$$

a minimum function, having a $k = 1$ transformer. If $k < 1$ in the network realization, a pole appears at infinity (representing the equivalent inductance of a transformer without perfect coupling) and a zero appears on the negative real axis. Changes in pole-zero locations are illustrated in Table 7-3. Observe the rapid movement of the real zero along the real negative axis with changes in k.

Another illustration of this sensitivity to element value changes makes use of a modified Bott-Duffin realization of a biquadratic (2nd degree in both numerator and denominator) $Z(s)$. In Fig. 7-20, the small pole and zero represent specification positions in the upper half plane, along with the three poles and three zeros which cancel in attaining the bridge balance of the Bott-Duffin realization. If elements are changed in some random fashion—in this case, three elements are assumed exact, two 10% high, and two 10% low—then all poles and zeros migrate, and, in particular, the bridge balance is

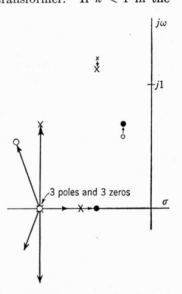

Fig. 7-20. The migration of the poles and zeros of a Bott-Duffin network due to small changes in four elements.

---

* Discussed in greater detail by F. F. Kuo in "Pole-zero sensitivity in network functions," and J. J. Mikulski, "A correlation between classical and pole-zero sensitivity," Ph.D. theses at the University of Illinois in 1958 and 1959.

destroyed and the three poles and zeros no longer cancel as shown in the figure.

A practical method of realization of networks of low sensitivity to changes in element values is not known for the general case. In many actual problems, it is possible to avoid ideal transformers by avoiding the case of zero minimum value for Re $Z(j\omega)$. One approach is to expand the impedance or its reciprocal in partial fraction form, then share the available resistance (or conductance) with each of the component fractions. Sometimes this will lead to a set of realizable series or parallel component networks.

FURTHER READING

The topics of this chapter are covered in greater detail by Tuttle in *Network Synthesis*, Vol. I, pp. 503–678. Other textbooks recommended to the student for further reading are those by Guillemin, *Synthesis of Passive Networks*, pp. 328–444; Balabanian, *Network Synthesis*, pp. 92–117; Storer, *Passive Network Synthesis*, pp. 15–46; and Cauer, *Synthesis of Linear Communication Networks*, pp. 181–220, 817–823. For a detailed study of the mathematics relating to minimum functions, see Guillemin's *The Mathematics of Circuit Analysis*, pp. 409–415. An excellent treatment in French is to be found in Bayard's *Théorie des réseaux de Kirchhoff*, Chapter 20. Another interesting driving-point synthesis method is due to F. Miyata and is described in his paper, "A new system of two-terminal network synthesis," *IRE Trans.*, **CT-2**, 297–302 (1955), and also in detail in Guillemin's *Synthesis of Passive Networks*.

For the serious student, a gold mine of new ideas relating to the topics of this chapter is to be found in the December 1955 issue of the *IRE Trans.*, **CT-2**.

PROBLEMS

7-1. In Prob. 4-18 it was shown that

$$Y(s) = K \frac{s^2 + a_1 s + a_0}{s^2 + b_1 s + b_0}$$

is positive real if

$$a_1 b_1 \geqq (\sqrt{a_0} - \sqrt{b_0})^2$$

What is the condition necessary that this $Y(s)$ be a minimum function? Express in a single equation the necessary and sufficient condition that the given $Y(s)$, sometimes called a biquadratic function, be positive real and minimum.

7-2. Show that the following impedance functions are positive real and minimum. Determine ω_1, the frequency at which Re $Z(j\omega) = 0$, and determine the value of $Z(j\omega_1) = jX_1$.

(a) $Z(s) = \dfrac{(s+1)(s+2)}{(s+\frac{1}{2})(s+\frac{1}{25})}$ (b) $Z(s) = \dfrac{5s^2 + 18s + 8}{s^2 + s + 10}$

7-3. Consider the admittance function

$$Y(s) = K \frac{(s + \alpha_1)(s + \alpha_2)}{(s + \beta_1)(s + \beta_2)}$$

where $\alpha_1, \alpha_2 = a \pm jb$ and $\beta_1, \beta_2 = c \pm jd$. The frequency is scaled so that $|\alpha_1| = 1$. Let $|\beta_1| = l$ and the angle of β_1 with respect to the negative real axis be θ. Then when $Y(s)$ is a minimum function, the possible pole locations are determined as a function of the zero locations by the equation

$$l = 1 + 2a \cos \theta \pm \sqrt{(1 + 2a \cos \theta)^2 - 1}$$

Also show that the frequency at which Re $Y(j\omega_1) = 0$ is

$$\omega_1 = (\alpha_1 \alpha_2 \beta_1 \beta_2)^{\frac{1}{4}}$$

7-4. Two bridge networks are shown in Fig. P7-4. Let the admittance of the network of Fig. P7-4(a) be $Y_a(s)$ and that of Fig. P7-4(b) be $Y_b(s)$.

(a) Show that

$$Y_a = 2G \frac{s^2 + \dfrac{k}{2LG} s + \dfrac{1}{2LC}}{s^2 + \dfrac{G}{kC} s + \dfrac{2}{LC}}$$

(b) Find the expression for $Y_b(s)$ in the form of $Y_a(s)$.
(c) Show that for both networks Re $Y(j\omega)$ vanishes at the frequency $\omega_1 = 1/\sqrt{LC}$.
(d) Show that

$$Y_a(j\omega_1) = jk \sqrt{C/L} \quad \text{and} \quad Y_b(j\omega_1) = -jk \sqrt{C/L}$$

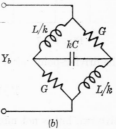

(a)   (b)

Fig. P7-4

7-5. Given the impedance

$$Z(s) = \frac{2s^3 + s^2 + 4s + 1}{s^3 + 3s^2 + 3s + 1}$$

which is to be realized by a network having the structure shown in Fig. P7-5, determine all element values for the network. The network is a Foster preamble.

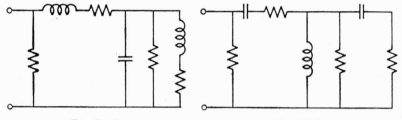

Fig. P7-5   Fig. P7-6

7-6. The positive real admittance function

$$Y(s) = \frac{s^3 + 3s^2 + 3s + 1}{s^3 + 4s^2 + s + 2}$$

is not a minimum function and so can be realized by a continuing pole removal and constant removal process. It is required that the network be realized in the form shown in Fig. P7-6. Determine the element values for this network.

7-7. The network illustrated in Fig. P7-7 has four reactive elements and with the proper choice of elements has the driving-point admittance

$$Y(s) = \frac{8s^4 + 6s^3 + 10s^2 + 3s + 2}{4s^4 + 12s^3 + 5s^2 + 6s + 1}$$

Determine the required values for the network elements.

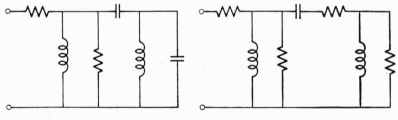

Fig. P7-7   Fig. P7-8

7-8. The driving-point admittance function

$$Y(s) = \frac{s^3 + 3s^2 + 2s + 2}{s^3 + 3s^2 + 3s + 1}$$

is positive real but is not minimum. By a process of pole removal and constant removal, the network can be realized in the form shown in Fig. P7-8. For this network and the given $Y(s)$, determine each element value.

7-9. Show that the condition that two coils for which L_1, L_2, and L_3 are inductances of the equivalent T network have unity coefficient of coupling is

$$L_1L_2 + L_2L_3 + L_3L_1 = 0$$

7-10. Combine Eqs. 7.23 with Eq. 7.32 to arrive at Eq. 7.33 for the impedance $Z_3(s)$ for Case 2. Find $Z_3(s)$ for Case 1 and show that it has the same form as Eq. 7.33, thereby demonstrating that $Z_3(s)$ for Case 2 is a positive real function.

7-11. Given the impedance function

$$Z(s) = \frac{s^2 + 2s + 16}{s^2 + 2s + 4}$$

find a network realization if one exists.

7-12. Find the Brune network realization of the impedance function

$$Z(s) = \frac{5s^2 + 18s + 8}{s^2 + s + 10}$$

both with the negative inductor and with the unity coupling coefficient transformer.

7-13. Consider the pseudo-positive-real function

$$Y_1(s) = \frac{1}{Z(s) - L_1s}$$

where L_1 is chosen so that Y_1 has poles at $s = \pm j\omega_1$. Show that the residue of $Y_1(s)$ evaluated at these poles, K_1, is real and positive.

7-14. The admittance function

$$Y(s) = \frac{1}{5} \frac{s^3 + \frac{5}{3}s^2 + \frac{76}{9}s + \frac{20}{3}}{s^3 + \frac{44}{15}s^2 + 4s + \frac{16}{15}}$$

is a minimum function and the real part of $Y(j\omega)$ vanishes at $\omega_1 = 2$. Find the Brune network realization with a transformer.

7-15. Specifications for an electronic amplifier require that the device terminate in a network having the impedance

$$Z(s) = \frac{s^4 + 2s^3 + 3s^2 + s + 1}{s^4 + s^3 + 3s^2 + 2s + 1}$$

This function is positive real and minimum since Re $Z(j\omega)$ vanishes at $\omega_1 = 1$ radian/sec. Determine a Brune network realization of this impedance function.

7-16. Given the driving-point impedance function

$$Z(s) = \frac{3s^3 + 4s^2 + 4s + 2}{s^3 + s^2 + s}$$

find a network realization if one exists.

7-17. At the frequency $\omega_1 = 1$, the driving-point admittance function

$$Y(s) = \frac{2s^4 + 5s^3 + 6s^2 + 3s + 1}{2s^4 + 4s^3 + 7s^2 + 7s + 3}$$

has a real part which vanishes. Find the Brune network realization with a transformer.

7-18. R. Leroy has pointed out* that the Brune procedure may be applied to cases where the even part of $Z(s)$ vanishes at the frequencies $s = \pm\sigma_1$. These are imaginary or neper frequencies. Since

$$Z(s) = \text{Ev } Z(s) + \text{Od } Z(s)$$

if $\text{Ev } Z(s) = 0$ for $s = \pm\sigma_1$, then $Z(\sigma_1) = \text{Od } Z(\sigma_1)$. Now $\text{Od } Z(s) = s M_1(s)$ where M_1 is an even function. Following the Brune procedure, we

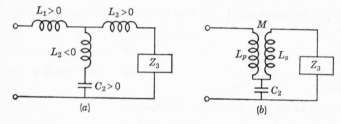

Fig. P7-18

first remove an inductor $L_1 = M_1(\sigma_1)$ and continue through the Brune cycle to arrive at the networks shown in Fig. P7-18.

(a) Show that L_1 and L_3 are positive, but that L_2 is negative as shown in the network. What does series resonance mean for a negative inductor? Show that the transformer requires unity coupling coefficient and determine the appropriate polarity markings on the transformer.

(b) Show that $Z_3(s)$ is positive real and that it has one less pole and one less zero than $Z(s)$.

(c) Apply the results obtained in parts (a) and (b) to the impedance function.

$$Z(s) = \frac{s + a}{s + b}$$

and show that the network realization has the values:

$$M = \frac{1}{b(1 + \sqrt{b/a})} \qquad\qquad C_2 = \frac{1 + \sqrt{b/a}}{a}$$

$$L_p = \frac{\sqrt{b/a}}{b(1 + \sqrt{b/a})} \qquad\qquad Z_3 = a/b$$

$$L_s = \frac{1}{b\sqrt{b/a}\,(1 + \sqrt{b/a})}$$

* See Bayard, *Théorie des réseaux de Kirchhoff*, p. 312.

7-19. Determine the Bott-Duffin realization of the biquadratic network function given in Prob. 7-11.

7-20. In Prob. 7-12, a biquadratic function was given to be realized by the Brune method. Using the Bott and Duffin method, find a network realization without transformers. Using the fact that this network is a balanced bridge, draw one equivalent to this network.

7-21. Find two Bott and Duffin network realizations for the impedance function

$$Z(s) = \frac{5s^2 + 18s + 8}{s^2 + s + 10}$$

7-22. Let $Z(s)$ be a positive real, minimum, biquadratic (degree of both numerator and denominator is 2) function. Show that k, the constant of the Richards transformation and the Bott and Duffin synthesis method, is given by either

$$k = \frac{1}{L_1} \sqrt{Z(0) Z(\infty)}$$

or

$$k = \frac{1}{C_1} [Z(0) Z(\infty)]^{-\frac{1}{2}}$$

Is the restriction to biquadratic functions necessary?

7-23. The network of Fig. P7-23 is adjusted so that $R = \sqrt{L/C}$. It is required that a network be designed which, when placed in parallel with the network shown, causes the admittance of the combination to be frequency invariant and, at the same time, equal to the maximum value of the real part of the admittance of the network given in Fig. P7-23. Make use of the Brune method of synthesis.

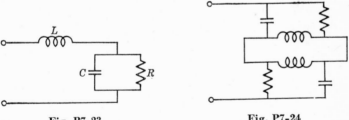

Fig. P7-23   **Fig. P7-24**

7-24. Find the result of Prob. 7-4(a) by considering the bridge network to be in the form illustrated in Fig. P7-24, and then use a π-T transformation.

7-25. Two impedance functions $Z_a(s)$ and $Z_b(s)$, are said to be *complementary* if $Z_a + Z_b = K$, where K is a real positive constant. Show that the necessary and sufficient conditions for two impedances to be complementary are:

(a) Z_a and Z_b must have identical poles.
(b) Z_a and Z_b must have no poles or zeros along the imaginary axis.

(c) The residue of Z_a at each of its poles must be the negative of the residue of Z_b.

(d) $K = \max \operatorname{Re} Z_a(j\omega)$ and $K = \max \operatorname{Re} Z_b(j\omega)$.

7-26. The network of Fig. P7-26 is to be connected in series with another one terminal-pair network in such a way that the combined impedance will be equal to R ohms, with the minimum possible value for R. Find the network.

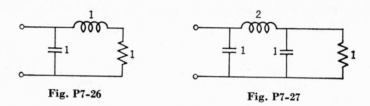

Fig. P7-26   Fig. P7-27

7-27. Find a network that, when placed in series or parallel with the network shown in Fig. P7-27, results in a constant resistance network, i.e., the combined networks have an impedance of R ohms for all frequencies.

Parts of
Network Functions

The "parts" to be studied in this chapter are (1) the *real* and *imaginary* parts, and (2) the *magnitude* and *phase* of $Z(j\omega)$ representing either a driving-point or transfer function. These parts are given the symbols

$$Z(j\omega) = R(\omega) + j\,X(\omega) \tag{8.1}$$

and

$$Z(j\omega) = |Z(j\omega)|\,e^{j\,\text{Arg}\,Z(j\omega)} \tag{8.2}$$

The parts in these two equations are routinely measured by instruments designed for operation in the sinusoidal steady state: the Wheatstone bridge measures real and imaginary parts (resistance, conductance, reactance, susceptance); the Z-angle meter, for example, measures magnitude and phase. The studies of this chapter will extend earlier studies of driving-point functions and introduce Chapter 9, which deals with approximation of sinusoidal steady-state characteristics by rational quotients of polynomials for both driving-point and transfer functions.

8.1 Properties of Ev $Z(s)$ when $Z(s)$ is positive real

If the impedance function $Z(s)$ is positive real and is represented in the form

$$Z(s) = \frac{m_1 + n_1}{m_2 + n_2} \tag{8.3}$$

then the resistance function, $R(\omega)$, in Eq. 8.1 is Re $Z(j\omega)$ or

$$R(\omega) = \text{Ev}\,Z(s)\bigg|_{s=j\omega} = \frac{m_1 m_2 - n_1 n_2}{m_2{}^2 - n_2{}^2}\bigg|_{s=j\omega} \tag{8.4}$$

This function was studied in Chapter 4, using the notation

$$\text{Ev } Z(s) \Big|_{s=j\omega} = \frac{A(\omega^2)}{B(\omega^2)} \tag{8.5}$$

where A and B are *even functions* in ω (although not in ω^2, of course). In Chapter 4, our attention was focused on $A(\omega^2)$ and particularly the requirement that $A(\omega^2) \geq 0$ for all ω in order that $Z(s)$ be positive real. Here we must also study the properties of the denominator function, $B(\omega^2)$.

If we substitute $-s^2$ for ω^2 in Eq. 8.5, an operation described as analytic continuation, then

$$\text{Ev } Z(s) = \frac{A(-s^2)}{B(-s^2)} \tag{8.6}$$

The zeros of Ev $Z(s)$ are the zeros of $A(-s^2)$ and the poles are the zeros of $B(-s^2)$. While we know more about the zeros than the poles from Chapter 4, we begin by tabulating the properties of the poles of Ev $Z(s)$.

(1) *If $Z(s)$ is positive real, Ev $Z(s)$ has no poles on the imaginary axis.* This conclusion follows from the nature of the even function Ev $Z(s)$. If there were such poles, the partial fraction expansion of Ev $Z(s)$ would contain an odd term

$$\frac{K_1}{s + j\omega_1} + \frac{K_1}{s - j\omega_1} = \frac{2K_1 s}{s^2 + \omega_1^2} \tag{8.7}$$

and Ev $Z(s)$ would be odd, which is contrary to assumption. From this property, we see that $R(\omega)$ found from a positive real function has no real-frequency poles and so is bounded.

(2) *The complex poles of Ev $Z(s)$ have quadrantal symmetry.* From Eqs. 8.4 and 8.6,

$$B(-s^2) = m_2{}^2 - n_2{}^2 = (m_2 + n_2)(m_2 - n_2) \tag{8.8}$$

Suppose that s_0 is a zero of $m_2 + n_2$ so that $m_2(s_0) + n_2(s_0) = 0$. Then since m_2 is even and n_2 is odd,

$$m_2(-s_0) - n_2(-s_0) = m_2(s_0) + n_2(s_0) = 0 \tag{8.9}$$

and we see that $-s_0$ is a zero of $m_2 - n_2$. Thus the poles of Ev $Z(s)$ appear in pairs, one always being the negative of the other. Possible locations for poles of Ev $Z(s)$ are those shown in Fig. 8-1. The symmetry with respect to real and imaginary axes which is illustrated in the figure is described as *quadrantal* symmetry.

(3) *If the denominator of $Z(s)$ is of degree t, then $B(-s^2)$ is of degree 2t and the degree 2r of $A(-s^2)$ is bounded by $0 \leq 2r \leq 2t$.* Since the degree of either $m_2{}^2$ or $n_2{}^2$ in $m_2{}^2 - n_2{}^2$ of Eq. 8.8 is $2t$ if the degree of $m_2 + n_2$ is t, $B(-s^2)$ is of degree $2t$. However, $A(-s^2)$ is found from the difference of two products, $m_1 m_2$ and $n_1 n_2$, and cancellation can result in a degree as small as 0 (a constant). The upper limit is established from the fact that $R(\omega) = \text{Re } Z(j\omega)$ is bounded at infinity for positive real functions so that the degree of $A(\omega^2)$ is at most equal to

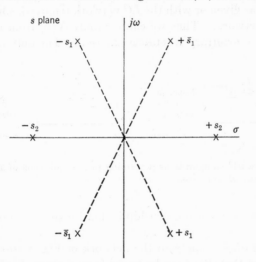

Fig. 8-1.   Poles of Ev $Z(s)$ with quadrantal symmetry.

that of $B(\omega^2)$, namely $2t$. From this conclusion, $R(\omega)$ may be written in the form

$$R(\omega) = \frac{A_0 + A_2\omega^2 + A_4\omega^4 + \cdots + A_{2r}\omega^{2r}}{B_0 + B_2\omega^2 + B_4\omega^4 + \cdots + B_{2t}\omega^{2t}}, \qquad r \leq t \quad (8.10)$$

(4) *Poles of Ev $Z(s)$ may be either simple or of higher multiplicity.* No restriction on pole multiplicity is made.

The zeros of Ev $Z(s)$ are not as restricted as the poles. We found in Chapter 4 that imaginary axis zeros were required to be of even multiplicity in order that Re $Z(j\omega)$ never be negative. (Such zeros are present in all minimum positive real functions.) Otherwise, zeros may have any s plane location and be of any multiplicity so long as they have quadrantal symmetry.

8.2   The Brune–Gewertz method

A method due to O. Brune* and C. M. Gewertz† makes it possible to find $Z(s)$ from either of its parts, $R(\omega)$ or $X(\omega)$. It will be described in this section, assuming that $R(\omega)$ is known and that $Z(s)$—or $X(\omega)$— is to be found. Before studying the details of the method, we observe a limitation inherent in any method of computing $X(\omega)$ from $R(\omega)$. Figure 8-2(a) shows two networks in series: one is an LC network and the other a network with minimum reactance [its $Z(s)$ has no imaginary axis poles or zeros]. The resistance function $R(\omega)$ is identical for the network as given or with the LC network removed, since $R(\omega) = 0$ for the LC network. Thus we can compute $X(\omega)$ from a given $R(\omega)$ only within an arbitrary reactance function. The only case in which

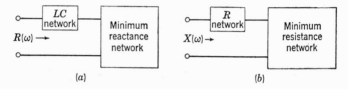

(a)   (b)

Fig. 8-2. Network configurations pertaining to the limitation of any method for finding $X(\omega)$ from $R(\omega)$ or vice versa.

there will be an explicit relationship is that for the minimum reactance network.

Similar arguments apply to the network of Fig. 8-2(b) and lead to the conclusion that $R(\omega)$ can be found from a given $X(\omega)$ only within an arbitrary constant, represented in the figure by the R network. The relationship between $R(\omega)$ and $X(\omega)$ is explicit only for the case of a minimum resistance network.

The conclusions concerning the arbitrariness of any method for finding $X(\omega)$ or $Z(s)$ from $R(\omega)$ allow us to deliberately exclude the possibility of a pole at infinity in $Z(s)$. Such a pole is identified with a series inductor which is a special case of the LC network of Fig. 8-2(a). We have already designated the degree of the denominator of $Z(s)$ to be t. Then the numerator of $Z(s)$ is at most of degree t, and at least of degree $t - 1$ if $Z(s)$ is positive real. It may be written

---

* "Synthesis of a finite two terminal network whose driving-point impedance is a prescribed function of frequency," *Jour. Math. and Phys.*, **10**, 191 (1931). Same as his MIT Sc.D. thesis (1930).

† *Network Synthesis*, The Williams and Wilkins Co., Baltimore, 1933, pp. 142–149. This book is identical with the article in *J. Math. and Phys.*, **12**, 1–257 (1933). This work is based on Gewertz's MIT doctoral thesis (1933). After teaching many years in Thailand, Gewertz now resides in Sweden.

$$Z(s) = \frac{a_0 + a_1 s + a_2 s^2 + \cdots + a_t s^t}{b_0 + b_1 s + b_2 s^2 + \cdots + b_t s^t} \tag{8.11}$$

where the a and b coefficients are to be determined.

The Brune-Gewertz method for finding $Z(s)$ from $R(\omega)$ may be described in two steps:

Step 1, the b coefficients. From the given $R(\omega) = A(\omega^2)/B(\omega^2)$, $B(-s^2) = (m_2 + n_2)(m_2 - n_2)$ is formed by replacing ω^2 by $-s^2$. The roots of $B(-s^2)$ have quadrantal symmetry and are not located on the imaginary axis. Those roots in the left half plane are identified with the Hurwitz polynomial, $m_2 + n_2$; those in the right half plane form the *anti-Hurwitz* polynomial, $m_2 - n_2$. Thus the left half plane roots of $B(-s^2)$ are the roots of $m_2 + n_2$ and so the poles of $Z(s)$. Expanding from these roots into polynomial form gives the denominator of Eq. 8.11,

$$b_0 + b_1 s + b_2 s^2 + \cdots + b_t s^t \tag{8.12}$$

with $b_t = 1$ and the b coefficients determined. Observe that $Z(s)$ formed by this procedure will never have poles on the imaginary axis (including infinity), and $Z(s)$ will therefore always be minimum reactive.

Step 2, the a coefficients. Starting from Eq. 8.11 with the b coefficients determined, we form Ev $Z(s)$, which is

$$\text{Ev } Z(s) = \frac{\begin{aligned}(a_0 + a_2 s^2 + \cdots)(b_0 + b_2 s^2 + \cdots)\\ - (a_1 s + a_3 s^3 + \cdots)(b_1 s + b_3 s^3 + \cdots)\end{aligned}}{m_2{}^2 - n_2{}^2} \tag{8.13}$$

Next, let $s^2 = -\omega^2$, and

$$R(\omega) = \frac{\begin{aligned}(a_0 - a_2 \omega^2 + \cdots)(b_0 - b_2 \omega^2 + \cdots)\\ + \omega^2(a_1 - a_3 \omega^2 + \cdots)(b_1 - b_3 \omega^2 + \cdots)\end{aligned}}{m_2{}^2 - n_2{}^2} \tag{8.14}$$

The numerator of this equation is next equated to $A(\omega^2)$ having known coefficients. Equating coefficients of like powers of ω gives a set of simultaneous equations in the a coefficients:

$$A_0 = a_0 b_0$$
$$A_2 = -a_0 b_2 + a_1 b_1 - a_2 b_0$$
$$A_4 = a_0 b_4 - a_1 b_3 + a_2 b_2 - a_3 b_1 + a_4 b_0$$
$$\cdot \tag{8.15}$$
$$\cdot$$
$$\cdot$$
$$A_{2t} = \pm a_t b_t$$

This set of equations has the characteristic shape of a wedge, starting and ending with one-term equations. Solving these simultaneous equations is not as much a task as it may appear, as an example will illustrate. With the a coefficients found, $Z(s)$ is determined and $X(\omega)$, if desired, may be found from

$$j\,X(\omega) = \mathrm{Od}\,Z(s)\Big|_{s=j\omega} = \frac{m_2 n_1 - m_1 n_2}{m_2{}^2 - n_2{}^2}\Big|_{s=j\omega} \qquad (8.16)$$

The necessary and sufficient conditions that the $Z(s)$ formed by the Brune-Gewertz method be positive real are simply stated. The function $Z(s)$ has no right half plane or imaginary axis poles. The sole requirement then is that $R(\omega) \geq 0$ or, the equivalent, that $A(\omega^2) \geq 0$. From our studies of Chapter 4, we know that this is accomplished providing the ω^2 roots of $A(\omega^2)$ which are real and positive be of even multiplicity. The corresponding roots of $A(-s^2)$ are on the imaginary axis. Thus the criterion for $Z(s)$ to be positive real is that (1) $A(\omega^2) \geq 0$, or (2) the imaginary axis roots of $A(-s^2)$ be of even multiplicity.

Example 1. Suppose that it is required that

$$R(\omega) = \frac{1}{1 + \omega^6} \qquad (8.17)$$

A plot of this resistance function is shown in Fig. 8-3, and is known as a

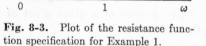

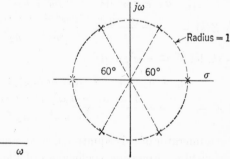

Fig. 8-3. Plot of the resistance function specification for Example 1.

Fig. 8-4. An s plane plot of the six roots of the equation $1 - s^6 = 0$.

maximally flat or Butterworth response. The first step in finding $Z(s)$ is the replacing of ω^2 by $-s^2$, giving the polynomial

$$1 - s^6 = 0 \qquad \text{or} \qquad s^6 = 1 \qquad (8.18)$$

The six roots of this equation are on the periphery of a unit circle and are separated by an angle of $60°$, as shown in Fig. 8-4. The Brune-Gewertz method requires that the poles in the right half plane be rejected. Hence the denominator polynomial for $Z(s)$ is made up of the roots in the left half plane of Fig. 8-4 and is

$$m_2 + n_2 = \left(s + \frac{1}{2} + j\frac{\sqrt{3}}{2}\right)\left(s + \frac{1}{2} - j\frac{\sqrt{3}}{2}\right)(s + 1) \tag{8.19}$$

$$= s^3 + 2s^2 + 2s + 1 \tag{8.20}$$

The impedance function is next constructed with a polynomial in the numerator of degree equal to that of the denominator polynomial:

$$Z(s) = \frac{a_0 + a_1 s + a_2 s^2 + a_3 s^3}{s^3 + 2s^2 + 2s + 1} \tag{8.21}$$

Arranging even and odd parts, we have

$$Z(s) = \frac{(a_0 + a_2 s^2) + (a_1 s + a_3 s^3)}{(1 + 2s^2) + (2s + s^3)} = \frac{m_1 + n_1}{m_2 + n_2} \tag{8.22}$$

The numerator of the even part of $Z(s)$ is

$$m_1 m_2 - n_1 n_2 = (a_0 + a_2 s^2)(1 + 2s^2) - (a_1 s + a_3 s^3)(2s + s^3) \tag{8.23}$$

Substituting $-\omega^2$ for s^2 gives

$$(a_0 - a_2 \omega^2)(1 - 2\omega^2) + \omega^2(a_1 - a_3 \omega^2)(2 - \omega^2) \tag{8.24}$$

This numerator function is next equated to the numerator of the given $R(\omega)$ to give the following set of equations:

$$a_0 = 1$$
$$a_2 + 2a_0 - 2a_1 = 0$$
$$2a_2 - 2a_3 - a_1 = 0 \tag{8.25}$$
$$a_3 = 0$$

Solving these equations gives $a_0 = 1$, $a_1 = \frac{4}{3}$, $a_2 = \frac{2}{3}$, and $a_3 = 0$. The required impedance function is thus found to be

$$Z(s) = \frac{\frac{2}{3}s^2 + \frac{4}{3}s + 1}{s^3 + 2s^2 + 2s + 1} \tag{8.26}$$

The reactance function associated with this $Z(s)$ is

$$X(\omega) = \frac{-\omega(\frac{2}{3}\omega^4 + \frac{1}{3}\omega^2 + \frac{2}{3})}{1 + \omega^6} \tag{8.27}$$

This reactance function corresponds to the specified $R(\omega)$ within an arbitrary reactance.

8.3   Bode's method

Another method for computing a function from its real part is due to H. W. Bode* and is based on the relationship

$$\text{Ev } Z(s) = \tfrac{1}{2}[Z(s) + Z(-s)] \tag{8.28}$$

The Bode method begins with Ev $Z(s)$ as a quotient of polynomials in s, $A(-s^2)/B(-s^2) = N(s)/D(s)$, which is expanded by partial fractions. We have already found in connection with the Brune-Gewertz method that the poles of Ev $Z(s)$ occur in quads so that

$$\text{Ev } Z(s) = \frac{N(s)}{[(s - p_1)(s - \bar{p}_1) \cdots][(s + p_1)(s + \bar{p}_1) \cdots]} \tag{8.29}$$

We assume for the time being that all of the poles in Ev $Z(s)$ are simple.

To complete the partial fraction expansion, we first find the residue of the pole p_1, which is (from Eq. 4.66)

$$K_{p_1} = \frac{N(p_1)}{D'(p_1)} \tag{8.30}$$

where the prime indicates differentiation with respect to s. The residue of the pole at $-p_1$ is simply related to K_{p_1} since

$$K_{-p_1} = \frac{N(-p_1)}{D'(-p_1)} = -K_{p_1} \tag{8.31}$$

because differentiation of the denominator changes it from an even to an odd function for which $D'(-p_1) = -D'(p_1)$, but for the even numerator $N(-p_1) = N(p_1)$. Then the partial fraction expansion of Ev $Z(s)$ is

$$\text{Ev } Z(s) = \left(\frac{K_{p_1}}{s - p_1} + \frac{\bar{K}_{p_1}}{s - \bar{p}_1} + \cdots + \frac{R_\infty}{2} \right)$$
$$+ \left(\frac{-K_{p_1}}{s + p_1} + \frac{-\bar{K}_{p_1}}{s + \bar{p}_1} + \cdots + \frac{R_\infty}{2} \right) \tag{8.32}$$

where R_∞ is the limit of Ev $Z(s)$ as s approaches infinity. Suppose that we identify the two parts of Eq. 8.32 in parentheses in terms of

---

* *Network Analysis and Feedback Amplifier Design*, Chapter 14. Hendrick W. Bode has been a member of the technical staff at the Bell Telephone Laboratories since 1926. He is best known for his contributions to the theory of filters and broadband feedback amplifiers and for the textbook cited.

their left or right half plane pole locations as

$$\text{Ev } Z(s) = Z_L(s) + Z_R(s) \tag{8.33}$$

Now since $Z_R(s) = Z_L(-s)$ from Eq. 8.32, the last equation may be written

$$\text{Ev } Z(s) = Z_L(s) + Z_L(-s) \tag{8.34}$$

Comparing this equation with Eq. 8.28, we see that

$$Z(s) = 2Z_L(s) = 2\left(\frac{K_{s_1}}{s - s_1} + \frac{\bar{K}_{s_1}}{s - \bar{s}_1} + \cdots\right) + R_\infty \tag{8.35}$$

and $Z(s)$ has been determined. The Bode method usually requires more computation than the Brune-Gewertz method and for this reason is seldom used. It does afford an understanding of the real-imaginary part relationships in that it arrives at the end result by a different route. A detailed justification of the Bode procedure for the multiple pole case is to be found in Tuttle.*

Example 2. The Bode method will be illustrated using the specification function of Example 1. First Ev $Z(s)$ is expanded as partial fractions using the poles shown in Fig. 8-4. The part of this expansion for poles in the left half plane is identified as Z_L by Eq. 8.33 and

$$Z_L(s) = \frac{K_{-1}}{s + 1} + \frac{K_{-2}}{s + \frac{1}{2} + j\frac{1}{2}\sqrt{3}} + \frac{\bar{K}_{-2}}{s + \frac{1}{2} - j\frac{1}{2}\sqrt{3}} \tag{8.36}$$

Employing Eq. 8.30 to evaluate the residues, we find that $K_{-1} = \frac{1}{6}$, and $K_{-2} = \frac{1}{12} + j\frac{1}{12}\sqrt{3}$. From Eq. 8.35,

$$Z(s) = \frac{1}{3}\left(\frac{1}{s + 1} + \frac{s + 2}{s^2 + s + 1}\right) \tag{8.37}$$

or

$$Z(s) = \frac{\frac{2}{3}s^2 + \frac{4}{3}s + 1}{s^3 + 2s^2 + 2s + 1} \tag{8.38}$$

in agreement with Example 1.

8.4   From magnitude to phase

The procedure for finding a phase function from a specified magnitude function is useful for both driving-point and transfer functions. So $Z(s)$ as employed from this point on in this chapter is *either kind* of network function. Transfer functions differ from driving-point functions in two respects important to the present study:

* *Network Synthesis*, Vol. I, pp. 461–465.

(1) The rules governing degree difference of numerator and denominator polynomials are different: the numerator may be of any degree lower than the denominator (including 0 degree) and may be 1 larger for transfer impedances or admittances or just equal for voltage or current ratios.

(2) Zeros may be located in the right half of the s plane. We define transfer functions with right half plane zeros to be *nonminimum-phase functions;* those without as *minimum-phase functions.*

In relating real and imaginary parts of network functions as studied in the past two sections, there was arbitrariness in one function determined from the other. The same kind of arbitrariness is found in relating phase and magnitude. Consider the networks connected in tandem in Fig. 8-5(a). The all-pass network identified there has the

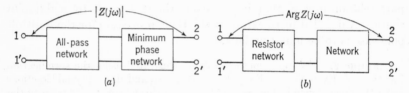

Fig. 8-5. Network structures used to point out the limitations on the relationships between parts of network functions.

special property that the magnitude of the output voltage is always equal to the magnitude of the input voltage (for sinusoidal voltages, of course) but the phase of the output measured with the input as a reference changes with frequency.* For the network of Fig. 8-5(a), the magnitude ratio of input and output voltages will be the same with or without the all-pass network. We anticipate, therefore, that for a given magnitude function we will be able to determine the corresponding phase function only within the phase contribution of an arbitrary number of all-pass networks. The relationship of magnitude and phase will be explicit only when the two terminal-pair network is a minimum phase network (no zeros in the right half plane).

In Fig. 8-5(b) is shown a network connected in tandem with a network made up entirely of resistive elements. (An ideal amplifier would do equally well.) The presence of the resistive network does not affect the phase relationship of input and output and the function $Z(j\omega)$ relating output to input will be the same with or without the resistive network. We anticipate that from a given phase character-

---

* See the author's *Network Analysis,* p. 265, for a specific example of an all-pass network. These two terminal-pair networks will be studied in Chapter 12.

istic we will be able to determine the magnitude function only within a multiplying constant.

The derivation of the method for finding phase from magnitude starts with the relationship

$$|Z(j\omega)|^2 = Z(j\omega)\,\overline{Z(j\omega)} = Z(j\omega)\,Z(-j\omega) \tag{8.39}$$

Analytic continuation—the substitution of s for $j\omega$—gives the product $Z(s)\,Z(-s)$. If $Z(s)$ is represented by

$$Z(s) = \frac{m_1 + n_1}{m_2 + n_2} \tag{8.40}$$

then

$$Z(-s) = \frac{m_1 - n_1}{m_2 - n_2} \tag{8.41}$$

The product of these last two functions, which will be equal to the squared magnitude function when $s = j\omega$, is

$$Z(s)\,Z(-s) = \frac{m_1 + n_1}{m_2 + n_2}\frac{m_1 - n_1}{m_2 - n_2} = \frac{m_1^2 - n_1^2}{m_2^2 - n_2^2} \tag{8.42}$$

From this result, we see that both numerator and denominator of $Z(s)\,Z(-s)$ are even polynomials. And when $s = j\omega$, both numerator and denominator are even in ω. Thus

$$|Z(j\omega)|^2 = \frac{C_0 + C_2\omega^2 + C_4\omega^4 + \cdots}{D_0 + D_2\omega^2 + D_4\omega^4 + \cdots} \tag{8.43}$$

From these results, a tabulation of the important properties of the magnitude squared function may be made. The first three of these properties apply to either driving-point or transfer functions.

(1) Both the magnitude and magnitude squared functions are even and positive for all ω. Testing of possible magnitude functions may therefore involve the use of the Sturm test of Chapter 4. All zeros of $Z(s)\,Z(-s)$ on the imaginary axis must be of even multiplicity.

(2) The C and D coefficients of Eq. 8.43 are real (although not necessarily positive) since the coefficients of $Z(s)$ from which this equation was derived are real. This requires that poles and zeros be conjugate if complex.

(3) Every pole and zero of $Z(s)\,Z(-s)$ is accompanied by its negative. The property of $B(-s^2)$ derived in Section 8.1 applies here to both numerator and denominator.

If $Z(s)$ is required to be a driving-point function, then another property can be added.

(4) The degrees of the numerator and denominator of either $Z(s)$ $Z(-s)$ or $|Z(j\omega)|^2$ are either equal or differ by 2. Further, when $Z(s)$ is separated from the product $Z(s) Z(-s)$, it must have only left half plane zeros.

This tabulation contains necessary conditions, but they are not sufficient for $Z(s)$ to be positive real since no use has been made of sufficiency conditions in their statement. If $Z(s)$ is required to be positive real, then the function found must be tested by the standard methods given in Chapter 4. There are no short cuts as there were in the last section.

Based on these results, we may now outline a procedure for finding the phase from a given magnitude.

(1) Given $|Z(j\omega)|^2$, replace ω^2 by $-s^2$ and so form $Z(s) Z(-s)$.

(2) If $Z(s)$ is to be positive real, form $m_1 + n_1$ and $m_2 + n_2$ by rejecting all zeros and poles of $Z(s) Z(-s)$ in the right half plane. For a nonminimum-phase transfer function, some or all of the right half plane zeros of $Z(s) Z(-s)$ may be chosen.

(3) Having found $Z(s)$ in the form of Eq. 8.40, the phase is determined to be

$$\text{Arg } Z(j\omega) = \tan^{-1} \frac{n_1(\omega)}{jm_1(\omega)} - \tan^{-1} \frac{n_2(\omega)}{jm_2(\omega)} \tag{8.44}$$

This difference can be simplified using the identity

$$\tan^{-1} x \pm \tan^{-1} y = \tan^{-1} \frac{x \pm y}{1 \mp xy} \tag{8.45}$$

Example 3. Given the magnitude function

$$|Z(j\omega)| = 2 \sqrt{\frac{\omega^4 - 3\omega^2 + 36}{\omega^4 - 4\omega^2 + 16}} \tag{8.46}$$

or

$$|Z(j\omega)|^2 = 4 \frac{\omega^4 - 3\omega^2 + 36}{\omega^4 - 4\omega^2 + 16} \tag{8.47}$$

then

$$Z(s) Z(-s) = 4 \frac{s^4 + 3s^2 + 36}{s^4 + 4s^2 + 16} \tag{8.48}$$

simply by replacing ω^2 by $-s^2$. Factoring numerator and denominator polynomials gives the following poles and zeros:

$$\text{zeros at } s_a, s_b, s_c, s_d \text{ are } \pm \left(\frac{-3 \pm j \sqrt{15}}{2} \right)$$

$$\text{poles at } s_1, s_2, s_3, s_4 \text{ are } \pm (-1 \pm j \sqrt{3})$$

Rejecting the right half plane poles and zeros gives

$$Z(s) = 2\frac{s^2 + 3s + 6}{s^2 + 2s + 4} \tag{8.49}$$

From this, the phase function is

$$\text{Arg } Z(j\omega) = \tan^{-1}\frac{3\omega}{6 - \omega^2} - \tan^{-1}\frac{2\omega}{4 - \omega^2} \tag{8.50}$$

Making use of Eq. 8.45, this equation may be simplified to the form

$$\text{Arg } Z(j\omega) = \tan^{-1}\frac{-\omega^3}{\omega^4 - 4\omega^2 + 24} \tag{8.51}$$

A comparison of the last two equations serves to introduce the next topic. How can we find an equation of the form of Eq. 8.50 given an equation like Eq. 8.51? It is not clear how we may use Eq. 8.45 in reverse. We need a new approach to solve the phase-to-magnitude problem.

8.5   From phase to magnitude

The next procedure to be described allows the magnitude to be found with an arbitrary multiplying constant from a given phase function. The properties of the phase function will first be tabulated before the procedure is described. The network function, again either driving-point or transfer in nature, is first written

$$Z(j\omega) = \text{Re } Z(j\omega) + j \text{ Im } Z(j\omega) \tag{8.52}$$

Then

$$\text{Arg } Z(j\omega) \equiv \theta = \tan^{-1}\frac{\text{Im } Z(j\omega)}{\text{Re } Z(j\omega)} \tag{8.53}$$

Since

$$\text{Od } Z(s) \Big|_{s=j\omega} = j \text{ Im } Z(j\omega)$$

and

$$\text{Ev } Z(s) \Big|_{s=j\omega} = \text{Re } Z(j\omega) \tag{8.54}$$

we have

$$\theta = \tan^{-1}\frac{1}{j}\frac{\text{Od } Z(s)}{\text{Ev } Z(s)}\Big|_{s=j\omega} \tag{8.55}$$

or

$$j \tan \theta = \frac{\text{Od } Z(s)}{\text{Ev } Z(s)}\Big|_{s=j\omega} \tag{8.56}$$

A generalization of this expression may be written if we let $j \tan \theta$

with $j\omega$ replaced by s be $T(s)$. Then

$$T(s) = \frac{\text{Od } Z(s)}{\text{Ev } Z(s)} \tag{8.57}$$

Still another useful form results if the even and odd parts of

$$Z(s) = \frac{m_1 + n_1}{m_2 + n_2} \tag{8.58}$$

are substituted into Eq. 8.56 and the common denominator of the two parts is canceled:

$$j \tan \theta = \frac{n_1 m_2 - n_2 m_1}{m_1 m_2 - n_1 n_2}\bigg|_{s=j\omega} \tag{8.59}$$

This function is the quotient of an odd to even polynomial in ω which is

$$\tan \theta = \frac{E_1\omega + E_3\omega^3 + \cdots}{F_0 + F_2\omega^2 + F_4\omega^4 + \cdots} \equiv \frac{N(\omega)}{M(\omega)} \tag{8.60}$$

From these various forms of writing the angle function, we may tabulate the following properties of $\tan \theta$:

(1) The angle function, $\tan \theta = \tan \text{Arg } Z(j\omega)$, is an odd function and, moreover, the quotient of an odd to even polynomial in ω.

(2) The E and F coefficients of this polynomial, Eq. 8.60, are real since they are derived from the real coefficients of $Z(s)$. Thus poles and zeros of $T(s)$ are conjugate if complex.

(3) The function $Z(s)$ derived from $\tan \theta$ is positive real if

$$|\theta| \leq 90°$$

for all ω. Using this criterion, we can tell in advance whether a positive real function can be found from a given $\tan \theta$ specification. This may require plotting.

The procedure used to find $Z(s)$ is suggested by the equation $T(s) = \text{Od } Z(s)/\text{Ev } Z(s)$ (Eq. 8.57). If we add numerator and denominator of $T(s)$, then

$$\text{Ev } Z(s) + \text{Od } Z(s) = Z(s) \tag{8.61}$$

and the objective is accomplished. Several details of this operation require further examination. We begin by assuming that we are given $\tan \theta$ as a quotient of polynomials, $N(j\omega)/M(j\omega)$. We first form $j \tan \theta = jN(j\omega)/M(j\omega)$ and then generalize by letting $j\omega = s$. Adding numerator to denominator gives, from Eq. 8.59,

$$M + N = n_1 m_2 - n_2 m_1 + m_1 m_2 - n_1 n_2 = (m_1 + n_1)(m_2 - n_2) \tag{8.62}$$

From this result, we see that

$$M + N = [m_1(s) + n_1(s)][m_2(-s) + n_2(-s)] \tag{8.63}$$

This equation tells us that if s_0 is a zero of $M + N$, either s_0 is a zero of $m_1 + n_1$ or $-s_0$ is a zero of $m_2 + n_2$. Then the sorting of the zeros of $M + N$ is accomplished by position in the s plane with respect to the imaginary axis. Zeros in the left half plane are zeros of $Z(s)$; zeros in the right half plane are poles of $Z(s)$ when reflected into the left half plane. This reflection operation automatically introduces a change in sign, as may be seen from the following construction.

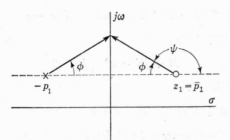

Fig. 8-6. Phasor diagram identifying $\phi = \text{Arg}\, 1/(j\omega + p_1)$ and $\psi = \text{Arg}\,(j\omega - z_1)$.

Figure 8-6 shows a right half plane zero z_1 and an image pole $-p_1$. From the figure, observe that $\psi + \phi = 180°$. The phase functions to be compared are

$$\text{Arg}\,(j\omega - z_1) = \psi \tag{8.64}$$

and

$$\text{Arg}\,\frac{1}{j\omega + p_1} = \phi \tag{8.65}$$

Thus

$$\text{Arg}\,(j\omega - z_1) + \text{Arg}\,\frac{1}{j\omega + p_1} = 180° \tag{8.66}$$

and the phase change associated with reflecting a zero into the left half plane and changing it to a pole is $180°$.

In summary, the following operations are sufficient to determine the magnitude from a given phase function, $\tan \theta$:

(1) From the specified $\tan \theta = N(\omega)/M(\omega)$, form $j \tan \theta$ and then $T(s) = N(s)/M(s)$.

(2) Add M and N and factor the resulting polynomial.

(3) Reflect right half plane zeros into left half plane poles and so construct $Z(s)$ within a constant multiplier, K.

(4) From $Z(s)$, form $|Z(j\omega)|$ if required.

Tuttle* gives a detailed procedure by which functions having the form of even to odd polynomials (in contrast to Eq. 8.60) may be modified by introducing a pole or zero at the origin in $Z(s)$, and also a method of modifying a function so that it will satisfy the requirement that $|\theta| \leq 90°$ if it does not already by introducing imaginary axis poles or zeros in $Z(s)$.

Example 4.   Suppose that we are given the function

$$\theta = \tan^{-1} \frac{-\omega}{\omega^2 + 2} \tag{8.67}$$

From this,

$$M = \omega^2 + 2 \quad \text{and} \quad N = -\omega \tag{8.68}$$

The polynomial $M + jN$ is

$$M + jN = \omega^2 - j\omega + 2 \tag{8.69}$$

Substituting s for $j\omega$ gives

$$M(s) + N(s) = -s^2 - s + 2 = -1(s^2 + s - 2) \tag{8.70}$$

The zeros of this function are -2 and $+1$, so

$$M + N = -(s + 2)(s - 1) \tag{8.71}$$

Changing the right half plane zero to a left half plane pole and introducing an arbitrary multiplier, K, gives

$$Z(s) = K \frac{s + 2}{s + 1} \tag{8.72}$$

The magnitude function is

$$|Z(j\omega)| = K \left| \frac{j\omega + 2}{j\omega + 1} \right| = K \sqrt{\frac{\omega^2 + 4}{\omega^2 + 1}} \tag{8.73}$$

Example 5.   The operations involved in finding the magnitude from a given phase require factoring polynomials that may be of high degree. For example, if the specification function is taken as

$$\tan \theta = \frac{-63\omega + 15\omega^3}{16 - 16\omega^2 + 4\omega^4} \tag{8.74}$$

then

$$M + N = 4(s^4 - \tfrac{15}{4}s^3 + 4s^2 - \tfrac{63}{4}s + 4) \tag{8.75}$$

---

* *Op. cit.*, pp. 437–456; see also Guillemin, *Synthesis of Passive Networks*, pp. 316–321.

Using Linn's method for factoring, we find that

$$M + N = 4(s - 3.732)(s - 0.268)(s + 0.125 + j1.992)(s + 0.125 - j1.992) \tag{8.76}$$

so that, finally,

$$Z(s) = K \frac{4s^2 + s + 16}{s^2 + 4s + 1} \tag{8.77}$$

FURTHER READING

A comprehensive treatment of the relationships of parts of network functions is given by Guillemin in Chapter 8, "Real-Part Sufficiency and Related Topics," of *Synthesis of Passive Networks*. Also highly recommended is the lucid development by Tuttle in *Network Synthesis*, Vol. I, Chapter 8. The topic is studied from an advanced point of view in Bode's *Network Analysis and Feedback Amplifier Design*, pp. 303–360, and in Bayard's *Théorie des réseaux de Kirchhoff*, pp. 254–261. See also Louis Weinberg, "On the phase function," *IRE Trans.*, **CT-3**, 200–201 (1956). For source material, see Marcel Bayard, "Relationship of the real and imaginary parts of impedance" (in French), *Rev. gén. élec.*, **37**, 659–664 (1935); T. Murakami and M. S. Corrington, "Relation between amplitude and phase in electrical networks," *RCA Rev.*, **9**, 602–631 (1948); and C. M. Gewertz, *Network Synthesis*, The Williams and Wilkins Co., Baltimore, 1933. For references relating to graphical computations of phase and magnitude, see D. E. Thomas, "Tables of phase associated with a semi-infinite unit slope of attenuation," *Bell Sys. Tech. J.*, **26**, 870–899 (1947), or Bode, *op. cit.*, pp. 337–360.

PROBLEMS

8-1. Given the positive real impedance function

$$Z(s) = \frac{5s^2 + 18s + 8}{s^2 + s + 10}$$

determine $R(\omega)$ and $X(\omega)$.

8-2. Using the Brune-Gewertz method, determine the minimum-reactance impedance functions whose real parts for $s = j\omega$ are

(a) $R_1(\omega) = \dfrac{1}{1 + \omega^2}$ (b) $R_2(\omega) = \dfrac{\omega^2}{1 + \omega^6}$

8-3. For the following two resistance functions, determine the corresponding minimum-reactance impedance function using the Brune-Gewertz method.

(a) $R_1(\omega) = \dfrac{\omega^6}{1 + \omega^6}$ (b) $R_2(\omega) = \dfrac{\omega^2}{(1 + \omega^2)(4 + \omega^2)}$

8-4. Determine $Z(s)$ given the following $R(\omega)$ functions. Make use of the Brune-Gewertz method. Explain the arbitrariness in your solution. What additional information would suffice to fix $Z(s)$ exactly?

$$\text{(a)} \quad R_1(\omega) = \frac{\omega^2(1 - \omega^2)^2}{1 + \omega^6} \qquad \text{(b)} \quad R_2(\omega) = \frac{\omega^4 + 25\omega^2 + 144}{\omega^4 + 5\omega^2 + 4}$$

8-5. The following $R(\omega)$ vanishes at the frequency $\omega = \sqrt{3}$ and therefore represents a minimum $Z(s)$. Using the Brune-Gewertz method, determine the minimum $Z(s)$ function.

$$R(\omega) = \frac{\omega^2(\omega^2 - 3)^2}{(1 + \omega^2)(2 + \omega^2)(3 + \omega^2)}$$

8-6. Given the resistance function

$$R(\omega) = \frac{1 - \omega^2 + \omega^4}{(1 + \omega^2)^4}$$

(a) Test this function to determine if the $Z(s)$ found from it will be positive real.

(b) If your answer to part (a) is in the affirmative, find $Z(s)$ by the Brune-Gewertz method.

8-7. Rework Prob. 8-2 using the Bode method.

8-8. Employ the Bode method in solving Prob. 8-3.

8-9. Use the Bode method to solve Prob. 8-4.

8-10. Make use of the Bode method in solving Prob. 8-5. Compare the number of steps required for the two methods on this particular problem.

8-11. Rework Prob. 8-6 using the Bode method.

8-12. Given the reactance function

$$X(\omega) = \frac{-\omega}{1 + \omega^2}$$

(a) Determine the associated resistance function, $R(\omega)$.

(b) If $R(0) = \frac{1}{2}$ ohm, find the driving-point impedance function corresponding to the given $X(\omega)$.

8-13. Prepare a list of properties of the reactance function $X(\omega)$ corresponding to a positive real $Z(s)$ similar to that given in the chapter for $R(\omega)$.

8-14. Based on the properties of $X(\omega)$ found in Prob. 8-13, outline a general method for finding $Z(s)$ and so $R(\omega)$ from a given $X(\omega)$ specification.

8-15. A driving-point impedance function has an associated reactance function

$$X(\omega) = \frac{\omega}{1 + \omega^6}$$

Determine $\text{Re } Z(j\omega) = R(\omega)$ for this reactance. What is the arbitrariness in your solution?

8-16. For the following two specifications for a magnitude squared function, determine $Z(s)$ in a form that is positive real if such a form exists.

(a) $|Z(j\omega)|^2 = \dfrac{\omega^4 + 6\omega^2 + 25}{\omega^4 - 6\omega^2 + 25}$ (b) $|Z(j\omega)|^2 = \dfrac{\omega^2 + 16}{\omega^4 + 10\omega^2 + 9}$

8-17. Given the magnitude squared function

$$|Z(j\omega)|^2 = \frac{1}{1 + \omega^8}$$

and assuming that this function is transfer in nature, sketch all possible pole-zero configurations for $Z(s)$.

8-18. (a) An impedance function has a real part which is

$$\mathrm{Re}\, Z(j\omega) = \frac{1 + \omega^2}{1 + \omega^2 + \omega^4}$$

Determine the corresponding $Z(s)$.

(b) An impedance function has a magnitude squared characteristic

$$|Z(j\omega)|^2 = \frac{1 + \omega^2}{1 + \omega^2 + \omega^4}$$

Determine the corresponding $Z(s)$. Compare this impedance function with that found in part (a).

8-19. Repeat Prob. 8-18(b) for the function

$$|Z(j\omega)|^2 = \frac{\omega^2 + \omega^4}{1 + \omega^6}$$

8-20. (a) A two terminal-pair network has a voltage-ratio transfer function with the phase characteristic

$$\tan\theta = -\omega^5$$

Find the corresponding transfer function and write an expression for the magnitude of this function when $s = j\omega$. Is this function minimum phase?

(b) Repeat part (a) for the phase characteristic.

$$\tan\theta = -\omega^7$$

8-21. Given the phase function

$$\tan\theta = -\frac{\omega(4 - \omega^2)}{1 - \omega^2}$$

(a) Can this phase characteristic represent a driving-point function? Justify your answer.

(b) Determine one $Z(s)$ corresponding to this phase function and state whether it is driving point or transfer.

8-22. Repeat Prob. 8-21 for the function

$$-\tan\theta = \frac{3\omega - \omega^3}{1 - 3\omega^2}$$

8-23. Show that

$$\frac{Z(s)}{Z(-s)} = \frac{1 + T(s)}{1 - T(s)}$$

Make use of this relationship to find $Z(s)$ for the function

$$\theta = \tan^{-1} \frac{-\omega}{2 + \omega^2}$$

Compare your result with Example 4.

8-24. Find a positive real impedance function $Z(s)$ corresponding to the following resistance function:

$$R(\omega) = \frac{2 + 3\omega^2 - 4\omega^4 + 4\omega^6}{1 + \omega^2 - 11\omega^4 + 4\omega^6}$$

8-25. A particularly simple form for the resistance function is

$$R(\omega) = \frac{\omega^{2i}}{1 + \omega^{2j}}, \qquad j = 1, 2, \cdots ; i = 0, 1, 2, \cdots , j$$

Outline a procedure for finding the associated minimum reactance function, $Z(s)$, for any value of i and j. Illustrate this procedure for several values of i and j.

Approximation I

. . . . *9*

9.1 Introduction

Past chapters have dealt with properties of networks and network functions and with realization methods. Another important aspect of synthesis, mentioned briefly in Chapter 1, is *approximation*. Our study will be of the approximation of frequency-domain quantities* like $R(\omega)$, $X(\omega)$, $|Z(j\omega)|$, and Arg $Z(j\omega)$. With these quantities determined, the methods of the last chapter are available for finding $Z(s)$.

Several new definitions and descriptions are needed first. We define the *error* $\Delta(\omega)$ to mean the difference between the approximating function and the specification function. The sign of this error is seldom significant; in most cases, we are interested in minimizing the magnitude of the error over some band of frequencies. In Fig. 9-1, the specification function is represented by the dashed lines. Three possible forms of the approximating function and the corresponding errors are shown in the figure. Which approximation is best? The answer to this question requires that we know the permissible *error tolerance*, the maximum error allowed. This error tolerance may be constant over the band of frequencies from 0 to 1 (a normalized scale) or may vary with frequency. In the cases shown in Fig. 9-1, a constant error tolerance from 0 to 1 identifies the approximation of (c) as the best. However, if the tolerance is small at frequencies centering around $\omega = \frac{1}{2}$, but relatively large for other frequencies, then the approximation of (a) appears to be the best.

Approximation in network synthesis often requires a compromise between minimizing error and satisfying realizability conditions (e.g., the requirement that driving-point functions be positive real) imposed

---

* For a discussion of time-domain approximation, see Guillemin's *Synthesis of Passive Networks*, Chapter 15.

on the approximating functions.   The "best" approximating function is the one that minimizes error while still satisfying realizability conditions.   Another important consideration is that the value of permissible error tolerance depends on the application for which it is intended.   In the design of filters such as those used in telephone transmission systems, tolerances are often small (fractions of a decibel); in the design of compensating networks for electromechanical servomechanisms or some electronic feedback amplifiers, tolerances are larger (perhaps a few decibels).   The methods of this chapter are

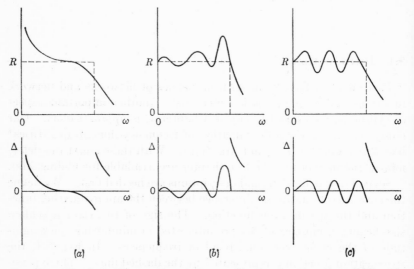

Fig. 9-1.   The dashed line represents the specification function, the solid line the approximating function, $R(\omega)$. $\Delta(\omega)$ is the error function for each of the three forms of approximation.

suited to the larger approximation error applications.   Other methods with approximation optimized in some sense are studied in Chapter 13.

9.2   A method of cut and try

A very direct method of approximation was suggested in Chapter 1. It is carried out in the following steps:

(1) A suitable form for the approximating function is chosen.

(2) This function is forced through selected points on the desired response curve.

(3) The resulting set of linear simultaneous algebraic equations are solved for the coefficients.

(4) The function so found is tested. If found lacking—the error exceeds set limits or realizability conditions are not satisfied—start over.

Such a method is described as *cut and try* or *trial and error*.* An example will illustrate its features.

Example 1. Figure 9-2 shows a desired resistance function variation. The corresponding $Z(s)$ is required to be positive real. A simple form that $R(\omega)$

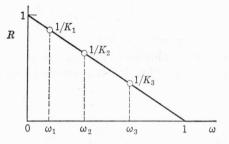

Fig. 9-2. The specification function, $R(\omega)$, used as an example for cut-and-try approximation.

may have is

$$R(\omega) = \frac{A_0}{B_0 + B_2\omega^2 + B_4\omega^4} \tag{9.1}$$

or dividing numerator and denominator by A_0 and letting $B_n/A_0 = b_n$,

$$R(\omega) = \frac{1}{b_0 + b_2\omega^2 + b_4\omega^4} \tag{9.2}$$

Suppose that we select three frequencies and require that the error in the approximating function be 0. Let

$$R(\omega_1) = 1/K_1, \qquad R(\omega_2) = 1/K_2, \qquad R(\omega_3) = 1/K_3 \tag{9.3}$$

Then
$$b_0 + \omega_1{}^2 b_2 + \omega_1{}^4 b_4 = K_1$$

$$b_0 + \omega_2{}^2 b_2 + \omega_2{}^4 b_4 = K_2 \tag{9.4}$$

and
$$b_0 + \omega_3{}^2 b_2 + \omega_3{}^4 b_4 = K_3$$

In this set of equations, the unknowns are b_0, b_2, and b_4. The simultaneous equations may be solved by any standard method: successive elimination, determinants, or by the digital computer (routine programs are available for this kind of problem). Determining the values for the b coefficients provides the approximating function. Some things can be determined by inspection of the coefficients, but the final test will require a complete plot of $R(\omega)$, a straightforward though tedious task.

---

* A detailed and comprehensive description of this method is available in Tuttle's *Network Synthesis*, Vol. I, pp. 746–756.

This last statement may be amplified by considering four possibilities for the signs of the b coefficients in Eq. 9.2:

Sign of:

Case	b_0	b_2	b_4
1	$-$	$+$	$+$
2	$+$	$+$	$-$
3	$+$	$-$	$+$
4	$+$	$+$	$+$

In Case 1, the negative value for b_0 implies a negative value for $R(0)$, resulting in the approximating function shown in Fig. 9-3(a). With

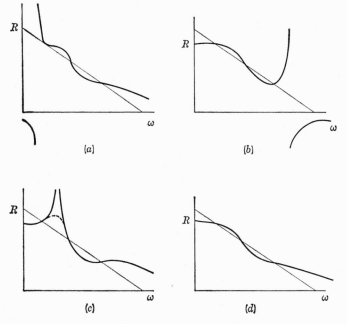

Fig. 9-3. Four possible variations of $R(\omega)$ depending on the signs of the b coefficients of Eq. 9.2.

b_4 negative, Case 2, $R(\omega)$ is negative for large ω, and $R(\omega)$ has a pole at the frequency at which the positive and negative terms in the denominator just cancel, as shown in Fig. 9-3(b). For Case 3, $R(\omega)$ may or may not become negative for some range of frequencies, as in Fig. 9-3(c). The Sturm test of Chapter 4 distinguished the two possibilities. Only for Case 4 with all coefficients positive is it certain that

$R(\omega)$ is positive for all ω, as in the response of Fig. 9-3(d). Since negative values for $R(\omega)$ exclude them from representing driving-point functions, we see that Cases 1 and 2 are not acceptable, Case 3 is conditionally acceptable (requiring further test), and Case 4 is acceptable. To determine whether $R(\omega)$ found by this method satisfies some error tolerance criterion requires plotting; failure necessitates starting at the beginning once more in selecting ω_1, ω_2, and ω_3. Users of the method have found that they develop skill in selecting appropriate points of zero error with practice. The reader is invited to test this statement by working several of the problems provided at the end of this chapter.

9.3   Break-point approximation: general considerations

Another approximation method has come to be known as *break-point approximation* and is due to Bode.* Figure 9-4 shows a response

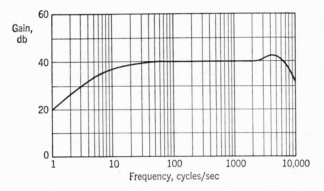

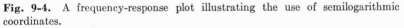

Fig. 9-4. A frequency-response plot illustrating the use of semilogarithmic coordinates.

plot for an audio amplifier. This semilogarithmic plot is typical of that used in describing other communications equipment in that the range of frequencies of interest dictates the use of a logarithmic frequency scale and gain (or the magnitude of a function) is usually given in decibels. Given this curve, our problem is to find an expression for a network function as a quotient of polynomials in s which has a magnitude approximating the curve within an allowable tolerance.

By definition, the number of decibels expressing the ratio of a magnitude of voltages (or currents) is† $20 \log |V_2/V_1|$ db. Let the ordinate of the semilogarithmic plot be y db for the time being. Since the

* *Network Analysis and Feedback Amplifier Design*, pp. 316 ff.
† Throughout the text, log denotes the base 10 and ln the base ϵ.

abscissa of the plot is log ω, the equation of a straight line on the semilogarithmic coordinates is

$$y = 20 \log \omega + K \quad \text{db} \qquad (9.5)$$

where, by analogy to the equation of a straight line, $y = mx + b$, familiar from analytic geometry,

$$\text{slope} = \frac{dy}{d \log \omega} = 20 \qquad (9.6)$$

and K is the value of y at $\omega = 1$.

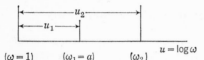

(ω = 1)   (ω₁ = a)   (ω₂) $u = \log \omega$

Fig. 9-5. The logarithmic scale used to illustrate the relationship of linear measurement to quantities on the logarithmic scale.

What units shall we use for the slope given by this equation? The dimension of y is the decibel. To find appropriate units for log ω, consider the units we may use for linear measurements on a logarithmic scale. Let the linear distance be designated as $u = \log \omega$. Let $u_1 = \log a$ be a general distance from the point at which $\omega = 1$ on the frequency axis of Fig. 9-5. A distance twice u_1 from $\omega = 1$ is

$$u_2 = 2u_1 = 2 \log a = \log a^2 \qquad (9.7)$$

and so occurs at $\omega_2 = a^2$. The solution for the general case is found by substituting n for 2 in the last equation so that the frequencies of equal distances are

$$\omega_n = a^n \qquad (9.8)$$

where n is a positive or negative integer. Thus the frequencies corresponding to a^{-2}, a^{-1}, 1, a^2, a^3, $\cdots$ are separated by the linearly measured distances, $u_n - u_{n-1} = \log a$. Figure 9-6 illustrates this conclusion for the general case and for the special cases of $a = 10$ and $a = 2$.

We can now answer the question about the units of the slope of a straight line in semilogarithmic coordinates. Equal spaces on the $u = \log \omega$ axis are defined by Eq. 9.8 for any value of a. What value or values of a shall we use? When $a = 10$, the frequencies so defined are said to be separated by a *decade* (from *deca*, a prefix meaning ten). When $a = 2$, the frequencies are separated by an *octave*. The word octave (from *octa*, a prefix meaning eight) is used in music to denote an interval consisting of eight diatonic degrees. Two notes, one twice the frequency of the other, are an octave apart. For our purposes we should associate octave with *two* (two times the frequency) rather than eight (eight notes per octave).   The slope in terms of the decade and

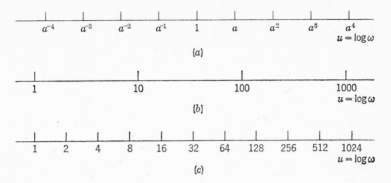

(a)

(b)

(c)

Fig. 9-6.   Illustrations of frequencies corresponding to equal linear measurements.

the octave is found by substituting Eq. 9.8 into Eq. 9.5 for $a = 10$ and $a = 2$.   Thus, with $a = 10$,

$$y_n = 20 \log 10^n + K = 20n + K \quad \text{db} \tag{9.9}$$

so that for each increase in the integer value of n, y increases (or decreases for negative n) by 20 db, and the slope is therefore 20 db/ decade.

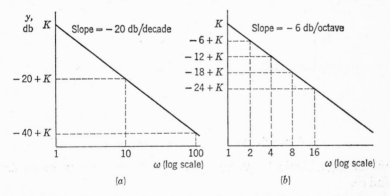

Fig. 9-7.   Plots illustrating the unit slope of a straight line in semilogarithmic coordinates.

With $a = 2$, the frequencies are separated by an octave so that

$$y_n = 20 \log 2^n + K = 20n \log 2 + K \quad \text{db} \tag{9.10}$$

or $$y_n = 6.0206n + K = 6n + K \quad \text{db} \tag{9.11}$$

and the slope is approximately 6 db/octave.   These conclusions are illustrated in Fig. 9-7.

In Fig. 9-8, two frequencies ω_1 and ω_2 are separated on logarithmic coordinates by the distance u_{12}. A third frequency ω_b is located a

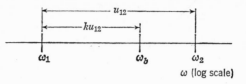

Fig. 9-8. The frequency, ω_b, is located at a fraction of the linear distance, u_{12}.

fraction of this distance from ω_1, ku_{12}. It is required to determine ω_b in terms of ω_1, ω_2, and k. From the figure, we see that

$$\log \omega_b = \log \omega_1 + k(\log \omega_2 - \log \omega_1) \tag{9.12}$$

$$= k \log \omega_2 + (1 - k) \log \omega_1 \tag{9.13}$$

$$= \log \omega_2{}^k \omega_1{}^{1-k} \tag{9.14}$$

Then $\qquad \omega_b = \omega_1{}^{1-k} \omega_2{}^k, \qquad 0 \leq k \leq 1 \tag{9.15}$

An important special case of this relationship occurs when $k = \frac{1}{2}$. For this case,

$$\omega_b = \sqrt{\omega_1 \omega_2} \tag{9.16}$$

This frequency is called the *geometrical mean frequency* and is located

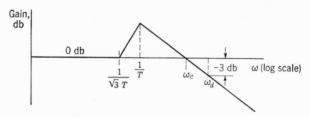

Fig. 9-9. Gain characteristic for Example 2.

on the logarithmic frequency scale at a point midway between ω_1 and ω_2.

Example 2. The gain characteristic made up of straight-line segments shown in Fig. 9-9* has 0 value from $\omega = 0$ to $\omega = 1/\sqrt{3}\,T$. At that frequency it increases at 12 db/octave until $\omega = 1/T$ and thereafter decreases at -6 db/octave for all larger ω. Let it be required to find the frequency ω_c at which the line crosses the 0 db line and the frequency ω_d where the characteristic is at -3 db (the so-called half-power frequency).

* Taken from H. Epstein, "Synthesis of passive RC networks with gains greater than unity," *Proc. I.R.E.*, **39**, 833 (1951).

By simple geometry, the linear distance from $\omega = 1/T$ to ω_c is twice that from $1/\sqrt{3}\ T$ to $1/T$. Then by Eq. 9.15,

$$\omega_c = 3/T \quad \text{radians/sec} \tag{9.17}$$

The piecewise linear curve has the value of -6 db at twice the frequency ω_c. Using Eq. 9.16, the mid-point frequency between ω_c and the -6 db frequency is found to be

$$\omega_d = \sqrt{\frac{6}{T}\frac{3}{T}} = \frac{3\sqrt{2}}{T} \quad \text{radians/sec} \tag{9.18}$$

which completes the solution.

9.4   Semilog plots of network function factors

In the first four chapters, we found that the poles and zeros of driving-point functions might be at the origin or on the imaginary axis if simple, might be on the negative real axis, or might be complex conjugate providing the real part was negative. Transfer functions, as later studies will reveal, are not so restricted in that there may be multiple zeros at the origin or on the imaginary axis, and zeros are permitted in the right half of the s plane. In this approximation study, we will be concerned with the magnitude and phase for $s = j\omega$ of network function factors corresponding to these pole and zero locations. The four factors to be considered are:

(1) s.
(2) $s + \alpha_1$ with α_1 real.
(3) $(s + \alpha + j\beta)(s + \alpha - j\beta) = (s + \alpha)^2 + \beta^2$, α and β real.
(4) A constant multiplier, K.

The discussion to follow is simplified if we take advantage of our study of magnitude and frequency scaling in Chapter 2. In terms of semilogarithmic coordinates, magnitude scaling provides vertical shifting of a given characteristic whereas frequency scaling corresponds to horizontal shifts, as shown in Fig. 9-10. In each case the characteristic is unaffected in its shape by scaling. The scaling operations for factors (2) and (3) are carried out as follows:

$$s + \alpha_1 = \alpha_1(s/\alpha_1 + 1) = \alpha_1(S + 1) \tag{9.19}$$

and

$$s^2 + 2\alpha s + \alpha^2 + \beta^2$$

$$= (\alpha^2 + \beta^2)\left(\frac{s^2}{\alpha^2 + \beta^2} + \frac{2\alpha}{\sqrt{\alpha^2 + \beta^2}} \times \frac{s}{\sqrt{\alpha^2 + \beta^2}} + 1\right) \tag{9.20}$$

$$= (\alpha^2 + \beta^2)(S^2 + 2\zeta S + 1) \tag{9.21}$$

where $\zeta = \alpha/(\alpha^2 + \beta^2)^{1/2} = \cos\theta$ and θ is identified in Fig. 9-11. With the understanding that we will be using normalized frequency, we will replace S by s in these equations and restore the multipliers in

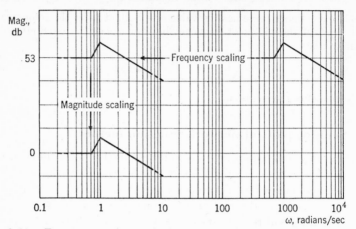

Fig. 9-10. Frequency and magnitude scaling in semilogarithmic coordinates.

later inverse scaling. The four factors for consideration then have the simplified forms: (1) s, (2) $s + 1$, (3) $s^2 + 2\zeta s + 1$, and (4) the constant multiplier, $K' = 1$.

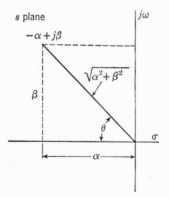

Fig. 9-11. The s plane identification of quantities in Eq. 9.20.

Now the logarithm of a complex function, $x + jy$, is

$$\log(x + jy) = \log|x + jy| + j\,\text{Arg}\,(x + jy) \quad (9.22)$$

This equation may be written in another form,

$$\log(x + jy) = \log(x^2 + y^2)^{1/2} + j\,\tan^{-1}\frac{y}{x} \quad (9.23)$$

We will use this equation to express the magnitude and the phase for each of the four factors just listed, with $s = j\omega$.

The factor $j\omega$. Consider the factor $(j\omega)^m$, where positive m indicates the number of zeros at the origin or negative m the number of poles. The magnitude is

$$20\log|(j\omega)^m| = 20\,m\log\omega \quad \text{db} \quad (9.24)$$

which is the equation of a straight line with a slope of $6m$ db/octave, having the value 0 db at $\omega = 1$. The phase of the factor is

$$\text{Arg } (j\omega)^m = m\pi/2 \quad \text{radians} \tag{9.25}$$

Plots of these two results are shown in Fig. 9-12. For positive real functions m is restricted to the values -1, 0, or $+1$, but for transfer functions m may have other positive values.

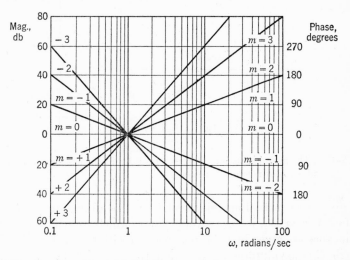

Fig. 9-12. Semilogarithmic plot of the magnitude and phase of the factor $(j\omega)^m$.

The factor $j\omega + 1$. The magnitude of this factor in decibels is

$$20 \log |j\omega + 1| = 20 \log (1 + \omega^2)^{\frac{1}{2}} \quad \text{db} \tag{9.26}$$

and the phase is

$$\text{Arg } (j\omega + 1) = \tan^{-1} \omega \tag{9.27}$$

In plotting this magnitude function, use is made of the low- and high-frequency asymptotes. For $\omega \ll 1$,

$$20 \log (1 + \omega^2)^{\frac{1}{2}} \cong 20 \log 1 = 0 \quad \text{db} \tag{9.28}$$

and for $\omega \gg 1$,

$$20 \log (1 + \omega^2)^{\frac{1}{2}} \cong 20 \log \omega \quad \text{db} \tag{9.29}$$

Thus both asymptotes are straight lines, one having 0 slope and the other with a slope of 6 db/octave. It is evident that the two asymptotes intersect when $20 \log \omega = 0$ or at $\omega = 1$. This frequency of intersection of the extended asymptotic lines is known as the *break frequency* or sometimes the *break point*. When the factor $j\omega + 1$ appears in the denominator of a network function, then the magnitude and phase functions are identical with Eqs. 9.26 and 9.27 except for a negative sign. The asymptotic lines for numerator and denominator factors are shown in Fig. 9-13.

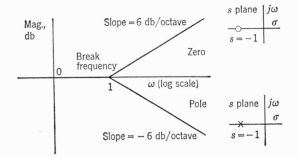

Fig. 9-13. The asymptotes for the factor $j\omega + 1$ and the associated positions of the poles and zeros of network functions.

Values of the actual magnitude of $j\omega + 1$ as a function of frequency are found from Eq. 9.26. Several values which we will find to be of significance are given in Table 9-1 together with the magnitudes of the straight-line asymptotes for the same frequencies. The variation of

TABLE 9-1

Frequency		Value of Magnitude from Eq. 9-26, db	Asymptotic Value Magnitude, db	Error, db
0.5	(octave below break frequency)	±1	0	±1
0.76		±2	0	±2
1	(break frequency)	±3	0	±3
1.31		±4.3	±2.3	±2
2	(octave above break frequency)	±7	±6	±1

the actual magnitude as given in the second column of Table 9-1 is shown in Fig. 9-14. The difference of the actual magnitude variation and the asymptotic lines is here defined as *error*, which is tabulated in the fourth column of Table 9-1. The magnitude of the error as a function of frequency is shown in Fig. 9-15, plotted with a logarithmic frequency scale. Observe that the error has symmetry with respect to the break point. Observe also that the error is nearly 3 db at the break point and is 1 db both an octave above and an octave below the

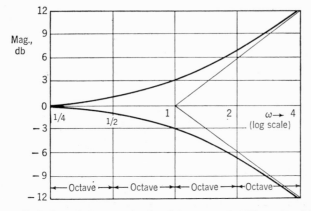

Fig. 9-14. Variation of the magnitude of $j\omega + 1$ and $1/(j\omega + 1)$ with ω from Eq. 9.26.

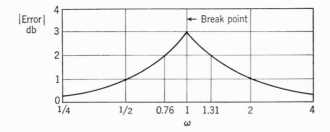

Fig. 9-15. The magnitude of the error (difference of asymptotic and actual curves) as a function of frequency. Note the symmetry with respect to the break point.

break point. These easily remembered numbers make the plotting of the magnitude characteristic routine:

(1) Locate the break point and draw the straight-line asymptotes.

(2) Locate the five points—in some cases three points will suffice—as tabulated in Table 9-1.

(3) Using these points and the asymptotes, draw a smooth magnitude characteristic.

There are no equivalent simple rules for plotting the phase function, Arg $(j\omega + 1) = \tan^{-1} \omega$. It is often helpful to remember that the tangent of θ is approximately equal to θ for angles less than 20° so that a linear approximation is valid from 0° to 20°. Several other angles and the corresponding values of ω that are easily remembered are given in Table 9-2 and illustrated in Fig. 9-16. When magnitude and phase

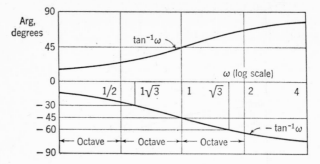

Fig. 9-16. The angle of $j\omega + 1$ and $1/(j\omega + 1)$ as a function of frequency, ω.

must be drawn repeatedly, a template matched to a particular kind of semilog graph paper is easily constructed of cardboard or plastic.

TABLE 9-2

ω	$\tan^{-1} \omega$
0	0
1/2	$\pm 26.6°$
$1/\sqrt{3}$	$\pm 30.0°$
1	$\pm 45.0°$
$\sqrt{3}$	$\pm 60.0°$
2	$\pm 63.4°$
∞	$\pm 90.0°$

The factor $1 - \omega^2 + j2\zeta\omega$. The magnitude of this factor is

$$20 \log |1 - \omega^2 + j2\zeta\omega| = 20 \log [(1 - \omega^2)^2 + (2\zeta\omega)^2]^{\frac{1}{2}} \quad \text{db} \quad (9.30)$$

and the phase is

$$\text{Arg}\,(1 - \omega^2 + j2\zeta\omega) = \tan^{-1}\frac{2\zeta\omega}{1 - \omega^2} \tag{9.31}$$

Just as for the last factor, it is helpful in plotting the magnitude function, Eq. 9.30, to determine the low- and high-frequency asymptotes. For low frequencies, $\omega \ll 1$, the magnitude function is approximately $20 \log 1 = 0$ db. For high values of frequency, $\omega \gg 1$, the magnitude function is approximately 40 log ω, which is a straight line of 12 db/octave slope. The low- and high-frequency asymptotes intersect when 40 log $\omega = 0$ or when $\omega = 1$. This frequency is identified as the break point as before or as the *resonant frequency*. The asymptotic straight lines together with the break point are shown in Fig. 9-17 with a positive slope for a numerator factor and negative slope for a denominator factor.

The development thus far parallels that given for the 1st-degree factor, $j\omega + 1$. In plotting the *actual* curves of magnitude and phase, the parameter ζ gives rise to a family of curves for each value of ζ between 0 and 1. Such plots are shown in Figs. 9-18 and 9-19 for

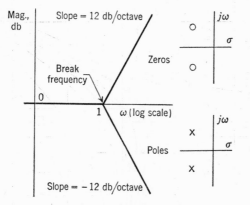

Fig. 9-17. The asymptotes for the 2nd-degree factor which may represent poles or zeros of network functions.

several values of ζ. The value $\zeta = 0$ corresponds to a zero or a pole on the imaginary axis, giving the very small (negative infinity when the plot is in decibels) or very large values for the magnitude suggested by the figure. Several features of these 2nd-degree factor characteristics should be noted: The error of the asymptotic lines with respect to the actual curves is symmetrical about the break frequency, as shown in Fig. 9-20. The break-point phase is 90° for all values of ζ. The low- and high-frequency asymptotic phases are 0° and 180°.

Factors for zeros in the right half plane. Some transfer functions have zeros in the right half of the s plane corresponding to the factors $s - 1$ and $s^2 - 2\zeta s + 1$. For $s = j\omega$, the magnitudes of these two factors are identical with those given by Eqs. 9.26 and 9.30 for left half plane locations. However, the phase function has the opposite sign to those for the left half plane zeros.

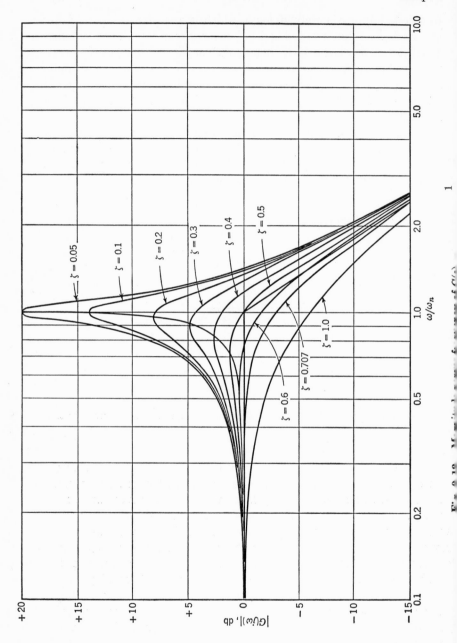

Fig. 9.19. Magnitude curves for responses of $G(s)$.

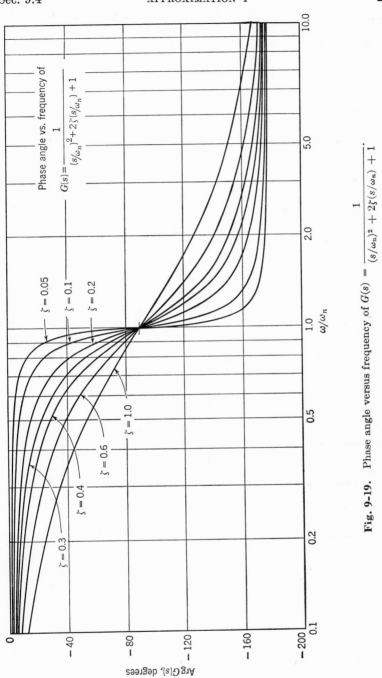

Fig. 9-19. Phase angle versus frequency of $G(s) = \dfrac{1}{(s/\omega_n)^2 + 2\zeta(s/\omega_n) + 1}$.

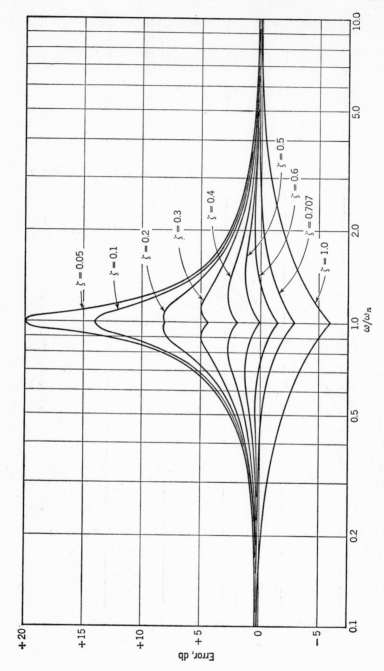

Fig. 9-20. Error in magnitude versus frequency.

9.5 Combinations of factors: analysis

The magnitude and phase characteristics for all factors which appear in the network functions we will study were tabulated in the last section. The total magnitude characteristic in logarithmic units is found by summing the logarithms of the individual factors, and the total phase is similarly found by summing the individual phase functions. For example, the function

$$G(j\omega) = K_1 \frac{j\omega + 1}{j\omega + 2} \qquad (9.32)$$

has a logarithmic magnitude in decibels of

$$20 \log |G(j\omega)| = 20 \log K_1 + 20 \log |j\omega + 1| - 20 \log |j\omega + 2| \qquad (9.33)$$

and a phase

$$\text{Arg } G(j\omega) = \text{Arg } (j\omega + 1) - \text{Arg } (j\omega + 2) \qquad (9.34)$$

since $\text{Arg } K_1 = 0$. An explanation of combinations of the magnitude and phase functions for a network function like that of Eq. 9.32 will be given by an example.

Example 3. Consider a network function with complex conjugate zeros and with two real poles as given by the equation

$$G_1(s) = 5 \frac{s^2 + 2s + 4}{(s + 1)(s + 4)} \qquad (9.35)$$

A voltage-ratio transfer function of this form describes one form of *notch network*, so called, used in servomechanisms for stabilization. The break frequencies for denominator factors are seen to be $\omega = 1$ and $\omega = 4$; for the numerator factor the break frequency is $\omega = 2$ with $\zeta = \frac{1}{2}$. These frequencies are displayed in Fig. 9-21 in relationship to the poles and zeros of $G_1(s)$. Inspection of the equation for $G_1(s)$ shows that both the low- and high-frequency values for this function are 5, or in logarithmic units, $20 \log 5 = 14$ db. Having determined all break frequencies and the corresponding asymptotic line slopes, as summarized in Fig. 9-22(a), the construction procedure may be described as in Fig. 9-22(b). Starting with the low-frequency asymptote, 14 db, locate the break point of smallest value, which

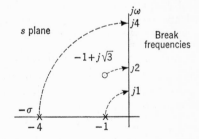

Fig. 9-21. Illustrating the relationship of the pole and zero locations in the s plane to the location of break frequencies on the $j\omega$ axis.

in this case is at $\omega = 1$. At this frequency, the asymptotic curve begins to decrease at -6 db/octave, continuing until the next break point at $\omega = 2$.

At this point, the 2nd-degree numerator factor begins to dominate and the net slope becomes $-6 + 12 = 6$ db/octave which continues until another break point is passed in traversing the ω axis. This occurs at $\omega = 4$ where the final value of 14 db and the final slope of 0 db/octave are attained. The last step in this construction involves plotting the actual curve. For the

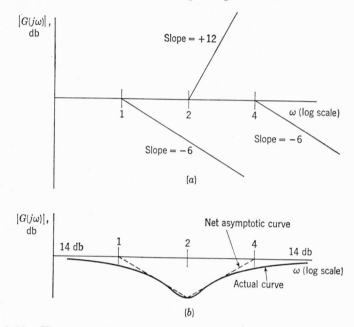

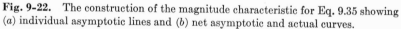

Fig. 9-22. The construction of the magnitude characteristic for Eq. 9.35 showing (a) individual asymptotic lines and (b) net asymptotic and actual curves.

1st-degree factors, the five points of Table 9-1 are located, and for the 2nd-degree factor the curve corresponding to $\zeta = \frac{1}{2}$ is plotted around the break frequency $\omega = 2$. The resulting curve is that shown solid in Fig. 9-22(b).

Other problems will differ from this example only in that other low- and high-frequency asymptotes will be given along with other patterns of break frequencies. This analysis is simple and is rapidly carried to completion.

9.6   Approximation by straight-line asymptotes

We now possess a number of building blocks, the magnitude and phase characteristics of the four factors: K (a constant), $j\omega$, $j\omega + 1$, and $(1 - \omega^2 + j2\zeta\omega)$. A network function factored in terms of its poles and zeros contains instructions on how the building blocks are to be put together to find a total characteristic, magnitude or phase.

Consider the converse problem: given the total characteristic, how do we find the component factors which will approximate the given characteristic to any degree of accuracy desired?

The method of approximation which will be described in this section is based on a number of observations which are now outlined.

(1) The low- and high-frequency asymptotes of any network function magnitude (with $s = j\omega$) have a slope of 0 or $\pm 6n$ db/octave, where n is an integer. There are no other possibilities! These asymptotes are readily determined from the network function. For example,

$$G(s) = \frac{8s^3 + 21s}{5s^4 + 7s^2 + 17} \tag{9.36}$$

has the limit for large s,

$$\lim_{s \to \infty} G(s) = \lim_{s \to \infty} \frac{8}{5} \frac{1}{s} \tag{9.37}$$

so that $20 \log |G(j\omega)|$ decreases at the rate of 6 db/octave for large ω. For small s,

$$\lim_{s \to 0} G(s) = \lim_{s \to 0} \frac{21}{17} s \tag{9.38}$$

so that $20 \log |G(j\omega)|$ increases at 6 db/octave for small ω.

(2) The magnitude characteristic at intermediate frequencies can be approximated by a number of straight-line segments of slopes 0 or $\pm 6n$ db/octave such that the actual characteristic, found by filling in the five points for 1st-degree factors or from the curves for a particular ζ for 2nd-degree factors, nearly coincides with the characteristic being approximated.

(3) Given an asymptotic representation of a semilogarithmic curve as described in step (2), an algebraic expression for the network function may be written from (a) the break frequencies, (b) values of the curve near 2nd-degree resonances, and (c) the level of the asymptotes. The factors $j\omega + 1$ and $1 - \omega^2 + j2\zeta\omega$ may be scaled to any break frequency ω_n by replacing ω by ω/ω_n.

(4) The evaluation of the gain constant K requires that we decide which factors in $G(j\omega)$ contribute to the asymptotic curve at a frequency chosen for this evaluation. In plotting the magnitude of $j\omega/\omega_n + 1$, where ω_n is the break frequency, we let this factor be 1 below ω_n and ω/ω_n above ω_n. In equation form,

$$\text{asymptotes of } 20 \log \left| j \frac{\omega}{\omega_n} + 1 \right| = \begin{cases} 20 \log \dfrac{\omega}{\omega_n} & \text{for } \omega > \omega_n \\ 20 \log 1 & \text{for } \omega < \omega_n \end{cases} \quad (9.39)$$

and similarly, for 2nd-degree factors,

$$\text{asymptotes of } 20 \log \left| 1 - \frac{\omega^2}{\omega_n{}^2} + j2\zeta \frac{\omega}{\omega_n} \right| = \begin{cases} 40 \log \dfrac{\omega}{\omega_n} & \text{for } \omega > \omega_n \\ 20 \log 1 & \text{for } \omega < \omega_n \end{cases}$$
$$(9.40)$$

To evaluate K, select some frequency ω_1. Each factor in $G(j\omega)$ is replaced by the approximation factor as in the above equations, depending on whether the individual ω_n is smaller or larger than ω_1. The resulting equation of the asymptote at ω_1 and the known value of the asymptotic curve at ω_1 determine the value of K. Table 9-3 gives useful numerical values. Examples will illustrate this procedure.

TABLE 9-3

Db	Voltage Ratio*	Db	Voltage Ratio*
0.1	1.0116	3.5	1.4962
0.2	1.0233	4.0	1.5849
0.3	1.0351	4.5	1.6788
0.4	1.0471	5.0	1.7783
0.5	1.0593	5.5	1.8836
0.6	1.0715	6.0	1.9953
0.7	1.0839	7.0	2.2387
0.8	1.0965	8.0	2.5119
0.9	1.1092	9.0	2.8184
1.0	1.1220	10.0	3.1623
1.2	1.1482	15.0	5.6234
1.4	1.1749	20.0	10.0000
1.6	1.2023	30.0	31.6230
1.8	1.2303	40.0	100.0000
2.0	1.2589	50.0	316.2300
2.2	1.2882	60.0	1000.0000
2.4	1.3183	70.0	3162.3000
2.6	1.3490	80.0	10000.0000
2.8	1.3804	90.0	31623.0000
3.0	1.4125	100.0	100000.0000

* Or current ratio, or any numerical ratio.

Example 4. Figure 9-23 shows a magnitude characteristic with the same low- and high-frequency value but with a dip reaching its lowest value at 400 radians/sec. Such a curve is identified with lead-lag networks which are important in the compensation of automatic control systems. It is

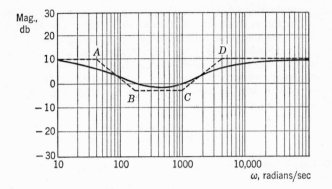

Fig. 9-23. Magnitude characteristic for Example 4.

required to find a network function which approximates this curve. Carrying out the steps in the order given above:

(1) The low- and high-frequency asymptotes have 0 db/octave slopes and values of 10 db. These are shown on Fig. 9-23 by dashed lines.

(2) Starting with these two asymptotes, we search for break frequencies. For 1st-degree factors, the break point occurs when the actual and asymptotic

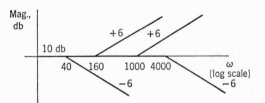

Fig. 9-24. Individual asymptotic plots for Example 4.

curves differ by 3 db. Since the curve is simple, we assume that only 1st-degree terms are required and that the break frequencies are widely separated, and we locate break frequencies at A and D in Fig. 9-23. From A, a line of -6 db/octave slope is constructed; from D, one of $+6$ db/octave slope. The actual and asymptotic curves are again separated by 3 db at points B and C. Since B and C are both at the -2 db level, the two points are connected with a straight line of 0 slope.

(3) To construct the network function, we observe that the asymptotic curve of Fig. 9-23 is constructed from individual asymptotic plots, as shown in Fig. 9-24. The break frequencies are 40, 160, 1000, and 4000 radians/sec. Scaling the factor $s + 1$ for these frequencies, and leaving magnitude-scaling

problems for the next step, we have

$$G(s) = K \frac{(s/160 + 1)(s/1000 + 1)}{(s/40 + 1)(s/4000 + 1)} \tag{9.41}$$

(4) An examination of this equation shows that very low frequencies are convenient for the evaluation of K since $G(j0) = K$. Since $20 \log |G(j0)| = 10$ db, $|G(j0)|$ has the value 3.16, which is the required value of K. Alternatively, we may select some other frequency such as $\omega = 500$ radians/sec, where the asymptote has the value -2 db. In plotting the asymptotic curve at this frequency, we have let $j\omega/160 + 1$ be $j\omega/160$, $j\omega/40 + 1$ be $j\omega/40$, $j\omega/1000 + 1$ be 1, and $j\omega/4000 + 1$ also be 1. Then Eq. 9.41 reduces to the following with $s = j\omega$:

$$|G(j\omega)| = K \frac{\omega/160}{\omega/40} = \frac{K}{4} \tag{9.42}$$

Since $20 \log |G(j500)| = -2$ db, then $G(j500) = 0.792$, so that

$$K = 0.792 \times 4 = 3.16 \tag{9.43}$$

as before. Finally, Eq. 9.41 is written to display poles and zeros as

$$G(s) = 3.16 \frac{(s + 160)(s + 1000)}{(s + 40)(s + 4000)} \tag{9.44}$$

Example 5. For the next example, consider the magnitude characteristic of an amplifier plotted in Fig. 9-25. The low-frequency asymptote (Fig.

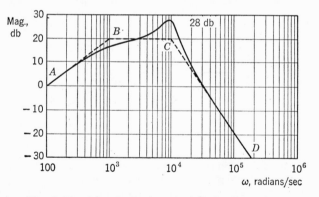

Fig. 9-25. Magnitude characteristic for Example 5.

9-26) is seen to have a slope of 6 db/octave, the high-frequency slope is -12 db/octave, and there is a "resonant peak," indicating a 2nd-degree factor, at $\omega = 10^4$ radians/sec. Starting at the low-frequency side of the curve, the point B is located where the actual and asymptotic curves differ by 3 db. A cut-and-try procedure is used to locate point C which is joined to point B by a line of 0 slope and to point D by a straight line with -12 db/octave slope. From these asymptotes, we see that the break frequencies

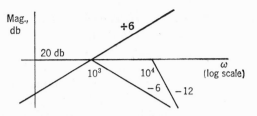

Fig. 9-26. Separate asymptotic plots for Example 5.

are 10^3 and 10^4 radians/sec, and the 8 db error at point C corresponds to $\zeta = 0.2$ from Fig. 9-18. The low-frequency asymptote corresponds to a numerator factor s so that

$$G(s) = K \frac{s}{(s/10^3 + 1)(s^2/10^8 + 4s/10^5 + 1)} \tag{9.45}$$

Point B, where $\omega = 10^3$ and the gain is 20 db, is used to evaluate K. Neglecting all factors except $s = j\omega$ in the last equation gives

$$|G(j1000)| = 10^3 K = 10 \tag{9.46}$$

so that $K = 10^{-2}$. Finally,

$$G(s) = 10^9 \frac{s}{(s + 1000)(s^2 + 4000s + 10^8)} \tag{9.47}$$

What are the limitations of this method of approximation? Clearly, the method works best when the break frequencies are widely separated so that the various asymptotic straight lines are easily recognized. When there are a large number of poles and zeros—say twenty or thirty clustered together—the limitations of the method will be most evident. For the numerous problems involving only a few poles and zeros, the method has advantages in the amount of time required, allows for easy modification to indicate changes in break frequencies, and provides an association of pole and zero locations with the approximation process.

9.7 Approximation from phase plots

The same philosophy of approximation as was given in the last section applies to phase plots, although the details are different. Low- and high-frequency asymptotes of a phase curve are $0°$ or $\pm n90°$, where n is an integer (no other values are possible!). The phase building blocks are those given in Fig. 9-16 for 1st-degree factors and in Fig. 9-19 for 2nd-degree factors. Straight-line approximations are not particularly useful, except for very small angles (less than $20°$).

However, the curves can be placed at various trial positions along the ω axis until a good approximation to the given curve is realized.   Once the individual building-block phase characteristics are in position, the break frequencies are fixed by the 45° point for 1st-degree factors and 90° for 2nd-degree factors.   A phase shift which does not change with frequency indicates the presence of poles or zeros at the origin for the network function, the number being m in $\pm m90°$ of constant phase shift.

9.8   The potential analog

Consider the problem of determining the voltage distribution from a point probe supplying a current I to an infinite sheet of resistance

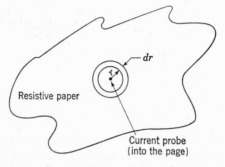

Fig. 9-27.   A current probe placed on an infinite sheet of resistance paper, the potential analog of the network function.

paper of thickness t and resistivity ρ.   The resistance of an annular ring a distance r from the probe and of width dr, as shown in Fig. 9-27, is

$$dR = \frac{\rho \, dl}{A} = \frac{\rho \, dr}{2\pi rt} \qquad (9.48)$$

where A is the cross-sectional area and dl is the length of path.   Now the current I spreads out as a sheet after entering from the probe and all current passes through the annular ring of resistance dR, causing a change in potential across the ring

$$dV = -I \, dR = \frac{-\rho I \, dr}{2\pi rt} \qquad (9.49)$$

The potential difference from one point to another on the sheet of resistance paper may be found by integrating the incremental potential dV. Suppose that we compute the potential at a point P a distance r from the current probe, this potential being with respect to a reference point a distance r' from the probe. This potential difference is

$$V = \int_{r'}^{r} dV \tag{9.50}$$

Substituting dV from Eq. 9.49 gives

$$V = \frac{-\rho I}{2\pi t} \int_{r'}^{r} \frac{dr}{r} = \frac{-\rho I}{2\pi t} \ln r + C \tag{9.51}$$

Let us next apply this result to a somewhat more complicated situation, as shown in Fig. 9-28. A number of probes have been introduced, all carrying the same magnitude of current, but some currents

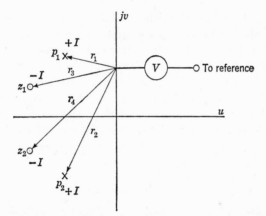

Fig. 9-28. A sheet of resistance paper with four current probes, two carrying current in and two carrying current out of the paper. The potential along the imaginary axis may be recorded on a cathode-ray oscilloscope by commutating points located on the jv axis at the same rate as the sweep of the oscilloscope.

are directed into the paper and some out of the paper. In order to make measurements of distances, the resistance paper has been designated the w plane, with $w = u + jv$, and a system of coordinates established. At a particular point, shown in the figure on the imaginary axis of the w plane, the potential with respect to a given reference may be found by superimposing the scalar potentials, giving

$$V_t = \frac{-\rho I}{2\pi t} (\ln r_1 + \ln r_2 - \ln r_3 - \ln r_4) + C_t \tag{9.52}$$

where C_t is a constant and r_1, r_2, r_3, and r_4 are defined in Fig. 9-28, or

$$V_t = \frac{\rho I}{2\pi t} (\ln |w - z_1| + \ln |w - z_2| - \ln |w - p_1| - \ln |w - p_2|) + C_t$$
(9.53)

Next consider the network function written in the form

$$Z(s) = \frac{a_0}{b_0} \frac{(s - z_1)(s - z_2) \cdots (s - z_n)}{(s - p_1)(s - p_2) \cdots (s - p_m)}$$
(9.54)

The logarithm of the magnitude of this network function is

$$\ln |Z(s)| = \ln \frac{a_0}{b_0} + \ln |s - z_1| + \ln |s - z_2| + \cdots$$
$$- \ln |s - p_1| - \ln |s - p_2| - \cdots - \ln |s - p_m| \quad (9.55)$$

A comparison of this result with Eq. 9.53 suggests the *analog* of the potential in this resistance paper system to the logarithm of the magnitude of network functions. If we have a large resistance paper sheet (Western Union *Teledeltos* paper, for example) with a marked coordinate system (the w plane), and locate probes carrying current into the sheet at points corresponding to poles of the network function and probes carrying current out of the sheet at the zeros, then along the imaginary axis in the w plane the measured potential will be proportional to the logarithm of the magnitude of the network function with $s = j\omega$. The analogs are then

$$V(jv) \quad \text{and} \quad \ln |Z(j\omega)|$$

zeros of $Z(s)$ and $-I$ probe locations

poles of $Z(s)$ and $+I$ probe locations

The logarithm of a complex quantity W is

$$\ln W = \ln |W| + j \operatorname{Arg} W$$
(9.56)

The real part of $\ln W$ has the form of the terms in the expression for V_t, suggesting that this potential be regarded as the real part of a *complex potential*

$$W = V + jU$$
(9.57)

with V and U at right angles when plotted in the w plane. Since contours of constant potential in the w plane (equipotential lines) are at right angles to the direction of current, U represents current in a given path.*   Hence another pair of useful analogs is

$$U(jv) \qquad \text{and} \qquad \text{Arg } Z(j\omega)$$

Figure 9-29 shows four probe distributions and the corresponding potential variations along the imaginary axis (jv) which are analogous

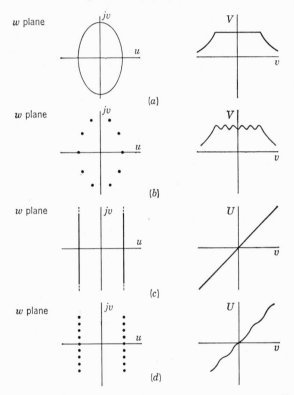

Fig. 9-29. Four distributions of current probes and the corresponding potential distributions.

to variations of the magnitude or phase of $Z(j\omega)$.   In (a) an infinite number of probes form an elliptically shaped figure.   The potential magnitude, V, is constant within the ellipse and falls off outside it, giving an approximation to a constant.   If only a finite number of probes are used, as in (b), then the potential distribution is similar to that of (a) but with small ripples.   Figure 9-29(c) shows two parallel lines of current probes.   The function U for this distribution increases linearly and corresponds to a linear phase increase for $Z(j\omega)$.   A finite number of probes replacing the infinite number of (c) are shown in (d)

* If the resistive sheet is replaced by a dielectric material, U represents flux.

and result in a rippling kind of approximation to the linear phase characteristic.

The potential analogy was first employed in network theory by Bode in 1940 and was used by Hansen and Lundstrom* in 1945. Tuttle and others† have made extensive use of it in theoretical studies in network synthesis.

The potential analogy has an interesting application in the experimental determination of network functions. In this use of the potential analog as a computer,‡ a number of changes are made in the system of Fig. 9-28. A metallic ring surrounds a sheet of resistance paper at some convenient radius, effectively transforming the rectangular coordinate system of Fig. 9-28 into the coordinates of the Smith chart of transmission-line theory. The potential of the imaginary axis in the w plane is scanned rapidly by inserting tiny probes, commonly phonograph needles, along the axis and then commutating the potential of the probes at a rate synchronized with the sweep of a cathode-ray oscilloscope. With this potential distribution displayed as the displacement of the oscilloscope, the current probes corresponding to the poles and zeros are manipulated in position until the oscilloscope trace matches some prescribed variation of the magnitude of the network function with frequency. Current probes not used in a particular study are located at infinity (the metallic ring) so that the number of poles is equal to the number of zeros (a property of rational network functions) and the current directed into the sheet equals that directed out.

The analog serves to transfer to the beginning student a "feel" or an intuition for network functions that he may already have for electrostatic problems.

FURTHER READING

A very comprehensive treatment of approximation is contained in Chapters 13, 14, 15, and Appendix A of Tuttle's *Network Synthesis*, Vol. I. The subject

* W. W. Hansen and O. C. Lundstrom, "Experimental determination of impedance functions by the use of an electrolytic tank," *Proc. I.R.E.*, **33**, 528–534 (1945). See also E. C. Cherry, "Application of the electrolytic tank techniques to network synthesis," *Proc. Symposium on Modern Network Synthesis*, Polytechnic Institute of Brooklyn, **1**, 140–160 (1952).

† Tuttle, *Network Synthesis*, Vol. I, Chapter 14. See also S. Darlington, "The potential analogue method of network synthesis," *Bell System Tech. J.*, **30**, 315–365 (1951).

‡ Such a computer is described by R. E. Scott, "Network synthesis by the use of potential analogs," *Proc. I.R.E.*, **40**, 970–973 (1952). A commercial computer of this type is manufactured by Electro-Measurements, Inc., Portland, Oreg.

of the relationship of the parts of network functions—including a graphical procedure—is treated by Bode, *Network Analysis and Feedback Amplifier Design*, Chapters 14 and 15, and explicit relationships between the parts are given in Chapter 14.

An excellent treatment of approximation using asymptotic straight lines is given by Truxal in *Automatic Feedback Control System Synthesis*, pp. 345–375. See also H. M. James, N. B. Nichols, and R. S. Phillip, *Theory of Servomechanisms* (Vol. 25 of the Radiation Laboratory series), McGraw-Hill Book Co., New York, 1947, pp. 163–179. A method for improving the accuracy of approximations is given by J. G. Linvill in "The selection of network functions to approximate prescribed frequency characteristics," MIT RLE Report 145, March 14, 1950, and in "The approximation with rational functions of prescribed magnitude and phase characteristics," *Proc. I.R.E.*, **40**, 711–721 (1952). First-degree factors are treated under the heading "corner plots" by W. L. Everitt and G. E. Anner in *Communication Engineering*, 3rd ed., McGraw-Hill Book Co., New York, 1956, pp. 515–530. For further advanced reading on the subject of approximation in general, the review paper by Stanley Winkler, "The approximation problem of network synthesis, *IRE Trans.*, **CT-2**, 5 (1954), listing some 240 references, is recommended.

PROBLEMS

9-1. The specification function is defined as

$$R(\omega) = \begin{cases} 1 - \omega, & 0 \le \omega \le 1 \\ 0, & \omega \ge 1 \end{cases}$$

A rational function approximation is required such that the magnitude of the maximum error is 0.1 from $\omega = 0$ to $\omega = 2$, and $R(\omega) \ge 0$ for all ω. Use the cut-and-try method of Section 9.2 to find $R(\omega)$. (*Note:* The solution of this problem will require the use of a desk calculator or the corresponding hand calculations. A slide rule is generally inadequate for the solution of such problems.)

9-2. For the $R(\omega)$ of Prob. 9-1, determine the positive real function, $Z(s)$.

9-3. The specification function is

$$R(\omega) = \begin{cases} \sqrt{1 - \omega^2}, & 0 \le \omega \le 1 \\ 0, & \omega \ge 1 \end{cases}$$

and the allowable error is 0.1 unit from $\omega = 0$ to $\omega = 2$. Use the cut-and-try method of Section 9.2 to find $R(\omega)$. See the note of Prob. 9-1.

9-4. From the $R(\omega)$ found in Prob. 9-3, find the positive real function, $Z(s)$.

9-5. Repeat Prob. 9-1 for the specification function

$$R(\omega) = 1/\sqrt{\omega}, \qquad \omega \ge 0$$

with the same error tolerance, 0.1 unit, from $\omega = 1$ to $\omega = 5$.

9-6. Two frequencies, $\omega_1 = 1$ radian/sec and $\omega_2 = 10$ radians/sec, are identified on a logarithmic scale.

   (a) What is the frequency at one-half of the linear distance between these two points?
   (b) At one-third and two-thirds of the linear distance?
   (c) At one-fourth and three-fourths of the linear distance?

9-7. A straight line on semilogarithmic coordinates is plotted with a slope of 6 db/octave instead of the more accurate $20 \times 0.30103 = 6.0206$ db/octave. How many octaves before the difference between the true and approximate line is 1 db?

9-8. A new interval is invented in which one frequency is sixteen times the other. The interval is called the sexadecade. What value of slope in decibels per sexadecade corresponds to 6 db/octave?

9-9. The straight-line characteristic shown in Fig. P9-9 is h db high and the sides have slopes of $\pm 6n$ db/octave. Determine the frequencies ω_1 and ω_2 as a function of h, n, and T.

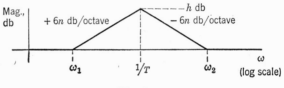

Fig. P9-9

9-10. The straight lines forming the characteristic shown in Fig. P9-10 have slopes of 0 and ± 6 db/octave with the line at low and high frequencies at the 0 db level. Break frequencies are identified at ω_1, ω_2, ω_3, and ω_4. The level at the interval ω_2 to ω_3 is at $-a$ db. Find as many relationships as you can between ω_1, ω_2, ω_3, ω_4, x, and a.

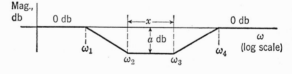

Fig. P9-10

9-11. A log-log duplex vector (or equivalent) slide rule can be used for computation of the magnitude and phase of the 1st-degree factor $j\omega T + 1$, following a procedure outlined in James, Nichols, and Phillips (see Further Reading). Outline this method in your own words, and use it to compute the magnitude and phase for $\omega T = 0.75$.

9-12. Consider the network function

$$G(j\omega) = \frac{j\omega T_2 + 1}{j\omega T_1 + 1}, \qquad T_1 > T_2$$

Show that the magnitude characteristic of this function has odd symmetry and the phase has even symmetry about the geometrical mean frequency, $\omega_a = 1/\sqrt{T_1 T_2}$. Show that the error between the actual and asymptotic curves is 0 at the geometrical mean frequency.

9-13. Consider a network function given by the equation

$$G(j\omega) = \frac{(\alpha - \frac{1}{2}) + j\omega}{(\alpha + \frac{1}{2}) + j\omega}$$

which has the magnitude characteristic illustrated in Fig. P9-13.

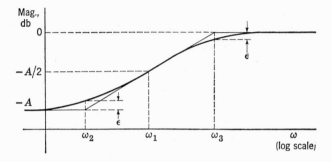

Fig. P9-13

(a) Show that ϵ as identified in the figure has the value

$$\epsilon = 10 \log \frac{\omega_3{}^2 + (\alpha + \frac{1}{2})^2}{\omega_3{}^2 + (\alpha - \frac{1}{2})^2} \quad \text{db}$$

(b) Show that the geometrical mean frequency is ω_1 in

$$\omega_1{}^2 = \omega_2 \omega_3 = \alpha^2 - \frac{1}{4}$$

and also that

$$\frac{\omega_3}{\omega_2} = \left(\frac{\alpha + \frac{1}{2}}{\alpha - \frac{1}{2}}\right)^{2\alpha}$$

(c) Show that at the frequency ω_1 the slope of the magnitude characteristic is a maximum and is

$$S = 3.01/\alpha \quad \text{db/octave}$$

(d) Show that the maximum value of phase occurs at the frequency ω_1 and is

$$\phi_m = \frac{1}{2}\pi - 2 \tan^{-1}\left(\frac{\alpha - \frac{1}{2}}{\alpha + \frac{1}{2}}\right)^{1/2}$$

For an interesting discussion of how these equations may be used in approximation, see an article by A. D. Bresler.*

* *Proc. I.R.E.*, **40**, 1724 (1952).

9-14. For the 2nd-degree magnitude curves of Fig. 9-18, show that the maximum magnitude has the value

$$20 \log \frac{1}{2\zeta \sqrt{1 - \zeta^2}} \quad \text{db}$$

for $\zeta \leq 0.707$.

9-15. Show that the maximum magnitude of the curves shown in Fig. 9-18 occurs at the frequency

$$\omega_M = \sqrt{1 - 2\zeta^2}, \quad \zeta < 0.707$$

9-16. Show that the magnitude of the curves in Fig. 9-18 has the following value at the break frequency:

$$20 \log \frac{1}{2\zeta} \quad \text{db}$$

9-17. For each of the following network functions, sketch the straight-line asymptotic magnitude curves and the phase angle. Use 3 or 4 cycle semilog paper.

(a) $G(s) = \dfrac{100}{s(0.01s + 1)(0.001s + 1)}$

(b) $G(s) = 50 \dfrac{(0.025s + 1)}{s(0.05s + 1)}$

(c) $G(s) = 192 \dfrac{s^2}{(0.16s + 1)(0.47s + 1)}$

(d) $G(s) = \dfrac{10(0.2s + 1)}{s(s^2 + 2s + 10)}$

9-18. Figure P9-18 shows a curve composed of straight-line segments having slopes of $\pm 6n$ db/octave which approximate given logarithmic magnitude characteristics. Assume that the low- and high-frequency asymptotes extend indefinitely. Find the network function $G(s)$ and evaluate the constant multiplier K.

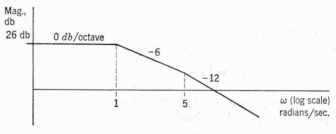

Fig. P9-18

9-19. The characteristic represented in Fig. P9-19 is the type that might be used to approximate the gain of an amplifier. For this characteristic, determine $G(s)$ as a quotient of polynomials in complex frequency s and evaluate K.

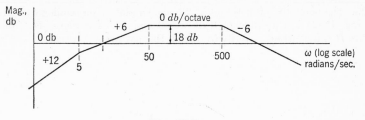

Fig. P9-19

9-20. Scale the network function found in Prob. 9-19 so that $\omega = 1$ becomes 10^6 and the magnitude so that 0 db becomes 20 db.

9-21. The magnitude curve of Fig. P9-21 is ever decreasing with increasing ω, but decreases most rapidly in the frequency interval, $100 \leq \omega \leq 200$. Determine the network function $G(s)$ having this asymptotic characteristic and evaluate the constant K.

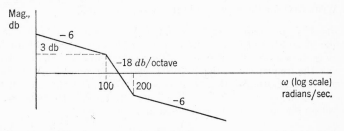

Fig. P9-21

9-22. In contrast to the characteristic of the last problem, the asymptotic magnitude characteristic of Fig. P-22 is ever increasing with increasing ω, attaining the value of 0 db at the frequency $\omega = 10$. Determine $G(s)$ including K.

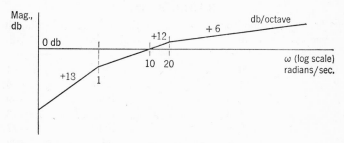

Fig. P9-22

9-23. Write an expression for the function $G(s)$ which corresponds to the asymptotic plot of Prob. 9-9.

9-24. The lead-lag response of Prob. 9-10 (so called because of the associated phase response) in asymptotic form corresponds to what network function $G(s)$?

9-25. The magnitude function, $|G(j\omega)|$, shown plotted on semilog coordinates in Fig. P9-25 has a value of 0 db at 10 and 10,000 radians/sec. In this figure H is a constant. Write $G(s)$ from this asymptotic curve.

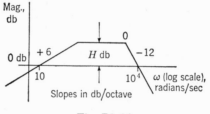

Fig. P9-25

9-26. (*a*) Decompose the response characteristic of Fig. 9-9 in the form of Fig. 9-22(*a*).

(*b*) Write $G(s)$ for the asymptotic response of Fig. 9-9.

9-27. Specifications require that the magnitude of a network function have the value of 20 db and 0 slope from 0 to 10,000 cycles/sec, and for higher frequencies decrease at the rate of -24 db/octave with a ± 1 db tolerance. First scale the frequencies so that 10,000 cycles/sec becomes 1 radian/sec, and then scale the magnitude so that 20 db becomes 0 db. Determine the network function that meets the scaled specifications. Determine the network function meeting the specifications before scaling.

9-28. Plot the points given in Table P9-28 on 3 or 4 cycle semilog graph paper and draw a smooth curve through these points. Approximate this curve using straight-line asymptotes of 0 or $\pm 6n$ db/octave slope and from this approximation determine the network function $G(s)$, including the constant multiplier K. Maintain a tolerance of ± 1 db.

TABLE P9-28

Frequency, radians/sec	Magnitude, db	Frequency, radians/sec	Magnitude, db
1	20	50	-4.2
2	14	70	-6.5
4	8.5	100	-9.5
8	4.0	150	-13.8
10	2.8	200	-17.0
15	0.8	300	-22.5
30	-1.8	500	-40.0
40	-3.0	1,000	-61.5

9-29. Repeat Prob. 9-28 for the data of Table P9-29.

TABLE P9-29

Frequency, radians/sec	Magnitude, db	Frequency, radians/sec	Magnitude, db
1	−20	2,000	3.0
10	0	3,000	3.0
30	8.3	4,000	5.5
50	11.0	5,000	14.0
90	13.0	6,000	0
200	13.6	9,000	−18.5
300	13.0	10,000	−21.5
500	11.0	50,000	−65.0

9-30. Plot the points listed in Table P9-30 on 3 or 4 cycle semilog graph paper and draw a smooth curve through these points. From the given phase characteristics, approximate the network function $G(s)$. What arbitrariness is there in your answer?

TABLE P9-30

Frequency, radians/sec	Phase, degrees	Frequency, radians/sec	Phase, degrees
1	−12	200	−32
2	−22	300	−40
4	−34	400	−46
8	−44	800	−66
10	−44	1,000	−70
20	−36	2,000	−80
40	−27	4,000	−85
80	−22	10,000	−87
100	−24		

9-31. It is required to design a network to use as the load of the pentode amplifier shown in Fig. P9-31. In this form of amplifier, the input and output

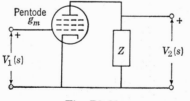

Fig. P9-31

voltages relate to the load impedance by the equation

$$\frac{V_2}{V_1} = -g_m Z(s)$$

where g_m is a constant. The required variation of the magnitude of $|Z(j\omega)|$ is given in Table P9-31. Find a network to meet these specifications within 1 db.

TABLE P9-31

ω, kiloradians/sec	$|Z(j\omega)|$, db	ω, kiloradians/sec	$|Z(j\omega)|$, db
0.1	150	70.0	106.5
1.0	130	100.0	105.0
5.0	117	200.0	103.0
10.0	113	500.0	102.0
20.0	110	1,000.0	102.0
40.0	108	10,000.0	102.0

9-32. Repeat Prob. 9-31 for the $|Z(j\omega)|$ data of Table P9-32.*

TABLE P9-32

ω, radians/sec	$|Z|$, db	θ, degrees	ω, radians/sec	$|Z|$, db	θ, degrees
0.1	100	−4.77	50	80.2	−41.8
0.2	99.8	−9.42	100	77.9	−44.1
0.5	99.1	−21.9	200	75.3	−54.5
1.0	97.2	−35.7	500	69.5	−72.1
2.0	93.6	−45.6	1,000	63.9	−80.6
5.0	88.6	−43.5	2,000	58.0	−85.3
10	86.1	−39.0	5,000	50.1	−88.1
20	83.9	−40.1	10,000	44.1	−89.1

9-33. Repeat Prob. 9-31 for the $|Z(j\omega)|$ data of Table P9-33.

TABLE P9-33

ω radians/sec	$|Z|$, db	θ, degrees	ω, radians/sec	$|Z|$, db	θ, degrees
0.1	114	+89.0	50	151	+39.5
0.2	120	+87.9	100	154	+45.4
0.5	128	+84.8	200	157	+43.7
1.0	134	+79.6	500	160	+43.2
2.0	139	+70.0	1,000	163	+53.7
5.0	145	+49.6	2,000	167	+67.9
10	147	+35.6	5,000	174	+80.5
20	148	+31.3	10,000	180	+85.2

* In typical applications, both magnitude and the corresponding phase would not be given. They are given here to assist in finding the approximation.

9-34. For the vacuum-tube amplifier of Fig. P9-31, the magnitude of the voltage ratio is

$$\left| \frac{V_2(j\omega)}{V_1(j\omega)} \right| = g_m \, |Z(j\omega)|$$

An equalizer application of this amplifier requires that $|Z|$ change with ω approximately as indicated in the data of Table P9-34. It is known that both low- and high-frequency asymptotes have 0 db/octave slopes. In the table, ω is in radians per second.

(a) From the data, find $Z(s)$ such that the numerator polynomial is of 3rd degree. Maintain a tolerance of at least ± 1 db.

(b) Show in detail that the $Z(s)$ you find is positive real. [Note that your solution must satisfy the requirement $|\text{Arg } Z(j\omega)| \leq 90°$.]

(c) Find one network realization.

TABLE P9-34

ω	$|Z|$, db	Arg Z, degrees*	ω	$|Z|$, db	Arg Z, degrees*
0.01	−0.177	0.153	1.30	+6.60	77.9
0.02	−0.179	0.307	1.40	+7.39	73.6
0.03	−0.182	0.460	1.50	+7.95	70.1
0.05	−0.192	0.767	1.70	+8.73	65.3
0.10	−0.283	1.54	2.00	+9.55	61.4
0.20	−0.432	3.15	3.00	+11.7	56.9
0.30	−0.792	4.96	5.00	+14.7	51.4
0.50	−2.29	11.0	10.00	+18.2	37.8
0.90	−2.29	82.6	20.00	+20.0	22.5
1.00	+1.07	89.2	30.00	+20.4	15.6
1.10	+3.66	87.5	50.00	+20.7	9.59
1.20	+5.43	82.9	100.00	+20.8	4.84

* In typical applications, both magnitude and the corresponding phase would not be given. They are given here to assist in finding the approximation.

Two Terminal-Pair
Synthesis
by
Ladder Development

$\cdot$ $\cdot$ $\cdot$ $\cdot$ $\cdot$ $\cdot$ $\cdot$ $\cdot$ $\cdot$ $\cdot$ $\cdot$ $\cdot$ $\cdot$ $\cdot$ *10*

With this chapter, we begin a study of synthesis methods for two terminal-pair networks. Such networks were studied with emphasis on analysis in Chapter 2. There it was shown that input voltage and current could be related to output voltage and current by three network functions—two driving-point and one transfer: z_{11}, z_{12}, z_{22}, or y_{11}, $-y_{12}$, y_{22}. Now of these six functions, z_{11}, z_{22}, y_{11}, and y_{22} are driving-point functions which must be positive real. We recall from problems in Chapter 2 that the transfer functions z_{12} and $-y_{12}$, as well as functions like Z_{12}, $-Y_{12}$, and G_{12}, are not generally positive real, although they can be. We have not yet examined the various conditions that must be satisfied by transfer functions in order that they represent two terminal-pair networks of the LLFPB variety. This property study begins in this chapter.

After giving several of the important properties of transfer functions, we will turn to a study of one significant method of two terminal-pair synthesis. This method is due to Cauer and results in ladder networks which are attractive from an engineering viewpoint in that they are unbalanced and contain no coupled coils. The Cauer ladder development, as it is called, is one of the most direct methods for synthesizing two terminal-pair networks and so most appropriate as an introduction to this subject. The method applies to a network model for which only two functions are known or important: one

248

driving-point and one transfer, say $-y_{12}$ and y_{22} or z_{12} and z_{11}. This model adequately describes a wide variety of engineering problems. In the synthesis of closed-loop control systems, for example, we often require a passive network to meet a transfer function specification with the output terminals of the network connected to the input of a high-impedance electronic amplifier and so not loaded. We found in Chapter 2 that for this model,

$$G_{12} = \frac{z_{12}}{z_{11}} = \frac{-y_{12}}{y_{22}} \qquad (10.1)$$

(See Fig. 10-1.) If we are given G_{12}, or find it by an approximation from a plot of magnitude or phase against frequency, then we may select, say, $-y_{12}$ and y_{22} by observing requirements to be discussed later in this chapter. The ladder development applies to other models

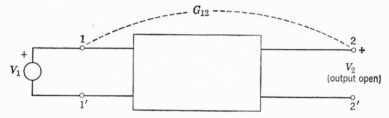

Fig. 10-1. The model of the network to which Eq. 10.1 applies.

than the one cited, e.g., Z_{12} and $-Y_{12}$ for two of the three functions, y_{11}, $-y_{12}$, y_{22} (or the z functions). Such terminated networks will be treated in a later chapter.

The name Cauer is already familiar from the ladder and RC synthesis methods of Chapter 6, and will be encountered repeatedly throughout the remaining chapters. Few men have left a greater imprint on network theory than Wilhelm Adolf Eduard Cauer. Born in 1900, the son of a professor of railroad engineering at Technischen Hochschule, Berlin, Cauer received his doctor's degree in 1924 from the school at which his father taught with the dissertation, "The realization of impedances with prescribed frequency dependence." This dissertation marked the beginning of a lifetime of tireless and devoted effort in the field of network theory, both as a university professor in Berlin and as an engineer in aircraft and telephone industries. Thirty-eight papers and a major textbook published in 1940 attest to his productivity. Cauer met an untimely death in Berlin during the closing days of World War II, the victim of a fate similar to that of Archimedes, who was killed when Syracuse was captured by the Romans in 212 B.C.

10.1 Some properties of $-y_{12}$ and z_{12}

We begin our study of transfer functions from the determinant equations of Chapter 2. The short-circuit admittance functions are

$$y_{11} = \frac{\Delta_{11}}{\Delta}, \qquad -y_{12} = \frac{-\Delta_{21}}{\Delta}, \qquad \text{and} \qquad y_{22} = \frac{\Delta_{22}}{\Delta} \qquad (10.2)$$

and the open-circuit impedance functions are

$$z_{11} = \frac{\Delta_{11}'}{\Delta'}, \qquad z_{12} = \frac{\Delta_{21}'}{\Delta'}, \qquad \text{and} \qquad z_{22} = \frac{\Delta_{22}'}{\Delta'} \qquad (10.3)$$

where the Δ's are loop-basis determinants and cofactors, and the Δ''s are node-basis determinants and cofactors. The similarity of the two sets of equations suggests that the conclusions reached for the y's will

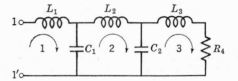

Fig. 10-2. The three-loop network from which the determinant of Eq. 10.4 was written.

hold for the z's. Though we consider only y functions for the remainder of the section, we understand that the same results apply to the z functions. Also, since $\Delta_{21} = \Delta_{12}$ for LLFPB networks, we represent either cofactor as Δ_{12} in the discussion to follow.

The determinants and cofactors of Eqs. 10.2 all have the same general forms: the summation of products of impedances of the forms Ls, $1/Cs$, and R. For the three-loop network, for example, of Fig. 10-2,

$$\Delta = \begin{vmatrix} L_1 s + \dfrac{1}{C_1 s} & \dfrac{-1}{C_1 s} & 0 \\[3mm] -\dfrac{1}{C_1 s} & L_2 s + \dfrac{1}{C_1 s} + \dfrac{1}{C_2 s} & \dfrac{-1}{C_2 s} \\[3mm] 0 & -\dfrac{1}{C_2 s} & L_3 s + R_4 + \dfrac{1}{C_2 s} \end{vmatrix} \qquad (10.4)$$

The expansion of the determinant will give a summation of terms like $L_1 L_2 L_3 s^3$, $L_1 R_4 / C_1$, $(R_4 / C_1{}^2) s^{-2}$, etc.* When these terms are put over

---

* These products may be formed in an elegant manner by means of topological formulas. See "Topological formulas for network functions," W. Mayeda and S. Seshu, Bull. 446, Engineering Experiment Station, University of Illinois (1957).

a common denominator, the resulting general form for Δ will be

$$\Delta = \frac{f_0 s^i + f_1 s^{i-1} + \cdots + f_{i-1} s + f_i}{s^t} \qquad (10.5)$$

and typical cofactors are

$$\Delta_{11} = \frac{g_0 s^j + g_1 s^{j-1} + \cdots + g_{j-1} s + g_j}{s^u} \qquad (10.6)$$

and $\qquad \Delta_{12} = \dfrac{h_0 s^k + h_1 s^{k-1} + \cdots + h_{k-1} s + h_k}{s^v} \qquad (10.7)$

where the f's, g's, h's, i, j, k, and t, u, v are constants. When we form the quotient of Δ and Δ_{11}, the resulting function must be positive real. This places constraints on the difference of t and u, and also on the degrees i and j. Some of the factors of the numerator polynomials of Δ and Δ_{11} may cancel in forming the quotient. We are assured, however, that the quotient of Δ_{11} and Δ simplifies so that y_{11} is a positive real function. But in forming the quotient of Δ_{12} to Δ in forming $-y_{12}$, we have no such assurance. What are the possible forms in which $-y_{12}$ will appear?

We will next show that, except for one special case, the poles of $-y_{12}$ are also poles of y_{11} and y_{22}, but that the converse situation does not follow. Since the functions $y_{11} = \Delta_{11}/\Delta$ and $-y_{12} = -\Delta_{12}/\Delta$ have the same denominator, the only way $-y_{12}$ can have a pole not present in y_{11} is for there to be a cancellation of a factor in Δ_{11} and Δ and not in Δ_{12} and Δ. Now Δ_{12} is not independent of Δ_{11} and Δ_{22}, being given by the equation*

$$\Delta_{12}{}^2 = \Delta_{11}\Delta_{22} - \Delta\Delta_{1122} \qquad (10.8)$$

where Δ_{1122} is the cofactor formed by deleting both the first and second rows and columns. Let us suppose that $s - s_0$ is a factor in both Δ_{11} and Δ so that it is not a factor in y_{11} because of cancellation. Then since

$$\Delta_{11} = (s - s_0)\Delta_{11}'' \qquad \text{and} \qquad \Delta = (s - s_0)\Delta'' \qquad (10.9)$$

we have, from Eq. 10.8,

$$\Delta_{12}{}^2 = (s - s_0)[\Delta_{11}''\Delta_{22} - \Delta''\Delta_{1122}] \qquad (10.10)$$

Now the cofactor Δ_{12} must be a rational function, meaning that the bracketed term of this equation must contribute in some manner

* M. Bocher, *Introduction to Higher Algebra*, The Macmillan Co., New York, 1938, p. 33.

another factor $s - s_0$. Let us separate the various ways in which this contribution can be made into two cases:

Case 1. The factor $s - s_0$ may be in Δ_{22} and in Δ_{1122}, or it may be formed in taking the difference of $\Delta_{11}''\Delta_{22}$ and $\Delta''\Delta_{1122}$ in Eq. 10.10; this case is intended to cover all possibilities except one, namely,

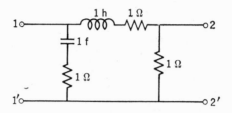

Fig. 10-3. Network for Example 1.

Case 2. The factor $s - s_0$ may be in Δ_{11}'' and in Δ'', and not occur in any other way in Eq. 10.10. This insures that $s - s_0$ is a factor in Δ_{12}, but that $(s - s_0)^2$ is not.

For Case 1, Δ_{12} also contains $s - s_0$ and so this term cancels in $-y_{12}$ also. Since we have ruled out the possibility that $s - s_0$ can cancel in Δ_{11} and Δ and not in Δ_{12} and Δ, we see that a pole of $-y_{12}$ must also be a pole of y_{11} (and of y_{22} by similar arguments). For Case 2, however, Δ_{12} contains $s - s_0$ and there is a single cancellation in forming

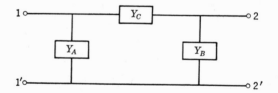

Fig. 10-4. Network analyzed in Eqs. 10.12.

y_{12}, but a double cancellation in the formation of y_{11} or y_{22}. For this case, a pole of y_{12} need not be present in y_{11} or in y_{22}. It turns out that the second case is very special compared to the first and seldom encountered. An example will show that it is a possibility.

Example 1. For the network shown in Fig. 10-3, it is easily verified that

$$y_{11} = 1, \qquad -y_{12} = \frac{1}{s+1}, \qquad \text{and} \qquad y_{22} = \frac{s+2}{s+1} \qquad (10.11)$$

For a simple illustration of our conclusion, consider the π network shown in Fig. 10-4. For this network,

$$y_{11} = Y_A + Y_C$$

$$y_{22} = Y_B + Y_C \qquad (10.12)$$

and $\qquad -y_{12} = Y_C$

Without special cancellation in the sum of $Y_A + Y_C$ and $Y_B + Y_C$ of the type in Example 1, the poles in $-y_{12}$ due to Y_C are seen to be present in both y_{11} and y_{22}. However, there are poles of y_{11} and y_{22}, due to Y_A and Y_B, which are not poles of $-y_{12}$.

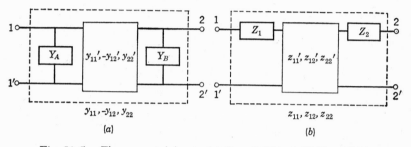

Fig. 10-5. Figures pertaining to (a) Eqs. 10.13 and (b) Eqs. 10.14.

These observations for the simple π network may be amplified by considering the more general network configuration shown in Fig. 10-5(a). Observe that

$$y_{11} = y_{11}' + Y_A$$

$$y_{22} = y_{22}' + Y_B \qquad (10.13)$$

and $\qquad -y_{12} = -y_{12}'$

and for the network shown in Fig. 10-5(b)

$$z_{11} = z_{11}' + Z_1$$

$$z_{22} = z_{22}' + Z_2 \qquad (10.14)$$

and $\qquad z_{12} = z_{12}'$

For the network of Fig. 10-5(a), a subnetwork connected from terminal 1 to terminal 1' appears only in y_{11}, and one connected from terminal 2 to 2' appears only in y_{22}. This suggests that a pole of y_{11} not present in $-y_{12}$ can be realized by a partial fraction expansion as a network in the position of that of admittance Y_A. A pole of y_{22} not present in $-y_{12}$ is similarly realized in the position of the network of admittance Y_B. Poles which are present in y_{11} and/or y_{22} but not in $-y_{12}$ are distinguished by the name *private* poles.

Our conclusions thus far may be summarized in two statements:

(1) Poles of $-y_{12}$ are poles of y_{11} and y_{22} for the usual case, Case 1, but not so for the special case, Case 2.

(2) Poles of y_{11} and y_{22} not present in $-y_{12}$, the private poles, arise from the shunt-connected networks represented by Y_A and Y_B in Fig. 10-5(a) respectively.

In the work to follow, we will make two simplifications. Since we often have some freedom in selecting $-y_{12}$ and y_{22}, say from a given G_{12} specification, we will avoid the special conditions associated with Case 2. And since the private poles in y_{11} and y_{22} are identified with the shunt-connected networks represented by Y_A and Y_B, we will assume that all private poles have been removed, say by a partial fraction expansion, before the main synthesis problem is encountered. In other words, we will assume that the poles of y_{11}, $-y_{12}$, and y_{22} are identical.

The coefficient conditions. Short-circuit admittance functions of the type just described may be written in the forms

$$-y_{12} = \frac{-\Delta_{12}}{\Delta} = \frac{a_0 + a_1 s + a_2 s^2 + \cdots + a_{m-1} s^{m-1} + a_m s^m}{q(s)}$$

(10.15)

$$y_{11} = \frac{\Delta_{11}}{\Delta} = \frac{b_0 + b_1 s + b_2 s^2 + \cdots + b_{n-1} s^{n-1} + b_n s^n}{q(s)}$$ (10.16)

and

$$y_{22} = \frac{\Delta_{22}}{\Delta} = \frac{c_0 + c_1 s + c_2 s^2 + \cdots + c_{l-1} s^{l-1} + c_l s^l}{q(s)}$$ (10.17)

A set of restrictions applying to the coefficients, a_i, b_i, and c_i, of the numerator polynomials will next be derived; this is due to Fialkow and Gerst.*

Consider a ladder network of the kind shown in Fig. 10-6(a) with a common ground connection (and so unbalanced) and without mutual inductance. We wish to represent this ladder network by an equivalent π section, as shown in Fig. 10-6(b). We have no assurance, of course, that the subnetworks of the equivalent π will be positive real and so realizable, but this is not essential to the derivation. We will

---

* A. D. Fialkow and I. Gerst, "The transfer function of general two terminal-pair RC networks," *Quart. Appl. Math.*, **10**, 113–127 (1952). See also P. M. Lewis II, "The concept of the one in voltage transfer synthesis," *IRE Trans.*, **CT-2**, 316–319 (Dec. 1952).

find the equivalent π network by successive application of the T-π transformation having the form,

$$Z_b = \frac{Y_2}{Y_1 Y_2 + Y_2 Y_3 + Y_3 Y_1} \tag{10.18}$$

with reference to the quantities in Fig. 10-7. The first time we make use of the transformation, we will start with the Y_1, Y_2, Y_3 that are positive real. The summation of products of these positive real functions in the denominator of the last equation will not generally result

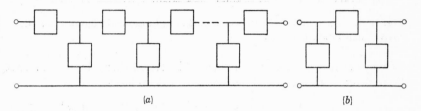

Fig. 10-6. (a) Ladder network with common ground connection and no mutual inductance. (b) The equivalent π network with arm impedances not necessarily positive real.

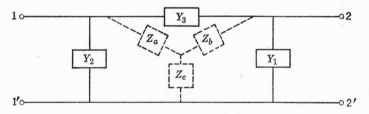

Fig. 10-7. Identification of the arm impedances and admittances for the T and π networks of the T-π transformation.

in a positive real Z_b. But all of the coefficients in Z_b will be positive simply because there is no way to get a negative sign in the product and summation operations. When the transformation is repeated in the process of arriving at the final equivalent π network, the same property will hold for each step up to the last: all coefficients will be real and positive. Nor is it necessary that we start with an unbalanced ladder network to reach the same conclusion. For a more complicated network structure with node bridging, the more general star-mesh transformation* which applies to situations with more branches and nodes than three may be used.

---

*See Guillemin, *Introductory Circuit Theory*, pp. 127–138, for an elaboration of the star-mesh transformation of which the T-π transformation is a special case.

In Chapter 2, the π equivalent of a general two terminal-pair network was derived in terms of the short-circuit admittance functions having the form shown in Fig. 10-8. The arms of the π network are equal to $-y_{12}$, $y_{11} + y_{12}$, and $y_{22} + y_{12}$. By the argument just given,

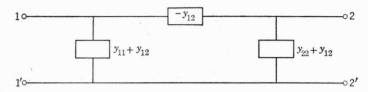

Fig. 10-8. The π network with arm admittances expressed in terms of the short-circuit admittance functions.

we see that it is necessary that the coefficients of these three quantities be positive. Then, from Eqs. 10.15–10.17, we have

$$-y_{12} = \frac{a_0 + a_1 s + a_2 s^2 + \cdots + a_{m-1} s^{m-1} + a_m s^m}{q(s)} \qquad (10.19)$$

$$y_{11} + y_{12} = \frac{(b_0 - a_0) + (b_1 - a_1)s + (b_2 - a_2)s^2 + \cdots}{q(s)} \qquad (10.20)$$

and

$$y_{22} + y_{12} = \frac{(c_0 - a_0) + (c_1 - a_1)s + (c_2 - a_2)s^2 + \cdots}{q(s)} \qquad (10.21)$$

Since all coefficients must be positive, it is required that

$$a_i \geq 0$$
$$b_i \geq a_i \qquad i = 0, 1, 2, \cdots \qquad (10.22)$$
$$c_i \geq a_i$$

which is the desired result. Furthermore, we see that the degree of the numerator polynomial of $-y_{12}$ cannot exceed the degree of the numerator polynomial of y_{11} or y_{22}, whichever is smaller.

The numerator polynomials of the positive real functions y_{11} and y_{22} must have no missing coefficients unless all even or all odd coefficients are missing in the LC case. But this is not true for $-y_{12}$. Any of the coefficients may be missing without violating the coefficient conditions of Eqs. 10.22. In applying the conditions, it should be remembered that the derivation is made for a common denominator for $-y_{12}$, y_{11}, and y_{22}. If a factor should cancel in the formation of any of these functions in the analysis of networks, then it is necessary that the factor be restored before the coefficient condition can be applied. (See Prob. 10-2.)

Important properties of the open-circuit voltage-ratio transfer function may be deduced from the properties of $-y_{12}$ and y_{22} (or z_{12} and z_{11}) just found, since

$$G_{12} = \frac{-y_{12}}{y_{22}} \left(= \frac{z_{12}}{z_{11}} \right) = \frac{N_{12}D_{22}}{D_{12}N_{22}} \tag{10.23}$$

where N and D refer to numerator and denominator. From this equation, we see that the poles of G_{12} are either (1) the zeros of y_{22} which are not also zeros of $-y_{12}$ or (2) poles of $-y_{12}$ which are not also poles of y_{22}. The second case is identified with the degenerate Case 2 which we will neglect as occurring infrequently. Similarly, we see that the zeros of G_{12} are the zeros of $-y_{12}$ plus the private poles of y_{22}. For example, if

$$-y_{12} = \frac{(s + 1.5)}{(s + 1)(s + 3)} \quad \text{and} \quad y_{22} = \frac{(s + 2)(s + 4)}{(s + 1)(s + 3)(s + 5)} \tag{10.24}$$

then
$$G_{12} = \frac{(s + 1.5)(s + 5)}{(s + 2)(s + 4)} \tag{10.25}$$

Since the poles of G_{12} are the zeros of a driving-point function, as this example illustrates, we see that these poles must be in the left half plane or on the imaginary axis and simple. However, the zeros of G_{12} are restricted only in the sense that those of $-y_{12}$ are restricted: they are required to occur in conjugate pairs if complex, but may have any s plane location (for a ladder they may not be in the right half plane, and for grounded networks may not be on the positive real axis*) and may have any multiplicity.

The transfer function G_{12} cannot have a pole at the origin or at infinity. If y_{22} has a zero at the origin, then $-y_{12}$ must have one there too or the coefficient condition is violated with $b_0 = 0$ and $a_0 \neq 0$. The same reasoning applies to the case of a pole of $-y_{12}$ at infinity, leading to the conclusion that y_{22} must also have one there for the coefficient condition to be satisfied. This implies that the numerator of G_{12} cannot be of degree higher than the denominator although it may be lower.

The reason for the conclusions of the last paragraph may be seen in terms of a physical network. If the driving-point admittance func-

---

* P. M. Lewis, II, "The concept of the one in voltage transfer synthesis," *IRE Trans*, **CT-2**, 316–319 (1955).

tion of the network has a pole at the origin, the network must have an inductor in shunt from one terminal to the other.   A pole at infinity likewise implies a shunt-connected capacitor at the driving-point terminals.   In neither case can any network configuration be imagined to produce infinite output, which implies a pole for the transfer function G_{12} at zero or infinite frequency respectively.*

In summary, we have arrived at the following properties for the transfer function G_{12}:

(1) Poles are in the left half of the s plane or on the imaginary axis and simple.

(2) Zeros may have any s plane location, except for the positive real axis, but must always occur in conjugate pairs.

(3) Poles may not be located at the origin or at infinity.

(4) The degree of the numerator may equal but not exceed the degree of the denominator.

Zeros of transmission.   Let the word *input* refer to the voltage or current source connected at terminals 1-1' of a two terminal-pair

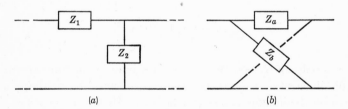

(a)   (b)

Fig. 10-9.   (*a*) In the ladder network, there may be zero transmission if $Z_1 = \infty$ or $Z_2 = 0$.   (*b*) In the lattice (or bridge) network, there is zero transmission if $Z_a = Z_b$.

network; let the word *output* similarly refer to voltage or current measurable at terminals 2-2'.   There is *transmission* through the network when, for finite input, there results an output.   When zero output occurs for finite input, the network is said to have zero transmission.   The frequencies at which this condition occurs are known as *zeros of transmission*.   Zeros of transmission play the major role in two terminal-pair synthesis much as poles do in the one terminal-pair case.

In terms of combination of elements (subnetworks) within a two terminal-pair network, there are a number of ways of producing zeros of transmission.   Combinations of elements may prevent the input from reaching the output by shortening together all transmission paths

* Other properties of G_{12} are given in Chapter 14 for resistively terminated networks.

or by opening all transmission paths by means of a series or parallel resonance. Or there may be a balance, as in a balanced bridge, such that all components of the output transmitted by different paths cancel. See Fig. 10-9.

How do these zeros of transmission relate to the network functions? From the defining equations for z_{12}, $-y_{12}$, and G_{12} of Chapter 2,

$$z_{12} = \frac{V_2}{I_1}\bigg|_{I_2=0} \tag{10.26}$$

$$-y_{12} = \frac{I_2}{V_1}\bigg|_{V_2=0} \tag{10.27}$$

and

$$G_{12} = \frac{V_2}{V_1}\bigg|_{I_2=0} \tag{10.28}$$

we see that zero output, $V_2 = 0$ and $I_2 = 0$, implies a zero for each of these functions. Zeros of transmission are zeros of z_{12}, $-y_{12}$, and G_{12}. For a given network, these three functions have the same zeros as suggested by the relationships of Chapter 2: $-y_{12} = z_{12}/\Delta_z$ and $G_{12} = z_{12}/z_{11} = -y_{12}/y_{22}$.

Table 10-1 summarizes some properties of $-y_{12}$ for grounded networks without mutual inductance.

Let us now turn our attention exclusively to the ladder network. In the ladder, there are no multiple paths by which fractions of the input might meet at the output in such a way as to cancel. The transmission path is direct and can be interrupted only by a short circuit in a shunt arm or an open circuit in a series arm. Now the shunt arm is a short circuit at the pole frequencies of its admittance, whereas the series arm is an open circuit at the pole frequencies of its impedance. This means that we can identify directly the zeros of transmission with the poles of the driving-point functions of the series and shunt arm networks of the ladder. And if we restrict the kinds of elements in the subnetworks of the ladder, we can restrict the s plane locations of the zeros of transmission. Thus:

(1) If all of the subnetworks of the ladder are RC or RL, then all zeros of transmission of the ladder are on the negative real axis of the s plane, since this is the location of the poles and zeros of the impedance of each subnetwork.

(2) Similarly, if all subnetworks are LC, then all zeros of transmission are on the imaginary axis, occurring in conjugate pairs.

To produce zeros of transmission at any other s plane location, it is necessary that either: (1) the ladder subnetworks be RLC, or (2) some

TABLE 10-1
Properties of $-y_{12}$ for Grounded Networks
without Mutual Inductance

1. Poles	Poles of $-y_{12}$ are poles of both y_{11} and y_{22} excluding the special resonance conditions of Case 2. However, all poles of y_{11} and/or y_{22} are not required to be poles of $-y_{12}$; such poles are called private poles.
2. Private poles	Private poles of y_{11} and y_{22} may be realized as shunt-connected networks as in Fig. 10-5(a).
3. Coefficients	The numerator polynomials of $-y_{12}$, y_{11}, and y_{22} must, after the private poles have been removed, satisfy the Fialkow-Gerst coefficient conditions of Eqs. 10.22. (If the coefficient condition is not satisfied, then $-y_{12}$ can be realized only within a multiplicative constant less than 1.) These equations imply that the degree of the numerator polynomial of $-y_{12}$ be equal to or less than the degree of the numerator polynomial of y_{11} or y_{22}, whichever is the lower degree.
4. Zeros	For ladder networks with only two kinds of elements, the zeros of transmission are on the negative real axis for RC and RL networks, and are on the imaginary axis for LC networks.
5. Polynomial form	For LC networks it is necessary that $-y_{12}$ be the quotient of odd to even or even to odd polynomials in order that $z_{12}(j\omega)$ have no real part. This is implied by item 3.

other network structure be used, like networks with node bridging or parallel ladders, in order that there be the required multiple transmission paths at the complex frequencies. In this chapter, we restrict our study to the RC and LC cases.

10.2 The LC ladder development*

For LC networks, the requirements made of z_{12} and z_{11} or $-y_{12}$ and y_{22} in order that they represent a two terminal-pair ladder are now simply stated. The driving-point function must be positive real, requiring that its poles and zeros be simple and interlaced on the imaginary axis. The transfer function z_{12} or $-y_{12}$, which is assumed to have the same poles as the driving-point function, must have all of

---

* W. Cauer, "Filters open circuited on the output side," *Elek. Nachr.-Tech.*, **16(6)**, 161–163 (June 1939).

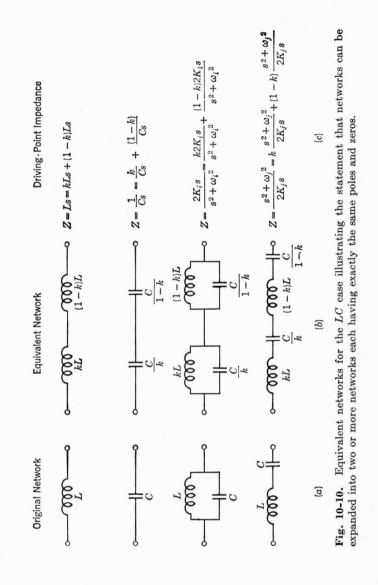

Fig. 10-10. Equivalent networks for the LC case illustrating the statement that networks can be expanded into two or more networks each having exactly the same poles and zeros.

its zeros on the imaginary axis, and the coefficient condition must be satisfied. The zeros need not be interlaced with the poles and it is not necessary that they be simple.

The Cauer ladder development is essentially a method of driving-point synthesis carried out in such a way that the zeros of transmission are realized. In this section, we will first justify the method, and then illustrate it by examples. We will arbitrarily use z_{11} and z_{12} for the LC case, and then $-y_{12}$ and y_{22} for the RC case of the next section.

The partial removal of a pole. The expressions "partial removal of a pole," "removing part of a pole," and "weakening of a pole" are used in describing a basic operation in the ladder development. Although these expressions sound strange at first, suggesting the subdivision of infinity, they are quite reasonable once explained. As described in Chapter 5, the removal of a pole implies the removal of an element or elements that produce the pole. The removal operation is carried out by subtracting an algebraic factor from the function being developed, and then identifying this factor with a simple network. The removal of a pole at infinity, for example, is accomplished by subtracting the term Hs from $Z(s)$ and the identification of Hs as the impedance of an inductor of H henrys. The *partial* removal of a pole means the removal of some fraction of the total network that possibly could be removed without destroying the positive real nature of the function being developed.

To amplify this last statement, consider the four networks shown in Fig. 10-10(a) and (b). The networks in the rows of (a) and (b) are equivalent to each other. Each of the two subnetworks of (b) has exactly the same poles as the networks in (a). Figure 10-11 makes use of these equivalents in illustrating partial pole removal for LC networks. The dashed-line boundaries identify the network remaining when one or more elements have been removed.

The partial removal of a pole is identified with the partial fraction expansion of a positive real function. When a term like one in the partial fraction expansion but with only a fraction of its residue is removed and identified with a network, then a part of the pole is said to have been removed.

Zero shifting by partial pole removal. In Chapter 5 we saw that the removal of a pole caused the zeros of the remaining function to be shifted with respect to the zeros of the original function. The partial removal of a pole produces this same zero-shifting effect. How far can a zero be shifted? What is the direction of the zero shift? These are questions we consider next.

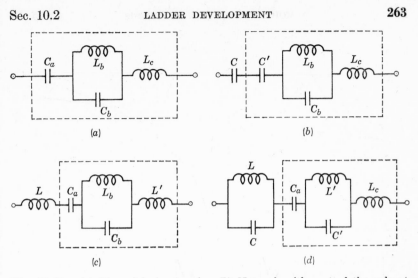

Fig. 10-11. (*a*) The original network. (*b*) Network with part of the pole at zero removed. (*c*) Network with part of the pole at infinity removed. (*d*) Network with part of a finite pole removed.

The partial removal of a pole of $Z(s)$ at infinity results in the formation of a new impedance function given by the equation

$$Z_1(s) = Z(s) - k_pLs \qquad (10.29)$$

where $\qquad L = \lim_{s \to \infty} \dfrac{1}{s} Z(s) \qquad$ and $\qquad k_p < 1 \qquad (10.30)$

and k_p is the fraction of the residue partially removed. Since all zeros of $Z_1(s)$ are located on the imaginary axis of the s plane, these zeros may be found by dealing with reactance functions,

$$X_1(\omega) = X(\omega) - k_p\omega L \qquad (10.31)$$

Zeros of X_1 occur when

$$X(\omega) = k_p\omega L \qquad (10.32)$$

Solutions to this equation may be determined graphically by plotting the reactance function, $X(\omega)$, and the straight line of slope k_pL, as shown in Fig. 10-12(*a*). This figure is useful in revealing the limitations of zero shifting by partial pole removal. All of the zeros are shifted toward the pole being removed, a consequence of the positive slope property of reactance functions. The amount of shift of the zeros depends on the value of k_p, being the largest for $k_p = 1$, and the

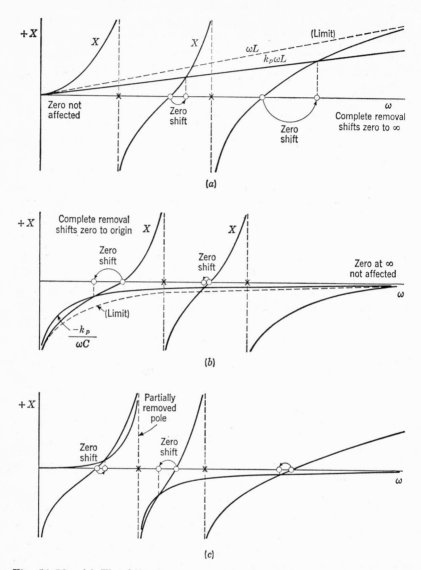

Fig. 10-12. (a) The shift of zeros caused by the partial removal of a pole at infinity, from the solution of $X(\omega) - k_p \omega L = 0$. (b) The shift of zeros caused by the partial removal of the pole at the origin, from the solution of $X(\omega) = k_p/\omega C$. (c) The partial removal of a finite pole.

smallest for $k_p = 0$. The amount of shift is different for the different zeros. The finite (interior) zero of largest value can be shifted any amount, since complete removal of the pole shifts this zero to infinity. Other zeros can be shifted only a limited distance along the frequency axis, the limit being the intersection of the $X(\omega)$ curve with the line of slope L (the dashed straight line of the figure).

Similar analysis shows that the removal of a part of a pole at the origin gives a new impedance function whose zeros are defined by the intersections of the plots of $X(\omega)$ and $-k_p/\omega C$ with ω,

$$X(\omega) = -k_p/\omega C \qquad (10.33)$$

The consequent shifting of the zeros is illustrated in Fig. 10-12(b). The final kind of pole remaining for LC networks is that occurring at a finite, nonzero frequency. In the partial fraction expansion of the impedance function, such poles result in factors of the form

$$Z_2(s) = \frac{2K_i s}{s^2 + \omega_i{}^2} \qquad (10.34)$$

The zeros of the function that results for the partial removal of terms of this form are defined by the intersection of the reactance curves, $X(\omega)$ and $X_2(\omega)$, given by the equation

$$X(\omega) = \frac{-k_p 2K_i \omega}{\omega^2 - \omega_i{}^2} \qquad (10.35)$$

as shown in Fig. 10-12(c).

A comparison of these three cases from the reactance plot analyses of Fig. 10-12 results in the following general observations:

(1) The partial removal of a pole shifts the zero toward that pole, the amount of shift depending on the value of k_p and the proximity of a zero to that pole.

(2) In no case can a zero be shifted beyond an adjacent pole. Typically, the shift can be only a fraction of that distance.

(3) The complete removal of a pole at infinity shifts the adjacent zero to infinity, the complete removal of a pole at the origin shifts the adjacent zero to the origin, and the complete removal of a finite pole shifts an adjacent zero toward the position of the removed pole [the other zero vanishing with the pole to maintain the equality of the number of zeros (including those at zero and infinity) to the number of poles]. These limiting situations are helpful in visualizing the effects of partial pole removals.

(4) The partial or complete removal of a pole at the origin does not affect a zero at infinity, nor does the partial or complete removal of a pole at infinity affect a zero at the origin.

(5) There are limits on the amount a given partial pole removal can shift a given zero. However, by using several steps of zero shifting (by weakening several poles or by successive weakening of poles of impedance and admittance), some zero can be moved to any location on the imaginary axis of the s plane.

How does the zero shifting just discussed tie in with the synthesis method under study? In the Cauer method, a zero of z_{11} (or $1/z_{11}$) is shifted by the partial removal of an appropriate pole so that it coincides with a zero of z_{12}. This is a zero-shifting step. In the zero-producing step, the pole of the reciprocal function corresponding to

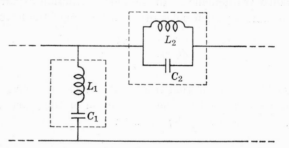

Fig. 10-13. Zero-producing LC networks for the shunt position (L_1 and C_1) and series position (L_2 and C_2).

the shifted zero is completely removed. A pole of impedance is removed as a series network; and similarly a pole of admittance is removed as a shunt network. These operations are repeated until all of the zeros of transmission are realized and the driving-point function is completely developed.

Zero producing by complete pole removal. A subnetwork in a shunt position must have zero impedance at the frequency of the zero of transmission, and a series subnetwork must have infinite impedance at such a frequency. For the LC case, a series connection of L and C has zero impedance at its resonant frequency, $\omega = 1/\sqrt{LC}$; this network is used in the ladder development in a shunt position to produce a zero of transmission. The parallel connection of L and C has infinite impedance when in resonance (sometimes called antiresonance) and is similarly used in a series position. These networks, shown in Fig. 10-13 in appropriate positions, are the two used for zero-producing sections for LC networks.

Let us now bring these several features of the ladder development into focus by a specific example.

Example 2. An LC network is to be synthesized to satisfy the following open-circuit impedance functions:

$$z_{11} = \frac{(s^2 + 9)(s^2 + 25)}{s(s^2 + 16)} \tag{10.36}$$

and

$$z_{12} = \frac{(s^2 + 1)(s^2 + 4)}{s(s^2 + 16)} \tag{10.37}$$

Both functions have the same poles and the coefficient condition of Eqs. 10.22 is satisfied at least for z_{11} and z_{12} (z_{22} is not given). The poles and zeros of z_{11} and $1/z_{11}$ in comparison with z_{12} are shown in Fig. 10-14. From this

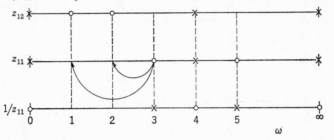

Fig. 10-14. Pole-zero configuration for the specifications of Example 2, with two possible zero shiftings indicated.

figure, we see that the zero of z_{11} at $s = j3$ can be shifted to $s = j1$ or $s = j2$ by the partial removal of the pole at the origin. There is no doubt that either shift can be accomplished since the total removal of the pole at the origin shifts the zero all of the way to the origin. Suppose that we choose to produce a zero in the new impedance function at $s = j2$. The new function is

$$z_1(s) = z_{11}(s) - k_p \frac{K_0}{s} \tag{10.38}$$

In order that $z_1(s)$ have a zero at $s = j2$, it is necessary that

$$z_{11}(j2) - k_p \frac{K_0}{j2} = 0 \tag{10.39}$$

from which we find that

$$k_p K_0 = j2 \frac{5 \times 21}{j2 \times 12} = \frac{35}{4} \tag{10.40}$$

Since the residue at the pole at the origin, K_0, is

$$K_0 = s z_{11} \Big|_{s=0} = \frac{9 \times 25}{16}$$

then

$$k_p = \frac{k_p K_0}{K_0} = \frac{28}{45} \tag{10.41}$$

which is less than 1 as required. The new impedance function is

$$z_1(s) = z_{11}(s) - \frac{35}{4s} \tag{10.42}$$

corresponding to the removal of a series capacitor of value $C_1 = \frac{4}{35}$ farad, or

$$z_1(s) = \frac{s^4 + 25.25s^2 + 85}{s(s^2 + 16)} = \frac{(s^2 + 4)(s^2 + 21.25)}{s(s^2 + 16)} \tag{10.43}$$

The $s^2 + 4$ numerator factor was anticipated, of course, since the objective of our operations was to produce a zero in the driving-point function at $s = j2$.

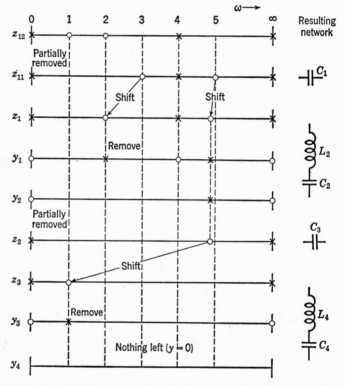

Fig. 10-15. Zero-shifting and zero-producing operations in the synthesis of a ladder network in Example 2.

We have completed the zero-shifting step and can now carry out the zero-producing operation. This is done by removing the pole of $y_1(s) = 1/z_1(s)$ at $s = j2$. Thus

$$y_1(s) = \frac{s(s^2 + 16)}{(s^2 + 4)(s^2 + 21.25)} = \frac{12s/17.25}{s^2 + 4} + \frac{5.25s/17.25}{s^2 + 21.25} \tag{10.44}$$

This removal gives the new admittance function

$$y_2(s) = \frac{5.25s/17.25}{s^2 + 21.25} \tag{10.45}$$

which must be expanded in such a way to realize the other transmission zero. Our progress to this point is summarized in Fig. 10-15. From this figure, we can see what should be done next. The admittance function $y_2(s)$ has a pole at $\omega = (21.25)^{1/2}$. The reciprocal function, $z_2(s) = 1/y_2(s)$, has a zero at this frequency which we can shift as near to the origin as we like by the

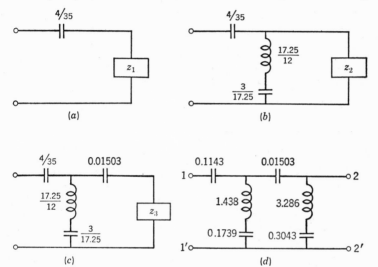

Fig. 10-16. Four stages of the ladder development of Example 2. The final network is shown in (d).

partial removal of the pole at $s = 0$. Shifting this zero to $s = j1$ is accomplished by starting with the impedance

$$z_2(s) = \frac{s^2 + 21.25}{5.25s/17.25} \tag{10.46}$$

which may be separated as

$$z_2(s) = \frac{20.25}{5.25s/17.25} + \frac{s^2 + 1}{5.25s/17.25} = k_p{'} \frac{K_0{'}}{s} + z_3(s) \tag{10.47}$$

where $k_p{'} = 0.953$, and the zero of transmission at $s = j1$ is produced from the admittance $y_3 = 1/z_3$, or

$$y_3(s) = \frac{5.25s/17.25}{s^2 + 1} = \frac{1}{\dfrac{17.25}{5.25}\dfrac{1}{s} + \dfrac{17.25}{5.25}s} \tag{10.48}$$

These concluding steps in the ladder development are also shown in Fig. 10-15. The ladder network at the various stages of development is shown in Fig. 10-16.

10.3 Other considerations

The poles of z_{12}. We know that the poles of z_{12} will be the same as those of z_{11} providing the ladder network is developed in such a way as to avoid starting or terminating in a series subnetwork (a shunt subnetwork when developing y_{11}). This requirement is illustrated by Fig. 10-17 for the development of z_{11} and y_{11}. It was discussed in

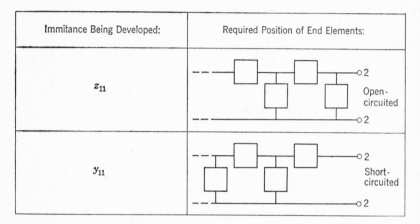

Immitance Being Developed:	Required Position of End Elements:
z_{11}	Open-circuited
y_{11}	Short-circuited

Fig. 10-17. Required position of end elements in the ladder development.

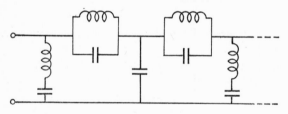

Fig. 10-18. General LC ladder network.

Section 10.1 in connection with the subnetworks identified with the private poles of z_{11}. We are, therefore, assured that the pole specifications of z_{12} are satisfied simultaneously with the zero specifications. Even though we have this assurance, it may be difficult at first to see why a zero-shifting section in the ladder is not *also* zero producing (why, for example, a parallel LC section in a series position resulting from zero shifting does not produce a zero of transmission at its pole frequency). What, we might ask, distinguishes zero-shifting and zero-producing subnetworks in the general LC ladder network such as that shown in Fig. 10-18?

A heuristic answer to this question starts with the defining equation for z_{12},

$$z_{12} = \frac{V_2}{I_1}\bigg|_{I_2=0} \qquad (10.49)$$

If we let the current source driving the network have a value of $I_1 = 1$ ampere for all frequencies, this equation simplifies to

$$z_{12} = V_2 \qquad (10.50)$$

and frequencies for which $V_2 = 0$ are zeros whereas those giving $V_2 = \infty$ are poles. Now when we have a short-circuited shunt arm

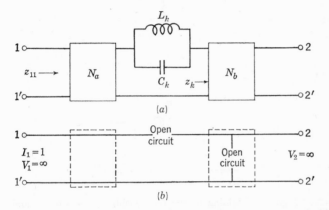

(a)

(b)

Fig. 10-19. (a) A ladder network with a zero-shifting subnetwork identified which is resonant at a pole frequency. (b) The equivalent network at the pole frequency if the $L_k C_k$ network is realized by partial pole removal.

or an open-circuited series arm in the ladder, $V_2 = 0$ and a zero of z_{12} is indicated. If $I_1 = 1$ at pole frequencies, then V_1 will be infinite. What about V_2 and so z_{12} at these pole frequencies? If a pole of z_{11} is partially removed, it must be done by a network like that shown in Fig. 10-19(a) because a shunt-connected LC series section results from the partial removal of an admittance pole and so has no bearing on the poles of the impedance z_{11}. At the pole frequency, $\omega = 1/\sqrt{L_k C_k}$, the impedance looking back into N_a from the $L_k C_k$ combination is finite. Since the $L_k C_k$ section results from the *partial* removal of a pole, the driving-point impedance of the network N_b, call it z_k, also contains this same pole and so is an open circuit. Then the equivalent network at the pole frequency is that shown in Fig. 10-19(b). The voltage V_2 is infinite because of voltage divider action, and $V_2 = \infty$ indicates a pole of z_{12}. Furthermore, there *is* transmission at the pole frequencies. We see that so long as there is partial pole removal, there is never a zero of transmission at a pole frequency.

Similar conclusions may be reached regarding the zeros of z_{11}. Such zeros will be poles of some admittance function, y_k, which may be partially removed, as shown in Fig. 10-20(a). At a zero frequency, L_k and C_k will be in resonance and so appear to be a short circuit. However, the network to the right of L_k and C_k will also have zero impedance at the same frequency provided that the pole of y_k has been partially removed. That such a network can have output voltage

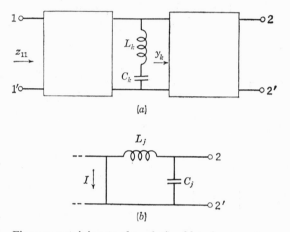

Fig. 10-20. Figures pertaining to the relationship of zeros of z_{11} and zeros of transmission. In (a), L_k and C_k resonate at a zero frequency of z_{11}, but $1/y_k = 0$ at that frequency due to partial pole removal. In (b), L_j and C_j resonate at the same frequency at which L_k and C_k are equivalent to a short circuit, and the voltage across C_j is not zero so that there is not a zero of transmission.

despite the short circuit is illustrated in Fig. 10-20(b). The L_j and C_j network is in resonance and so represents a short circuit in parallel with that due to L_k and C_k. However, the voltage across C_j which is the voltage V_2 will be finite and nonzero. Hence there is transmission at frequencies which are the zeros of z_{11}.

Finally, we observe that good engineering design requires that we avoid situations in which too great a part of any pole is removed, for then the parasitic loss in the elements may obscure the pole, producing thereby an unwanted zero of transmission. Rather than overweakening any one pole, the required zero shifting can be accomplished by a number of shifting steps, even though the cost is that more elements will be required in the network.*

* F. F. Kuo, "Sensitivity of transmission zeros in RC network synthesis," 1959 *IRE Convention Record*, Pt. 2, pp. 18–22.

Is the method general?   If the degree of the denominator of
z_{12} is n, then z_{12} has n zeros of transmission, counting those at zero
and infinity.   Since the poles of z_{11} and z_{12} are the same, we see that
the total number of zeros of transmission is always equal to the degree
of the denominator of z_{11} and so to the number of non-infinite poles
of z_{11}.   We thus have just the right number of poles of z_{11} to spend in
realizing the zeros of z_{12}.   Can we be assured that we need spend only
one pole in getting one zero of transmission so that the ladder development will end with all zeros of transmission realized?

The zero-shifting step, while it gives network elements, does *not*
reduce the degree of the numerator or denominator of the impedance
being developed.   On the other hand, a pole and zero* of the driving-
point impedance are removed in the zero-producing step.   When a
pole and a zero in the range $\omega = 0$ to $\omega = \infty$ are removed, the conjugate pole and zero are also removed, meaning that the degree of both
numerator and denominator of the driving-point function is reduced
by 2.   This reduction of degree by 2 produced two (conjugate) zeros
of transmission.   We see that the degree-reducing steps are identified
only with the zero-producing operation, and there is no danger that
z_{11} will be developed before all zeros of transmission are produced.
In this sense, the method is general.

The scale factor of z_{12}.   Even though the ladder development
always realizes the poles and zeros of z_{12} in developing z_{11}, the Cauer
method gives no control over the scale factor of z_{12}.   Different network realizations may have different z_{12} scale factors.   Since $G_{12} =$
z_{12}/z_{11} and z_{11} is always realized exactly, the scale factor of the voltage-
ratio transfer function is proportional to the scale factor of z_{12}.   In
applications like servomechanisms, a large scale factor of G_{12} is desired
for otherwise it must be compensated by the gain of an electronic
amplifier.   This need for a large scale factor of z_{12} has resulted in the
definition of a quality factor which is identified with each network
realization, a frequency-independent constant multiplier defined by
the equation†

$$k_m = \frac{z_{12} \text{ from network realization}}{z_{12} \text{ from specifications}} \tag{10.51}$$

The constant k_m is ordinarily computed from the given z_{12} and from
the realized network.   Rather than going to the trouble of computing

---

* The zero disappears to preserve the balance of poles and zeros (counting
those at 0 and ∞) in quotients of polynomials.

† In some cases, it is more meaningful to define a factor as the quotient of z_{12}
from a network realization to the z_{12} with the largest scale factor allowable by the
Fialkow-Gerst condition.

z_{12} for the network realized, we select some frequency at which z_{12} may be computed from the network for comparison with the value of z_{12} of the specifications at the same frequency. It is, of course, necessary to avoid frequencies corresponding to the zeros and poles of z_{12} which lead to the indeterminate form for k_m. Zero and infinite frequencies, when appropriate, are especially convenient choices, as later examples will show.

The constant k_m is allowed to have any value, larger or smaller than unity, since the scale factor of the specification z_{12} can be arbitrarily small or arbitrarily large.

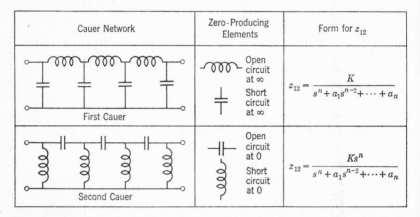

Cauer Network	Zero-Producing Elements	Form for z_{12}
First Cauer	Open circuit at ∞ Short circuit at ∞	$z_{12} = \dfrac{K}{s^n + a_1 s^{n-2} + \cdots + a_n}$
Second Cauer	Open circuit at 0 Short circuit at 0	$z_{12} = \dfrac{Ks^n}{s^n + a_1 s^{n-2} + \cdots + a_n}$

Fig. 10-21. Networks having all zeros of transmission at zero or at infinity.

It is interesting to note that the coefficient condition of Eqs. 10.22 has bearing on the scale factor of z_{12} and so on the constant multiplier, k_m. The maximum value of the scale factor of z_{12} which may be realized by a ladder development is the largest constant k_s which can multiply z_{12} and still permit $k_s z_{12}$ and z_{11} to satisfy the coefficient condition.

Example 3. For the specification functions

$$z_{11} = \frac{s^4 + 10s^2 + 9}{s(s^2 + 4)(s^2 + 16)} \quad \text{and} \quad z_{12} = k_s \frac{s^4 + 61s^2 + 900}{s(s^2 + 4)(s^2 + 16)} \quad (10.52)$$

the maximum possible value of k_s is, from the coefficient condition, $k_s = \frac{1}{100}$ for the given z_{11}. The impedance z_{22}, when known, may impose further restrictions on the scale factor, k_s.

Special cases: all zeros of z_{12} at zero or infinity. The first Cauer and second Cauer forms of LC networks studied in Chapter 5 have a special role in the ladder development. As shown in Fig. 10-21, all of the elements of the first Cauer form produce zeros of transmission at infinity. The second Cauer networks have elements associated with zeros of transmission at zero only, as in Fig. 10-21. If we are given z_{12} with zeros only at the origin or at infinity, or if at some point in the impedance development there remain to be realized only zeros at the origin or infinity, then the remainder of the ladder network will have one of the two Cauer forms and the element values may be found by a routine continued fraction expansion.

From the developed ladder, the constant multiplier, k_m, may be determined for the network realized in Example 2. By inspection of the network shown in Fig. 10-16(d), we see that the behavior of the network is dominated by the shunt-connected inductors at very high frequencies. The equivalent of these two parallel inductors is found from the equation

$$\frac{1}{L_{eq}} = \frac{1}{1.438} + \frac{1}{3.286} = 1 \tag{10.53}$$

where $L_{eq} = 1$ henry. For this equivalent network consisting of a 1-henry inductor in a shunt position, we see that

$$\lim_{s \to \infty} z_{12} = \lim_{s \to \infty} s \tag{10.54}$$

and since this same equation results from the specification function given by Eq. 10.37, we see that

$$k_m = \frac{z_{12}(\infty) \text{ from network realized}}{z_{12}(\infty) \text{ from specifications}} = 1 \tag{10.55}$$

meaning that the specifications are satisfied exactly by the network we have found.

There are many possible forms for the ladder networks synthesized by the Cauer method (see Fig. 10-22), depending on such factors as: (1) the order in which zeros of transmission are realized, (2) the choice that we have in using shunt arms or series arms to realize zeros of transmission, (3) the choice we have in developing impedance or admittance—at least there is this choice after the first step, and (4) whether one or several partial pole removal operations are employed for shifting a given zero. With this number of more or less arbitrary choices to be made in carrying out the synthesis from given specifications, we see that the number of different realizations is indeed large.

Which of the possible realizations should be selected? Factors which might influence a decision include these:

(1) Element values may be more favorable in one ladder structure than in another, in terms of components available from the stockroom.

(2) There is no way of completely controlling z_{22} in the ladder development, but we can compute this function for several alternative networks to see which is best for a particular application.

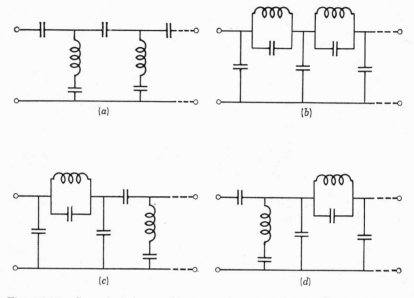

Fig. 10-22. Several of the possible forms of ladder networks developed by the Cauer method.

(3) The constant multiplier, k_m, may be larger for one network than for others. Since this constant is akin to network "gain" in some applications, a large value of k_m is preferred.

10.4   The *RC* ladder development

We will next study the application of the Cauer method to one other two-element-kind case. *RC* ladder networks are regarded to be of more interest than *RL* networks because of their application as compensating devices in feedback control systems* where size and weight considerations often preclude the use of inductors. For variety, our discussion here will be in terms of the short-circuit admittance functions, and with application to synthesis from $G_{12} = -y_{12}/y_{22}$ specifications in mind, we will use y_{22} rather than y_{11}. This means that the

* See Chapter 5 of Truxal's *Automatic Feedback Control System Synthesis*.

discussions of Section 10.1 apply directly while those of Section 10.2, which were in terms of z functions, apply on a *dual* basis.

With the inductor replaced by the resistor as a network element, we must examine the new zero-shifting operations in terms of RC driving-point functions. This requires a knowledge of properties of RC functions which were derived in Chapter 6 and can be summarized in the following statements:

(1) All poles and zeros of $Z(s)$ are simple, are located on the negative real axis of the s plane, and are interlaced. The residue at each pole is real and positive.

(2) The critical frequency of smallest magnitude is a pole which may or may not be at the origin. The critical frequency of largest magnitude is a zero which may or may not be at infinity.

(3) The slope of $Z(\sigma)$ plotted as a function of σ is always negative.

(4) The impedance at zero frequency is greater than or equal to the impedance at infinite frequency,

$$Z(\infty) \leq Z(0) \qquad (10.56)$$

The driving-point admittance function for RC networks has properties which are duals of those given for impedance functions:

(1) All poles and zeros of $Y(s)$ are simple, are located on the negative real axis of the s plane, and are interlaced. The residues at the poles of $Y(s)$ are negative, but the residues of $Y(s)/s$ are positive.

(2) The critical frequency of smallest magnitude is a zero which may or may not be at the origin. The critical frequency of largest magnitude is a pole which may or may not be at infinity.

(3) The slope of $Y(\sigma)$ plotted as a function of σ is always positive.

(4) The admittance at zero frequency is always less than or equal to the admittance at infinite frequency,

$$Y(0) \leq Y(\infty) \qquad (10.57)$$

Zero shifting for RC functions. There are three different operations used for zero shifting in RC driving-point functions. These are:

(1) The removal of a constant, $k_p Z(\infty)$, from $Z(s)$; $k_p \leq 1$.

(2) The removal of a constant, $k_p Y(0)$, from $Y(s)$; $k_p \leq 1$.

(3) The partial removal of a pole from $Z(s)$ or $Y(s)$ like

$$Z_1(s) = Z(s) - k_p \frac{K_i}{s + p_i}, \qquad k_p < 1 \qquad (10.58)$$

where K_i is the residue at the pole p_i.

The first operation is permitted since $Z(\infty)$ is not only smaller than $Z(0)$ but is the smallest value of Re $Z(j\omega)$ so that any fraction of $Z(\infty)$ may be removed and the resulting impedance function will be positive real. In other words,

$$Z_1(s) = Z(s) - k_p Z(\infty), \qquad k_p \leq 1 \tag{10.59}$$

is positive real if $Z(s)$ is positive real, and the zeros of $Z_1(s)$ are defined by the condition,

$$Z(s) = k_p Z(\infty) \tag{10.60}$$

Let us examine the plots of $Z(\sigma)$ and $k_p Z(\infty)$ in Fig. 10-23. The $Z(\sigma)$ plot and the straight line intersect the same number of times as

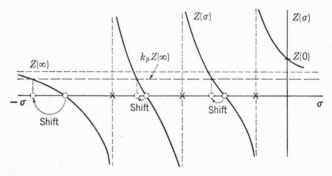

Fig. 10-23. A plot of $Z(\sigma)$ and the constant $k_p Z(\infty)$ showing the shifting of the zeros toward infinity by the partial or complete removal of $Z(\infty)$.

there are zeros of $Z(s)$. Hence the zeros of $Z_1(s)$ as defined by Eq. 10.60 all occur with $s = \sigma$ under the condition

$$Z(\sigma) = k_p Z(\infty) \tag{10.61}$$

Comparing the zeros of $Z_1(s)$ with those of $Z(s)$ in Fig. 10-23 shows that all zeros are shifted toward infinity ($s = -\infty$) by the partial or complete removal of $k_p Z(\infty)$, and that the larger the value of k_p the more the zeros of $Z(s)$ are shifted. Furthermore, the complete removal of $Z(\infty)$, with $k_p = 1$, shifts the zero of largest magnitude all the way to infinity.

Justification of the second operation parallels the first. The constant $Y(0)$ is the minimum value of Re $Y(j\omega)$ and so may be partially or completely removed from $Y(s)$ and the resulting function be positive real. There results an admittance function,

$$Y_1(s) = Y(s) - k_p Y(0), \qquad k_p \leq 1 \tag{10.62}$$

The zeros of $Y_1(s)$ occur with $s = \sigma$ and are defined by the equation

$$Y(\sigma) = k_p \, Y(0) \qquad (10.63)$$

The intersections of the $Y(\sigma)$ curve with the straight line $k_p \, Y(0)$ are shown in Fig. 10-24. We see that the zeros of $Y_1(s)$ are shifted toward the origin ($s = 0$) in comparison with the zeros of $Y(s)$. The amount of shift depends on the value of k_p, and the zero of smallest magnitude is shifted to the origin for $k_p = 1$.

The third operation has already been described by Eq. 10.58 for the impedance case. The partial removal of a finite pole or a pole at

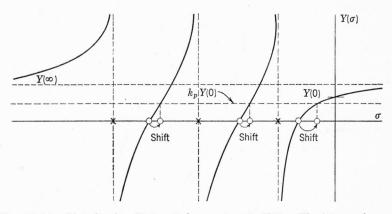

Fig. 10-24. Plot showing $Y(\sigma)$ and the constant $k_p \, Y(0)$. The intersections of these two curves define the new zero positions. Note the shifting toward the origin.

the origin from $Z(s)$ results in a zero shift defined by the condition $Z_1(s) = 0$ in Eq. 10.58, or

$$Z(\sigma) = k_p \, \frac{K_i}{\sigma + p_i} \qquad (10.64)$$

where $p_i = 0$ for the case of a pole at the origin. That these zeros are indeed on the negative real axis of the s plane is shown in Fig. 10-25. Observe from the figure that the partial removal of a pole causes the zeros of $Z_1(s)$ to be shifted toward the partially removed pole in comparison to the zeros of $Z(s)$, the amount of shift depending on the magnitude of k_p.

The conclusions just given for the RC network case bear close resemblance to those for the LC case. In each of the three operations, the partial or complete removal of a constant or a pole results in the shifting of the zeros of the remaining function *toward* the quantity removed, be it $Z(\infty)$, or $Y(0)$, or a pole.

Observe that in the three removal operations we allow $k_p = 1$ for the two constant removal possibilities, but impose the restriction, $k_p < 1$, for the partial pole removal case. By analogy to the LC ladder development of the last section, the zero-shifting operation always corresponds to $k_p < 1$, and the zero-producing step has been identified with $k_p = 1$. But the removal of a constant is not a zero-producing step—a resistor is not resonant at any frequency—and so $k_p = 1$ is permitted. This complete removal of a constant step is frequently

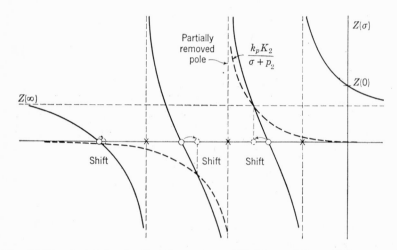

Fig. 10-25. A plot showing that the zeros are shifted toward the partially removed pole, for $k_p < 1$. A similar conclusion is reached from the plot of $Y(\sigma)$.

used in the RC ladder development since it shifts a zero to the origin or to infinity. The removal of a pole operation, on the other hand, can be either zero shifting ($k_p < 1$) or zero producing ($k_p = 1$). The kinds of networks used for the arms of the RC ladder are tabulated in Fig. 10-26. The series or parallel combinations of R and C are in resonance (zero impedance in series, infinite impedance in parallel) at the frequency, $s = -1/RC$. Single capacitors as arms produce zeros of transmission at zero or infinity as shown. Resistors serve only for zero shifting.

We will assume initially that the driving-point function y_{22} has the same poles as $-y_{12}$. Synthesis is accomplished by a procedure*

* See, for example, E. A. Guillemin, "A note on the ladder development of RC networks, *Proc. I.R.E.*, **40**, 482–485 (1952).

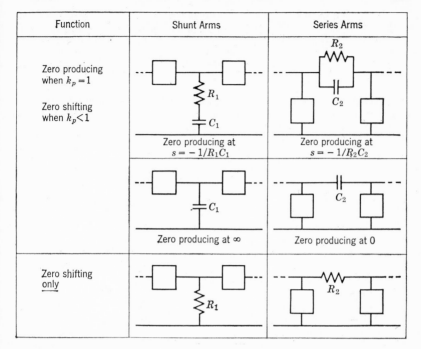

Function	Shunt Arms	Series Arms
Zero producing when $k_p = 1$ Zero shifting when $k_p < 1$	Zero producing at $s = -1/R_1C_1$	Zero producing at $s = -1/R_2C_2$
	Zero producing at ∞	Zero producing at 0
Zero shifting <u>only</u>		

Fig. 10-26.   Series and shunt arm networks used in the RC ladder development.

analogous to that given for the LC case, and will be illustrated by two examples.

Example 4.   Consider the following specification functions:

$$y_{22} = \frac{(s+1)(s+3)}{(s+2)(s+4)} \quad \text{and} \quad -y_{12} = \frac{s(s+\frac{1}{2})}{(s+2)(s+4)} \qquad (10.65)$$

The function y_{22} is clearly positive real, and the coefficient condition is satisfied. From the pole-zero plot of Fig. 10-27, we see that there are two obvious zero-shifting operations for y_{22}. The zero at $s = -1$ can be shifted to either of the zero of transmission locations, $s = -\frac{1}{2}$ or to $s = 0$, by the partial or complete removal of $y_{22}(0)$. There are other possibilities, to be sure, involving multiple shiftings of the zeros; these will be illustrated by Example 5. Suppose that we select the second of the possibilities listed and shift the zero all the way to the origin. This is done by forming the new admittance function:

$$y_1 = y_{22} - y_{22}(0) = y_{22} - \tfrac{3}{8} \qquad (10.66)$$

or $\qquad y_1 = \dfrac{(s+1)(s+3)}{(s+2)(s+4)} - \dfrac{3}{8} = \dfrac{5}{8}\dfrac{s(s+\frac{14}{5})}{(s+2)(s+4)} \qquad (10.67)$

This zero shifting is shown in the second and third rows of Fig. 10-27. Having shifted the zero to the origin, the removal of the corresponding pole, that of

$z_1 = 1/y_1$, will realize one zero of transmission. The residue of the pole at the origin is $\frac{32}{7}$. Removal of this pole in the form of a series arm capacitor leaves a new impedance function z_2:

$$z_2 = \frac{1}{y_1} - \frac{\frac{32}{7}}{s} = \frac{8}{5}\frac{s + \frac{22}{7}}{s + \frac{14}{5}} \tag{10.68}$$

The next step in the development is made evident from the pole and zero record of Fig. 10-27. The zero of $y_2 = 1/z_2$ at $s = -\frac{14}{5}$ can be shifted to

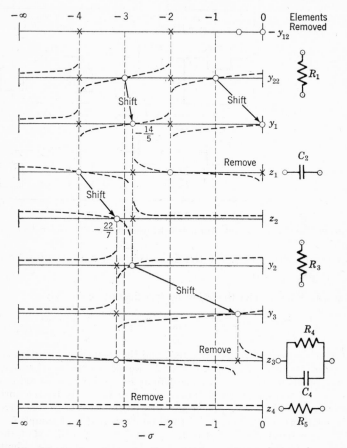

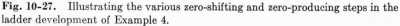

Fig. 10-27. Illustrating the various zero-shifting and zero-producing steps in the ladder development of Example 4.

$s = -\frac{1}{2}$ to realize the second required zero of transmission. This shifting requires the removal of $y_2(-\frac{1}{2}) = \frac{161}{296}$ mho. Thus

$$y_3 = \frac{1}{z_2} - \frac{161}{296} = \frac{3}{37}\frac{s + \frac{1}{2}}{s + \frac{22}{7}} \tag{10.69}$$

The pole of $z_3 = 1/y_3$ at $s = -\frac{1}{2}$ can next be removed in a zero-producing step, giving the parallel RC network made up of R_4 and C_4. To find element values, we expand z_3, giving

$$z_3 = \frac{(37)^2/42}{s + \frac{1}{2}} + \frac{37}{3} \tag{10.70}$$

The last term in this equation is identified with the resistor R_5 which is removed in a series position, and the ladder development is complete, both zeros of transmission having been realized. Four stages in the ladder development of y_{22} are shown in Fig. 10-28. Inspection of the final network, part (d), shows that series arms have been used to produce both zeros of transmission and shunt arms have been used for zero shifting.

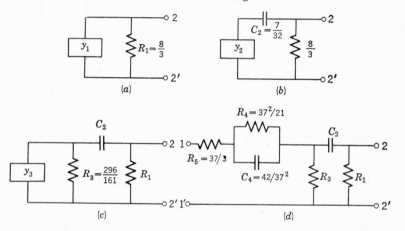

Fig. 10-28. Four stages of the ladder development of y_{22} for Example 4.

From Fig. 10-27, we see that the zero of y_{22} at $s = -1$ might have been shifted to $s = -\frac{1}{2}$ as the first step rather than to $s = 0$. There is yet another interesting possibility which we will next introduce by an example.

Example 5. We begin from the same set of specification functions used for Example 4 (Eqs. 10.65). Let us shift the zero of y_{22} at $s = -1$ to $s = -\frac{1}{4}$, rather than either $s = 0$ or $s = -\frac{1}{2}$. This is a different approach certainly since $s = -\frac{1}{4}$ is not a zero of transmission. Let us examine what this accomplishes from Fig. 10-29. There we see that the function $z_1 = 1/y_1$ has a pole at $s = -\frac{1}{4}$ and a zero at $s = -2$, and that $s = -\frac{1}{2}$ is between this pole and the zero to be shifted. If the pole at $s = -\frac{1}{4}$ is now "weakened" by partial removal, the zero at $s = -2$ can be shifted to the $s = -\frac{1}{2}$ position and so one of the required zeros of transmission can be realized. The function z_2 is next inverted to create the pole at $s = -\frac{1}{2}$ which is completely removed in a zero-producing step. The resulting admittance function y_3 has a zero which can be shifted to the origin by the removal of $y_3(0)$, and the corresponding pole at the origin can be removed to realize the second zero of transmission. The network that results from these operations is shown in Fig. 10-30. With this network and this plan of approach in mind, let us carry out the detailed steps of the ladder development.

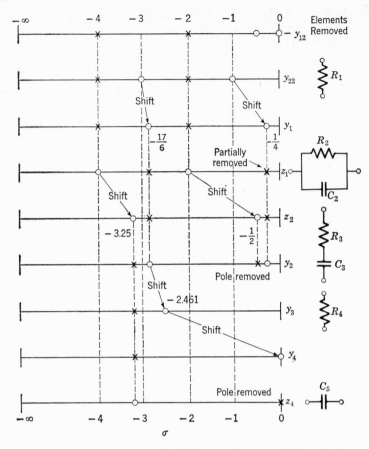

Fig. 10-29. Illustrating the ladder development of Example 5.

The shifting of the zero from $s = -1$ to $s = -\frac{1}{4}$ requires that $y_{22}(-\frac{1}{4}) = \frac{33}{105}$ mho be subtracted from y_{22} to give the admittance function y_1:

$$y_1 = y_{22} - \frac{33}{105} = \frac{72}{105} \frac{(s + \frac{1}{4})(s + \frac{17}{6})}{(s + 2)(s + 4)} \tag{10.71}$$

The next step is the shifting of the zero of z_1 at $s = -2$ to $s = -\frac{1}{2}$ by the partial removal of the pole at $s = -\frac{1}{4}$. This requires that

$$z_1 - \frac{k_p K_1}{s + \frac{1}{4}} = 0 \qquad \text{when } s = -\frac{1}{2} \tag{10.72}$$

which may be solved to find that $k_p K_1 = \frac{105}{32}$, and $k_p = \frac{31}{35}$ which is less than 1 as required. The partial removal of this pole defines the impedance function z_2:

$$z_2 = \frac{1}{y_1} - \frac{\frac{105}{32}}{s + \frac{1}{4}} = \frac{105}{72} \frac{(s + \frac{1}{2})(s + 3.25)}{(s + \frac{1}{4})(s + \frac{17}{6})} \tag{10.73}$$

The residue at the pole of y_2/s at $s = -\frac{1}{2}$ is found to be $\left(\frac{72}{105}\right)\left(\frac{14}{33}\right)$. The removal of this pole as a zero-producing step gives

$$y_3 = y_2 - \frac{\frac{72}{105} \times \frac{14}{33}s}{s + \frac{1}{2}} = 0.3948 \frac{s + 2.461}{s + 3.250} \tag{10.74}$$

This admittance function must be altered in such a way that its zero is shifted to the origin to realize the second zero of transmission located there. This

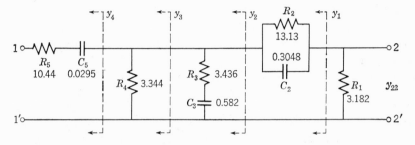

Fig. 10-30. Network realization for Example 5. Element values in ohms and farads.

shifting of the zero at $s = -2.461$ to $s = 0$ is done by the removal of $y_3(0) = 0.2990$ mho from $y_3(s)$, giving

$$y_4 = y_3 - 0.2990 = \frac{0.0958s}{s + 3.25} \tag{10.75}$$

The corresponding impedance function, $z_4 = 1/y_4$, is expanded as follows,

$$z_4 = 10.44 + \frac{1}{0.0295s} \tag{10.76}$$

and the ladder development is complete.

Element values are found from the several equations just given. The resistor R_1 has the value

$$R_1 = \frac{1}{y_{22}(-\frac{1}{4})} = 3.182 \text{ ohms} \tag{10.77}$$

The elements R_2 and C_2 of the zero-shifting network are found from the subtracted factor in Eq. 10.73, which gives $R_2 = 13.13$ ohms and $C_2 = 0.3048$ farad. The elements of the shunt-connected zero-producing network, R_3 and C_3, are found from the subtracted factor in Eq. 10.74 to be $R_3 = 3.436$ ohms and $C_3 = 0.582$ farad. The shunt resistor R_4 which shifts the zero to the origin has the value, from Eq. 10.75, $R_4 = 1/y_3(0) = 3.344$ ohms. The remaining elements, C_5 and R_5, serve to produce the zero of transmission at the origin (R_5 simply completes the development) and have values given in Eq. 10.76 as $R_5 = 10.44$ ohms and $C_5 = 0.0295$ farad. These element values might next be scaled for impedance level or frequency, using techniques in Chapter 2, depending on the nature of the problem from which the specification equations were derived.

Two different RC networks have been found from the same two specification functions. As in the LC case, it is clear from the methods employed that there are a large number of other network realizations. This is a situation which is characteristic of design or synthesis in contrast with analysis. From a large number of possible solutions, we must select one. Our choice will be dictated by such factors as the number and size of the elements and the value of the "gain" factor, k_m. In some cases we might be more interested in *any* solution than in a choice of solutions. The expense for the time consumed in running through several alternative developments might be greater than the added cost of elements of inconvenient size. Amplifiers, which are already in some systems for which we might design networks of the type being studied, can compensate for network loss which is implied by a low value of k_m. The variety of manipulations available, the number of tricks it is possible to use in reducing the number of elements or realizing favorable element sizes, all make ladder network synthesis something of a game of skill, especially for an unusual combination of specifications.

Something should be said of the obvious role of the desk calculator in problems like Example 5. In carrying out the arithmetic of the various steps, it is often helpful to substitute a desk calculator for a slide rule. And with the calculator comes the question of the number of figures to carry through the calculations. In the examples given thus far, nothing has been said about the number of significant figures in the specifications. This being the case, it is not possible to make a statement about the number of significant figures required in the solution. It has become conventional practice to give four to six figures in the network element values. It should be understood by both the designer and the user that once the number of significant figures in the specifications has been established, the meaningless figures in element values should be dropped. If the specifications are accurate to only two places, then it is wasted effort to attempt to realize element values to within more than two or three significant figures.

The calculations in the ladder development sometimes involve small differences of two large numbers. Accuracy difficulties can be avoided by suitable manipulations of the variables in some cases. Rather than anticipate such difficulties in terms of algebraic operations, it is common to carry a large number of significant figures through the calculations so that accuracy is still attained in the small-difference case.

Let us return to the matter of the constant multiplier k_m (also called the gain factor or the loss constant). In RC networks, infinite frequency is often a particularly convenient choice for computation for at infinite frequency the resistor is not changed in value but the capacitor becomes a short circuit. Thus RC networks reduce to simple resistor networks at infinite frequency for many cases. At infinite frequency, the networks found for Examples 4 and 5, those shown in Figs. 10-28(d) and 10-30, reduce to the networks given in Fig. 10-31. If terminals 2-2′ of these networks are short-circuited, $-y_{12}$ may be

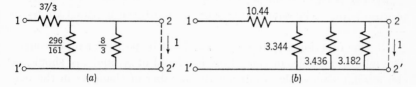

Fig. 10-31. Infinite frequency equivalent networks for (a) the RC ladder of Example 4, (b) the RC ladder of Example 5. These networks are used to compute k_m.

computed by assuming 1 ampere of current in this short circuit and then finding the corresponding input voltage. The value is

$$-y_{12}(\infty) = \frac{I_2}{V_1}\bigg|_{V_2=0} = \frac{1}{V_1}\bigg|_{V_2=0} \tag{10.78}$$

For these two networks, we see that only the series arm resistor has any bearing on the value for $-y_{12}(\infty)$ computed from this equation. Since $-y_{12}(\infty)$ from the specifications is

$$-y_{12}(\infty) = \lim_{s\to\infty} \frac{s(s+\frac{1}{2})}{(s+2)(s+4)} = 1 \tag{10.79}$$

we see that for the network of Example 4

$$k_m = \frac{\frac{3}{37}}{1} = 0.0811 \tag{10.80}$$

and for the network of Example 5

$$k_m = \frac{(1/10.44)}{1} = 0.0957 \tag{10.81}$$

The second network has a slight advantage as far as k_m is concerned.

Synthesis from $G_{12} = V_2/V_1$ specifications. From the equation

$$G_{12} = \frac{V_2}{V_1}\bigg|_{I_2=0} = \frac{z_{12}}{z_{11}} = \frac{-y_{12}}{y_{22}} \tag{10.82}$$

we see that synthesis from G_{12} specifications requires a proper choice of z_{12} and z_{11} or $-y_{12}$ and y_{22}. Such a choice must meet the following conditions:

(1) The poles and zeros of G_{12} must be identified with those of z_{12} and z_{11} or $-y_{12}$ and y_{22}. There are, of course, many possible choices, the most direct being to assign the zeros of G_{12} to be zeros of z_{12} or $-y_{12}$ and the poles to be zeros of z_{11} or y_{22}.

(2) The poles of z_{11} or y_{22} must be selected to make these functions positive real. The same poles will ordinarily be assigned to z_{12} or $-y_{12}$.

(3) The functions z_{12} and $-y_{12}$ need not be positive real, of course. The number of poles of these functions, and of z_{11} and y_{22}, should be the minimum possible number if the number of elements in the network is important.

Example 6. In order to meet specifications, it is required that a closed-loop control system be compensated by the insertion of a tandem-connected RC network with open-circuit output terminals described by the function,

$$G_{12}(s) = \frac{s(s + \frac{1}{2})}{(s + 1)(s + 3)} \tag{10.83}$$

One possible selection of values for y_{22} and $-y_{12}$ is

$$y_{22} = \frac{(s + 1)(s + 3)}{(s + 2)(s + 4)}, \qquad -y_{12} = \frac{s(s + \frac{1}{2})}{(s + 2)(s + 4)} \tag{10.84}$$

These specifications coincide with those for Examples 4 and 5, and the network realizations of Figs. 10-28(d) and 10-30 will satisfy the specifications of Eq. 10.83. The minor role of the poles for synthesis from G_{12} specifications alone is illustrated by this example. Zeros are often the important part of specifications in two terminal-pair problems.

FURTHER READING

For a more extended treatment of the Cauer ladder development, see Guillemin's *Synthesis of Passive Networks*, especially pp. 231–247. Cauer's *Synthesis of Linear Communication Networks* (the English translation by Knausenberger and Warfield) covers the ladder development in Chapter 5. A brief account is given by Storer in his *Passive Network Synthesis*, Chapter 22.

The basis of the ladder development method is to be found in the pioneer paper by Cauer, "The realization of impedances with prescribed frequency dependence," *Arch. Elektrotech.*, **17**, 355–388 (1926–27), amplified in "Filters open circuited on the output side," *Elek. Nachr.-Tech.,* **16(6),** 161–163, (June 1939).

A lucid treatment of *RC* ladder networks is given by Truxal in *Automatic Feedback Control System Synthesis,* Chapter 3. For a detailed description of the parallel *RC* ladder development, see Guillemin's *Synthesis of Passive Networks,* Chapter 23.

The serious student will realize that the treatment of this and the last chapter is intended to serve only as an introduction to the subject. Those interested in further pursuit of the subtleties of the ladder development will be rewarded by studying a series of papers by Fialkow and Gerst, for example, "The transfer function of an *RC* ladder network, *Jour. Math. and Phys.,* **30,** 49–71 (1951) and "The transfer function of networks without mutual reactance," *Quart. Appl. Math,* **12,** 117–131 (1954). Another interesting paper is that of J. L. Bower and P. F. Ordung, "The synthesis of resistor-capacitor networks," *Proc. I.R.E.,* **38,** 263–269 (1950). An important extension of the Cauer method to cover the realization of complex zeros using tandem-connected bridged ladders is given by B. J. Dasher, "Synthesis of *RC* transfer functions as unbalanced two terminal-pair networks," *IRE Trans.,* **CT-1,** 20–34 (1952) and is also described by Truxal, *op. cit.,* pp. 206–218. This method has been extended to cover right half plane zeros by Hakimi and Seshu, who also describe Dasher-like synthesis in terms of the "overremoval" of poles in shifting the zeros from the real axis into the complex plane. See their "Realization of complex zeros of transmission by means of *RC* networks," *Proc. N.E.C.,* **13,** 1013–1025 (1957).

PROBLEMS

10-1. For the network shown in Fig. P10-1, determine y_{11}, $-y_{12}$, and y_{22}, taking care to cancel common numerator and denominator factors if possible. Show that the coefficient conditions of Eqs. 10.22 are satisfied.

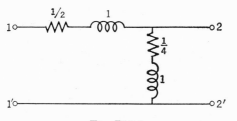

Fig. P10-1

10-2. Find z_{11}, z_{12}, and z_{22} for the network of Fig. P10-2. By canceling common factors in the numerator and denominator of z_{11} show that $z_{11} = 1$. Show that the computed functions satisfy the coefficient conditions of Eqs. 10.22.

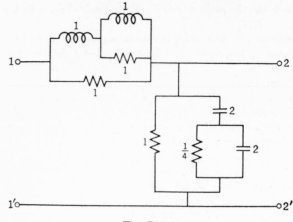

Fig. P10-2

10-3. The networks of the two problems above are examples of a special class of networks. Outline a method by which other networks of this class can be synthesized. Illustrate by examples.

10-4. Given the three open-circuit impedance functions

$$z_{11} = \frac{8s^5 + 46s^3 + 44s}{(s^2 + 1)(s^2 + 4)}$$

$$z_{12} = H\frac{16s^5 + 56s^3 + 64s}{(s^2 + 1)(s^2 + 4)}$$

$$z_{22} = \frac{8s^5 + 58s^3 + 56s}{(s^2 + 1)(s^2 + 4)}$$

what is the maximum value of H, the scale factor of z_{12}, that can be realized?

10-5. The three impedance functions

$$z_{11} = \frac{4s^3 + 20s}{(s^2 + 1)(s^2 + 9)}$$

$$z_{12} = \frac{q(s)}{(s^2 + 1)(s^2 + 9)}$$

$$z_{22} = \frac{2s^3 + 8s}{(s^2 + 1)(s^2 + 9)}$$

are to represent an LC network. Prepare a list of restrictions on the polynomial $q(s)$ based only on results of this chapter. Give one example of a possible form for $q(s)$ of each permitted degree.

10-6. For each of the networks shown in Fig. P10-6, determine the zeros of transmission. How can you distinguish zero-shifting from zero-producing subnetworks of the ladder? Discuss.

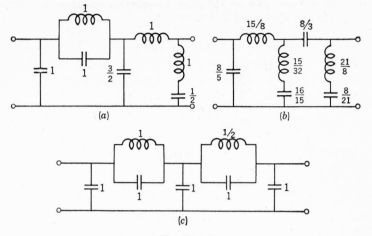

Fig. P10-6

10-7. At a certain point in a ladder development, it is found that

$$y_2(s) = \frac{10s(s^2 + 5.5)}{(s^2 + 1)(s^2 + 9)}$$

What element (size and kind) must be removed from $z_2(s) = 1/y_2(s)$ to shift a zero of $z_2(s)$ to $s = \pm j5$ ($\omega = 5$)?

10-8. Near the completion of a ladder development, we are left with

$$y_7(s) = \frac{10s}{s^2 + 6.25}$$

and we have yet to realize a zero of transmission at $s = \pm j6$ ($\omega = 6$). Complete the ladder development if the original function being developed is z_{11}.

10-9. This problem is somewhat different from the usual synthesis problem in that the specification functions are given and, in addition, the desired form of network is shown (to guide you in making the ladder development). Synthesize a ladder network (find element values) for the specifications

$$z_{11} = \frac{(s^2 + 4)(s^2 + 16)}{s(s^2 + 9)(s^2 + 25)}, \qquad z_{12} = \frac{(s^2 + 1)(s^2 + 36)}{s(s^2 + 9)(s^2 + 25)}$$

in the form shown in Fig. P10-9.

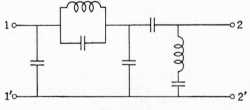

Fig. P10-9

10-10. Repeat Prob. 10-9 for the same specification functions, but for the network structure shown in Fig. P10-10.

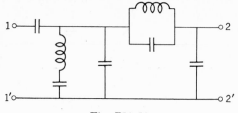

Fig. P10-10

10-11. Find a ladder network to meet the specifications of Example 2, by initially shifting a zero of z_{11} to $s = j1$ rather than to $s = j2$.

10-12. Given the open-circuit impedance functions

$$z_{11} = \frac{(s^2 + 1)(s^2 + 3)}{s(s^2 + 2)(s^2 + 4)}, \qquad z_{12} = \frac{q(s)}{s(s^2 + 2)(s^2 + 4)}$$

synthesize a ladder network for these specifications with:

(a) $q(s) = 1$,   (b) $q(s) = s^2$,   (c) $q(s) = s^4$.

10-13. The impedance functions z_{11} and z_{12} both have poles at $\omega = 2$ and $\omega = 4$ and z_{11} has zeros at $\omega = 0$ and $\omega = 3$. If z_{11} has no private poles, synthesize a ladder network when:

(a) There is one zero of transmission at the origin and three at infinity.
(b) Three zeros of transmission at the origin and one at infinity.

10-14. Show, referring to the ladder development, that if a series subnetwork becomes an open circuit or a shunt subnetwork becomes a short circuit, a zero of transmission is realized only if the network beyond this subnetwork presents a finite impedance or admittance respectively. Figure P10-14 gives an illustration of what is to be shown.

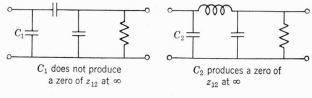

C_1 does not produce C_2 produces a zero of
a zero of z_{12} at ∞ z_{12} at ∞

Fig. P10-14

10-15. Explain in terms of the behavior of the arms of the ladder network how it is possible to have a zero of z_{11} which is not also a zero of z_{12}.

10-16. The figures of Prob. 10-6 show the forms of network resulting from the Cauer ladder development. The parallel LC networks are open circuits when in resonance and the series LC networks appear as short circuits when in resonance. Now some of the sections in the shunt and series positions are "zero shifting" while some are "zero producing."

(a) How can you distinguish zero-producing sections from zero-shifting sections?

(b) Show that networks used for zero shifting are not zero producing.

10-17. Determine a ladder network to realize the open-circuit impedance function specifications

$$z_{22} = \frac{s(s^2 + 16)(s^2 + 36)}{(s^2 + 1)(s^2 + 25)}, \qquad z_{12} = \frac{s(s^2 + 4)}{(s^2 + 1)(s^2 + 25)}$$

Realize the zero of transmission at $s = j2$ last.

10-18. Determine a ladder network to realize the following short-circuit admittance functions:

$$y_{22} = \frac{s(s^2 + 16)(s^2 + 36)}{(s^2 + 1)(s^2 + 25)}, \qquad -y_{12} = \frac{s(s^2 + 4)}{(s^2 + 1)(s^2 + 25)}$$

Find the constant multiplier, k_m, for your network realization.

10-19. The specifications for an RC ladder network have the general form

$$y_{22} = \frac{(s + 1)(s + 3)}{(s + 2)(s + 4)}, \qquad -y_{12} = \frac{q_{12}(s)}{(s + 2)(s + 4)}$$

Find a ladder network for $q_{12}(s) = 1$ and find the corresponding k_m. Prepare a chart showing the movement of the poles and the zeros in the various stages of the development, indicating zero shifting and poles removed.

10-20. Repeat Prob. 10-19 with $q_{12}(s) = s$.

10-21. Repeat Prob. 10-19 with $q_{12}(s) = (s + \frac{5}{2})(s + \frac{9}{4})$.

10-22. Given the RC ladder network specifications

$$y_{22} = \frac{(s + 1)(s + 6)}{(s + 4)(s + 8)}, \qquad -y_{12} = \frac{q_{12}(s)}{(s + 4)(s + 8)}$$

when $q_{12}(s) = (s + 2)(s + 3)$, find a ladder network. Chart the development and find the constant factor, k_m, of the network you find.

10-23. Repeat Prob. 10-22 for $q_{12}(s) = (s + 3)(s + 5)$.

10-24. Repeat Prob. 10-22 for $q_{12}(s) = (s + 5)(s + 7)$.

10-25. Find an RC ladder network to meet the specifications

$$y_{11} = K \frac{(s + \frac{1}{2})(s + 2)}{(s + 1)}, \qquad -y_{12} = \frac{s(s + \frac{3}{2})}{(s + 1)}$$

in which $-y_{12}$ is realized exactly. Determine K.

10-26. Synthesize an RC network containing not more than five elements to realize the transfer voltage specification:

$$G_{12}(s) = \frac{V_2(s)}{V_1(s)} = \frac{(s+2)(s+3)}{(s+1)(s+4)}$$

Compare the scale factor of the G_{12} of the network you find with that specified.

10-27. Figure P10-27 shows a block-diagram representation of a closed-loop control system (servomechanism). The synthesis of closed-loop systems is usually accomplished by choosing convenient fixed parts of the system (such as motors, amplifiers, transducers, etc., available in the stockroom) and then meeting the specifications by a *compensating network*. The two parts of the system are shown in the figure as $G_f(s)$ and $G_c(s)$. The servo engineer has decided that he requires a network approximating the voltage-ratio variation with frequency given in Table P10-27. The network is to be excited by a voltage source and is to drive a high input-impedance amplifier. Synthesize a network suitable for this purpose. Attempt to use convenient (stockroom) element sizes and use as few elements as possible. Maintain a tolerance of ± 1 db.

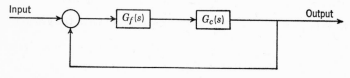

Fig. P10-27

TABLE P10-27

ω, radians/sec	$\lvert G_c(j\omega)\rvert$, db	Arg $G_c(j\omega)$, degrees
10	−0.00152	−1.65
30	−0.0172	−4.93
60	−0.0696	−9.84
100	−0.192	−16.3
200	−0.740	−31.8
300	−1.57	−46.0
500	−3.70	−69.7
700	−6.07	−87.7
1,000	−9.55	−107
2,000	−18.8	−139
3,000	−25.1	−152
4,000	−29.9	−158
6,000	−36.7	−166
10,000	−45.5	−171
30,000	−64.5	−177

10-28. Repeat Prob. 10-27 for the data of Table P10-28.

TABLE P10-28

ω, radians/sec	$\left|G_c(j\omega)\right|$, db	Arg $G_c(j\omega)$, degrees
10	-0.0427	-5.82
30	-0.374	-17.0
60	-1.34	-31.6
100	-3.01	-46.1
200	-7.00	-65.6
300	-10.0	-74.8
500	-14.2	-84.1
700	-17.1	-89.4
1,000	-20.2	-94.9
2,000	-26.6	-108
3,000	-30.8	-118
4,000	-34.0	-125
6,000	-39.1	-138
10,000	-46.6	-151
30,000	-64.7	-170

10-29. Repeat Prob. 10-27 for the data given in Table P10-29.

TABLE P10-29

ω, radians/sec	$\left|G_c(j\omega)\right|$, db	Arg $G_c(j\omega)$, degrees
10	-0.0435	-6.53
30	-0.382	-19.2
60	-1.37	-35.9
100	-3.10	-53.1
200	-7.33	-79.4
300	-10.7	-94.8
500	-15.9	-114
700	-20.0	-127
1,000	-24.9	-139
2,000	-35.7	-158
3,000	-42.4	-165
4,000	-47.3	-169
6,000	-54.3	-172
10,000	-63.1	-175
30,000	-82.2	-179

10-30. (a) Show that when a two terminal-pair network is terminated in a 1-ohm resistor, $Z_L = 1$, then

$$Z_{12}(s) = \frac{V_2}{I_1(s)} = \frac{z_{12}}{1 + z_{22}}$$

(b) Using this equation, synthesize a network to the specification

$$Z_{12}(s) = \frac{1}{s^3 + 2s^2 + 2s + 1}$$

(c) Show that the poles of this Z_{12} are three roots of the equation,

$$1 - s^6 = 0$$

The network found in part (b) is known as a third-order Butterworth network in the literature.

10-31. Synthesize a network to meet the specification

$$Z_{12}(s) = \frac{s^3 + 7s}{s^3 + s^2 + 3s + 1}$$

using the method suggested in Prob. 10-30.

10-32. Adapting the results of Prob. 2-21 to the network shown in (a) of Fig. P10-32, it follows that

$$z_{12} = \frac{z_{12a}z_{12b}}{z_{22a} + Z_1 + z_{11b}}$$

and similarly for the network of (b)

$$-y_{12} = \frac{-y_{12a}y_{12b}}{y_{22a} + Y_1 + y_{11b}}$$

Using these equations, examine the conditions under which the poles of Z_1 and the poles of Y_1 will be zeros of transmission of the system. Discuss completely.

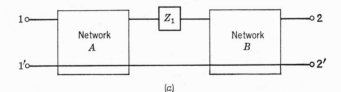

(a)

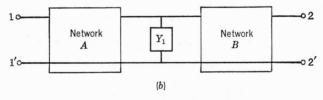

(b)

Fig. P10-32

Series and
Parallel Realizations

The two synthesis methods to be studied in this chapter apply to two terminal-pair networks containing two kinds of elements: LC, RC, and RL. These methods, due to Cauer and to Guillemin, depend upon a special manner in which subnetworks are connected together in satisfying specification functions. In these studies, a knowledge of the isolating and impedance transforming properties of the ideal transformer is important and will be the first topic treated.

11.1 The ideal transformer

The ideal transformer represented in Fig. 11-1 is defined to operate so that the ratio of voltage transforms is a real constant, a, which

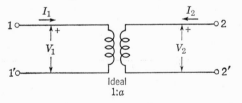

Fig. 11-1. The ideal transformer represented as a two terminal-pair network.

may be either positive or negative

$$\frac{V_2(s)}{V_1(s)} = a \tag{11.1}$$

and the corresponding current transforms are related by the equation

$$\frac{I_2(s)}{I_1(s)} = \frac{-1}{a} \tag{11.2}$$

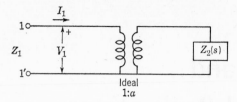

Fig. 11-2. The ideal transformer terminated in an impedance, $Z_2(s)$.

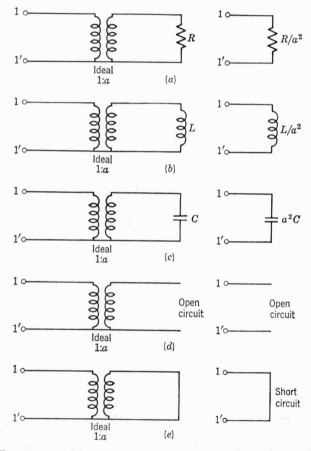

Fig. 11-3. Table of equivalent networks derived from Eq. 11.4.

This ideal transformer is customarily described in terms of the voltage ratio of Eq. 11.1. If $V_2(s) = a\,V(s)$ when $V_1(s) = V(s)$, then the transformer is described by the ratio, $1:a$.

    In synthesis applications, we are interested in two properties of the ideal transformer: (1) its impedance transformation properties, and

(2) its isolating properties. To explore the first of these, we divide
Eq. 11.1 by Eq. 11.2 and rearrange
so that

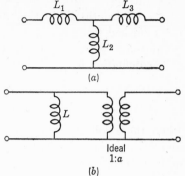

$$\frac{-V_2(s)}{I_2(s)} = a^2 \frac{V_1(s)}{I_1(s)} \quad (11.3)$$

or $\qquad Z_1(s) = \frac{1}{a^2} Z_2(s) \quad (11.4)$

(a)

(b)

From this result, we see that the
input impedance of an ideal transformer terminated in $Z_2(s)$ is $1/a^2$
times that impedance (Fig. 11-2).
Several applications of this relationship are shown in Fig. 11-3. Note
that these relationships hold independent of whether the lower terminals of the ideal transformer are con-

Fig. 11-4. An equivalent network
for the Brune transformer when

$L = L_1 + L_2$ and
$a = [(L_2 + L_3)/(L_1 + L_2)]^{1/2}$

nected together or not, i.e., whether one part of the network is *isolated*
from the other.

The use of a transformer for impedance transformation but not
necessarily for isolation is familiar from our study of the Brune method
of synthesis in Chapter 7.   In the Brune method, either L_1 or L_3 in

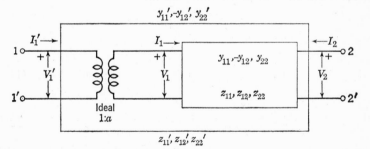

Fig. 11-5. An ideal transformer connected in tandem with a two terminal-pair
network used to find the relationship between the primed and unprimed y and z
functions.

Fig. 11-4(*a*) is negative.   The "Brune transformer" is seen to be equivalent to an inductor and an ideal transformer, as shown in Fig. 11-4(*b*),
since this network is described by the same z_{11}, z_{12}, and z_{22} functions
as that of Fig. 11-4(*a*).

Figure 11-5 shows a general two terminal-pair network connected in
tandem with an ideal transformer.   We know that the two terminal-

pair network may be described by either the short-circuit admittance functions (y_{11}, $-y_{12}$, y_{22}) or the open-circuit impedance functions (z_{11}, z_{12}, z_{22}). Let these functions for the tandem-connected networks be distinguished from those of the general network by primes. We are interested in the relationship of the primed and unprimed quantities.

The definition for z_{11}' for the combined system is

$$z_{11}' = \left. \frac{V_1'}{I_1'} \right|_{I_2=0} \tag{11.5}$$

where these voltages and currents are defined by Fig. 11-5. Now V_1' and I_1' are related to V_1 and I_1 by Eqs. 11.1 and 11.2, and the ratio of V_1 to I_1 with $I_2 = 0$ defines z_{11}. We thus find z_{11}' in terms of z_{11} as follows:

$$z_{11}' = \left. \frac{V_1'}{I_1'} \right|_{I_2=0} = \left. \frac{1}{a^2} \frac{V_1}{I_1} \right|_{I_2=0} = \frac{1}{a^2} z_{11} \tag{11.6}$$

Similarly,

$$z_{12}' = \left. \frac{V_2}{I_1'} \right|_{I_2=0} = \left. \frac{1}{a} \frac{V_2}{I_1} \right|_{I_2=0} = \frac{1}{a} z_{12} \tag{11.7}$$

and

$$z_{22}' = \left. \frac{V_2}{I_2} \right|_{I_1'=0} = z_{22} \tag{11.8}$$

The short-circuit admittance functions are

$$y_{11}' = \left. \frac{I_1'}{V_1'} \right|_{V_2=0} = \left. a^2 \frac{I_1}{V_1} \right|_{V_2=0} = a^2 y_{11} \tag{11.9}$$

$$-y_{12}' = \left. \frac{I_2}{V_1'} \right|_{V_2=0} = \left. a \frac{I_2}{V_1} \right|_{V_2=0} = -a y_{12} \tag{11.10}$$

and

$$y_{22}' = \left. \frac{I_2}{V_2} \right|_{V_1'=0} = y_{22} \tag{11.11}$$

From these six equations, we observe that the driving-point quantities have positive signs for either sign of a, but that the sign of the transfer functions is the sign of a which may be either positive or negative. This fact finds application in various methods of synthesis.

We next turn to an application in which the isolating properties of the ideal transformer are important. Figure 11-6(a) shows two networks, N_a and N_b. When these two networks are connected together as shown in Fig. 11-6(b), either with the ideal transformer or without it, the two networks are said to be connected together in *series* (in contrast with the tandem or cascade connection discussed in Chapter 2).

An important relationship for series-connected networks relates the z functions of the composite network in terms of those of the component networks.

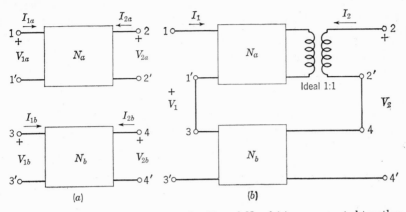

Fig. 11-6. Two terminal-pair networks, N_a and N_b, of (a) are connected together in *series* in (b).

Network N_a of Fig. 11-6(a) is described in terms of the open-circuit impedance functions by the equations

$$V_{1a} = z_{11a}I_{1a} + z_{12a}I_{2a}$$
$$V_{2a} = z_{12a}I_{1a} + z_{22a}I_{2a}$$

(11.12)

and similarly network N_b by the equations

$$V_{1b} = z_{11b}I_{1b} + z_{12b}I_{2b}$$
$$V_{2b} = z_{12b}I_{1b} + z_{22b}I_{2b}$$

(11.13)

For this network connection, we may write

$$V_1 = V_{1a} + V_{1b} \quad \text{and} \quad V_2 = V_{2a} + V_{2b} \quad (11.14)$$

With the ideal transformer connected as shown in the figure,

$$I_1 = I_{1a} = I_{1b} \quad \text{and} \quad I_2 = I_{2a} = I_{2b} \quad (11.15)$$

Without the ideal transformer, we cannot be sure that these current relationships are valid. It is possible to connect networks in series without the ideal transformers using criteria outlined by Cauer;* for our purposes, the ideal transformer provides the necessary isolation.

* *Synthesis of Linear Communication Networks*, pp. 97–108.

Substituting Eqs. 11.12 into Eqs. 11.14 and simplifying through Eqs. 11.15 result in expressions relating V_1 and V_2 in terms of I_1 and I_2:

$$V_1 = (z_{11a} + z_{11b})I_1 + (z_{12a} + z_{12b})I_2$$
$$V_2 = (z_{12a} + z_{12b})I_1 + (z_{22a} + z_{22b})I_2 \qquad (11.16)$$

These equations show that the open-circuit impedance functions add for this connection, suggesting the reason that the connection is called *series*.

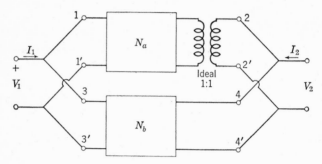

Fig. 11-7. The parallel connection of N_a and N_b.

For the parallel networks of Fig. 11-7, we start with the equations

$$I_{1a} = y_{11a}V_{1a} + y_{12a}V_{2a}$$
$$I_{2a} = y_{12a}V_{1a} + y_{22a}V_{2a} \qquad (11.17)$$

and

$$I_{1b} = y_{11b}V_{1b} + y_{12b}V_{2b}$$
$$I_{2b} = y_{12b}V_{1b} + y_{22b}V_{2b} \qquad (11.18)$$

and impose the conditions made possible by the use of the ideal transformer.

$$I_1 = I_{1a} + I_{1b} \qquad \text{and} \qquad I_2 = I_{2a} + I_{2b} \qquad (11.19)$$

$$V_1 = V_{1a} = V_{1b} \qquad \text{and} \qquad V_2 = V_{2a} = V_{2b} \qquad (11.20)$$

These equations are the duals of those given for the series connection with the role of voltages and currents interchanged and with impedance replaced by admittance. Combining the equations gives

$$I_1 = (y_{11a} + y_{11b})V_1 + (y_{12a} + y_{12b})V_2$$

and

$$I_2 = (y_{12a} + y_{12b})V_1 + (y_{22a} + y_{22b})V_2 \qquad (11.21)$$

showing that the admittance functions add for the parallel networks just as the impedances do for the series network.

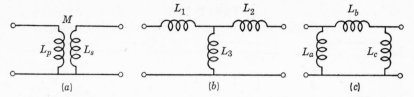

Fig. 11-8. Representation of (a) a transformer and (b) potentially equivalent T and (c) π networks.

We shall find it useful to study the equivalence of coupled coils to inductive T or inductive π networks. These three networks, with the symbols we shall assign to the different inductors for our discussion, are shown in Fig. 11-8. Networks (a) and (b) are equivalent if

$$L_1 = L_p \mp M$$
$$L_2 = L_s \mp M \tag{11.22}$$
$$L_3 = \pm M$$

Solving the equations for L_p, L_s, and M gives

$$L_p = L_1 + L_3$$
$$L_s = L_2 + L_3 \tag{11.23}$$
$$M = \pm L_3$$

The condition for unity coefficient of coupling is $L_p L_s - M^2 = 0$, or, in terms of L_1, L_2, and L_3,

$$L_1 L_2 + L_2 L_3 + L_3 L_1 = 0 \tag{11.24}$$

How may this equation be satisfied? If the inductances are all either positive (or negative), then this equation can never be satisfied and the coefficient of coupling must be less than unity. If either one or two of the three inductances are negative, however, then $k = 1$ is a possibility. Observe that with $L_1 L_2 + L_2 L_3 + L_3 L_1 = 0$ both L_p and L_s will be positive if $L_1 + L_3$ and $L_2 + L_3$ are positive, from Eqs. 11.23. Further, with L_1, L_2, and L_3 finite, both L_p and L_s will be finite. This is a description of the Brune equivalent networks studied in Chapter 7.

A parallel study of the possibility of representing an ideal transformer by a π network with one or more negative elements may be made in terms of the equivalent networks of Table 11-1.* These equivalences may be verified by using Eqs. 11.22 and 11.23 together

---

* A table similar to the one shown is given by Milton Dishal in "Design of dissipative band-pass filters producing desired exact amplitude-frequency characteristics," *Proc. I.R.E.*, **37**, 1050–1069 (1949).

TABLE 11-1

Table of Equivalent T, π, and Transformer Networks

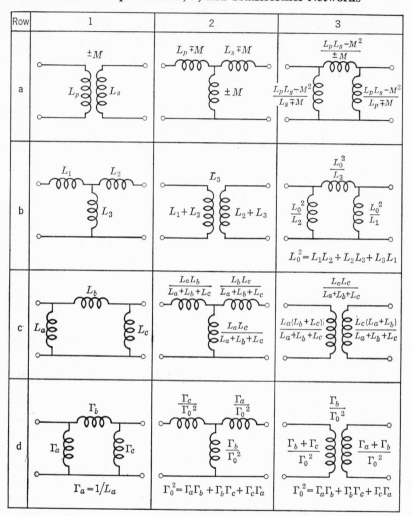

with the equations for the T-π transformation. In this table, inverse inductance is symbolized as $\Gamma_j = 1/L_j$ in the equivalent networks of row d. The condition for unity coefficient of coupling may be found by writing k in terms of the equations in Table 11-1 (row d, column 3) as

$$k^2 = \frac{M^2}{L_p L_s} = \frac{\Gamma_b{}^2}{\Gamma_a \Gamma_b + \Gamma_b \Gamma_c + \Gamma_c \Gamma_a + \Gamma_b{}^2} \qquad (11.25)$$

From this equation, we see that if

$$\Gamma_0{}^2 = \Gamma_a\Gamma_b + \Gamma_b\Gamma_c + \Gamma_c\Gamma_a = 0 \qquad (11.26)$$

then $k = 1$ and unity coefficient of coupling is accomplished. The only way this equation can be satisfied is, as before, for one or two of the inverse inductances be to negative.

As a network "element," the ideal transformer is avoided if at all possible because of "practical" realization difficulties. If, however, there exists an inductor in shunt with either the input or output terminals of the ideal transformer, the transformer and inductor may be combined and realized as a lossless transformer with less than unity coupling. If, in addition, there is an inductor in series with the unity-

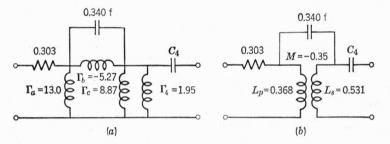

Fig. 11-9. Equivalent networks showing how a π network with negative inductance (*a*) may be altered to represent a realizable network (*b*) by combining Γ_4 with Γ_c.

coupled lossless transformer, the inductor can be absorbed into the transformer to reduce the coefficient of coupling to a value less than unity. As an example of such an operation, consider the network of Fig. 11-9(*a*) which contains one negative inductor.* Considering this π network alone, we observe that $\Gamma_a\Gamma_b + \Gamma_b\Gamma_c + \Gamma_c\Gamma_a = 13 \times -5.27 + 8.87 \times -5.27 + 8.87 \times 13.0 = 0$, indicating unity coupling coefficient. If, however, we first combine Γ_4 with the adjacent inverse inductance of the π network, an equivalent network with less than unity coefficient of coupling results, as shown in Fig. 11-9(*b*).

11.2   Further restrictions on z_{12}

Since z_{12} need not be positive real, what are the conditions imposed in order that z_{12} together with z_{11} and z_{22} represent a passive net-

* G. L. Matthaei, "Synthesis of Tchebycheff impedance-matching networks, filters, and interstages," *IRE Trans.*, **CT-3**, 163–172 (1956).

work?* The derivation to follow, due to Gewertz and others,† makes use of the ideal transformer of the preceding section to provide restrictions on z_{12} to add to those found in the last chapter. The equations which relate the voltages and currents in terms of the open-circuit impedance functions are

$$V_1 = z_{11}I_1 + z_{12}I_2$$
$$V_2 = z_{12}I_1 + z_{22}I_2$$

(11.27)

Suppose that we modify the usual two terminal-pair network by the addition of an ideal transformer for each terminal pair, as shown in

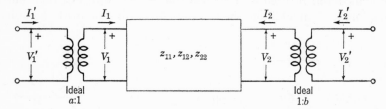

Fig. 11-10. A general two terminal-pair network isolated by two ideal transformers.

Fig. 11-10. If the transformation ratios of the transformers are $a:1$ and $1:b$ as shown, then the ideal transformer voltages are related by the equations

$$V_1' = aV_1; \qquad I_1' = (1/a)I_1$$

(11.28)

and

$$V_2' = bV_2; \qquad I_2' = (1/b)I_2$$

(11.29)

If we substitute these equations into Eqs. 11.27 and solve for the primed voltages, we have

$$V_1' = a^2 z_{11}I_1' + abz_{12}I_2'$$

and

$$V_2' = abz_{12}I_1' + b^2 z_{22}I_2'$$

(11.30)

As our next step, we connect the terminals of the network of Fig. 11-10 with the two ideal transformers in such a way that the two terminal-pair network becomes a one terminal-pair structure, shown in Fig. 11-11. By this maneuver, we tie in with the store of knowledge we already possess—the properties of one terminal-pair networks and positive real functions. We thus develop our new ideas by building

---

* Proof for the y functions parallels that given here for the z's and makes use of the network connection of Fig. 11-7.

† See B. MacMillan, "Introduction for formal realizability theory," *Bell System Tech. J.*, **31**, 217–279 and 541–600 (1952).

on the foundation of topics already familiar. The connections of Fig. 11-11 are such that at the driving-point terminals

$$V = V_1' + V_2' \tag{11.31}$$

and

$$I = I_1' = I_2' \tag{11.32}$$

Substituting Eqs. 11.30 into Eq. 11.31 and simplifying the resulting equation by Eq. 11.32 give

$$V(s) = (a^2 z_{11} + 2ab z_{12} + b^2 z_{22})\, I(s) \tag{11.33}$$

and the driving-point impedance is

$$Z(s) = \frac{V(s)}{I(s)} = a^2 z_{11} + 2ab z_{12} + b^2 z_{22} \tag{11.34}$$

In this equation, a^2 and b^2 are always positive, but since a or b may be either positive or negative, the term $2ab$ can have either a positive or

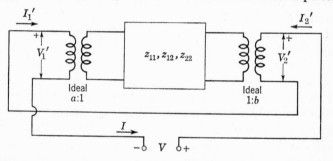

Fig. 11-11. Two terminal-pair network connected to form a one terminal-pair network.

a negative sign. The function $Z(s)$, being a driving-point impedance, is required to be positive real as are both $z_{11}(s)$ and $z_{22}(s)$. Thus we see that Eq. 11.34 provides us with a means of relating the properties of the transfer function $z_{12}(s)$ to the already familiar positive real function. Having hemmed in $z_{12}(s)$, we may now extend the list of properties of transfer functions compiled in Chapter 10.

As a simple example of the application of Eq. 11.34, consider this equation with $s = \sigma$:

$$Z(\sigma) = a^2 z_{11}(\sigma) + 2ab z_{12}(\sigma) + b^2 z_{22}(\sigma) \tag{11.35}$$

Since Z, z_{11}, and z_{22} are positive real functions, $Z(\sigma)$, $z_{11}(\sigma)$, and $z_{22}(\sigma)$ are real. The only way the last equation can be satisfied is for $z_{12}(\sigma)$ to be real. This requires that the zeros of $z_{12}(s)$ *always occur in conjugate pairs* when complex or imaginary.

Another application of Eq. 11.34 leads to conclusions similar to those found in the last chapter concerning the poles and zeros of $z_{12}(s)$ at zero and infinity. Since Eq. 11.34 holds for all values of a and b, consider the case $a = b = \frac{1}{2}$, which gives

$$4Z_1 = z_{11} + 2z_{12} + z_{22} \tag{11.36}$$

Next let $a = -b = \frac{1}{2}$ define a different driving-point impedance Z_2,

$$4Z_2 = z_{11} - 2z_{12} + z_{22} \tag{11.37}$$

Subtracting these two equations gives

$$z_{12} = Z_1 - Z_2 = \frac{N_1 - N_2}{D} \tag{11.38}$$

where N_1 and N_2 are the numerator polynomials of Z_1 and Z_2 and D is the denominator polynomial of both Z_1 and Z_2. This result tells us that z_{12} may be expressed as the *difference* of two positive real functions and is therefore *not* necessarily positive real. This equation also leads to a number of conclusions about the poles and zeros of z_{12} at zero and infinity.

Since Z_1 and Z_2 are positive real, N_1 and N_2 can differ in degree from D at most by 1. If N_1 and N_2 are either or both of degree higher than D, and if the highest degree terms of each do not cancel, then z_{12} may have at most a simple pole at infinity. If the higher degree terms do cancel one by one, so long as they do not all cancel, then z_{12} may have multiple zeros or a simple zero at infinity. Similarly, if terms of lower degree cancel one by one starting from the lowest degree term and working toward the highest in N_1 and N_2, then we have either a simple zero or multiple zeros at zero frequency. In other words, expressions like

$$z_{12} = \frac{1}{s^3 + 5s^2 + 11s + 6} \quad \text{or} \quad z_{12} = \frac{s^3}{s^3 + 5s^2 + 11s + 6} \tag{11.39}$$

are permitted, a conclusion reached in Chapter 10 from the coefficient condition of Fialkow and Gerst.

The results given for z_{11}, z_{12}, and z_{22} apply to the short-circuit admittance functions, y_{11}, $-y_{12}$, and y_{22}.

11.3   The residue condition and related topics

An important property of the residue of $z_{12}(s)$ at each pole in relationship to the corresponding residues of $z_{11}(s)$ and $z_{22}(s)$ stems from

Eq. 11.34.   Consider a function having only simple poles which may be expanded as a partial fraction having the form

$$Z(s) = \frac{k_1}{s - p_1} + \frac{k_2}{s - p_2} + \cdots + \frac{k_i}{s - p_i} + \cdots + \frac{k_m}{s - p_m} \quad (11.40)$$

For values of s as near as we like to pole p_i, as shown in Fig. 11-12, the value of $Z(s)$ is approximately,

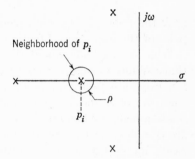

$$Z(s) \cong \frac{k_i}{s - p_i} \quad (11.41)$$

Fig. 11-12. Showing the region near a pole where the impedance function may be approximated by a single term.

Now assume that we are given the three impedance functions z_{11}, z_{12}, and z_{22} and further that the poles of these functions are all simple. Let the partial fraction expansions for these three functions be written in the following form with a superscript used to identify the various residues evaluated at a given pole:

$$z_{11} = \frac{k_{11}^{(1)}}{s - p_1} + \frac{k_{11}^{(2)}}{s - p_2} + \cdots + \frac{k_{11}^{(i)}}{s - p_i} + \cdots + \frac{k_{11}^{(m)}}{s - p_m} \\ + k_{11} + k_{11}^{(\infty)}s$$

$$z_{12} = \frac{k_{12}^{(1)}}{s - p_1} + \frac{k_{12}^{(2)}}{s - p_2} + \cdots + \frac{k_{12}^{(i)}}{s - p_i} + \cdots + \frac{k_{12}^{(m)}}{s - p_m} \\ + k_{12} + k_{12}^{(\infty)}s \quad (11.42)$$

$$z_{22} = \frac{k_{22}^{(1)}}{s - p_1} + \frac{k_{22}^{(2)}}{s - p_2} + \cdots + \frac{k_{22}^{(i)}}{s - p_i} + \cdots + \frac{k_{22}^{(m)}}{s - p_m} \\ + k_{22} + k_{22}^{(\infty)}s$$

In the neighborhood of the pole p_i, the following approximations may be made:

$$z_{11} \cong \frac{k_{11}^{(i)}}{s - p_i}$$

$$z_{12} \cong \frac{k_{12}^{(i)}}{s - p_i} \quad (11.43)$$

and

$$z_{22} \cong \frac{k_{22}^{(i)}}{s - p_i}$$

Now the positive real impedance function $Z(s)$ of Eq. 11.34 may also have the pole p_i and the residue at that pole is $k^{(i)}$. Then we may substitute Eqs. 11.43 together with the similar equation for $Z(s)$ into Eq. 11.34 and cancel the common denominator, $s - p_i$, to give

$$k^{(i)} = a^2 k_{11}^{(i)} + 2ab k_{12}^{(i)} + b^2 k_{22}^{(i)} \qquad (11.44)$$

near the pole p_i. This is a general result that applies to all simple poles of the impedance functions.

What do we know about these residues? In Chapter 3, we found that residues evaluated at poles on the imaginary axis for positive real functions are positive and real. Further, the residues evaluated at the poles of Z and Y/s for RC networks and Y and Z/s for RL networks are also real and positive. Residues for complex poles, however, are complex except for special cases. Then for the LC, RC, and RL cases, an impedance or admittance function has real and positive residues. For these three two-element-kind cases, the poles are simple as already assumed in the derivation.

For the special cases of poles on the imaginary axis and on the real axis for RC and RL networks, we see that since $k^{(i)}$ is required to be real and positive the summation $a^2 k_{11}^{(i)} + 2ab k_{12}^{(i)} + b^2 k_{22}^{(i)}$ is also required to be real and positive. This, in turn, requires that $k_{12}^{(i)}$ be real even though it may be either positive or negative. From this point on, let us drop the superscript which identifies the pole to which the equation is being applied. For the special case with k real and positive, we pose this problem: Given that k_{11} and k_{22} are real and positive but with k_{12}, a, and b real but either positive or negative, is there a condition that may be imposed on the residues k_{11}, k_{12}, and k_{22} such that k is *always* real and positive, independent of the values of a and b? Starting with Eq. 11.44, but dropping the superscript for the time being, we see that k is positive when the product $2ab k_{12}$ is positive. However, if this product is negative, then it is necessary that

$$2ab k_{12} \leq a^2 k_{11} + b^2 k_{22} \qquad (11.45)$$

or
$$k_{12} \leq \frac{1}{2}\left[\left(\frac{a}{b}\right) k_{11} + \left(\frac{b}{a}\right) k_{22}\right] \qquad (11.46)$$

To find the minimum value of the right-hand side of this equation for any a/b, we differentiate with respect to a/b and equate to 0. There results

$$k_{11} - \left(\frac{b}{a}\right)^2 k_{22} = 0 \qquad (11.47)$$

which is a minimum since the second derivative of Eq. 11.46 is positive for this value of a/b. Combining the last equation with Eq. 11.46 gives

$$k_{12} \leq \sqrt{k_{11}k_{22}} \tag{11.48}$$

or, finally,

$$k_{11}k_{22} - k_{12}{}^2 \geq 0 \tag{11.49}$$

This equation is known as the *residue condition*.* It applies to poles on the imaginary axis or on the real axis for RC impedance and RL admittance functions, but does not apply to simple, complex, or multiple poles of other functions. When the residue condition is fulfilled with the equals sign, then the poles and

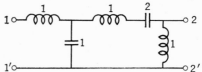

Fig. 11-13. Network employed in Example 1.

the subsequent realization of a network are described by the term *compact*, a term first used by Dasher.

Example 1.   The following open-circuit impedance functions characterize the network shown in Fig. 11-13:

$$z_{11} = \frac{4s^4 + 7s^2 + 1}{s(4s^2 + 3)} = \frac{1}{3s} + \frac{\frac{8}{3}s}{4s^2 + 3} + s$$

$$z_{22} = \frac{s(2s^2 + 3)}{4s^2 + 3} = 0 + \frac{\frac{3}{2}s}{4s^2 + 3} + \tfrac{1}{2}s \tag{11.50}$$

$$z_{12} = \frac{2s}{4s^2 + 3} = 0 + \frac{2s}{4s^2 + 3} + 0$$

At the pole at $s = \pm \sqrt{\frac{3}{4}}$, the residue condition is satisfied since

$$k_{11}k_{22} - k_{12}{}^2 = \tfrac{1}{4}(\tfrac{8}{3} \times \tfrac{3}{2} - 2^2) = 0 \tag{11.51}$$

Similarly, at $s = 0$ and $s = \infty$, we observe that the residue condition is satisfied since $\frac{1}{3} \times 0 - 0 = 0$ and $1 \times \frac{1}{2} - 0 = \frac{1}{2}$.

The real part of $z_{12}(j\omega)$.   Once again starting with Eq. 11.34, we see that $Z(s)$ is positive real and therefore Re $Z(j\omega) \geq 0$ for all ω, which requires that

$$\text{Re } Z(j\omega) = a^2 \text{ Re } z_{11}(j\omega) + 2ab \text{ Re } z_{12}(j\omega) + b^2 \text{ Re } z_{22}(j\omega) \geq 0 \tag{11.52}$$

---

* This equation may be alternatively derived making use of the properties of positive definite quadratic forms. See, for example, Guillemin's *The Mathematics of Circuit Analysis*, Chapter IV.

Now this equation is similar to Eq. 11.49 both in form and in the nature of Re z_{11}, Re z_{22}, and Re z_{12} compared to the residues k_{11}, k_{22}, and k_{12}. Both Re z_{11} and Re z_{22} are always positive, but Re z_{12} need not be. Following the same procedure as was used in arriving at the

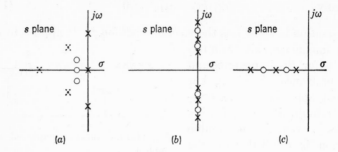

Fig. 11-14. Three plots showing poles of z_{11}, z_{12}, and z_{22}. (Zero locations are incomplete, since they will be different for the three functions.) The residue condition does not apply to the poles drawn with dashed lines, but does apply to those drawn with solid lines.

residue condition, we see that Eq. 11.52 will always be satisfied for any sign and values for a and b if

$$\text{Re } z_{11}(j\omega) \text{ Re } z_{22}(j\omega) - \text{Re } z_{12}(j\omega)^2 \geq 0 \qquad (11.53)$$

Similarly, since for positive real functions we require that Re $Z(s) \geq 0$ when Re $s \geq 0$, it is necessary that

$$\text{Re } (a^2 z_{11} + 2ab z_{12} + b^2 z_{22}) \geq 0 \text{ when Re } s \geq 0 \qquad (11.54)$$

If we introduce the notation

$$\text{Re } z_{11} = r_{11}, \qquad \text{Re } z_{12} = r_{12}, \qquad \text{and} \qquad \text{Re } z_{22} = r_{22} \quad (11.55)$$

then we may write Eq. 11.54 in the form

$$a^2 r_{11} + 2ab r_{12} + b^2 r_{22} \geq 0, \qquad \sigma \geq 0 \qquad (11.56)$$

This requirement is analogous to that which gave the residue condition, and we may conclude that this equation is satisfied when

$$r_{11} r_{22} - r_{12}^2 \geq 0, \qquad \sigma \geq 0 \qquad (11.57)$$

These transfer function properties are summarized in Table 11-2. The restriction as to the poles for which the residue condition applies is illustrated by Fig. 11-14.

TABLE 11-2
Residue and Real Part Requirements of z_{11}, z_{12}, z_{22}

Residues at Poles	Real Part of z_{12}
1. The residues at poles on the imaginary axis for LC networks or on the real axis for the impedance of RC networks and admittance of RL networks must satisfy the residue condition $$k_{11}k_{22} - k_{12}^2 \geq 0$$	1. For all ω, $$\operatorname{Re} z_{12}^2(j\omega) \leq \operatorname{Re} z_{11}(j\omega) \operatorname{Re} z_{22}(j\omega)$$ 2. For all $\sigma \geq 0$, $$r_{11}r_{22} - r_{12}^2 \geq 0$$

11.4   Cauer's partial fraction network realization

One of Cauer's early contributions to network theory* was his method of synthesis of two terminal-pair LC, RC, and RL networks based on the partial fraction expansion of z_{11}, z_{12}, and z_{22}. This method makes it possible to satisfy all three specification functions rather than only two as was the case for the ladder development. The network structures that result are not attractive, but the method is interesting for historical reasons and because of the understanding of the problems of two terminal-pair synthesis which it provides.

We will restrict our discussion of the method to the LC case, leaving the RC and RL cases for problems. Then z_{11} and z_{22} are functions having their poles and zeros interlaced on the imaginary axis. Equation 11.34, repeated here,

$$Z(s) = a^2 z_{11} + 2ab z_{12} + b^2 z_{22}$$

tells us that z_{12} cannot have poles other than simple imaginary axis poles. In order that Z, z_{11}, and z_{22} for $s = j\omega$ be reactance functions, it is necessary that z_{12} be the quotient of odd to even or even to odd polynomials. Other restrictions on z_{12} have been derived in this chapter and in Chapter 10.

The partial fraction expansions for the open-circuit impedance functions are

---

* "A reactance theorem" (in German), *Sitzber. preuss. Akad. Wiss., Physik-math. Kl.*, Jahrg. 1931. See also Chapter 5 of Cauer's *Synthesis of Linear Communication Networks*.

$$z_{11} = \frac{k_{11}^{(0)}}{s} + \frac{2k_{11}^{(1)}s}{s^2 + \omega_1^2} + \frac{2k_{11}^{(2)}s}{s^2 + \omega_2^2} + \cdots + k_{11}^{(\infty)}s$$

$$z_{22} = \frac{k_{22}^{(0)}}{s} + \frac{2k_{22}^{(1)}s}{s^2 + \omega_1^2} + \frac{2k_{22}^{(2)}s}{s^2 + \omega_2^2} + \cdots + k_{22}^{(\infty)}s \qquad (11.58)$$

$$z_{12} = \frac{k_{12}^{(0)}}{s} + \frac{2k_{12}^{(1)}s}{s^2 + \omega_1^2} + \frac{2k_{12}^{(2)}s}{s^2 + \omega_2^2} + \cdots + k_{12}^{(\infty)}s$$

where the superscript identifies the pole associated with a given residue. Here the k_{11}'s and k_{22}'s are real and positive, but the k_{12}'s may be either negative or positive.

The Cauer method is based on the conclusion reached in Section 11.1 that the z functions add for networks connected in series when properly isolated by ideal transformers. Thus for networks a, b, and c connected in series, the z functions for the combination are of the form

$$z_{11} = z_{11a} + z_{11b} + z_{11c} \qquad (11.59)$$

and similar expressions apply to z_{12} and z_{22}. Comparison of this equation with Eq. 11.58 suggests that the networks to be connected in series be selected from terms for the same poles in Eq. 11.58 so that for network ν, for example,

$$z_{11} = \frac{2k_{11}^{(\nu)}s}{s^2 + \omega_\nu^2}, \qquad z_{12} = \frac{2k_{12}^{(\nu)}s}{s^2 + \omega_\nu^2}, \qquad \text{and} \qquad z_{22} = \frac{2k_{22}^{(\nu)}s}{s^2 + \omega_\nu^2} \qquad (11.60)$$

and similar expressions may be written for the terms of the s and $1/s$ forms.

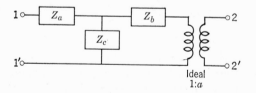
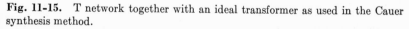

Fig. 11-15. T network together with an ideal transformer as used in the Cauer synthesis method.

A significant part of the Cauer method is the choice of the T network of Fig. 11-15 as the model for each of the subnetworks to be connected in series. For this network, the open-circuit impedance functions are

$$z_{11} = Z_a + Z_c$$

$$z_{12} = aZ_c \qquad (11.61)$$

and
$$z_{22} = a^2 Z_b + a^2 Z_c$$

Solving for the three impedances of the T network gives

$$Z_a = z_{11} - \frac{1}{a} z_{12}$$

$$Z_b = \frac{1}{a^2} z_{22} - \frac{1}{a} z_{12}, \qquad (11.62)$$

and
$$Z_c = \frac{1}{a} z_{12}$$

If the network under study, that of Fig. 11-15, is to play a part in a successful synthesis procedure, it is necessary that Z_a, Z_b, and Z_c be positive real functions. From Eqs. 11.62, we see that this requirement restricts the possible values that may be assigned to z_{11}, z_{12}, and z_{22}. The transfer impedance z_{12} is not necessarily positive real, and the sum or difference of a positive real function and a transfer function is also not necessarily positive real.

Suppose that we restrict the form of the open-circuit impedance functions to the three kinds of terms in Eqs. 11.58 taken one kind at a time. In other words, we assume that either

$$z_{11} = \frac{k_{11}^{(0)}}{s}, \qquad z_{22} = \frac{k_{22}^{(0)}}{s}, \qquad z_{12} = \frac{k_{12}^{(0)}}{s} \qquad (11.63)$$

or
$$z_{11} = \frac{2k_{11}^{(\nu)}s}{s^2 + \omega_\nu^2}, \qquad z_{22} = \frac{2k_{22}^{(\nu)}s}{s^2 + \omega_\nu^2}, \qquad z_{12} = \frac{2k_{12}^{(\nu)}s}{s^2 + \omega_\nu^2} \qquad (11.64)$$

or
$$z_{11} = k_{11}^{(\infty)}s, \qquad z_{22} = k_{22}^{(\infty)}s, \qquad z_{12} = k_{12}^{(\infty)}s \qquad (11.65)$$

For these three cases, the impedance functions differ only in the values of the residues. For any value of ν, it is necessary that the following condition on the residues be met in order that Z_a given by Eqs. 11.62 be positive real:

$$k_{11} - (1/a)k_{12} \geq 0 \qquad (11.66)$$

Similarly, for Z_b to be positive real,

$$(1/a^2)k_{22} - (1/a)k_{12} \geq 0 \qquad (11.67)$$

For Z_c to be positive real, it is necessary that

$$(1/a)k_{12} \geq 0 \tag{11.68}$$

This last condition is satisfied simply by choosing the proper sign for a. The value of a is limited by Eq. 11.66 to

$$|a| \geq \frac{|k_{12}|}{k_{11}} \tag{11.69}$$

and by Eq. 11.67 to

$$a \leq \frac{k_{22}}{|k_{12}|} \tag{11.70}$$

The last two equations tell us that for all values of ν (indicated by inserting the superscripts once more) the magnitude of a is required to be between the limits

$$\frac{\left|k_{12}^{(\nu)}\right|}{k_{11}^{(\nu)}} \leq \left|a^{(\nu)}\right| \leq \frac{k_{22}^{(\nu)}}{\left|k_{12}^{(\nu)}\right|} \tag{11.71}$$

and the sign of a must be chosen to make

$$\frac{1}{a^{(\nu)}} k_{12}^{(\nu)} \geq 0 \tag{11.72}$$

This accomplished, the residue condition is satisfied, since

$$\frac{k_{22}^{(\nu)}}{\left|k_{12}^{(\nu)}\right|} \geq \frac{\left|k_{12}^{(\nu)}\right|}{k_{11}^{(\nu)}} \tag{11.73}$$

implies that

$$k_{11}^{(\nu)} k_{22}^{(\nu)} - [k_{12}^{(\nu)}]^2 \geq 0 \tag{11.74}$$

which is the residue condition.

The network of Fig. 11-15 realizes one term in each of the partial fraction expansions for z_{11}, z_{12}, and z_{22}. By repeated application of the procedure just outlined, networks like that of Fig. 11-15 can be found for every term in the partial fraction expansions of the open-circuit impedance functions of Eqs. 11.58, as shown in Fig. 11-16. The Cauer partial fraction synthesis method realizes a network for *each column* of like terms in the partial fraction expansion for the impedances and then meets the specifications by the manner in which these individual networks are connected together.

From this discussion, we may outline the steps in the Cauer partial fraction method of synthesis of two terminal-pair networks. To begin with, we presume that the given impedance functions satisfy the residue condition. Then the following steps are carried out:

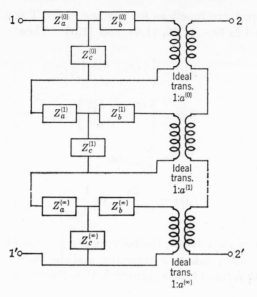

Fig. 11-16.   The connection of the networks of Fig. 11-15 for the Cauer synthesis method.

(1) Expand z_{11}, z_{22}, and z_{12} as partial fractions.   These equations will have the form of Eqs. 11.58 with the possibility that some of the k's will be 0.

(2) Select the magnitude and sign for a from Eqs. 11.71 and 11.72, which may be written as

$$\frac{\left|k_{12}^{(\nu)}\right|}{k_{11}^{(\nu)}} \leq \left|a^{(\nu)}\right| \leq \frac{k_{22}^{(\nu)}}{\left|k_{12}^{(\nu)}\right|} \tag{11.75}$$

If k_{12} is positive, and $k_{11} > k_{12}$, and $k_{22} > k_{12}$, then $a = +1$ may be selected and the ideal transformer removed by a procedure outlined in Fig. 11-18.

(3) From Eqs. 11.62, we next determine the values of the elements of the several T networks.   These values are

$$Z_a^{(\nu)} = z_{11}^{(\nu)} - \frac{1}{a^{(\nu)}} z_{12}^{(\nu)}$$

$$Z_b^{(\nu)} = \frac{1}{a^{(\nu)2}} z_{22}^{(\nu)} - \frac{1}{a^{(\nu)}} z_{12}^{(\nu)} \tag{11.76}$$

and
$$Z_c^{(\nu)} = \frac{1}{a^{(\nu)}} z_{12}^{(\nu)}$$

Now the impedance functions for any one of the T sections have the form assumed in Eqs. 11.63, 11.64, and 11.65   Then

$$Z_a^{(\nu)} = \left[k_{11}^{(\nu)} - \frac{k_{12}^{(\nu)}}{a^{(\nu)}} \right] f_\nu(s)$$

$$Z_b^{(\nu)} = \left[\frac{k_{22}^{(\nu)}}{a^{(\nu)2}} - \frac{k_{12}^{(\nu)}}{a^{(\nu)}} \right] f_\nu(s) \tag{11.77}$$

and

$$Z_c^{(\nu)} = \frac{k_{12}^{(\nu)}}{a^{(\nu)}} f_\nu(s)$$

where

$$f_\nu(s) = \frac{2s}{s^2 + \omega^2} \text{ or } \frac{1}{s} \text{ or } s \tag{11.78}$$

For the first of these forms, the network is a parallel LC combination, the second corresponds to a capacitor, and the third to an inductor. The resulting form of Cauer network is thus that shown in Fig. 11-17.

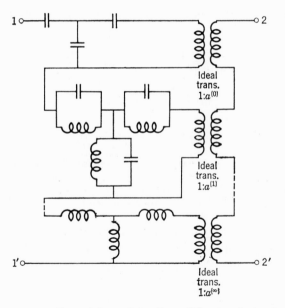

Fig. 11-17. General form of the Cauer LC network structure.

(4) For the special case that $a^{(\nu)} = +1$, the ideal transformer may be removed. The steps in the development in removing 1:1 ideal transformers are illustrated in Figs. 11-18 and 11-19.

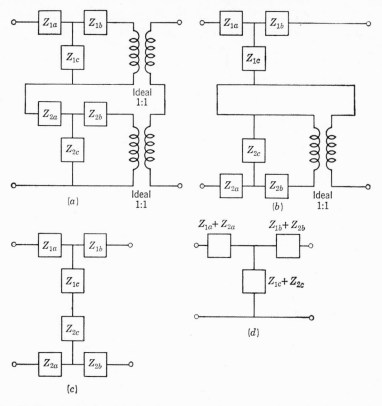

Fig. 11-18.   A step-by-step development of the process of eliminating 1:1 ideal transformers in the Cauer partial fraction network realization.

Example 2.   Consider the following open-circuit impedance functions:

$$z_{11} = \frac{2s^2 + 1}{s} = \frac{1}{s} + 2s$$

$$z_{22} = \frac{2s^2 + 1}{s} = \frac{1}{s} + 2s \tag{11.79}$$

$$z_{12} = \frac{1}{s} = \frac{1}{s} + 0s$$

For $\nu = 0$, we see that $1 \le a^{(0)} \le 1$.   Using the value $a = +1$ in Eqs. 11.77, we find that $Z_a = Z_b = 0$ and $Z_c = 1/s$ which is realized by a 1-farad capacitor.   For $\nu = \infty$, $0 \le a^{(\infty)} \le \infty$.   If we choose the value $+1$, then $Z_a = Z_b = 2s$, realized by a 2-henry inductor, and $Z_c = 0$.   The Cauer partial fraction network realization is shown in Fig. 11-20(a).   Since both ideal transformers are 1:1, the transformers may be removed to give the simple T network shown in Fig. 11-20(b).

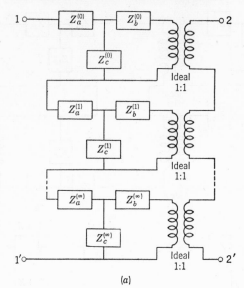

(a)

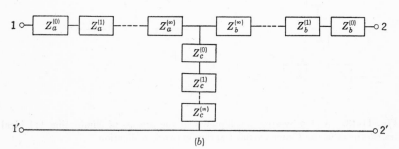

(b)

Fig. 11-19. Two equivalent networks when all ideal transformers have $1:1$ transformation ratios.

Example 3.   It is required to find a network realization for the impedance functions

$$z_{11} = \frac{s(s^2 + 4)}{s^2 + 1} = \frac{3s}{s^2 + 1} + s$$

$$z_{22} = \frac{s}{s^2 + 1} = \frac{s}{s^2 + 1} + 0s \tag{11.80}$$

$$z_{12} = \frac{-s}{s^2 + 1} = \frac{-s}{s^2 + 1} + 0s$$

The term s in z_{11} represents a private pole which may be realized directly without an ideal transformer, as shown in Fig. 11-21, or, alternatively, may be regarded as part of a network with $a = 1$ and $Z_a = s$. For $\nu = 1$, $\frac{1}{3} \leq |a^{(1)}| \leq 1$, and because the sign of $k_{12}^{(1)}$ is negative, $a^{(1)}$ must be negative. Suppose

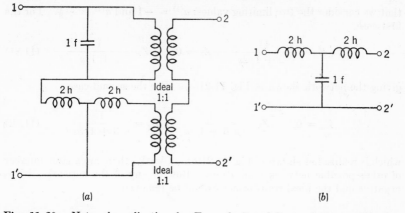

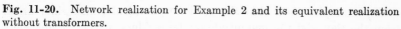

Fig. 11-20. Network realization for Example 2 and its equivalent realization without transformers.

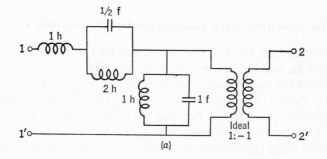

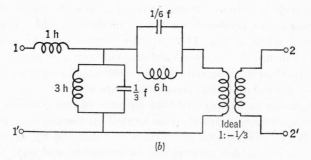

Fig. 11-21. Two network realizations of Example 3.

that we consider the two limiting values: $a^{(1)} = -1$ and $a^{(1)} = -\frac{1}{3}$. For the first case,

$$Z_a = \frac{1}{s/2 + 1/2s}, \qquad Z_b = 0, \qquad Z_c = \frac{1}{s + 1/s} \qquad (11.81)$$

giving the network shown in Fig. 11-21(a). For the second case,

$$Z_a = 0, \qquad Z_b = \frac{1}{s/6 + 1/6s} \qquad Z_c = \frac{1}{s/3 + 1/3s} \qquad (11.82)$$

which is realized as shown in Fig. 11-21(b). Clearly, there are a large number of other possible network realizations. But for any of the networks, $a^{(1)}$ is negative and the ideal transformer cannot be removed.

The examples show that the need for the ideal transformer arises from the sign and the magnitude of the residues of z_{12}. Using ideal transformers for this purpose, it is possible to satisfy the three specification functions z_{11}, z_{12}, and z_{22} exactly.

11.5 RC synthesis with parallel ladders (Guillemin's method)

In deriving Eqs. 11.21, it was shown that for two networks properly connected in parallel, as in Fig. 11-7, the short-circuit admittance functions of the two (or more) networks add. For this addition to be generally valid, it is necessary that an ideal transformer be used. In terms of the network of Fig. 11-22(a), we know that $I_2 = I_{2a} + I_{2b} = I_{2a}' + I_{2b}'$, but we do not know that $I_{2a} = I_{2a}'$ and $I_{2b} = I_{2b}'$ unless there is an ideal transformer at position x-y to so constrain the currents. In the case that the two networks have a common ground (each network is a three-terminal network), then the use of the ideal transformer is not necessary for the y functions to add. For in the two ground wires of Fig. 11-22(b), the currents can be arbitrarily assigned to insure the required current conditions just given. In the synthesis method to be described in this section, all networks will have a common ground and ideal transformers are not necessary.

It was shown in Chapter 10 that all zeros of transmission for RC ladder networks are required to be located on the negative real axis of the s plane. The reason given there was that the RC networks of the arms of the ladder network are in resonance and equivalent to short circuits or open circuits only at frequencies like $s = -1/RC$. Now some applications require zeros of transmission on the imaginary axis or in the complex frequency plane. Might it be possible to use RC networks for these applications? If we restrict consideration to

RC ladder networks, the answer is no.   Earlier in the chapter, it was
pointed out that zeros of transmission can be produced by multiple
transmission paths between input and output terminals.   The use of
parallel *RC* ladder networks to provide the multiple paths was first

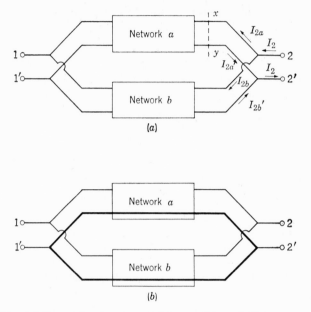

Fig. 11-22.   (*a*) Two networks connected in parallel, and (*b*) two grounded networks in parallel.   The *y* parameters add for (*a*) only with an ideal transformer
at *x*-*y*, but always add for (*b*).

suggested by Guillemin,* who showed that this structure was capable
of producing imaginary or complex zeros of transmission.   Thus it is
possible to use *RC* networks to realize imaginary zeros of transmission
which are usually associated with *LC* networks (suggesting filter
applications†) or complex zeros needed for certain phase-correction
applications.

* "Synthesis of *RC* networks," *Jour. Math. and Phys.*, **28**, 22–42 (1949).
Ernst A. Guillemin (1898–   ) has been a teacher of network theory at MIT
since 1927.   He is widely known for his textbooks, including *Communications
Networks* (two volumes), *The Mathematics of Circuit Analysis*, *Introductory Circuit
Theory*, and *Synthesis of Passive Networks*, and a host of journal articles.   Some
of his contributions and those of his students are described in the last-named book,
which is devoted entirely to the synthesis problem.

† A familiar *RC* "filter" is the twin-T network used in impedance measuring
instruments and many electronic applications.

For several grounded two terminal-pair networks connected in parallel, as in Fig. 11-23, we have for the combination

$$y_{11} = y_{11\alpha} + y_{11\beta} + \cdots + y_{11\omega}$$

$$y_{12} = y'_{12\alpha} + y'_{12\beta} + \cdots + y'_{12\omega} \qquad (11.83)$$

$$y_{22} = y_{22\alpha} + y_{22\beta} + \cdots + y_{22\omega}$$

(The primes on the y_{12} terms are for algebraic convenience in a later step in the derivation.) In satisfying the equation for y_{11}, we have two choices: We can subdivide y_{11}, say by a partial fraction expansion, and assign different parts to $y_{11\alpha}$, $y_{11\beta}$, and $y_{11\gamma}$. Or we can let each of these three functions have the same poles and zeros, but different

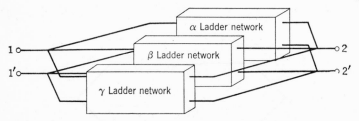

Fig. 11-23. Three ladder networks connected in parallel used in the Guillemin method.

scale factors (meaning simply an adjustment in impedance level) such that

$$y_{11\alpha} = B_\alpha y_{11}, \qquad y_{11\beta} = B_\beta y_{11}, \qquad y_{11\gamma} = B_\gamma y_{11} \qquad (11.84)$$

where the B's are constants. Substituting these equations into that for y_{11} gives the requirement that

$$B_\alpha + B_\beta + B_\gamma = 1 \qquad (11.85)$$

in order that the parallel ladders meet the specifications of y_{11}.

The equation for $-y_{12}$ will next be modified to take into account one of the properties of the Cauer ladder development, the fact that $-y_{12}$ is realized only within the multiplicative or gain constant, k_m. In addition, we must take into account the fact that the adjustment of the impedance level of $y_{11\alpha}$, $y_{11\beta}$, and $y_{11\gamma}$ by the B factors will also affect the impedance level of the functions $y_{12\alpha}$, $y_{12\beta}$, and $y_{12\gamma}$. Thus the transfer admittance functions actually realized by the individual ladders will be

$$y'_{12\alpha} = k_{m\alpha}B_\alpha y_{12\alpha}, \qquad y'_{12\beta} = k_{m\beta}B_\beta y_{12\beta}, \qquad y'_{12\gamma} = k_{m\gamma}B_\gamma y_{12\gamma} \qquad (11.86)$$

Substituting into the second of Eqs. 11.83 gives

$$y_{12} = k_{m\alpha}B_\alpha y_{12\alpha} + k_{m\beta}B_\beta y_{12\beta} + k_{m\gamma}B_\gamma y_{12\gamma} \qquad (11.87)$$

Now we have little control over the k_m's in this equation, but we can choose values for the B's so long as their sum is equal to 1, as required by Eqs. 11.83. One possible way (of many) that this can be accomplished is to let

$$k_{m\alpha}B_\alpha = k_{m\beta}B_\beta = k_{m\gamma}B_\gamma = K_g \qquad (11.88)$$

for under this condition, Eq. 11.87 has a particularly simple form,

$$y_{12} = K_g(y_{12\alpha} + y_{12\beta} + y_{12\gamma}) \qquad (11.89)$$

where K_g is the multiplicative constant which is realized by the paralleled ladders.

For λ ladder networks in parallel, we must satisfy the equations

$$k_{m\alpha}B_\alpha = k_{m\beta}B_\beta = k_{m\gamma}B_\gamma = \cdots = K_g \qquad (11.90)$$

and
$$B_\alpha + B_\beta + B_\gamma + \cdots + B_\lambda = 1 \qquad (11.91)$$

These equations constitute λ simultaneous equations with the B's as unknowns once realized values of the k's have been determined. When these equations are solved and the B values determined, the impedance level of each of the ladder networks can accordingly be scaled. This amounts to multiplying all capacitance values by B and dividing all resistance values by B, as in our study of scaling in Chapter 2. The λ ladder networks are then connected in parallel to realize the y_{12} specifications within the constant multiplier, K_g, of Eq. 11.88, and the y_{11} (or y_{22}) specifications exactly. The derived relationships hold only for the short-circuit admittance functions, and not for z_{12} and z_{11} of course. Parallel ladder synthesis is always accomplished from the y functions, never from the z's directly.

We still have to consider the expansion of the specification function, $-y_{12}$, into a sum of the form of Eq. 11.89. Let us write $y_{11} = p(s)/q(s)$, and

$$-y_{12} = \frac{a_0 + a_1 s + a_2 s^2 + \cdots + a_n s^n}{q(s)} = \frac{r(s)}{q(s)} \qquad (11.92)$$

This equation can be expanded into a sum in at least two simple ways:

(1) We can write

$$-y_{12} = \frac{a_0}{q(s)} + \frac{a_1 s}{q(s)} + \frac{a_2 s^2}{q(s)} + \cdots + \frac{a_n s^n}{q(s)} \tag{11.93}$$

(2) Also, we can take numerator terms two at a time so long as they last and write

$$-y_{12} = \frac{a_0 + a_1 s}{q(s)} + \frac{a_2 s^2 + a_3 s^3}{q(s)} + \cdots + \frac{a_{n-1} s^{n-1} + a_n s^n}{q(s)} \tag{11.94}$$

In these two forms, and possibly in others, the zeros of transmission are all at zero or at infinity or on the negative real axis, so long as all of the a coefficients are real and positive. This being the case, each component of $-y_{12}$ can be realized as an RC ladder network. Furthermore, the ladder networks will often have simple forms since the first and second Cauer forms, which are realized by a simple continued fraction expansion, are identified with all zeros of transmission at infinity and zero respectively.

Example 4. As an example of the Guillemin method of parallel ladder synthesis, consider the following specification functions:

$$y_{22} = \frac{(s+1)(s+3)}{(s+2)(s+4)}, \qquad -y_{12} = \frac{s^2 + s + 1}{(s+2)(s+4)} \tag{11.95}$$

where the complex zeros are in the left half of the s plane and where y_{22}, the given specification function, reflects the fact that these functions were selected from a $G_{12} = -y_{12}/y_{22}$ specification. The method requires that

$$y_{22\alpha} = y_{22\beta} = \frac{(s+1)(s+3)}{(s+2)(s+4)} \tag{11.96}$$

which will later be scaled by B factors. We may arbitrarily select the transfer functions

$$-y_{12\alpha} = \frac{s+1}{(s+2)(s+4)}, \qquad -y_{12\beta} = \frac{s^2}{(s+2)(s+4)} \tag{11.97}$$

to satisfy the $-y_{12}$ specifications. The two required ladder networks, here called the α ladder and the β ladder, are next synthesized as shown in Fig. 11-24.

The α ladder. From Fig. 11.24(a), we see that the zero of transmission at $s = -1$ can be realized by removing a pole of the function $1/y_{22\alpha}$ at $s = -1$. The residue of this pole is $\frac{3}{2}$, and the impedance that remains when this pole is removed is

$$z_1 = \frac{1}{y_{22\alpha}} - \frac{\frac{3}{2}}{s+1} = \frac{s + 3.5}{s+3} \tag{11.98}$$

The remaining transmission zero is at infinity, and can be realized by developing the remainder of the network as a first Cauer ladder. Then

$$
\begin{array}{c}
s + 3)s + 3.5(1 \\
\underline{s + 3} \\
\tfrac{1}{2})s + 3(2s \\
\underline{s} \\
3)\tfrac{1}{2}(\tfrac{1}{6}
\end{array}
\tag{11.99}
$$

The network is shown in Fig. 11-24(a).

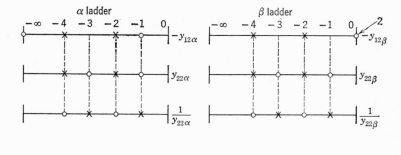

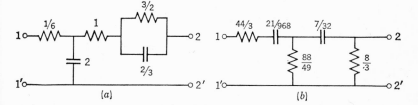

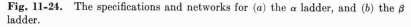

Fig. 11-24. The specifications and networks for (a) the α ladder, and (b) the β ladder.

The β ladder. The transmission zeros of the β ladder are at the origin, as shown in Fig. 11-24(b). The continued fraction development of $y_{22\beta}$ gives

$$
y_{22\beta} = \frac{3}{8} + \cfrac{1}{\cfrac{32}{7}\cfrac{1}{s} + \cfrac{1}{\cfrac{49}{88} + \cfrac{1}{\cfrac{968}{21}\cfrac{1}{s} + \cfrac{1}{\frac{3}{44}}}}}
\tag{11.100}
$$

and the second Cauer form of network shown in Fig. 11-24(b) results.

Our next task is that of connecting the two ladders in parallel such that the y_{22} specifications are realized. From the networks given in Fig. 11-24, we find that

$$
k_{m\alpha} = 3 \qquad \text{and} \qquad k_{m\beta} = \tfrac{3}{44}
\tag{11.101}
$$

Then, from Eqs. 11.90 and 11.91, we have

$$B_\alpha + B_\beta = 1 \tag{11.102}$$

and

$$3B_\alpha = \tfrac{3}{44}B_\beta \tag{11.103}$$

Solving these two equations simultaneously gives

$$B_\alpha = \tfrac{1}{45} \quad \text{and} \quad B_\beta = \tfrac{44}{45} \tag{11.104}$$

so that

$$k_{m\alpha}B_\alpha = k_{m\beta}B_\beta = \tfrac{1}{15} \tag{11.105}$$

Thus our realization gives for $-y_{12}$,

$$-y_{12} = \frac{1}{15}\frac{s^2 + s + 1}{(s + 2)(s + 4)} \tag{11.106}$$

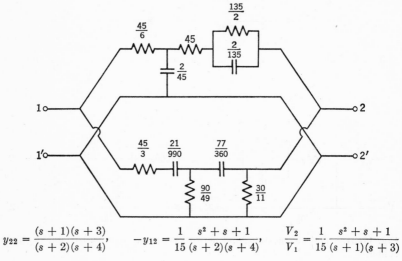

$$y_{22} = \frac{(s + 1)(s + 3)}{(s + 2)(s + 4)}, \quad -y_{12} = \frac{1}{15}\frac{s^2 + s + 1}{(s + 2)(s + 4)}, \quad \frac{V_2}{V_1} = \frac{1}{15}\frac{s^2 + s + 1}{(s + 1)(s + 3)}$$

Fig. 11-25. Final network composed of two ladder networks in parallel by Guillemin's method for Example 4.

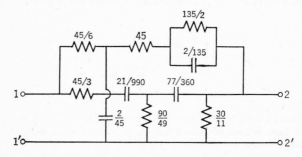

Fig. 11-26. Alternative method of representing the parallel ladder networks of Fig. 11-25.

and the y_{22} specification is realized exactly. The complete network with the ladders paralleled is shown in Figs. 11-25 and 11-26. Element values in the ladders were found by multiplying capacitances by the appropriate B value, and dividing resistance values by the appropriate B.

The Guillemin method applied to RC ladder networks depends on the coefficients of the numerator polynomial of $-y_{12}$ being positive. This does not imply that the zeros of transmission must be in the left half plane. For example, the specifications

$$y_{22} = \frac{(s + \tfrac{1}{2})(s + 1.5)(s + 3)}{(s + 1)(s + 2)(s + 5)} \tag{11.107}$$

and

$$-y_{12} = \frac{(s^2 - 2s + 10)(s + 4)}{(s + 1)(s + 2)(s + 5)} = \frac{s^3 + 2s^2 + 2s + 40}{(s + 1)(s + 2)(s + 5)} \tag{11.108}$$

can be realized by two parallel RC ladders, and give two complex right half plane zeros. Zeros on the positive real axis cannot be realized by any method using a common terminal for input and output.

FURTHER READING

Elementary treatments of the ideal transformer are to be found in the MIT Electrical Engineering Staff's *Electric Circuits*, John Wiley & Sons, New York, 1940, pp. 384–389, and *Magnetic Circuits and Transformers*, John Wiley & Sons, New York, 1943, pp. 268–271, and in A. E. Fitzgerald and C. Kingsley's *Electric Machinery*, McGraw-Hill Book Co., New York, 1952, pp. 646–655. A more advanced summary is given by Cauer in a special appendix devoted to the subject in *Synthesis of Linear Communication Networks*, pp. 167–179.

For further reading on the Cauer partial fraction method, see Cauer, *op. cit.*, pp. 200–220; Guillemin, *Synthesis of Passive Networks*, pp. 218–228; or Balabanian, *Network Synthesis*, pp. 220–226. An excellent description of the parallel ladder method is given by Guillemin, *op. cit.*, pp. 550–562. Also pertinent to this subject is the augmentation of polynomials to secure all positive coefficients (relating to Prob. 11–23) given by Guillemin, *op. cit.*, pp. 437–444. See also E. S. Kuh, "Parallel ladder realization of transfer admittance functions," *Proc. N.E.C.*, **10**, 198–206 (1954). For extensions to this method, see the Further Reading section in Chapter 10.

Of historical interest is the pioneer paper by C. M. Gewertz, "Synthesis of a finite, four-terminal network from its prescribed driving-point functions and transfer function," *Jour. Math and Phys.*, **12**, 1–257 (1932–33), which also appeared in book form as *Network Synthesis*, The Williams and Wilkins Co., Baltimore, 1933.

PROBLEMS

11-1. Find the necessary relationships between C and C_1, R and R_1, and L and L_1 in order that the networks shown in Fig. P11-1 are equivalent. Show the method clearly.

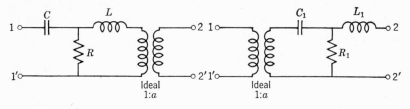

Fig. P11-1

11-2. For the network of Fig. P11-2, show that $z_{11} = z_{22} = s + 1/s$, and $z_{12} = 1/s$.

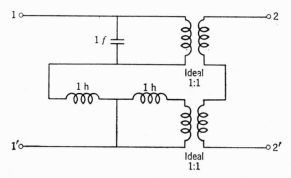

Fig. P11-2

11-3. For the network illustrated in Fig. P11-3, find z_{11}, z_{12}, and z_{22} in terms of Z_1 and Z_2.

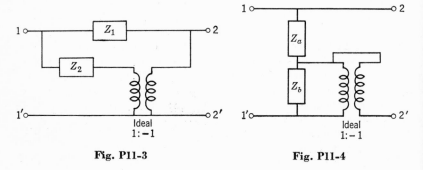

Fig. P11-3   **Fig. P11-4**

11-4. Find the values of the open-circuit impedance functions, z_{11}, z_{12}, and z_{22}, in terms of Z_a and Z_b for the network of Fig. P11-4.

11-5. If the two networks shown in Fig. P11-5 are to be equivalent, find the values for M, L_a, and L_b in terms of L_1, L_2, and a, and compute the coefficient of coupling k of the transformer.

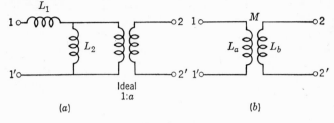

Fig. P11-5

11-6. For the network of Fig. P11-6, determine the coupled coil equivalent (with $k < 1$), the equivalent T network, and the equivalent π network.

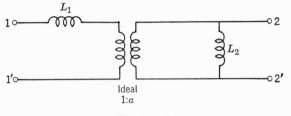

Fig. P11-6

11-7. Figure P11-7 shows a network made up of an ideal transformer with two inductors. Show that this network has a single transformer equivalent (with $k < 1$), and determine both the equivalent T and the equivalent π networks.

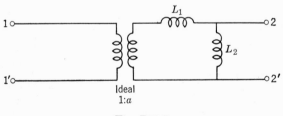

Fig. P11-7

11-8. The network of Fig. P11-8 is one given by Matthaei.* By combining L_s with L_3, show that the unity coupling coefficient transformer may be replaced by one with a coupling coefficient of 0.64.

* *Loc. cit.*

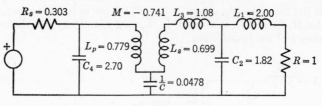

Fig. P11-8

11-9. Figure P11-9 shows a network having a coupling coefficient of 0.496. Find a network equivalent to the one given but containing a unity coefficient of coupling transformer.

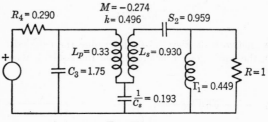

Fig. P11-9

11-10. Determine the residues of the open-circuit impedance functions,

$$z_{11} = \frac{5s^4 + 13.217s^2 + 5.060}{2.964s^3 + 4.458s}$$

$$z_{22} = \frac{s^4 + 5.193s^2 + 2.530}{2.964s^3 + 4.458s}$$

$$z_{12} = \frac{\sqrt{5}\,(s^4 + 1.6s^2 + 1.6)}{2.964s^3 + 4.458s}$$

and show that the residue condition is satisfied with the equality sign at each of the poles.

11-11. For the network of Fig. P11-11,

$$y_{11} = \frac{(s+1)(s+3)}{(s+2)(s+4)} \quad \text{and} \quad -y_{12} = \frac{(s+1)}{(s+2)(s+4)}$$

Find y_{22} and show that the residue condition is satisfied at each pole.

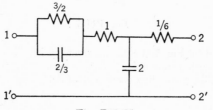

Fig. P11-11

11-12. Given

$$z_{11} = \frac{s(s^2 + 4)(s^2 + 16)}{(s^2 + 1)(s^2 + 9)}$$

$$z_{22} = \frac{s(s^2 + 6)}{(s^2 + 1)(s^2 + 9)}$$

$$z_{12} = \frac{Ks}{(s^2 + 1)(s^2 + 9)}$$

What is the largest value K may have if the impedance functions are to represent a network?

11-13. Show that when $z_{12}(s) = 0$, i.e., at the zeros of z_{12}, (a) $y_{11} = 1/z_{11}$ and $z_{22} = 1/y_{22}$, and (b) this result implies that impedance and admittance measurements made at the input terminals will be the same whether the output terminals are open-circuited or short-circuited.

11-14. An alternative method of Cauer synthesis makes use of a π network with ideal transformer, with these network-transformer combinations connected in parallel as shown in Fig. P11-14. Complete a derivation parallel to that of Section 11.4 for this case, working in terms of y_{11}, y_{12}, and y_{22}.

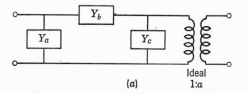

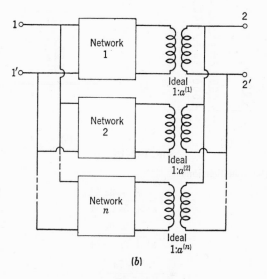

Fig. P11-14

11-15. Synthesize a Cauer network to meet the following specifications:

$$z_{11} = \frac{3s + 4}{(s + 1)(s + 2)}$$

$$z_{22} = \frac{3s + 4}{(s + 1)(s + 2)}$$

$$z_{12} = \frac{s}{(s + 1)(s + 2)}$$

11-16. Given

$$z_{11} = \frac{2s}{s^2 + 1} + \frac{3s}{s^2 + 4} + s$$

$$z_{22} = \frac{4s}{s^2 + 1} + 0 + 3s$$

$$z_{12} = \frac{s}{s^2 + 1} + 0 - s$$

find a Cauer network realization. Select values of a such that the network has only one ideal transformer. For the network shown in Fig. P11-16(a), show how two of the three ideal transformers may be removed to give the network of (b).

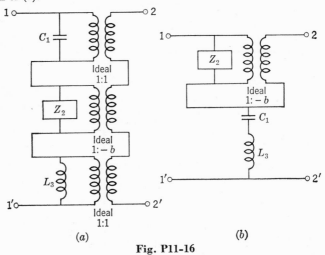

(a) (b)

Fig. P11-16

11-17. Given the specifications

$$z_{11} = 3\frac{s^3 + 3s}{s^4 + 5s^2 + 4}$$

$$z_{22} = 6\frac{s^3 + 3s}{s^4 + 5s^2 + 4}$$

$$z_{12} = \frac{s^3 + 7s}{s^4 + 5s^2 + 4}$$

determine one Cauer network realization and remove as many ideal transformers as possible.

11-18. From the following open-circuit impedance functions

$$z_{11} = \frac{s(s^2 + 4)(s^2 + 16)}{(s^2 + 1)(s^2 + 9)}$$

$$z_{22} = \frac{s(s^2 + 6)}{(s^2 + 1)(s^2 + 9)}$$

$$z_{12} = \frac{Hs}{(s^2 + 1)(s^2 + 9)}$$

synthesize a network by the Cauer method. For this problem, choose H such that $k_{11}^{(3)}k_{22}^{(3)} = [k_{12}^{(3)}]^2$, and choose the lower limit as the value for $a^{(1)}$.

11-19. Synthesize a Cauer network to meet the following specifications:

$$y_{11} = \frac{6s^2 + 2}{s^3 + s}, \qquad y_{22} = \frac{3s^2 + 2}{s^3 + s}, \qquad y_{12} = \frac{H}{s^3 + s}$$

Choose H so that the resulting network has the simplest (nontrivial) form.

11-20. Given the specifications

$$y_{22} = \frac{(s + 1)(s + 3)}{(s + 2)(s + 4)} \qquad \text{and} \qquad -y_{12} = \frac{s^2 + s + 1}{(s + 2)(s + 4)}$$

the choice

$$-y_{12\alpha} = \frac{s^2}{(s + 2)(s + 4)}$$

$$-y_{12\beta} = \frac{s}{(s + 2)(s + 4)}$$

$$-y_{12\gamma} = \frac{1}{(s + 2)(s + 4)}$$

and
$$y_{22\alpha} = y_{22\beta} = y_{22\gamma} = \frac{1}{3}\frac{(s + 1)(s + 3)}{(s + 2)(s + 4)}$$

is made for parallel ladder synthesis. Clearly the three parallel networks combine to meet the specification for y_{22} as required providing there is no subsequent level scaling. What, if anything, is *wrong* with this solution?

11-21. Determine an RC network satisfying the requirements that

$$y_{22} = \frac{(s + 1)(s + 3)}{(s + 2)(s + 4)} \qquad \text{and} \qquad -y_{12} = \frac{s^2 + s + 4}{(s + 2)(s + 4)}$$

Find k_m for your network realization.

11-22. A network is required which is described by the two specification functions:

$$y_{22} = \frac{s^2 + 2s + \frac{3}{4}}{s^2 + 4s + \frac{13}{4}} \quad \text{and} \quad -y_{12} = \frac{s^2 + 1}{s^2 + 4s + \frac{13}{4}}$$

Find k_m for your network realization.

11-23. Synthesize an RC network to realize the specification given by the voltage-ratio transfer function

$$G_{12}(s) = \frac{V_2(s)}{V_1(s)} = \frac{s^2 - s + 9}{s^2 + 5s + 4}$$

11-24. Figure P11-24 shows a three terminal-pair network of a special kind with both output terminal pairs open-circuited.

(a) Show that the poles and zeros of the voltage ratio function $V_1(s)/V_2(s)$ may have any s plane location providing they occur in conjugate pairs if complex.

(b) Suppose that it is required that

$$\frac{V_1(s)}{V_2(s)} = K(s - 1)(s - 3)$$

Outline the necessary properties of $V_1(s)/V_0(s)$ and $V_2(s)/V_0(s)$ and select a set of functions appropriate for the given specification.

(c) Repeat part (b) for

$$\frac{V_1(s)}{V_2(s)} = \frac{1}{(s - 1)(s^2 - s + 1)}$$

(d) What is the significance of V_1/V_2 having poles in the right half plane with respect to (1) stability, and (2) phase in the sinusoidal steady state?

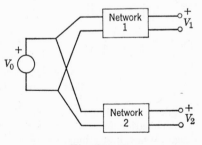

Fig. P11-24

11-25. For the ideal transformer, what are the values of L_p, L_s, and M? Compare these values with those possible for the Brune transformer. Resolve and explain any differences in the two answers. Suppose that you were assigned the task of building a transformer that closely approximated the ideal transformer. Describe your design. What size wire would you use? etc.

Symmetrical Lattice and Constant-Resistance Networks

. . . . *12*

In this chapter, we first study the symmetrical *lattice*, a name suggested by the geometrical form shown in Fig. 12-1. The lattice has long been used in communications systems and is important in both the historical development of network theory and in applications. We then turn to several network structures which have constant-resistance input impedance when terminated in a resistive load.

12.1 Impedance equations for the lattice

If the symmetrical lattice network of Fig. 12-1(a) is unwrapped to the equivalent form of Fig. 12-1(b), it is recognized that the symmetrical lattice is identical with a bridge network. The bridge representation is more convenient for the analysis of a single section. But if a number of lattice sections are connected in tandem, then the form of Fig. 12-1(a) is the only practical representation. The open-circuit impedance functions are found from Fig. 12-1(b) to be

$$z_{11} = z_{22} = \tfrac{1}{2}(Z_a + Z_b) \tag{12.1}$$

and
$$z_{12} = \tfrac{1}{2}(Z_b - Z_a) \tag{12.2}$$

The first of these equations is derived by inspection of the network. The driving-point impedance at terminals 1-1′ with terminals 2-2′ open

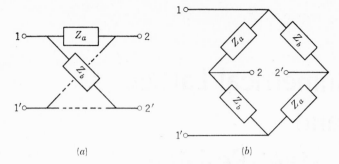

Fig. 12-1. (*a*) The standard representation of the symmetrical lattice. The dashed cross arm represents Z_b and the dashed series arm Z_a. (*b*) The bridge form of the symmetrical lattice.

is the impedance of two identical branches in parallel, the impedance of each branch being $Z_a + Z_b$. The second equation, Eq. 12.2, may be found by first computing the voltage of terminal 2 with respect to terminal 2′, which is

$$V_2 = \frac{Z_b V_1}{Z_a + Z_b} - \frac{Z_a V_1}{Z_a + Z_b} \qquad (12.3)$$

Now the voltage V_1 is related to the current I_1 with terminals 2-2′ open by Eq. 12.1:

$$V_1 = I_1[\tfrac{1}{2}(Z_a + Z_b)] \qquad (12.4)$$

Substituting this value of V_1 into Eq. 12.3 gives

$$\frac{V_2}{I_1} = z_{12} = \tfrac{1}{2}(Z_b - Z_a) \qquad (12.5)$$

which is in Eq. 12.2. From Eqs. 12.1 and 12.2, we express Z_a and Z_b in terms of the open-circuit impedance functions as

$$Z_a = z_{11} - z_{12} \qquad (12.6)$$

and $$Z_b = z_{11} + z_{12} = z_{22} + z_{12} \qquad (12.7)$$

Similar expressions may be found for the short-circuit admittance functions in terms of the lattice arm admittances, $Y_a = 1/Z_a$ and $Y_b = 1/Z_b$. These are

$$y_{11} = y_{22} = \tfrac{1}{2}(Y_a + Y_b) \qquad (12.8)$$

and $$y_{12} = \tfrac{1}{2}(Y_b - Y_a) \qquad (12.9)$$

Solving these equations for Y_a and Y_b gives

$$Y_a = y_{11} - y_{12} = y_{22} - y_{12} \qquad (12.10)$$

and $$Y_b = y_{11} + y_{12} = y_{22} + y_{12} \qquad (12.11)$$

These equations are keystones for synthesis procedures for the symmetrical lattice.

Can we be sure that the impedance functions Z_a and Z_b and the admittance functions Y_a and Y_b will always be positive real? This is clearly an important question in synthesis. The answer may be given in terms of a property of two terminal-pair networks given in Chapter 11. If we let $\mathrm{Re}\, z_{11}(s) = r_{11}$, $\mathrm{Re}\, z_{22}(s) = r_{22}$, and $\mathrm{Re}\, z_{12}(s) = r_{12}$, then by Eq. 11.57

$$r_{11}r_{22} - r_{12}{}^2 \geq 0 \text{ for } \sigma \geq 0 \qquad (12.12)$$

For a symmetrical network, $r_{11} = r_{22}$, so that

$$r_{11}r_{22} = r_{11}{}^2 = r_{22}{}^2 \qquad (12.13)$$

and Eq. 12.12 may be written

$$(r_{11} + r_{12})(r_{11} - r_{12}) \geq 0 \text{ for } \sigma \geq 0 \qquad (12.14)$$

Now r_{12} can be negative, but r_{11}, the real part of a positive real function, cannot. From the equation, we see that there is no way for both factors to be negative. The equation is satisfied only when both factors are positive. The factors in this equation remind us of Eqs. 12.6 and 12.7 which have the following real parts:

$$\mathrm{Re}\, Z_b = r_{11} + r_{12} \qquad (12.15)$$

and $$\mathrm{Re}\, Z_a = r_{11} - r_{12} \qquad (12.16)$$

From this we see that if Eq. 12.12 holds, which must be the case for *any* two terminal-pair network realization to exist at all, then

$$\mathrm{Re}\, Z_b(s) \geq 0 \text{ for } \sigma \geq 0 \qquad (12.17)$$

and $$\mathrm{Re}\, Z_a(s) \geq 0 \text{ for } \sigma \geq 0 \qquad (12.18)$$

These equations tell us that Z_a and Z_b found from the given z_{11}, z_{12}, and z_{22} functions (or the y functions) which satisfy the residue condition are always positive real and can therefore always be realized as a one terminal-pair network for the arms of the lattice. Thus, if there is any symmetrical network realization for a set of specification functions at all, then there is a symmetrical lattice realization! This is an important conclusion.

12.2   Several synthesis procedures for the unloaded lattice

There are a large number of methods by which unloaded symmetrical lattices may be synthesized, and most are simple and direct.   Several representative methods will be described in this section for the LC, RC, and RL cases, and *sometimes* for the general RLC case.

Given z_{11} and z_{12}.   In the Cauer ladder development studied in Chapter 10, networks were found to satisfy z_{11} specifications exactly and z_{12} specifications within a multiplicative constant.   For similar specifications for the lattice, we assign a multiplicative constant to z_{12} as the first step.   Replacing z_{12} by $k_l z_{12}$ in Eqs. 12.6 and 12.7, we have

$$Z_a = z_{11} - k_l z_{12} \tag{12.19}$$

and

$$Z_b = z_{11} + k_l z_{12} \tag{12.20}$$

If both z_{11} and z_{12} are expanded by partial fractions, then the range of values of k_l that will make Z_a positive real can usually be found by inspection.   An example will illustrate this simple synthesis method.

Example 1.   Given the open-circuit impedance specifications

$$z_{11} = \frac{s^4 + 4s^2 + 1}{s(s^2 + 1)}, \qquad z_{12} = \frac{2s^4 + 9s^2 + 1}{s(s^2 + 1)} \tag{12.21}$$

The impedance z_{11} (which is equal to z_{22} of course) is seen to be positive real and LC.   Expanding z_{11} and $k_l z_{12}$ by partial fractions,

$$z_{11} = \frac{1}{s} + \frac{2s}{s^2 + 1} + s \tag{12.22}$$

$$k_l z_{12} = \frac{k_l}{s} + \frac{6k_l s}{s^2 + 1} + 2k_l s \tag{12.23}$$

We consider these two equations one column at a time.   From the first column, it is necessary that $k_l \leq 1$, from the second that $k_l \leq \frac{1}{3}$, and from the last that $k_l \leq \frac{1}{2}$.   Then $Z_a = z_{11} - k_l z_{12}$ will be positive real for $k_l \leq \frac{1}{3}$, each term in the partial fraction expansion for Z_a being positive real under this condition.   If we select that value $k_l = \frac{1}{3}$, then Z_a and Z_b are found to be

$$Z_a = \frac{\frac{2}{3}}{s} + \frac{1}{3}s \tag{12.24}$$

and

$$Z_b = \frac{\frac{4}{3}}{s} + \frac{4s}{s^2 + 1} + \frac{5}{3}s \tag{12.25}$$

The LC networks for Z_a and Z_b are those shown in the lattice network realization of Fig. 12-2.   Other choices of k_l will give other networks.   While this example has been for an LC network, it is clear that the approach applies to RC or RL and sometimes to RLC networks.

Satisfying z_{12} only. Suppose that the only specification function is z_{12} but that it must be realized exactly. For this case, only Eq. 12.5 need be satisfied; i.e.,

$$z_{12} = \tfrac{1}{2}(Z_b - Z_a) \tag{12.26}$$

or $$2z_{12} = Z_b - Z_a \tag{12.27}$$

This equation applies to the network shown in Fig. 12-1 which is an unloaded lattice. The expression of z_{12} in terms of the difference of two positive real functions reminds us that z_{12} is not necessarily positive real. But we must always be able to select positive real forms for both Z_a and Z_b for any z_{12} specification. This is always possible, as can be seen from the following argument. The poles of z_{12} are required to be in the left half of the s plane. Therefore the poles of Z_a and Z_b

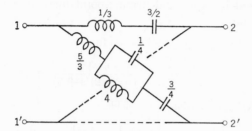

Fig. 12-2. The lattice network realization of Example 1.

are in the left half plane. It is always possible to add a constant, representing resistance, to both Z_a and Z_b without affecting z_{12}. By adding resistance to both Z_a and Z_b until the real parts of these impedance functions are positive for all values of $s = j\omega$, we can insure that both Z_a and Z_b are positive real. There will never be a unique form for Z_a and Z_b, however, so that the number of possible realizations is unlimited. But as a practical matter, we can always try a number of possibilities with little expenditure of time or effort with such a simple synthesis procedure.

The actual steps in synthesis may be carried out in the following order:

(1) We first factor the denominator of the given z_{12} into 1st-degree terms for real roots and into 2nd-degree terms for conjugate complex roots.

(2) We expand z_{12} into a partial fraction summation.

(3) Every term in this partial fraction expansion must be made positive real *except for sign*. First-degree factors will always satisfy

this requirement. Second-degree factors like

$$\frac{a_1 + jb_1}{s + \sigma_1 + j\omega_1} + \frac{a_1 - jb_1}{s + \sigma_1 - j\omega_1} \tag{12.28}$$

are positive real if

$$\frac{a_1}{|b_1|} \geq \frac{\omega_1}{\sigma_1} \tag{12.29}$$

(4) Nonpositive real terms in the expansion are then expressed as the difference of two terms with the proper distribution of residues or with the addition of a constant such that every term is positive real except for sign.

(5) Finally, we designate the terms with positive signs to be Z_b and those with negative signs to be Z_a. The impedances Z_a and Z_b may then be realized by the usual driving-point methods and the lattice synthesis is complete.

Example 2. Consider the specification function

$$2z_{12} = \frac{3s^2 + 6s + 1}{(s + 1)(s + 2)(s + 3)} \tag{12.30}$$

The partial fraction expansion of z_{12} yields

$$2z_{12} = Z_b - Z_a = \frac{-1}{s + 1} + \frac{-1}{s + 2} + \frac{5}{s + 3} \tag{12.31}$$

Suppose that we arbitrarily assign terms in this expansion to Z_a and Z_b as follows:

$$Z_b = \frac{5}{s + 3}, \qquad Z_a = \frac{1}{s + 1} + \frac{1}{s + 2} \tag{12.32}$$

One other possibility is to let

$$Z_b = \frac{1}{s + 1} + \frac{5}{s + 3}, \qquad Z_a = \frac{2}{s + 1} + \frac{1}{s + 2} \tag{12.33}$$

The lattice network corresponding to the first choice, Eqs. 12.32, is shown in Fig. 12-3

This method of synthesis is fairly general and has been applied to the RLC case* as well as the RC, LC, and RL cases.†

---

* Louis Weinberg, "RLC lattice networks," *Proc. I.R.E.*, **41**, 1139–1144 (1953); correction 1667. In the case of multiple poles, a special procedure is required and is given in this paper.

† E. A. Guillemin, "RC-coupling networks," MIT Rad. Lab. Report 43, 1944, and J. L. Bower and P. F. Ordung, "The synthesis of resistor-capacitor networks," *Proc. I.R.E.*, **38**, 263–269 (1950).

Given the transfer function G_{12}.   The open-circuit voltage-ratio transfer function for the symmetrical lattice structure may be found directly from Eq. 12.3.   Then

$$G_{12}(s) = \frac{V_2(s)}{V_1(s)}\bigg|_{I_2=0} = \frac{Z_b - Z_a}{Z_b + Z_a} = \frac{1 - (Z_a/Z_b)}{1 + (Z_a/Z_b)} \qquad (12.34)$$

Solving this equation for the impedance ratio Z_a/Z_b, we have

$$\frac{Z_a}{Z_b} = \frac{1 - G_{12}}{1 + G_{12}} \qquad (12.35)$$

Since G_{12} is a quotient of polynomials in s, $G_{12}(s) = p(s)/q(s)$, the last equation may be written in the form,

$$\frac{Z_a}{Z_b} = \frac{q(s) - p(s)}{q(s) + p(s)} \qquad (12.36)$$

This equation relates the polynomials $q \pm p$ to the quotient of driving-point impedance functions.

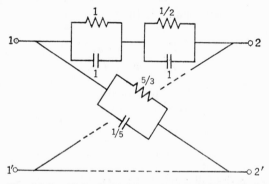

Fig. 12-3.   Unloaded lattice network of Example 2.

Using these three basic equations and the associated conclusions, several synthesis possibilities may be formulated.*   The most direct choice in satisfying Eq. 12.35 is to let

$$Z_a = 1 - G_{12}(s) \qquad \text{and} \qquad Z_b = 1 + G_{12}(s) \qquad (12.37)$$

or

$$Z_a = \frac{1}{1 + G_{12}(s)} \qquad \text{and} \qquad Z_b = \frac{1}{1 - G_{12}(s)} \qquad (12.38)$$

* See A. D. Fialkow and I. Gerst, "*RLC* lattice transfer functions," *Proc. I.R.E.*, **43**, 462 (1955), and P. M. Lewis II, "Voltage transfer synthesis—*RLC* lattice," *IRE Trans.*, **CT-2**, 282 (1955).

Let us expand $G_{12}(s)$ by partial fractions. The terms in this partial fraction expansion may or may not be positive real and so realizable by one terminal-pair techniques. However, those terms which are not positive real can be made positive real by the addition of a constant (resistance), as discussed earlier in this section. If it is possible to modify the G_{12} specification function to be

$$k_1 G_{12} = k_1 \frac{p_1(s)}{q(s)} \tag{12.39}$$

where k_1 can be made sufficiently small, then the 1 in $1 \pm G_{12}$ can be regarded as a reservoir from which resistance can be taken as needed to make the individual terms in the partial fraction expansion positive real. It is interesting to note that the input impedance of a lattice designed on the basis of Eqs. 12.37 is

$$z_{11} = z_{22} = \tfrac{1}{2}(Z_a + Z_b) = \tfrac{1}{2}(1 - G_{12} + 1 + G_{12}) = 1 \text{ ohm} \tag{12.40}$$

Another interesting synthesis procedure* is possible for the special condition that either the even or the odd parts of the polynomials $q(s) \pm p(s)$ are proportional. If the odd parts are proportional, then we may write

$$\frac{Z_a}{Z_b} = \frac{m_1 + n_1}{m_2 + kn_1} \tag{12.41}$$

where k is the constant of proportionality. Dividing numerator and denominator of this equation by n_1 gives

$$\frac{Z_a}{Z_b} = \frac{1 + m_1/n_1}{k + m_2/n_1} \tag{12.42}$$

If we next make the following assignments,

$$Z_a = 1 + m_1/n_1 \tag{12.43}$$

and $$Z_b = k + m_2/n_1 \tag{12.44}$$

then we see that each impedance can be realized by a resistor in series with a network synthesized from the functions m_1/n_1 and m_2/n_1. Now in Chapter 4 it was shown that such functions as these are reactance functions representing a one terminal-pair LC network. Hence each arm of the lattice synthesized by this procedure is a single resistor in series with an LC network. If we assign the impedances

* Lewis, *loc. cit.*

of Eq. 12.42 in the alternative form,

$$Z_a = \frac{1}{k + m_2/n_1} \qquad (12.45)$$

$$Z_b = \frac{1}{1 + m_1/n_1} \qquad (12.46)$$

then Z_a and Z_b can be synthesized as a single resistor in parallel with an LC network. Similar derivations can be made for the case with the even parts of $q - p$ and $q + p$ proportional. (See Prob. 12-11.)

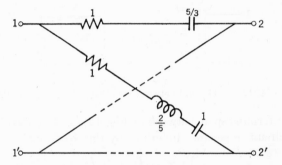

Fig. 12-4. Unloaded lattice network synthesized from open-circuit voltage-ratio transfer function specifications in Example 3.

Example 3. It is required that the voltage-ratio transfer function

$$G_{12}(s) = \frac{s^2 + 1}{s^2 + 5s + 4} \qquad (12.47)$$

be realized as a balanced lattice network. By the Lewis method,

$$q(s) \pm p(s) = (s^2 + 5s + 4) \pm (s^2 + 1) \qquad (12.48)$$

so that from Eq. 12.36,

$$\frac{Z_a}{Z_b} = \frac{5s + 3}{2s^2 + 5s + 5} = \frac{1 + 3/5s}{1 + (2s^2 + 5)/5s} \qquad (12.49)$$

Here the odd parts of the numerator and denominator polynomials are equal to each other and $k = 1$. Then by Eqs. 12.43 and 12.44,

$$Z_a = 1 + 3/5s$$

and $\qquad\qquad Z_b = 1 + 2s/5 + 1/s \qquad (12.50)$

The lattice realization of the specifications of Eq. 12.47 is shown in Fig. 12-4.

12.3   The constant-resistance symmetrical lattice

The methods of lattice synthesis of the last section applied to the *unloaded* lattice with terminals 2-2′ open or the value of the terminating resistance so large that the loading is negligible. The new problem we will consider in this section is that of synthesis of lattice networks terminated in a load of constant resistance R. With the lattice so terminated, we will inquire into the possibility that the elements of the lattice can be adjusted so that the driving-point impedance at terminals 1-1′ will always have the *same* value of R.

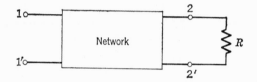

Fig. 12-5.   General network terminated in a resistor, R.

The two terminal-pair network of Fig. 12-5 is described in terms of the open-circuit impedance functions by the equations

$$V_1 = z_{11}I_1 + z_{12}I_2 \tag{12.51}$$

and

$$V_2 = z_{12}I_1 + z_{22}I_2 \tag{12.52}$$

With the network terminated in R, the voltage V_2 has the value $-RI_2$ (negative because of the direction of current). Substituting $V_2 = -RI_2$ into Eq. 12.52 makes it possible to eliminate I_2 from the equations and to solve for the ratio of V_1 to I_1, which is the driving-point impedance

$$Z(s) = \frac{z_{11}z_{22} - z_{12}{}^2 + z_{11}R}{z_{22} + R} \tag{12.53}$$

or

$$Z(s) = \frac{\Delta_z + z_{11}R}{z_{22} + R} = \frac{z_{11}[(\Delta_z/z_{11}) + R]}{z_{22} + R} \tag{12.54}$$

In Chapter 2, it was shown that $z_{11}/\Delta_z = y_{22}$ so that the last equation may also be written as

$$Z(s) = \frac{z_{11}[(1/y_{22}) + R]}{z_{22} + R} \tag{12.55}$$

Observe that this equation expresses the driving-point function $Z(s)$ in terms of four other driving-point quantities. With $R = 1$ ohm, the usual normalized value, the driving-point impedance of a two terminal-pair network terminated in a resistor is given by Eq. 12.54 with $R = 1$. The requirement that the driving-point impedance be R is equivalent to the requirement that $Z(s) = R = 1$ in this equation. Then

$$\frac{\Delta_z + z_{11}}{1 + z_{22}} = 1 \tag{12.56}$$

Since $\Delta_z = z_{11}z_{22} - z_{12}{}^2$ by definition and $z_{11} = z_{22}$ for the symmetrical lattice, the last equation becomes

$$z_{11}{}^2 = 1 + z_{12}{}^2 \tag{12.57}$$

Expressions for z_{11} and z_{12} for the lattice have already been found as Eqs. 12.1 and 12.2, which are

$$z_{11} = \tfrac{1}{2}(Z_b + Z_a) \quad \text{and} \quad z_{12} = \tfrac{1}{2}(Z_b - Z_a) \tag{12.58}$$

Substituting these two equations into Eq. 12.57 gives

$$\tfrac{1}{4}(Z_b{}^2 + Z_a{}^2 + 2Z_aZ_b) = 1 + \tfrac{1}{4}(Z_b{}^2 + Z_a{}^2 - 2Z_aZ_b) \tag{12.59}$$

or
$$Z_aZ_b = 1 \tag{12.60}$$

This result tells us that it is necessary that Z_a and Z_b be *reciprocal* impedances for the input impedance to have the constant value, $Z(s) = 1$. With the lattice terminated in R ohms, this equation has the more general form, $Z_aZ_b = R^2$.

For the network terminated in R, the transfer impedance Z_{12} is defined by Eq. 2.95, which is, for $Z_L = 1$ ohm:

$$Z_{12} = \frac{V_2}{I_1} \text{ (with } R = 1 \text{ in network)} = \frac{z_{12}}{1 + z_{22}} \tag{12.61}$$

With the 1-ohm resistor termination, $V_2 = -1 \times I_2$ so that Z_{12} may also be expressed as the current ratio, $-I_2/I_1$. In order to express Z_{12} in terms of Z_a and Z_b, we substitute the values of z_{12} and z_{22} given in Eqs. 12.58 into Eq. 12.61 to give

$$Z_{12} = \frac{Z_b - Z_a}{2 + Z_a + Z_b} \tag{12.62}$$

To eliminate Z_b from this equation, we next substitute $Z_b = 1/Z_a$ as expressed by Eq. 12.60 to give

$$Z_{12} = \frac{1 - Z_a{}^2}{Z_a{}^2 + 2Z_a + 1} = \frac{(1 - Z_a)(1 + Z_a)}{(1 + Z_a)(1 + Z_a)} = \frac{1 - Z_a}{1 + Z_a} \tag{12.63}$$

If $Z_L = R$ rather than $Z_L = 1$, this equation has the form

$$Z_{12} = R\left(\frac{R - Z_a}{R + Z_a}\right) = R\left[\frac{1 - (Z_a/R)}{1 + (Z_a/R)}\right] \tag{12.64}$$

Solving Eq. 12.63 for Z_a and Eq. 12.60 for Z_b, we have

$$Z_a = \frac{1 - Z_{12}}{1 + Z_{12}} \quad\text{and}\quad Z_b = \frac{1}{Z_a} \tag{12.65}$$

This important relationship makes it possible to find Z_a and Z_b from a given Z_{12} specification.

What are the requirements which must be satisfied by Z_{12} in order that a constant-resistance lattice realization will exist? Clearly these requirements will stem from the basic requirement that Z_a and Z_b be positive real. Equations 12.65 have the forms of Eqs. 4.96 which was used in the Talbot alternative derivation for positive real functions. In that derivation, it was shown that Z_a in Eqs. 12.65 will be positive real providing

(1) Z_{12} has no poles in the right half plane or on the imaginary axis, and

(2) $|Z_{12}(j\omega)| \leq 1$.

The first requirement that there be no right half plane poles is imposed on all output-to-input transfer functions, and clearly Z_{12} can have no imaginary axis poles if $|Z_{12}(j\omega)|$ is to be bounded as required in (2). The reason for (2) is suggested by a power ratio interpretation, which we give next.

Consider a lattice network composed entirely of L and C elements except for the termination. For this network both Z_a and Z_b are reactance functions. Then for the sinusoidal steady state, $Z_a(j\omega) = jX_a$ and Eq. 12.63 becomes

$$|Z_{12}(j\omega)| = \frac{|1 - jX_a|}{|1 + jX_a|} \tag{12.66}$$

In this equation, the magnitude of the numerator is always equal to the magnitude of the denominator, so that for the lossless case

$$|Z_{12}(j\omega)| = 1 \tag{12.67}$$

Next suppose that there is loss in the lattice. The power input and power output for a sinusoidal source may be written

$$P_{\text{in}} = |I_1|^2 R \quad\text{and}\quad P_{\text{out}} = |I_2|^2 R \tag{12.68}$$

and with loss P_{out} must be less than P_{in}.   This requires that

$$\left| I_2(j\omega) \right| < \left| I_1(j\omega) \right| \tag{12.69}$$

Now with a termination of 1 ohm, $V_2 = -1 \times I_2$, so that the last equation implies that

$$\left| \frac{I_2(j\omega)}{I_1(j\omega)} \right| = \left| \frac{V_2(j\omega)}{I_1(j\omega)} \right| = \left| Z_{12}(j\omega) \right| \le 1 \tag{12.70}$$

as required.

There is one more important property of the constant-resistance lattice network.   For lattice networks with the *same* constant-R specification, the input impedance of the cascade connection of any number

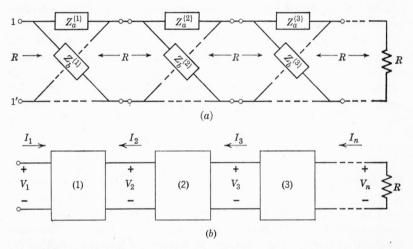

(a)

(b)

Fig. 12-6.   (a) Cascade connection of constant-resistance lattice networks to meet Z_{12} specifications, and (b) voltage and current reference directions for Eq. 12.72.

of lattices, as shown in Fig. 12-6, is still R ohms.   Given a single lattice terminated in R ohms.   Its input impedance is also R ohms and so this terminated lattice will serve as a proper termination of R ohms for another lattice.   This argument may be repeated any number of times for the cascade connection of lattices in Fig. 12-6.   Similarly, for n lattices connected in cascade, the current ratios are related by the equation,

$$\frac{I_n}{I_1} = \frac{I_2}{I_1} \times \frac{I_3}{I_2} \times \frac{I_4}{I_3} \times \frac{I_5}{I_4} \times \cdots \times \frac{I_n}{I_{n-1}} \tag{12.71}$$

This equation is justified as above by starting with one terminated lattice, and then repeatedly adding new sections in cascade for which the new current ratio may be written. If $R = 1$ ohm for each of the cascaded lattices, then $V_2 = -I_2$, $V_3 = -I_3$, $\cdots$, $V_n = -I_n$, and

$$\frac{V_n}{I_1} = \frac{V_2}{I_1} \times \frac{V_3}{-I_2} \times \frac{V_4}{-I_3} \times \frac{V_5}{-I_4} \times \cdots \times \frac{V_n}{-I_{n-1}} \qquad (12.72)$$

or

$$Z_{12} = Z_{12}^{(1)} Z_{12}^{(2)} Z_{12}^{(3)} \cdots Z_{12}^{(n)} \qquad (12.73)$$

In this equation, the superscript refers to the order in which the individual lattice networks appear in the cascade connection. Thus the total or net Z_{12}, the specification of the problem, can be regarded as the product of a number of transfer impedance functions and synthesis can be accomplished by a cascade connection of constant-resistance lattice networks.

In summary, we see that lattice network synthesis starts from the specification of a $Z_{12}(s)$ or equivalent function. This function must not have poles in the right half plane and must satisfy the magnitude condition, $|Z_{12}(j\omega)| \leq R$ for all ω, where R is the terminating resistance. Synthesis requires the use of the equations, for $R = 1$ ohm,

$$Z_a = \frac{1 - Z_{12}}{1 + Z_{12}} \qquad \text{and} \qquad Z_b = \frac{1}{Z_a} \qquad (12.74)$$

The network may often be realized as a single lattice or as a cascade of lattices. If several cascade lattices are used, then the poles and zeros of Z_{12} must be judiciously arranged in order that each of the product functions $Z_{12}^{(n)}$ also meets the magnitude condition. This may require that multiplying constants be introduced into the equation for Z_{12}.

Still other lattice realizations can be found by introducing surplus factors into Z_{12} by multiplying both numerator and denominator by factors of the form $s - s_1$, provided that s_1 be in the left half of the s plane. In some cases, the introduction of such surplus factors will help in meeting the magnitude condition for the individual factors in Eq. 12.73. As is characteristic of lattice synthesis, the number of different lattice realizations of a given specification is unlimited, especially if the introduction of surplus factors is considered.

Example 4. It is required to synthesize a lattice network terminated in a 1-ohm resistor to meet the specification

$$Z_{12} = \frac{s^2 - s + 1}{s^2 + s + 1} \qquad (12.75)$$

We observe that the poles are safely in the left half plane and that the magnitude of Z_{12} for $s = j\omega$ is

$$|Z_{12}(j\omega)| = \left| \frac{(1 - \omega^2) - j\omega}{(1 - \omega^2) + j\omega} \right| = 1 \qquad (12.76)$$

This result tells us that the magnitude condition is satisfied and further that the lattice realization will be lossless and so composed of L and C elements only. From Eqs. 12.74, we find that

$$Z_a = \frac{s}{s^2 + 1} = \frac{1}{s + (1/s)} \qquad \text{and} \qquad Z_b = s + \frac{1}{s} \qquad (12.77)$$

The lattice network realization is that shown in Fig. 12-7(a). Such a network is known in network theory as an *all-pass* network* since the magnitude of

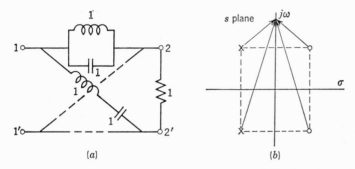

Fig. 12-7. (a) All-pass lattice network of Example 4 and (b) the poles and zeros of $Z_{12}(s)$ with phasors drawn to a given frequency.

$Z_{12}(j\omega)$ is unity for all values of ω. The phase of $Z_{12}(j\omega)$ does change with frequency, as may be found analytically from Eq. 12.75 with $s = j\omega$, or from the s plane representation of the poles and zeros of Eq. 12.75, shown in Fig. 12-7(b). Observe that these poles and zeros constitute a quad. Now the magnitude of $Z_{12}(j\omega)$ may be found graphically by determining the distance from each pole and each zero to a point on the imaginary axis. The magnitude function is then found as the product of the distances from the zeros to the product of the distances from the poles. Applying this method to quads, we see that there is always a phasor from a pole to match every phasor from a zero and the magnitude therefore does not vary with frequency. From this phasor model, we see that an all-pass function has a zero in the right half plane for every pole in the left half plane, with pole-zero pairs placed symmetrically with respect to the imaginary axis (Fig. 12-8). Networks synthesized from all-pass functions find applications as phase-correcting networks.

Example 5. Specifications require that the transfer impedance

$$Z_{12}(s) = \frac{-s + 1}{4s^2 + 3s + 1} \qquad (12.78)$$

* Properties of the all-pass network were considered earlier in Chapter 9.

be realized as a lattice terminated in a 1-ohm resistor. The poles of this function are in the left half plane and the magnitude condition is satisfied since

$$|Z_{12}(j\omega)| = \sqrt{\frac{1 + \omega^2}{(1 - 4\omega^2)^2 + (3\omega)^2}} = \sqrt{\frac{1 + \omega^2}{1 + 16\omega^4 + \omega^2}} \quad (12.79)$$

is less than 1 for all ω. From Eqs. 12.74, we have

$$Z_a = \frac{2s(s + 1)}{2s^2 + s + 1}, \qquad Z_b = \frac{2s^2 + s + 1}{2s(s + 1)} \quad (12.80)$$

The synthesized RLC lattice network corresponding to these impedance functions is shown in Fig. 12-9.

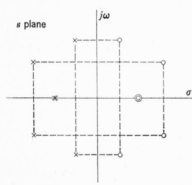

Fig. 12-8. Several quads of poles and zeros that characterize an all-pass Z_{12} function.

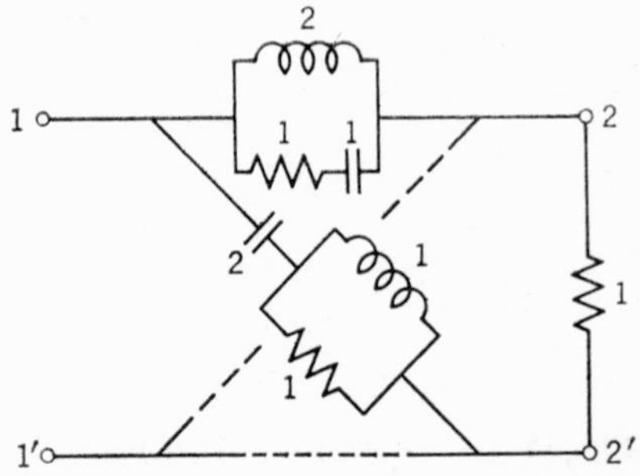

Fig. 12-9. Lattice network realization for Example 5.

12.4 Lattice decomposition

It is sometimes possible to modify the lattice network in such a way that we arrive at an equivalent network in the form of a ladder. This process of modification is known as lattice *decomposition* or the ladder development of the lattice.*

Figure 12-10(a) shows a symmetrical lattice network arranged so that the same impedance $Z(s)$ appears in the series arm and the cross arm. For this network, the open-circuit impedance functions are found from Eqs. 12.1 and 12.2. Thus

$$z_{11} = z_{22} = \tfrac{1}{2}(Z_a + Z_b) = \tfrac{1}{2}(Z_a' + Z_b' + 2Z) = Z + \tfrac{1}{2}(Z_a' + Z_b')$$
$$(12.81)$$

---

* See Bode, *Network Analysis and Feedback Amplifier Design*, p. 268, and Guillemin, *Introductory Circuit Theory*, p. 168, for further discussion.

This result suggests the network shown in Fig. 12-10(b), which is equivalent to that shown in (a) as far as z_{11} and z_{22} are concerned. The transfer impedance z_{12} is, for the network of Fig. 12-10(a),

$$z_{12} = \tfrac{1}{2}(Z_b - Z_a) = \tfrac{1}{2}(Z_b' + Z - Z_a' - Z) = \tfrac{1}{2}(Z_b' - Z_a') \quad (12.82)$$

showing that z_{12} for this network is independent of the impedance Z. The two networks have the same values for z_{11}, z_{22}, and z_{12} and are therefore equivalent networks.

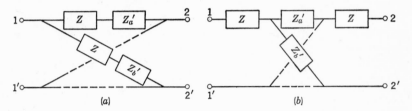

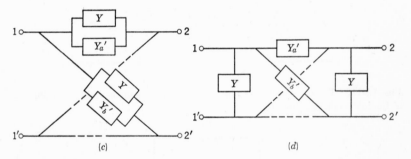

Fig. 12-10.   The two sets of equivalent lattice networks which are the basis of lattice decomposition.

The same analysis may be applied to the two networks of Fig. 12-10(c) and (d).   For each network

$$y_{11} = y_{22} = \tfrac{1}{2}(Y_a + Y_b) = Y + \tfrac{1}{2}(Y_a' + Y_b') \quad (12.83)$$

and $\qquad y_{12} = \tfrac{1}{2}(Y_b - Y_a) = \tfrac{1}{2}(Y_b' - Y_a') \qquad\qquad (12.84)$

so that the two networks are equivalent.

Lattice decomposition is accomplished by the successive use of these two network equivalences, as in Fig. 12-10.   This decomposition is illustrated by two examples.

Example 6.   In the lattice network shown in Fig. 12-11(a), the 1-ohm resistor is first removed, giving the network of Fig. 12-11(b).   We next recognize that there are equal R and L elements in parallel positions in both the series and cross arms which may be removed. Finally, the remaining series capacitor in the lower terminals is combined with a like capacitor in the

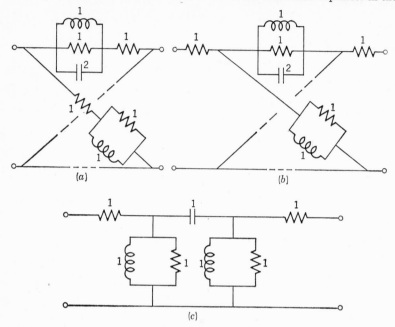

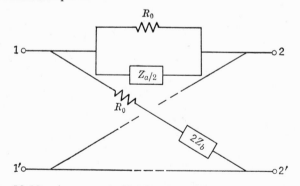

Fig. 12-11. Three networks showing successive stages of the ladder development of the lattice in Example 6.

Fig. 12-12. A symmetrical lattice network as used in Example 7.

upper terminals, giving the network of Fig. 12-11(c). In this example, a ladder equivalent to the symmetrical lattice has been found.

Example 7. Complete decomposition is not possible in many cases. Consider, as an example, the lattice network shown in Fig. 12-12. In this lattice, there are no common elements in series or in parallel in the two arms. Sup-

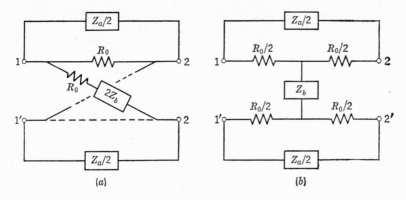

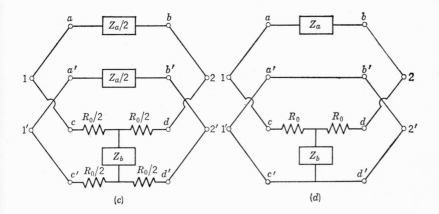

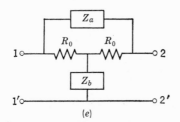

Fig. 12-13. Stages of the special decomposition of the symmetrical lattice of Fig. 12-12 into the form of a bridged-T network.

pose that we temporarily remove the impedance $Z_a/2$ from consideration, as in Fig. 12-13(a). We then recognize that R_0 occupies a series position in both the series and cross arms of the lattice. But before removing R_0, we see that the two impedances $Z_a/2$ may be combined into a single impedance Z_a since currents in the two $Z_a/2$ elements are equal but opposite for this symmetrical network. After removing R_0 and combining the parallel impedances of value $2Z_b$ that remain, we arrive at the network of Fig. 12-13(e). This network is known as a *bridged-T*. While not the desired ladder, it is nevertheless an important network structure.

The decomposition procedure just described makes it possible for a symmetrical lattice to be changed to an equivalent ladder network *for some networks*. It seems reasonable that this equivalence should be a two-way street, that it will be possible to find a symmetrical lattice equivalent of ladder networks. It is this topic we study next.

12.5   Bartlett's bisection theorem

A theorem due to Bartlett* makes it possible to find the lattice equivalent of ladder and other networks. Although the theorem is general, we will restrict our consideration to the case of networks that

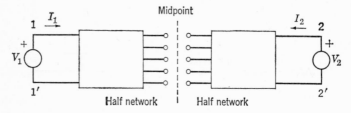

Fig. 12-14. Bisected network used in the discussion of Bartlett's bisection theorem.

are symmetrical in the sense that they can be divided at their mid-point, as in Fig. 12-14, and one of the half networks can be the mirror image of the other. In the network of Fig. 12-14, suppose that we first adjust the generators so that $V_1 = V_2$. The currents in each of the wires as the mid-point will also be equal because of symmetry but will be oppositely directed so that the net current in each wire is 0. With no current in any of the wires, each wire may be cut and no

---

*See A. C. Bartlett, *Theory of Electrical Artificial Lines and Filters*, John Wiley & Sons, New York, 1930, pp. 28–32, and Otto Brune, "Note on Bartlett's bisection theorem," *Phil. Mag.*, **14**, 806–811 (1932). Bartlett, an English engineer, made early contributions to the theory of lines and filters.

changes will result at either of the driving-point terminals. The voltage at terminals 1-1' is related to the two currents I_1 and I_2 by the familiar equation first written as Eq. 12.51:

$$V_1 = z_{11}I_1 + z_{12}I_2 \tag{12.85}$$

But I_2 has been made equal to I_1 so that

$$\frac{V_1}{I_1} = z_{11} + z_{12} \tag{12.86}$$

Now the ratio V_1/I_1 is, from our discussion, the input impedance at terminals 1-1' of the half network with the mid-point terminals open-circuited. A special subscript will be used to remind us of the way this impedance will be measured by letting $V_1/I_1 = Z_{\frac{1}{2}oc}$. Returning to the last equation, we recall that the sum $z_{11} + z_{12}$ is a familiar quantity in the theory of the lattice and is, by Eq. 12.7, the impedance of the cross arm of the symmetrical lattice, Z_b. Then

$$Z_b = Z_{\frac{1}{2}oc} \tag{12.87}$$

Suppose that we next reverse the polarity of the voltage source V_2 in the network of Fig. 12-14 while keeping the magnitudes of V_1 and V_2 equal. Under this condition, let us *short*-circuit all of the terminals at the mid-point and find the current in this short circuit. Because of the symmetry of the network, all currents will be equal but opposite in all parts of the half networks related by the mirror symmetry. In the short circuit the current caused by V_1 will be equal and opposite to the current caused by V_2, making the net current in the short circuit 0. At the input terminals, there is no way to tell whether the mid-point terminals of the two half networks now short-circuited are connected together or not. Thus the short-circuited half networks can be considered separately as far as conditions at the input terminals, 1-1' and 2-2', are concerned.

Since $I_2 = -I_1$, the voltage given by Eq. 12.85 becomes

$$V_1 = z_{11}I_1 + z_{12}(-I_1) \tag{12.88}$$

or

$$\frac{V_1}{I_1} = z_{11} - z_{12} \tag{12.89}$$

For the case now being considered, V_1/I_1 is the input impedance at terminals 1-1' for the half network with its mid-point terminals short-circuited. Let this impedance be designated as $V_1/I_1 = Z_{\frac{1}{2}sc}$ to suggest the method of measurement or computation. The impedance difference, $z_{11} - z_{12}$, is recognized to be the impedance of the series arm of the symmetrical lattice, by Eq. 12.6.   Then

$$Z_a = Z_{\frac{1}{2}sc} \tag{12.90}$$

Summarizing our findings: To find the impedance of the cross arm of the symmetrical lattice equivalent of a symmetrical network, open-circuit the terminals at the mid-point of the bisected network and compute the driving-point impedance.   To find the impedance of the series arm, short-circuit the terminals of the bisected network and again compute the driving-point impedance of the short-circuited half

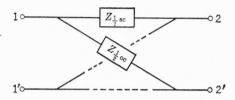

Fig. 12-15. Symmetrical lattice found from network computations using Bartlett's bisection theorem.

network.   This result is illustrated in Fig. 12-15.   Several examples of the application of Bartlett's theorem are shown in Fig. 12-16.

12.6   Constant-resistance bridged-T and ladder networks

The constant-resistance lattice studied in Section 12.3 has the property that the input impedance is resistive and equal to R ohms when the lattice is terminated in a resistor of R ohms.   Two other network structures having this constant-resistance property are the constant-resistance bridged-T network and the constant-resistance ladder.   Two reasons may be given for the importance of these networks.   (1) The networks are grounded (or unbalanced) and so attractive in electronic and transmission applications.   (2) The synthesis methods, as we shall show, are simple and routine.   Offsetting this second advantage, the realizations are often wasteful of elements in comparison to realizations found by other methods.

The synthesis methods to be described depend on our ability to express the quotient of polynomials with all poles and zeros in the left half plane or on the imaginary axis as a product of positive real functions.*   Given such a quotient of polynomials, $p(s)/q(s)$, where

---

* E. A. Guillemin, "A summary of modern methods of network synthesis," *Advances in Electronics*, Vol. III.   Important applications of this property are due to R. H. Pantell, "Minimum phase transfer function synthesis," *IRE Trans.*, **CT-2**, 133–137 (1955), and E. C. Ho, "*RLC* transfer function synthesis," *IRE Trans.*, **CT-2**, 146–153 (1955).

Network   Bisected Network   Equivalent Lattice

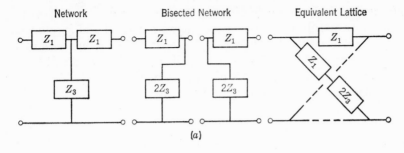

(a)

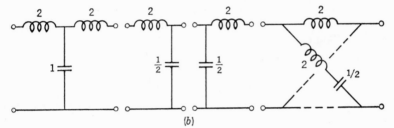

(b)

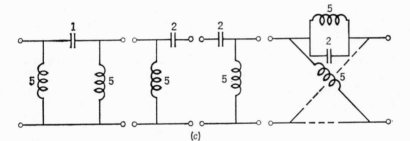

(c)

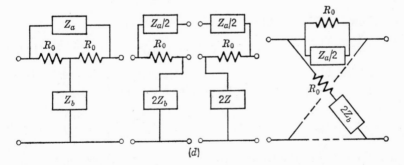

(d)

Fig. 12-16. The application of Bartlett's bisection theorem to four different ladder networks.

$p(s)$ and $q(s)$ are products of terms like $s + \alpha$ and $s^2 + \beta s + \gamma$, the numerator and denominator factors may be shuffled and surplus factors introduced in such a way that $p(s)/q(s)$ is the product of a number of positive real functions. To explain how this is accomplished in general, we consider a number of simple situations.

Typical terms in the product of functions

$$\frac{p(s)}{q(s)} = \prod_{j=a}^{n} G_{12j}(s) \qquad (12.91)$$

having simple forms like $G_{12a} = K_1/(s + a_1)$ or its inverse or $G_{12b} = K_2(s + a_2)/(s + b_2)$ are positive real for all real, positive values of a and b. The expression

$$G_{12c} = K_3 \frac{1}{s^2 + a_3 s + b_3} \qquad (12.92)$$

is not positive real, however. If we multiply by the surplus factor, $s + c_3$, there results

$$G_{12c} = \left(K_{3a} \frac{s + c_3}{s^2 + a_3 s + b_3}\right)\left(K_{3b} \frac{1}{s + c_3}\right) \qquad (12.93)$$

Then the second term is positive real for all real and positive c_3 and the first term is positive real under the condition that $c_3 \leq a_3$. Thus a value of c_3 can always be found to make each term positive real.

The biquadratic function

$$G_{12d} = K_4 \frac{s^2 + c_4 s + d_4}{s^2 + a_4 s + b_4} \qquad (12.94)$$

was shown in Prob. 4-18 to be positive real when

$$a_4 c_4 \geq (\sqrt{d_4} - \sqrt{b_4})^2 \qquad (12.95)$$

Clearly the biquadratic function is not always positive real. If we multiply by another biquadratic surplus factor so that

$$G_{12d} = \left(K_{4a} \frac{s^2 + e_4 s + f_4}{s^2 + a_4 s + b_4}\right)\left(K_{4b} \frac{s^2 + c_4 s + d_4}{s^2 + e_4 s + f_4}\right) \qquad (12.96)$$

then the terms in the product are each positive real providing

$$a_4 e_4 \geq (\sqrt{f_4} - \sqrt{b_4})^2 \quad \text{and} \quad c_4 e_4 \geq (\sqrt{f_4} - \sqrt{d_4})^2 \qquad (12.97)$$

Both equations can always be satisfied by assigning any value to f_4 and then selecting a value of e_4 such that both inequalities hold.

The last possibility that we need consider is a factor corresponding to a pole or a zero on the imaginary axis.   Let

$$G_{12e} = K_5 \frac{1}{s^2 + \omega_5{}^2} \tag{12.98}$$

This function is altered to be the product of two positive real functions by multiplying and dividing by s or, if LC functions are to be avoided, by a quadratic surplus factor such that

$$G_{12e} = \left(K_{5a} \frac{s^2 + a_5 s + b_5}{s^2 + \omega_5{}^2} \right) \left(K_{5b} \frac{1}{s^2 + a_5 s + b_5} \right) \tag{12.99}$$

Now the first factor is positive real providing $b_5 = \omega_5{}^2$; the second factor has the form of Eq. 12.92, and a second surplus factor like that used in Eq. 12.93 expands G_{12e} into the product of three positive real functions.   Having exhausted the possible forms of factors in Eq. 12.91, we may conclude that any $p(s)/q(s)$ with poles and zeros in the left half plane including the imaginary axis may be expressed as a product of positive real functions.*   As an example of such an expansion, consider the following function:

$$G_{12} = \frac{s^2 + 2}{s^2 + 4s + 6} \tag{12.100}$$

This G_{12} is not positive real.   By introducing appropriate surplus factors in the following pattern

$$G_{12} = \left(\frac{s^2 + 2}{s} \right) \left(\frac{s}{s^2 + 4s + 6} \right) \tag{12.101a}$$

each term in the product is made to be positive real.   (Test using Eq. 12.97.)   If LC functions are to be avoided, we may use the expansion

$$G_{12} = \left(\frac{s^2 + 2}{s^2 + As + 2} \right) \left(\frac{s^2 + As + 2}{s^2 + 4s + 6} \right), \qquad A \geq 2 - \sqrt{3} \tag{12.101b}$$

The result we have just found applies to the realization of a voltage-ratio transfer function by a cascade of pentode amplifiers each having the form shown in Fig. 12-17.   For this network, the transfer function is simply related to a driving-point function by the equation

$$G_{12} = \frac{V_2}{V_1} = -g_m Z \tag{12.102}$$

---

* For an extension of this result to include right half plane zeros and all-pass functions, see Prob. 12-40.

where g_m is the pentode transconductance and Z is the impedance of the termination. For a cascade of n such stages, we have

$$\frac{V_{n+1}}{V_1} = KZ_1Z_2Z_3 \cdots Z_n \qquad (12.103)$$

where

$$K = (-1)^n g_{m1}g_{m2} \cdots g_{mn} \qquad (12.104)$$

Since we now know that we may always express a transfer function like V_{n+1}/V_1 as the product of positive real functions, we can always identify the impedance functions in Eq. 12.103 and so find a network realization. This simple method is particularly suited when gain is specified in addition to a frequency response specification.* An example will illustrate these statements.

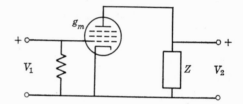

Fig. 12-17. A pentode amplifier for which $G_{12} = -g_mZ$.

Suppose that it is specified that the ratio of output voltage to input voltage meet the specification

$$G_{12} = 4\frac{(s + \frac{1}{4})(s + \frac{3}{2})}{(s + \frac{1}{2})(s + 1)} \qquad (12.105)$$

This function is not positive real, but it may be expressed as the product of two or more positive real functions. One combination is

$$Z_1 = \frac{4s + 1}{2s + 1} = 1 + \frac{2s}{2s + 1} \qquad (12.106)$$

and

$$Z_2 = \frac{2s + 3}{s + 1} = 2 + \frac{1}{s + 1} \qquad (12.107)$$

These impedance functions realize Eq. 12.105 directly. The cascade of amplifiers shown in Fig. 12-18 realizes the given G_{12} with $g_{m1} = g_{m2} = 1$.

Let us next turn our attention to the ladder networks of Fig. 12-19 and study the possibility that this network has a constant-resistance

---

* A number of examples are given in the author's *Network Analysis*, Chapter 14.

characteristic. The input impedance of the network of Fig. 12-19(a) is

$$Z = \frac{1 + Y_b}{Y_b + Y_a(1 + Y_b)} \tag{12.108}$$

The requirement that $Z = 1$ imposes a relationship between $Z_a = 1/Y_a$ and Y_b, i.e.,

$$Z_a = 1 + Y_b \tag{12.109}$$

The voltage-ratio transfer function for this network is

$$G_{12} = \frac{V_2}{V_1} = \frac{1}{1 + Z_b} \tag{12.110}$$

The last two equations have especially simple form. Together they constitute the design equations for a constant-resistance ladder. From

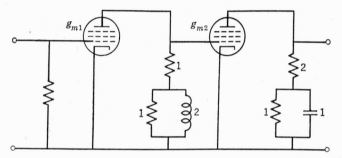

Fig. 12-18. A cascade of pentode amplifiers meeting the specification of Eq. 12.105.

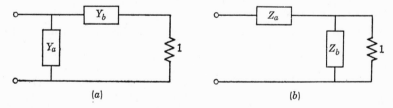

Fig. 12-19. The network of (a) is described by Eqs. 12.109 and 12.110; the network of (b) is described by dual equations: $Y_a' = 1 + Z_b'$ and $G_{12}' = 1/(1 + Y_b')$.

a specified G_{12}, Z_b is found from the second equation and Z_a from the first. From Eq. 12.110, we can make a number of pertinent observations. If Z_b is positive real, then G_{12} is also positive real, but not vice versa. The magnitude function for $s = j\omega$ is bounded and is

$$|G_{12}(j\omega)| \leq 1 \tag{12.111}$$

This in turn implies that G_{12} has no poles on the imaginary axis including infinity. These are necessary conditions imposed on G_{12}, but are they sufficient? They are, of course, if they are sufficient to insure that Z_a and Z_b are positive real. To study this question, we solve for Z_b from Eq. 12.110:

$$Z_b = \frac{1}{G_{12}} - 1 \tag{12.112}$$

Provided that we exclude the possibility of zeros of G_{12} in the right half of the s plane, the poles of Z_b will be in the left half plane or on the imaginary axis. Then for Z_b to be positive real, it is necessary only that Re $Z_b(j\omega) \geq 0$ for all ω, which will be the case if

$$\text{Re } \frac{1}{G_{12}(j\omega)} - 1 \geq 0 \text{ or if Re } \frac{1}{G_{12}(j\omega)} \geq 1 \tag{12.113}$$

This last equation may be written

$$\frac{\text{Re } G_{12}(j\omega)}{|G_{12}(j\omega)|^2} \geq 1 \tag{12.114}$$

Since the denominator of this equation is required by Eq. 12.111 to be no greater than 1, this equation can be satisfied only if we require that Re $G_{12}(j\omega)$ never vanish and, in addition, if we have the flexibility of multiplying G_{12} by a constant of such value that Eq. 12.114 is satisfied for all ω.

Let this constant be K in the equation

$$G_{12} = KG_{12}' \tag{12.115}$$

The usual philosophy of design of two terminal-pair networks places a premium on a large value of K, the gain constant. But by Eq. 12.113, rewritten in terms of KG_{12}',

$$\text{Re } \frac{1}{KG_{12}'(j\omega)} - 1 \geq 0 \tag{12.116}$$

we see that an upper limit is placed on the value that K may assume. It must be selected sufficiently small that the last equation, and so Eq. 12.114, is satisfied.

In summary, for a constant-resistance network of the form of Fig. 12-19(a) or (b) to exist, it is necessary and sufficient that G_{12} be (1) a minimum phase function with (2) a nonvanishing real part for $s = j\omega$ (called a nonminimum resistance function if G_{12} is an impedance function) with (3) no poles on the imaginary axis including infinity, and (4) with a multiplying constant of sufficiently small value that Eq. 12.116 is satisfied for ω. If these requirements are satisfied, then we are assured that Z_a and Z_b will be positive real and so realizable. Furthermore, any number of sections of the form shown in Fig. 12-19 may be connected in cascade, in which case the over-all G_{12} is related to the component G_{12} functions by the equation

$$G_{12} = G_{12a}G_{12b}G_{12c} \cdots G_{12n} \qquad (12.117)$$

and the theory developed for the expression of a transfer function as a product of positive real functions applies to the design of constant-resistance ladders.

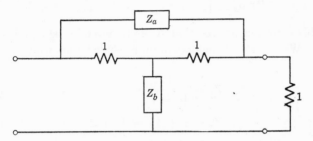

Fig. 12-20.   The constant-resistance bridged-T network described by Eqs. 12.118 and 12.119.

Before turning to examples, consider the network studied in Fig. 12-13(e), shown again as Fig. 12-20, which resulted from the decomposition of the constant-resistance lattice. It was shown in Prob. 2-25 that this is indeed a constant-resistance network providing, for $R_0 = 1$,

$$Z_a Z_b = 1 \qquad (12.118)$$

in which case
$$G_{12} = \frac{1}{1 + Z_a} \qquad (12.119)$$

Now this equation has exactly the same form as Eq. 12.110 (with Z_a replacing Z_b) so that the conclusions reached for the constant-resistance ladder apply directly to the constant-resistance bridged-T network. Furthermore, the design procedures differ only in that the requirement $Z_a Z_b = 1$ is used in place of $Z_a = 1 + Y_b$. We are now ready for examples.

Let us use the same specifications as given earlier for the cascade of pentodes. We are required to satisfy Eq. 12.105, which we write as the product of the following two positive real functions:

$$G_{12a} = K_a \frac{4s + 1}{2s + 1} \tag{12.120}$$

and

$$G_{12b} = K_b \frac{2s + 3}{s + 1} \tag{12.121}$$

Here K_a and K_b are to be selected to satisfy the requirement that $|G_{12}(j\omega)| \leq 1$ such that Z_a and Z_b are positive real. From Eq. 12.112, we have

$$Z_b = \frac{1}{K_a \dfrac{4s + 1}{2s + 1}} - 1 = \frac{(1 - 2K_a)2s + (1 - K_a)}{K_a(4s + 1)} \tag{12.122}$$

From this equation, we see that K_a is required to be equal to or less than $\frac{1}{2}$. We will select the maximum possible value, which is $K_a = \frac{1}{2}$. Then

$$Z_b = \frac{1}{4s + 1} \tag{12.123}$$

and

$$Z_a = 1 + Y_b = 4s + 2 \tag{12.124}$$

A similar analysis of Eq. 12.121 shows that the maximum value of the gain constant is $K_b = \frac{1}{3}$ (which can be seen by inspection), and the resulting impedance functions are

$$Z_b = \frac{s}{2s + 3} \tag{12.125}$$

and

$$Z_a = \frac{3(s + 1)}{s} \tag{12.126}$$

The network realized from the last four equations is shown in Fig. 12-21.

For the bridged-T realization, the first section is described by the impedance functions

$$Z_a = \frac{1}{4s + 1} \quad \text{and} \quad Z_b = 4s + 1 \tag{12.127}$$

and the second section by

$$Z_a = \frac{s}{2s + 3} \quad \text{and} \quad Z_b = \frac{2s + 3}{s} \tag{12.128}$$

The network realization is given in Fig. 12-22.

This example illustrates our claim that the synthesis methods of this section are simple and direct.   They are particularly well suited to applications in which only a few networks are required and to cases in which the engineer's time is more valuable than the saving of a few

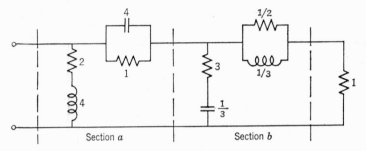

Fig. 12-21. Two-section constant-resistance ladder network satisfying the specification of Eq. 12.105 except that the gain constant realized is $K = \frac{1}{6}$.

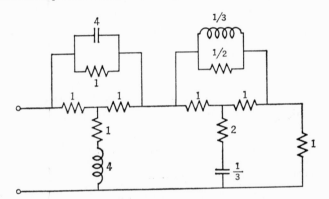

Fig. 12-22. Two-section constant-resistance bridged-T network satisfying the specification of Eq. 12.105 but with a gain constant of $K = \frac{1}{6}$.

network elements.   In applications requiring the production of thousands of networks, the saving of elements takes on new importance and more sophisticated methods are usually employed.

FURTHER READING

For general references on lattice synthesis, see Guillemin's *Synthesis of Passive Networks*, Chapters 11 and 12; Guillemin's review in *Advances in Electronics*, Vol. III, pp. 283–286; and Balabanian's study in *Network Synthesis*, pp. 169–181 and 323–331.   For filter applications of the lattice, see Guillemin's *Communication Networks*, Vol. II, especially Chapter 10; Reed's

Electric Network Synthesis, Chapters 3 and 4; and Bode's *Network Analysis and Feedback Amplifier Design,* pp. 233–244. See also Weber's *Linear Transient Analysis,* Vol. II, pp. 133–138, and Stewart's *Circuit Theory and Design,* pp. 258–264. On Bartlett's bisection theorem, Bode, *op. cit.,* pp. 266–270, and Reed, *op. cit.,* Chapter 5, are recommended. The reader will enjoy the characterization of the synthesizer of lattice networks in H. J. Carlin, "The champions," *IRE Trans.,* **CT-1,** 33 (1954). For further reading on the subject of constant-resistance networks including an explanation of the matrix factorization methods of Ho and Pantell, Balabanian, *op. cit.,* Chapter 8, is recommended.

PROBLEMS

12-1. It is required to synthesize a network to the specifications

$$z_{11} = z_{22} = \frac{s^3 + 4s}{(s^2 + 1)(s^2 + 9)}, \qquad z_{12} = \frac{2s}{(s^2 + 1)(s^2 + 9)}$$

Find a lattice network realization for the largest possible value of the lattice constant, k_l.

12-2. A lattice network is to be found subject to the specifications

$$z_{11} = z_{22} = \frac{s(s^2 + 16)(s^2 + 36)}{(s^2 + 1)(s^2 + 25)}, \qquad z_{12} = \frac{s(s^2 + 4)}{(s^2 + 1)(s^2 + 25)}$$

Find one network and state the range of possible values of k_l.

12-3. Find a lattice network to realize the specifications made in Prob. 11-21.

12-4. Determine the element values in an RC lattice network which satisfies the requirements stated in Prob. 11-22.

12-5. Find an RC lattice meeting the specification that

$$z_{12} = \frac{s^2 + 1}{(s + 1)(s + 3)}$$

exactly. Choose a network realization with the smallest number of elements in it.

12-6. The specification function

$$z_{12} = \frac{3s^2 + 5s + 1}{(s + 2)(s + 3)(s + 5)}$$

is to be realized using a lattice network. Find such a network.

12-7. Repeat Prob. 12-6 for the specification that

$$2z_{12} = \frac{(s - 1)(s + 2)(s + 3)}{(s + 1)(s + 2)(s + 3)}$$

12-8. Find a lattice network to realize the specification that

$$2z_{12} = \frac{(s^2 + 1)(s^2 + 36)}{s(s^2 + 9)(s^2 + 25)}$$

for the unloaded network.

12-9. Find an unloaded lattice network for the requirement that

$$G_{12} = \frac{s^2 - 4}{s^2 + 4}$$

12-10. Synthesize a lattice network having a voltage-ratio transfer function

$$G_{12}(s) = \frac{s^2 + s + 10}{2s^2 + 14s + 20}$$

if the lattice loading is so large that it can be neglected.

12-11. Show that if the even parts of $q(s) - p(s)$ and $q(s) + p(s)$ are proportional in Eq. 12.36, then a lattice may be synthesized having arms made up of one resistor in series with an LC network.

12-12. A network application requires that the voltage-ratio transfer function be

$$G_{12} = \frac{s^3 + s^2 + 4s + 1}{s^4 + \frac{1}{2}s^3 + 10s^2 + 2s + 9}$$

Synthesize a network in the form of a lattice without load to meet this specification.

12-13. Realize an unloaded lattice having the voltage-ratio transfer function

$$G_{12} = \frac{s(s + 10)(s + 20)(s + 40)}{(s + 1)(s + 3)(s + 5)(s + 80)}$$

The lattice is to be made up entirely from R and C elements.*

12-14. Find two lattice networks terminated in a 1-ohm resistor described by the transfer function

$$Z_{12}(s) = \frac{s^2 + 3s + 2}{s^2 + 5s + 6}$$

12-15. A constant-resistance lattice with a terminating resistance of 1 ohm is to be synthesized to the requirement that

$$Z_{12}(s) = \frac{1}{4s + 3}$$

(a) Draw a schematic of the network. Show all element values.
(b) Using lattice decomposition, find an equivalent ladder network.

* Cf. J. L. Bower and P. F. Ordung, Proc. IRE, **38**, 263–269 (1950).

12-16. Design a lattice network with a 1-ohm termination to give the voltage-ratio transfer function

$$G_{12} = \frac{V_2}{V_1} = \frac{4}{s + 6}$$

(*a*) Find element values.

(*b*) Find an equivalent ladder network.

(*c*) If the lattice is to be used with a 600-ohm termination, how must the element values be changed?

12-17. Given that

$$Z_{12}(s) = \frac{(s^2 - 2s + 5)(s^2 - 8s + 20)}{(s^2 + 2s + 5)(s^2 + 8s + 20)}$$

is specified for a network terminated in a 1-ohm resistor, find the network and give element values. Sketch the magnitude and phase characteristic of $Z_{12}(j\omega)$.

12-18. Decompose the lattice network shown in Fig. P12-18 to the form of a ladder network or bridged-ladder network.

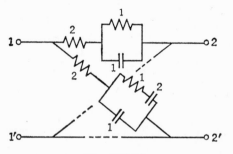

Fig. P12-18

12-19. Given that the lattice network shown in Fig. P12-19 does have a ladder equivalent, what must be the relationship of the element values in the arms of the lattice?

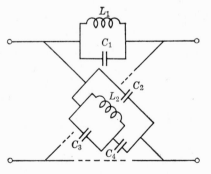

Fig. P12-19

12-20. The network shown in Fig. P12-20 is known as a *twin-T RC* network. Does this network have a lattice equivalent? If so, find it and simplify the impedance expressions for the arms.

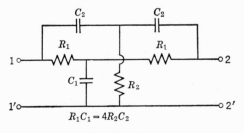

Fig. P12-20

12-21. Show that the two lattice networks of Fig. P12-21 are equivalent provided that (1) they are terminated in the same value of resistance, and (2)

$$Z_{x_1} Z_{y_1} = Z_{x_2} Z_{y_2}$$

(Bode, *Network Analysis and Feedback Amplifier Design*, p. 270.)

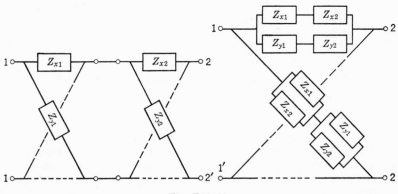

Fig. P12-21

12-22. The following functions are to be expanded into the product of a number of positive real functions:

(a) $G_{12} = \dfrac{1}{s^2 + 3s + 3}$ (b) $G_{12} = \dfrac{s + 5}{s^2 + s + 1}$

(c) $G_{12} = \dfrac{s^2 + \frac{1}{4}s + 1}{(s + 3)(s^2 + s + 5)}$ (d) $G_{12} = \dfrac{s^2 + 4s + 3}{s^2 + \frac{1}{2}s + 1}$

12-23. The following function is related to a third-order Butterworth function:

$$G_{12} = \frac{1}{s^3 + 2s^2 + 2s + 1}$$

Show that it may be expanded as a product of positive real functions.

12-24. Show that the first term in Eq. 12.99 is positive real provided only that $b_5 = \omega_5{}^2$.

12-25. Expand the following three functions as products of positive real functions:

(a) $G_{12} = \left(\dfrac{s+1}{s^2 + 2s + 2}\right)^2$ (b) $G_{12} = \dfrac{(s^2 + 3)(s^2 + s + 1)}{(2s^2 + s + 1)(s^2 + \frac{1}{2}s + 1)}$

(c) $G_{12} = \dfrac{(s^2 + 3)^2}{(2s^2 + s + 1)(s^2 + \frac{1}{2}s + 1)}$

12-26. Realize the transfer functions given in Prob. 12-22(a) and (b) in the form of a cascade of pentode amplifiers.

12-27. Repeat Prob. 12-26 for the specifications of Prob. 12-22(c) and (d).

The following twelve problems relate to the three structures studied in Section 12.6. For realizations found as constant-resistance ladders and bridged-T networks, use the maximum value of the gain constant, K. For the following G_{12} specifications, find a network realization in the prescribed form.

	Synthesize a network in the form of:		
G_{12} given by Prob.:	Cascade of pentodes	Constant-R ladder	Constant-R bridged-T
12-22(d)	12-28	12-32	12-36
12-23	12-29	12-33	12-37
12-25(a)	12-30	12-34	12-38
12-13	12-31	12-35	12-39

12-40. The voltage-ratio transfer function

$$\frac{V_2}{V_1} = \frac{s^2 - as + b}{s^2 + as + b}$$

describes a constant-resistance network for which the termination is $R = 1$ ohm. (a) Show that the lattice realization of this all-pass function may be decomposed to the unbalanced form shown in the accompanying figure. Determine C_1, C_2, L_p, L_s, and M in terms of a and b. Is the coefficient of coupling of the transformer equal to or less than 1?

(b) Using the result of part (a), synthesize a grounded network to meet the following specification and maximize the value of K.

$$\frac{V_2}{V_1} = \frac{2s^2 - s + 2}{s^2 + 2s + 3}$$

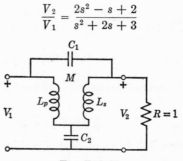

Fig. P12-40

Approximation II

. . . . *13*

The approximation of arbitrary semilogarithmic curves by straight-line segments of $\pm 6n$ db/octave slope and cut-and-try procedures were studied in Chapter 9.   A different approximation procedure is directed toward writing mathematical expressions which approximate the ideal forms of response shown in Fig. 13-1.   The magnitude response shown

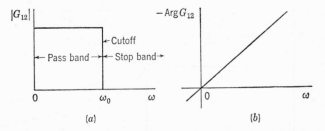

Fig. 13-1. (a) An ideal magnitude response with pass band, stop band, and cutoff frequency identified, and (b) an ideal linear phase response.

in Fig. 13-1(a), sometimes called a "brick wall," is constant from $\omega = 0$ to $\omega = \omega_0$, and zero for all greater ω.   Since no quotient of rational, finite-degree polynomials can represent this response exactly, what function $G_{12}(s)$ will approximate it best?   Similarly, the straight-line variation of phase with frequency shown in Fig. 13-1(b) is desired in some applications.   How might it be approximated within some tolerance?   These topics are to be studied in this chapter.

13.1   The Butterworth form of response

The response function

$$\left| G_{12}(j\omega) \right| = \frac{1}{\sqrt{1 + \omega^{2n}}} \tag{13.1}$$

is known as the nth-order Butterworth or maximally flat low-pass response,* and is an approximation to the ideal response of Fig. 13-1(a). The nature of the approximation function is seen from two observations:

(1) From the binomial series expansion

$$(1 \pm x)^{-n} = 1 \mp nx + \frac{n(n+1)x^2}{2!} \mp \frac{n(n+1)(n+2)x^3}{3!}$$
$$+ \cdots, \qquad x^2 < 1 \quad (13.2)$$

we see that near $\omega = 0$,

$$(1 + \omega^{2n})^{-\frac{1}{2}} = 1 - \tfrac{1}{2}\omega^{2n} + \tfrac{3}{8}\omega^{4n} - \tfrac{5}{16}\omega^{6n} + \cdots \quad (13.3)$$

and from this expression that the first $2n - 1$ derivatives are zero at $\omega = 0$.

(2) The magnitude $\left|G_{12}(j1)\right| = 0.707$ for all n.

The form of the Butterworth responses of several orders is shown in Fig. 13-2, in comparison with the ideal response of Fig. 13-1(a).

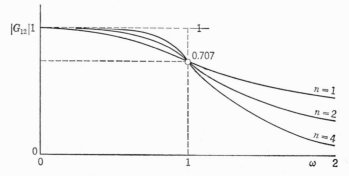

Fig. 13-2. The form of the Butterworth response for $n = 1$, $n = 2$, and $n = 4$. All curves have the value 1 at $\omega = 0$, and 0.707 at $\omega = 1$.

To determine the pole locations corresponding to the Butterworth response, we study the analytic continuation of $\left|G_{12}\right|^2$ of Eq. 13.1. The poles of this function are defined by the equation,

$$1 + (-s^2)^n = 0 \qquad (13.4)$$

* For a more detailed discussion of this response, see the author's *Network Analysis*, pp. 365–372. The maximally flat response was first studied in relationship to electronic amplifiers by the British engineer S. Butterworth in his paper, "On the theory of filter amplifiers," *Wireless Engineer*, **7**, 536–541 (1930). The term "maximally flat" was coined by V. D. Landon in "Cascade amplifiers with maximal flatness," *RCA Rev.*, **5**, 347–362 (1941).

Then the pole locations are

$$s_k = e^{j\frac{2k-1}{n}\frac{\pi}{2}}, \qquad n \text{ even}$$

$$s_k = e^{j\frac{2k}{n}\frac{\pi}{2}}, \qquad n \text{ odd} \tag{13.5}$$

or $\qquad s_k = e^{j\frac{2k+n-1}{n}\frac{\pi}{2}}, \qquad k = 1, 2, \cdots, 2n \tag{13.6}$

The poles so defined are located on a unit circle in the s plane and have symmetry with respect to both the real and the imaginary axes. For n odd, a pair of poles are located on the real axis, but the poles are not located on the imaginary axis for either n even or n odd. These properties follow because the poles are separated by π/n radians, and are located $\pi/2n$ radians from the real axis for n even and on the real axis for n odd. Pole locations for the $n = 4$ and $n = 5$ cases are shown in Fig. 13-3. Information useful in computing the pole locations is given in Table 13-1.

TABLE 13-1

n	Angles from Either Real Axis, degrees	$|\cos\theta|$	$|\sin\theta|$
1	0	1.00000	0.00000
2	± 45	0.70711	0.70711
3	0	1.00000	0.00000
	± 60	0.50000	0.86603
4	± 22.5	0.92388	0.38268
	± 67.5	0.38268	0.92388
5	0	1.00000	0.00000
	± 36	0.80902	0.58779
	± 72	0.30902	0.95106
6	± 15	0.96593	0.25882
	± 45	0.70711	0.70711
	± 75	0.25882	0.96593

To form the function $G_{12}(s)$ from the given $|G_{12}|^2$, we reject the right half plane poles, and from the left half plane poles form the all-pole function,

$$G_{12}(s) = \frac{1}{1 + a_1 s + a_2 s^2 + \cdots + a_n s^n} \tag{13.7}$$

which we know to have the $|G_{12}(j\omega)|$ characteristic expressed by Eq. 13.1. The coefficients of the denominator polynomials of $G_{12}(s)$, sometimes called Butterworth polynomials, are tabulated in Table 13-2.

TABLE 13-2

n	a_1	a_2	a_3	a_4	a_5	a_6	a_7	a_8
1	1.0000							
2	1.4142	1.0000						
3	2.0000	2.0000	1.0000					
4	2.6131	3.4142	2.6131	1.0000				
5	3.2361	5.2361	5.2361	3.2361	1.0000			
6	3.8637	7.4641	9.1416	7.4641	3.8637	1.0000		
7	4.4940	10.0978	14.5918	14.5918	10.0978	4.4940	1.0000	
8	5.1258	13.1371	21.8462	25.6884	21.8462	13.1371	5.1258	1.0000

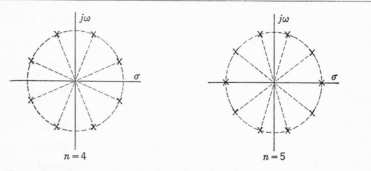

Fig. 13-3. Pole locations for the Butterworth response function for the cases $n = 4$ and $n = 5$.

13.2 Chebyshev polynomials in approximation

Another function which is used to approximate the ideal characteristic of Fig. 13-1(a) has the squared magnitude form

$$|G_{12}|^2 = \frac{1}{1 + \epsilon^2 C_n^2(\omega)} \tag{13.8}$$

where $C_n(\omega)$ is the nth-order Chebyshev polynomial* and $\epsilon < 1$ is a

---

* P. L. Chebyshev, "Théorie des mécanismes connus sous le nom de parallelogrammes," *Oeuvres*, Vol. I, St. Petersburg, 1899. Chebyshev first used these functions in studying the construction of steam engines. The transliteration of his Russian name Чебышёв has led to a variety of spellings, the most common of these being the English transliteration Chebyshev and the German transliteration Tschebyscheff.

real constant. Chebyshev polynomials are defined in terms of the real variable z by the equation

$$C_n(z) = \cos(n \cos^{-1} z) \tag{13.9}$$

To show that this transcendental function is indeed a polynomial, we define w such that $z = \cos w$ and

$$C_n(w) = \cos nw \tag{13.10}$$

Then

$$C_{n+1}(w) = \cos(n+1)w = \cos nw \cos w - \sin nw \sin w \tag{13.11}$$

and

$$C_{n-1}(w) = \cos(n-1)w = \cos nw \cos w + \sin nw \sin w \tag{13.12}$$

Adding these two equations gives

$$C_{n+1} + C_{n-1} = 2 \cos nw \cos w = 2zC_n \tag{13.13}$$

which may be rearranged in the form of a recursion formula,

$$C_{n+1}(z) = 2zC_n(z) - C_{n-1}(z) \tag{13.14}$$

Since we know that $C_0(z) = 1$ and $C_1(z) = z$ from Eq. 13.9, the Chebyshev polynomials given in Table 13-3 may be constructed.

TABLE 13-3

Order n	Chebyshev Polynomial
0	1
1	z
2	$2z^2 - 1$
3	$4z^3 - 3z$
4	$8z^4 - 8z^2 + 1$
5	$16z^5 - 20z^3 + 5z$
6	$32z^6 - 48z^4 + 18z^2 - 1$
7	$64z^7 - 112z^5 + 56z^3 - 7z$
8	$128z^8 - 256z^6 + 160z^4 - 32z^2 + 1$
9	$256z^9 - 576z^7 + 432z^5 - 120z^3 + 9z$
10	$512z^{10} - 1280z^8 + 1120z^6 - 400z^4 + 50z^2 - 1$

We thus have the forms of polynomials defined for all real z. Observe that when $|z| > 1$, then $\cos^{-1} z = j \cosh^{-1} z$, so that Eq. 13.9 becomes

$$C_n(z) = \cosh(n \cosh^{-1} z) \tag{13.15}$$

Several useful properties of these polynomials are illustrated in Fig. 13-4.   The zeros of the polynomials are all located in the interval, $-1 \leq z \leq 1$, and within this interval the maximum value attained is $+1$, the minimum value -1; i.e.,

$$|C_n| \leq 1 \text{ for } -1 \leq z \leq 1 \tag{13.16}$$

Outside of this interval, the magnitude of the polynomial becomes very large in comparison with unity.   It is precisely these properties that

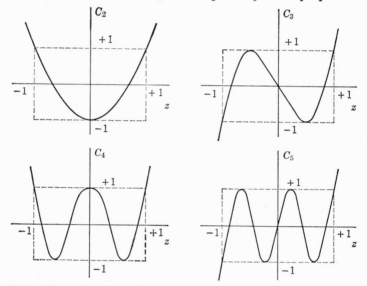

Fig. 13-4.   Plots of the behavior of Chebyshev polynomials for small values of $|z|$. Four orders of polynomials are shown.

make the Chebyshev polynomials useful in the approximation problem we are studying.

We now turn to an examination of the manner in which the Chebyshev polynomials as used in the response function of Eq. 13.8 approximate the "brick wall" of Fig. 13-1(a).   Equation 13.8 directs that we square $C_n(\omega)$, multiply it by the constant $\epsilon^2 \leq 1$, add unity, form the reciprocal, and extract the square root.   The response that results is shown in Fig. 13-5.   A number of features of this response are important in work to follow.   From the curves of Fig. 13-4 or from Table 13-3, we observe that

$$C_n(0) = (-1)^{n/2} \quad \text{and} \quad C_n(\pm 1) = 1, \qquad n \text{ even}$$

and
$$\tag{13.17}$$

$$C_n(0) = 0 \quad \text{and} \quad C_n(\pm 1) = \pm 1 \text{ (respectively)}, \qquad n \text{ odd}$$

The maximum value of the response is unity and this value corresponds to points of ω where $C_n(\omega) = 0$. The minimum value of the response in the pass band is $1/(1 + \epsilon^2)^{1/2}$, occurring when $|C_n(\omega)| = 1$. Thus we see that $|G_{12}(0)|$ is unity for all odd n and $1/(1 + \epsilon^2)^{1/2}$ for all even n. Similarly, $G_{12}(1) = 1/(1 + \epsilon^2)^{1/2}$ for *all* n, as shown in Fig. 13-5. The

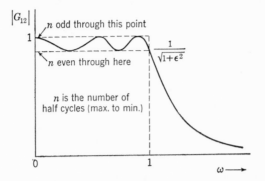

Fig. 13-5. Several identifying features of the Chebyshev magnitude response are shown.

ripple width or distance from maxima to minima in the pass band may be approximated for small ϵ by

$$1 - \frac{1}{(1 + \epsilon^2)^{1/2}} \cong \frac{\epsilon^2}{2}, \qquad \epsilon \ll 1 \tag{13.18}$$

For large values of ω, the magnitude response function of Eq. 13.8 has the approximate form

$$|G_{12}(j\omega)| = \frac{1}{\epsilon C_n(\omega)}, \qquad \omega \gg 1 \tag{13.19}$$

These last two equations suggest the procedure to be used in selecting a response function to match a particular set of specifications. The permissible ripple width fixes ϵ. The rate of decrease of the magnitude function in the stop band, as in Eq. 13.19, fixes n. With ϵ and n fixed, the response function is determined, except for the usual magnitude and frequency scaling.

Our next task is to locate the poles that give this equal ripple form of response. We start with the magnitude squared function of Eq. 13.8. By analytic continuation, we have

$$\frac{1}{1 + \epsilon^2 C_n{}^2(\omega)} = \frac{1}{1 + \epsilon^2 C_n{}^2(-js)} \bigg|_{s=j\omega} \tag{13.20}$$

To put this in a form more convenient for study, let $z = -js$. Then the poles of interest occur when

$$C_n(z) = \pm \frac{j}{\epsilon} \qquad (13.21)$$

If we now let $z = \cos w$, as in Eq. 13.10, and also let $w = u + jv$, then Eq. 13.21 becomes

$$C_n(z) = \cos nw = \cos nu \cosh nv - j \sin nu \sinh nv = \pm \frac{j}{\epsilon} \quad (13.22)$$

This equation is satisfied when

$$\cos nu \cosh nv = 0$$

and $\qquad\qquad\qquad\qquad\qquad\qquad\qquad\qquad\qquad (13.23)$

$$\sin nu \sinh nv = \pm \frac{1}{\epsilon}$$

Since $\cosh nv \neq 0$, the first of Eqs. 13.23 is satisfied only when $\cos nu = 0$, or when

$$u = \frac{1}{n}(2k - 1)\frac{\pi}{2}, \qquad k = 1, 2, \cdots, 2n \qquad (13.24)$$

At these values of u, $\sin nu = \pm 1$, so that

$$nv = \sinh^{-1} \frac{1}{\epsilon} \qquad (13.25)$$

We define the value of v satisfying this equation to be a, so that

$$a = \frac{1}{n} \sinh^{-1} \frac{1}{\epsilon} \qquad (13.26)$$

Since we have found the value of v and the values of u that locate the poles of the function under study, we next determine the pole positions in the s plane from the relationship,

$$s = j \cos w = j \cos (u + jv) = j \cos \left[\frac{\pi}{2n}(2k - 1) + ja \right] \quad (13.27)$$

Expanding this equation, we find that the pole locations are

$$\sigma_k = \pm \sinh a \sin \frac{2k - 1}{n}\frac{\pi}{2}$$

and $\qquad\qquad\qquad\qquad\qquad\qquad\qquad k = 1, 2, 3, \cdots, 2n \quad (13.28)$

$$\omega_k = \cosh a \cos \frac{2k - 1}{n}\frac{\pi}{2}$$

Squaring these expressions and adding yield

$$\frac{\sigma_k^2}{\sinh^2 a} + \frac{\omega_k^2}{\cosh^2 a} = 1 \tag{13.29}$$

This is the equation of an ellipse whose axes are the σ and ω axes of the s plane. The major semiaxis of the ellipse has the value $\cosh a$, the minor semiaxis is $\sinh a$, and the foci are located at $\omega = \pm 1$.

Consider the frequency $\omega_a = \cosh a$ at which this ellipse crosses the imaginary axis of the s plane. At this frequency,

$$C_n(\omega_a) = \cosh n \cosh^{-1} \cosh a = \cosh na \tag{13.30}$$

The quantity na has the value given by Eq. 13.26 of $\sinh^{-1} 1/\epsilon$, or $\sinh na = 1/\epsilon$. Using the relationship $\cosh^2 na - \sinh^2 na = 1$, we find that

$$na = \cosh^{-1}\left(1 + \frac{1}{\epsilon^2}\right)^{\frac{1}{2}} \tag{13.31}$$

Substituting this value into Eq. 13.30 gives

$$C_n(\omega_a) = \left(1 + \frac{1}{\epsilon^2}\right)^{\frac{1}{2}} \tag{13.32}$$

Then the magnitude response $|G_{12}|$ has the value

$$|G_{12}(j \cosh a)| = \frac{1}{[1 + \epsilon^2 C_n^2(\cosh a)]^{\frac{1}{2}}} = \frac{1}{(2 + \epsilon^2)^{\frac{1}{2}}} \tag{13.33}$$

If $\epsilon \ll 1$, then this result may be approximated as

$$|G_{12}(j \cosh a)| \cong 1/\sqrt{2} = 0.707 \tag{13.34}$$

which is the half-power or the cutoff frequency of the Butterworth response. This result tells us that we may compare the Butterworth and Chebyshev responses by comparing the frequency $\omega = 1$ of the Butterworth result with the frequency $\omega = \cosh a$ of the Chebyshev case. Better yet, we will normalize the frequency of the Chebyshev response by the factor $\cosh a$ in order that we may compare the two results directly. Then Eqs. 13.28 become

$$\sigma_k' = \pm \tanh a \sin \frac{2k-1}{n} \frac{\pi}{2}$$

and

$$\omega_k' = \cos \frac{2k-1}{n} \frac{\pi}{2}$$

                              (13.35)

The sine and cosine terms in these equations remind us of the equation of the pole locations for the Butterworth case with n even,

$$\sigma_k = \cos \frac{2k - 1}{n} \frac{\pi}{2}$$

and (13.36)

$$\omega_k = \sin \frac{2k - 1}{n} \frac{\pi}{2}$$

except that the sine and cosine terms are interchanged. This difference is explained by observing that different poles are associated with

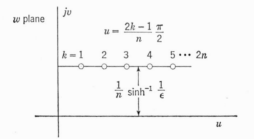

Fig. 13-6. Pole locations identified by Eqs. 13.36 for $n = 4$ and $n = 5$. Note order of appearance of poles with k.

Fig. 13-7. Positions in the w plane that locate the poles in the s plane for the Chebyshev response function.

the k values, $k = 1, 2, \cdots, 2n$ in the two sets of equations. The pole locations for the various k found from Eq. 13.36 are shown in Fig. 13-6. (The Butterworth case uses a different equation for n odd, but the Chebyshev results of Eqs. 13.35 are identified with the same sine and cosine terms for *all* n.) The u values and v value which located the poles and zeros through the transformation $s = j \cos (u + jv)$ in Eqs. 13.25 and 13.26 are shown in Fig. 13-7. In carrying out this transformation, the k values are associated with pole locations as shown in Fig. 13-8, with a different starting point and a different direction of "rotation."

Comparing the two figures, Fig. 13-6 and 13-8 for the cases $n = 4$ and $n = 5$, we arrive at the following procedure to locate the poles for the Chebyshev case: Locate the poles on a unit circle using Eqs.

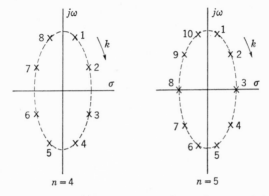

$n = 4$ $n = 5$

Fig. 13-8. The points shown in Fig. 13-7 for the w plane map into the positions shown here in the s plane. Note order of k numbers in comparison with those of Fig. 13-6.

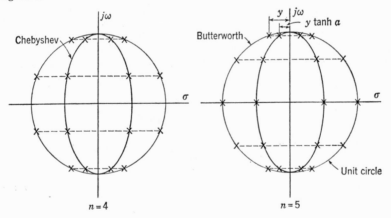

$n = 4$ $n = 5$

Fig. 13-9. The construction of the positions of the Chebyshev response poles from the poles of the Butterworth response poles.

13.36, as illustrated in Fig. 13-6. As directed by Eqs. 13.35, reduce the imaginary part so obtained by multiplying by $\tanh a$ and this becomes the real part for the Chebyshev case. The real part found from Eqs. 13.36 is the imaginary part for the Chebyshev case directly.

But because of the different order of appearance for the two cases (illustrated for typical cases in Figs. 13-6 and 13-8), this procedure may be simplified to the following: Locate poles for the Butterworth case using different forms of Eqs. 13.5 depending on whether n is even or odd. Reduce the real part by multiplying by tanh a, but use the imaginary part directly. That's all. The $n = 4$ and $n = 5$ cases are shown in Fig. 13-9 to illustrate this procedure. We note that, if necessary, frequency can be inversely scaled by the cosh a factor so that the ellipse has a form described by Eq. 13.29.

To find the coordinates for the poles for the Chebyshev case, Table 13-1 may be used by simply multiplying constants in the cos θ column by the constant tanh a. The right half plane poles are rejected as before in constructing the $G_{12}(s)$ function required in synthesis procedures.

Example 1. For tanh $a = \frac{3}{4}$ and $n = 3$, the left half plane poles are found using Table 13-1 to be located at -0.750 and $-0.375 \pm j0.866$. Multiplying together the corresponding factors, $s + \frac{3}{4}$ and $(s + \frac{3}{8})^2 + \frac{3}{4}$, we find that

$$G_{12}(s) = \frac{\frac{171}{256}}{s^3 + 1.5s^2 + \frac{93}{64}s + \frac{171}{256}} \qquad (13.37)$$

where the numerator constant has been introduced in order that $G_{12}(0) = 1$ as required.

There are two other respects in which the Butterworth and the Chebyshev responses can be compared: their magnitudes in the stop band and their phase characteristics. For large ω, the Chebyshev magnitude squared function is approximately the following when only the first term of the Chebyshev polynomial is retained

$$|G_C|^2 = \frac{1}{\epsilon^2 C_n{}^2(\omega)} = \frac{1}{\epsilon^2 2^{2(n-1)} \omega^{2n}} \qquad (13.38)$$

The corresponding large-value form of the Butterworth response is similarly

$$|G_B|^2 = \frac{1}{\omega^{2n}} \qquad (13.39)$$

We may plot these asymptotic values on semilogarithmic coordinates by expressing the magnitude squared in decibels. Thus, since $\alpha = 10 \log |G|^2$ db, we have

$$10 \log |G_B|^2 = -20n \log \omega \quad \text{db} \qquad (13.40)$$

and $\quad 10 \log |G_C|^2 = -20n \log \omega - 6(n-1) - 20 \log \epsilon \quad \text{db} \quad (13.41)$

The Butterworth response is seen to have an asymptotic slope of $-6n$ db/octave, whereas the Chebyshev response has the same slope but is offset by a value depending on both n and ϵ. Since ϵ is less than or equal to unity, the log ϵ term in Eq. 13.41 is either zero or negative, meaning that the second and third terms are of opposite sign. Consideration of two limiting conditions is helpful in interpreting the difference in Eqs. 13.40 and 13.41.

First, let $\epsilon = 1$ so that the lower limit of the ripple width is 0.707, a convenient value for comparison with all Butterworth cases. Then $20 \log \epsilon = 0$, and the high-frequency asymptote is displaced downward

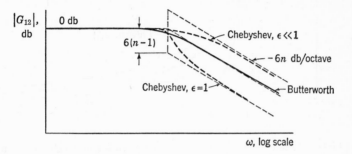

Fig. 13-10. A semilog plot showing the stop band response of the Chebyshev function in comparison with the Butterworth function for two limiting situations.

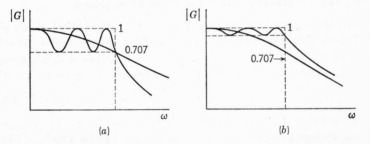

Fig. 13-11. Linear plots corresponding to the semilog plots of Fig. 13-10.

by $6(n-1)$ db, as shown in Fig. 13-10. For this case, the Chebyshev response has a smaller value in the stop band for all values of n and is a better approximation to the ideal response of Fig. 13-1(a).

This large ripple width shows the Chebyshev response in its most favorable light, of course. For small ϵ, we gain advantage in the pass band and so expect to pay some price in the stop band. For this small ripple width corresponding to small ϵ, the third term of Eq. 13.41 becomes larger than the second, meaning that the response asymptote is displaced upward, as shown in Fig. 13-10. The linear interpretation of these two cases is shown in Fig. 13-11. Comparisons of Chebyshev and Butterworth phase responses are shown in Fig. 13-12.

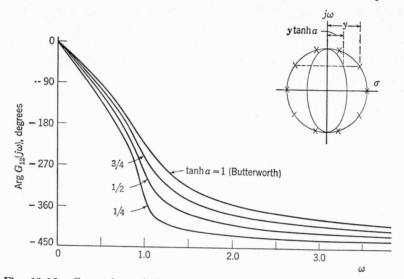

Fig. 13-12. Comparison of the phase characteristics of Chebyshev functions with the Butterworth function, plotted for $n = 5$.

13.3   The maximally flat delay form of response

The third approximating function we will study is that which gives maximally flat time delay. Like the Butterworth and Chebyshev responses, we shall study only an all-pole function with all zeros at infinity. From a fundamental theorem from Laplace transformation,

$$\mathcal{L}\, v(t - T) = e^{-sT}\, \mathcal{L}\, v(t) \tag{13.42}$$

We let $\mathcal{L}\, v(t) = V_1(s)$ be the input voltage transform. We desire the output voltage to be delayed T sec in time, but to be otherwise identical and so given by the equation $\mathcal{L}\, v(t - T) = V_2(s)$. Then

$$\frac{V_2(s)}{V_1(s)} = G_{12}(s) = e^{-sT} \tag{13.43}$$

When $s = j\omega$, the magnitude and phase characteristics may be identified. That is,

$$G_{12}(j\omega) = e^{-j\omega T} \tag{13.44}$$

and $\qquad \left| G_{12}(j\omega) \right| = 1 \qquad$ and $\qquad \operatorname{Arg} G_{12}(j\omega) = -\omega T \tag{13.45}$

are the desired properties of $G_{12}(s)$. This result also shows that

$$T = -\frac{d}{d\omega} \operatorname{Arg} G_{12}(j\omega) \tag{13.46}$$

meaning that the time delay is equal to the slope of the phase as a function of frequency curve, an important result.

The transfer function which is to approximate the ideal response shown in Fig. 13-13 must be in the form of a quotient of polynomials.

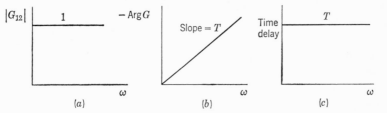

Fig. 13-13.   The ideal characteristics required for a constant time delay function.

To accomplish this, we first normalize frequency by letting $T = 1$ sec, and then observe that

$$G_{12}(s) = e^{-s} = \frac{1}{e^s} = \frac{1}{\cosh s + \sinh s} \qquad (13.47)$$

There are many ways this function can be approximated. The particular method we shall describe is due to L. Storch.* We begin by rearranging the last equation into the form

$$G_{12}(s) = \frac{1/\sinh s}{\cosh s/\sinh s + 1} \qquad (13.48)$$

The series expansions of the $\cosh s$ and $\sinh s$ functions are

$$\cosh s = 1 + \frac{s^2}{2!} + \frac{s^4}{4!} + \frac{s^6}{6!} + \cdots \qquad (13.49)$$

and

$$\sinh s = s + \frac{s^3}{3!} + \frac{s^5}{5!} + \frac{s^7}{7!} + \cdots \qquad (13.50)$$

From these expressions we may compute $\cosh s/\sinh s = \coth s$ in the form of an infinite continued fraction:

$$\coth s = \frac{1}{s} + \cfrac{1}{\cfrac{3}{s} + \cfrac{1}{\cfrac{5}{s} + \cfrac{1}{\cfrac{7}{s} + \cdot}}} \qquad (13.51)$$

---

* "Synthesis of constant-time delay ladder networks using Bessel polynomials," *Proc. I.R.E.*, **42**, 1666–1675 (1954).

The approximation employed is that of truncating this series with the $(2n - 1)/s$ term. For example, for $n = 3$, the truncated continued fraction is

$$\coth s = \frac{1}{s} + \cfrac{1}{\cfrac{3}{s} + \cfrac{1}{\cfrac{5}{s}}} = \frac{6s^2 + 15}{s^3 + 15s} \tag{13.52}$$

which is seen to be a quotient of polynomials in s. Let the general numerator polynomial be M and the denominator be N so that $\coth s$ is M/N. These letters are appropriately chosen since M/N is a Hurwitz ψ function (or reactance function) as studied in Chapter 4, and since all of the coefficients of the continued fraction expansion of Eq. 13.51 are positive we know that $M + N$ is a Hurwitz polynomial.

Let us identify M with $\cosh s$ and N with $\sinh s$ so that Eq. 13.48 becomes

$$G_{12}(s) = \frac{b_0}{M + N} \tag{13.53}$$

where b_0 is introduced to insure that $G_{12}(0) = 1$ as required in Eqs. 13.45. For the example of Eq. 13.52, we see that for $T = 1$,

$$G_{12}(s) = \frac{15}{15 + 15s + 6s^2 + s^3} \tag{13.54}$$

By truncating the infinite continued fraction at different n, we arrive at the table of coefficients for the denominator polynomials $B_n(s)$ as given in Table 13-4. Polynomials of higher order may be found from

TABLE 13-4

Coefficients of $B_n(s) = b_0 + b_1 s + \cdots + b_n s^n$

Order n	b_0	b_1	b_2	b_3	b_4	b_5	b_6	b_7
0	1							
1	1	1						
2	3	3	1					
3	15	15	6	1				
4	105	105	45	10	1			
5	945	945	420	105	15	1		
6	10,395	10,395	4,725	1,260	210	21	1	
7	135,135	135,135	62,370	17,325	3,150	378	28	1

the recursion formula

$$B_n = (2n - 1)B_{n-1} + s^2 B_{n-2} \tag{13.55}$$

How closely do these functions approximate the desired phase (and so time delay) characteristic? We have anticipated the answer to this question by naming our study *maximally flat* time delay. Proof that these functions have this desired time delay characteristic has been given by Storch* by identifying the polynomials $B_n(s)$ with the Bessel polynomials studied by H. L. Krall and O. Fink.† [Thus $B_n(s)$ is properly termed a Bessel polynomial, although the polynomials given by Krall and Fink are of the form $B_n(1/s)$, but they are related

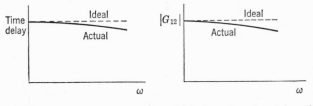

Fig. 13-14. Illustrating the manner in which functions involving the Bessel polynomials deviate from the ideal characteristic.

by the equation, $B_n(s) = s^n B_n(1/s)$.] The actual curves in comparison with the ideal are shown in Fig. 13-14. The deviation from the ideal time delay characteristic in per cent of the ideal is shown in Fig. 13-15, and Fig. 13-16 shows the deviation from the magnitude function in decibels. When specifications are given in terms of these two deviations, it is possible to fix a value of n satisfying the more stringent requirement. This n, the order of the Bessel polynomial, together with the value of T are sufficient to specify the function $G_{12}(s)$—or other functions like $Z_{12}(s)$ or $-Y_{12}(s)$—from which a network can be synthesized in either terminated or open-circuited output form.

We next examine the consequences of our choice of scaling so that $T = 1$ upon the frequency scaling. Suppose that the specifications of the problem are delay time T and also delay error and magnitude error, both at a particular frequency. What happens to the product

---

* *Loc. cit.*

† "A new class of orthogonal polynomials: the Bessel polynomials," *Trans. Amer. Math. Soc.*, **65**, 100–115 (1949). The polynomials satisfy the differential equation

$$p^2 \frac{d^2 y}{dp^2} + (2p + 2) \frac{dy}{dp} = n(n + 1)y$$

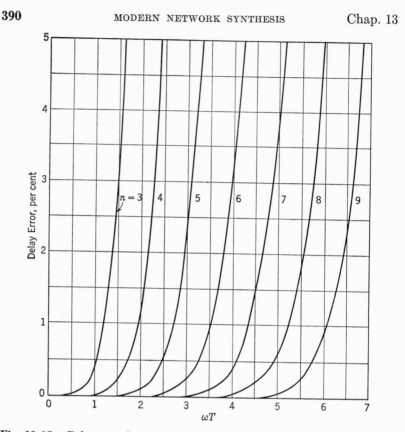

Fig. 13-15. Delay error in per cent as a function of ωT, with n as a parameter.

ωT when ω is scaled? Let us answer in terms of an example. Let the input to an ideal delay network be a sine wave so that the transform of the output is

$$V_0(s) = \frac{\omega}{s^2 + \omega^2}\, e^{-Ts} \tag{13.56}$$

This function is scaled so that

$$V_0{}'(s) = \frac{1}{a}\, \frac{\omega/a}{s^2 + (\omega/a)^2}\, e^{-aTs} \tag{13.57}$$

If we let

$$\omega' = \omega/a \qquad \text{and} \qquad T' = aT \tag{13.58}$$

then

$$v_0{}'(t) = \frac{1}{a} \sin \omega'(t - T') \tag{13.59}$$

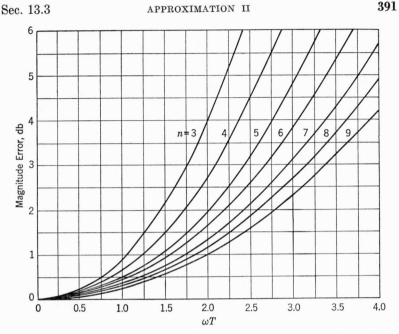

Fig. 13-16. Magnitude error in decibels as a function of frequency, ωT.

Observe that $\omega' T' = \omega T$; i.e., this product remains constant when fre-
quency is scaled. The consequence of this result is that frequency scaling should not be used before the order of approximation is determined. Then, however, the resulting function can be frequency-scaled in order to make computations easy.

It is interesting to compare the relative pole positions of $G_{12}(s)$ found from the Bessel polynomial with those found for the Butterworth and Chebyshev cases. As shown in Fig. 13-17, the poles for maximally flat delay have more nearly the same imaginary part in comparison with the maximally flat and equal ripple configurations. Thus as the poles move toward the imaginary axis, the maximally flat response changes to equal ripple;

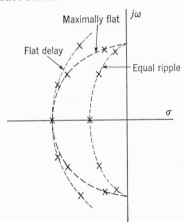

Fig. 13-17. Plot showing the relative position of the poles for the maximally flat delay, maximally flat magnitude, and equal ripple magnitude responses.

as they move away, the phase response becomes more nearly linear.

Many other possible response functions, in addition to the all-pole functions of this chapter, may be studied.   One of the most interesting is that giving equal ripple response in both the pass and stop bands, as shown in Fig. 13-18(a).   The pole positions corresponding to this

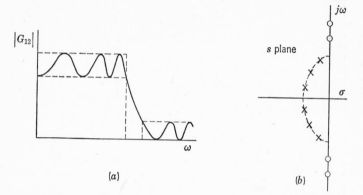

(a)

(b)

Fig. 13-18.   (a) An equal ripple function in both the pass and stop bands.   (b) The pole configuration that gives this magnitude response, found from the Jacobian elliptic function.

form of response, found through the use of the Jacobian elliptic function, are illustrated in Fig. 13-18(b).   Detailed discussions of these rather complicated relationships are given by Guillemin and Tuttle.*

13.4   Frequency transformations

The magnitude characteristic approximated in the first two sections of this chapter was low pass in character.   Frequency transformations which make it possible to apply the theory of this chapter to the high-pass, band-pass, band-elimination, and other cases are given in Chapter 16.

FURTHER READING

A discussion of the approximation problem in greater detail is given by Guillemin in *Synthesis of Passive Networks*, Chapter 14.   For an introduction to the subject by way of the potential analog, see Tuttle, *Network Synthesis*, Vol. I, Chapter 14.   See also Chapter 5 of Stewart, *Circuit Theory and Design*, and Chapter 9 of Balabanian, *Network Synthesis*.   An excellent introduction

* Guillemin, *Synthesis of Passive Networks*, pp. 607–614, and Tuttle, *Network Synthesis*, Vol. I, Chapter 14.   Tuttle's discussion is in terms of the potential analog.

to various aspects of approximation is given by Storer, *Passive Network Synthesis*, Chapters 27 through 31.

PROBLEMS

13-1. For each of the following functions, determine $|f(j\omega)|^2$. Compare your result with the general form of the Butterworth functions.

(a) $f_1(s) = 1 + 2s + s^2$
(b) $f_2(s) = 1 + 2s + 2s^2 + s^3$
(c) $f_3(s) = 1 + 2.613s + 3.414s^2 + 2.613s^3 + s^4$

13-2. Locate the poles of $G_{12}(s)$ for a maximally flat response for $n = 6$ and $n = 7$.

13-3. A Chebyshev response function is defined by $n = 5$ and $\epsilon^2 = 0.2$.

(a) Determine the maximum and minimum value of $|G_{12}(j\omega)|$ in the pass band.

(b) Determine the ripple width in decibels.

(c) Find the half-power frequency, i.e., the frequency at which $|G_{12}(j\omega)| = 0.707$.

13-4. An equal ripple response function is required to have a half-power frequency (see Prob. 13-3) at $\omega = 1.1$, and to have a ripple width not greater than 0.5 db. What is the minimum value that n may have?

13-5. It is required that $|G_{12}(j\omega)|$ be equal ripple in nature from $\omega = 0$ to $\omega = 1$, and that at $\omega = 1.3$, it be equal to or less than 0.40. The lower limit of the ripple width is to be 0.90. From these specifications, illustrated in Fig. P13-5, find the function $G_{12}(s)$ that comes closest to meeting the $\omega = 1.3$ magnitude specification.

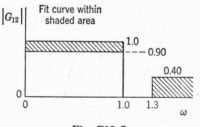

Fig. P13-5

13-6. Use the recursion formula, Eq. 13.14, to check the Chebyshev polynomial of order 9 in Table 13-3, starting with the polynomials of orders 7 and 8.

13-7. Show that

$$C_n^2(z) = [C_{2n}(z) + 1]/2$$

13-8. Prove that the quantities ϵ, n, and a of the Chebyshev response function are related by the equation

$$e^a = \left(\sqrt{\frac{1}{\epsilon^2} + 1} + \frac{1}{\epsilon}\right)^{1/n}$$

13-9. Figure P13-9 shows an ellipse constructed by a method commonly studied in descriptive geometry.

(a) By reference to a descriptive geometry textbook if necessary, explain the procedure for constructing the ellipse.

(b) A procedure for the location of the poles on the ellipse for the Chebyshev response case is shown by the construction lines of the figure. Justify this construction procedure. (How can you be sure that the poles so located are the proper ones?)

(c) Apply the method of part (b) for $n = 5$ to find all of the poles.

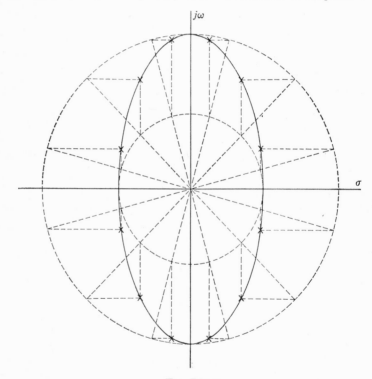

Fig. P13-9

13-10. It is asserted that the pole configuration shown in Fig. P13-10 gives approximately linear phase. All poles are separated by $\Delta\omega$.

(a) Derive an expression for the phase function.

(b) Show that the phase characteristic is equal ripple approximately, except near the poles located the greatest distance from the real axis.

(*c*) Derive an expression for the time delay associated with the function described by these poles.

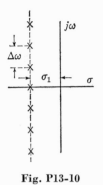

Fig. P13-10

13-11. We have shown that $2n - 1$ derivatives of the Butterworth response function, Eq. 13.1, are zero at $\omega = 0$. How many derivatives of the Chebyshev response function are zero at $\omega = 0$? Of the maximally flat delay function? Is the choice of the words "maximally flat" (sometimes "flat-flat") a good one for describing the Butterworth magnitude function?

13-12. Design a delay network in the form of a ladder having a delay of 1 millisec. The delay error is required to be less than 3 % up to the frequency, $\omega = 1500$ radians/sec. The loss to this frequency should be no more than 3 db.

13-13. Repeat Prob. 13-12 for a delay of 10 microsec.

(*a*) Determine the appropriate network function in terms of a Bessel polynomial to meet these specifications.

(*b*) Assuming that the specifications are to be applied to the function Z_{12} for a resistively terminated network, determine a ladder network terminated in a 500-ohm resistor.

13-14. Consider the magnitude squared function

$$|G_{12}|^2 = \frac{2C_n^2(1/\omega)}{1 + \epsilon^2 C_n^2(1/\omega)}$$

(*a*) Sketch $|G_{12}(j\omega)|$ as a function of ω, pointing out significant features of this response characteristic such as equal ripple characteristics, flat characteristics, etc.

(*b*) Locate the poles and zeros of $G_{12}(s)$. Explain the method.

13-15. A response function of the form shown in Fig. P13-15 is required to be equal ripple in the pass band and to fall off at a rate of -12 db/octave when well into the stop band. Draw the pole-zero location for $Z_{12}(s)$ to give the desired response. Give the coordinates of the poles and zeros.

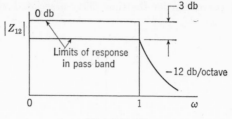

Fig. P13-15

13-16. The specification for $|Z_{12}(j\omega)|$ is as shown in Fig. P13-16(a) with equal ripple required in the pass band. Find a network of the form shown in (b) which meets the specifications. Give element values. (The driver of the network approximates a pentode.)

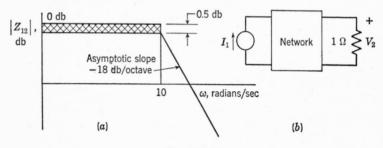

Fig. P13-16

13-17. A. Papoulis* has suggested a new amplitude characteristic

$$A(\omega) = \frac{A_0}{\sqrt{1 + L(\omega)^2}}$$

where

$$L(\omega^2) = \int_{-1}^{2\omega^2 - 1} v(x)\, dx$$

$$v(x) = a_0 + a_1 P_1(x) + \cdots + a_k P_k(x)$$

and

$$a_0 = a_1/3 = \cdots = a_k/(2k + 1) = \frac{1}{\sqrt{2(k + 1)}}$$

The P_k's are the Legendre polynomials of the first kind.

(a) What is the nature of this response function in the pass band? Compare it with the Butterworth response.

(b) Compare this response in the stop band with the Chebyshev response and with the Butterworth response. For comparable conditions, which response gives the greatest rate of decrease with frequency?

(c) Outline how you would compute the pole locations which give this response.

---

* "A new class of filters," *Proc. I.R.E.*, **46**, 649 (1958).

Resistively Terminated
Networks

· · · · · · · · · · · · · *14*

The design of a network to couple an energy source to a load, the system represented in Fig. 14-1, is important in electrical communications. If R_1 in the network illustrated is very small compared to the impedance level of the network, the energy source may be approximated as an ideal voltage source. When R_1 is very large, the energy

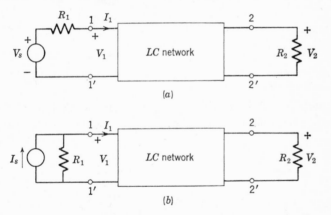

(a)

(b)

Fig. 14-1. Two forms of the double-terminated LC network.

source may be similarly approximated as an ideal current source. For these two cases, the system is described by the phrase *terminated network*, or terminated coupling network. The more general case, with a finite, nonzero value of R_1, is described as a *double-terminated network* and will be studied in Chapter 15.

What specification functions are suitable to describe the terminated network just discussed? The most important design specification of these networks is the transfer function. For the ideal voltage source, suitable transfer functions are $-Y_{12} = I_2/V_1$ and $G_{12} = V_2/V_1$; for the current source, $Z_{12} = V_2/I_1$ or $-\alpha_{12} = I_2/I_1$. Equations for these transfer functions in terms of the open-circuit impedance and short-circuit admittance functions were derived in Chapter 2, and are summarized in Fig. 14-2. Comparing the equations of this figure for each network, we make the interesting observation that if the impedance level is adjusted so that R_2 is 1 ohm, then $-Y_{12} = G_{12}$ and $Z_{12} = -\alpha_{12}$. Since the impedance level scaling results in no loss of

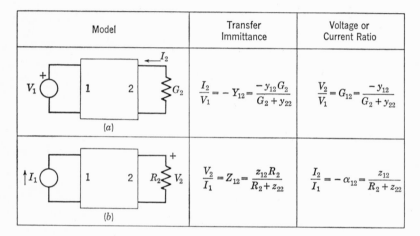

Model	Transfer Immittance	Voltage or Current Ratio
(a)	$\dfrac{I_2}{V_1} = -Y_{12} = \dfrac{-y_{12}G_2}{G_2 + y_{22}}$	$\dfrac{V_2}{V_1} = G_{12} = \dfrac{-y_{12}}{G_2 + y_{22}}$
(b)	$\dfrac{V_2}{I_1} = Z_{12} = \dfrac{z_{12}R_2}{R_2 + z_{22}}$	$\dfrac{I_2}{I_1} = -\alpha_{12} = \dfrac{z_{12}}{R_2 + z_{22}}$

Fig. 14-2. Summary of network function expressions for terminated networks.

generality, we will follow this standard practice of design on the basis of a 1-ohm termination. Then when $R_2 = 1$ ohm,

$$Z_{12} = -\alpha_{12} = \frac{z_{12}}{1 + z_{22}} \tag{14.1a}$$

and

$$-Y_{12} = G_{12} = \frac{-y_{12}}{1 + y_{22}} \tag{14.1b}$$

and the two kinds of specifications are related to z_{12} and z_{22} or $-y_{12}$ and y_{22}. Observe that these equations do not involve the driving-point functions z_{11} and y_{11}.

Expressions were also given in Chapter 2 for the double-terminated network to relate V_2 and I_2 to V_s and I_s (the s for source) rather than V_1 and I_1. These equations will be used in the synthesis of double-terminated networks in Chapter 15.

14.1   Elementary synthesis procedures

Let us consider the transfer admittance function $-Y_{12}$ which may be written as a quotient of polynomials of the form

$$-Y_{12}(s) = \frac{p(s)}{q(s)} = \frac{a_0 s^n + a_1 s^{n-1} + \cdots + a_{n-1} s + a_n}{b_0 s^m + b_1 s^{m-1} + \cdots + b_{m-1} s + b_m} \quad (14.2)$$

The problem associated with the synthesis of terminated networks is stated in terms of this equation in comparison with Eq. 14.1b. If we are given $-Y_{12}$ as a specification, how can we determine $-y_{12}$ and y_{22} in suitable form for synthesis, say by a Cauer ladder development? One answer to this question is given by writing $q(s)$ of Eq. 14.2 as a sum,

$$q(s) = q_1(s) + q_2(s) \quad (14.3)$$

so that $-Y_{12}$ may be written

$$-Y_{12}(s) = \frac{p(s)}{q_1(s) + q_2(s)} = \frac{\dfrac{p(s)}{q_2(s)}}{1 + \dfrac{q_1(s)}{q_2(s)}} \quad (14.4)$$

Comparison of this equation with Eq. 14.1b suggests the identification,

$$-y_{12}(s) = \frac{p(s)}{q_2(s)} \quad \text{and} \quad y_{22}(s) = \frac{q_1(s)}{q_2(s)} \quad (14.5)$$

Two special cases are well suited to the use of these equations. The first is for the all-pole functions of the last chapter, the second is for the synthesis of terminated RC networks.

For the special all-pole functions of Chapter 13 (Butterworth, Chebyshev, maximally flat delay), $p(s) = 1$ and $q(s)$ is a Hurwitz polynomial. If we select q_1 and q_2 to be the even and odd parts respectively of the Hurwitz polynomial, the quotient, q_1/q_2, is a Hurwitz ψ function (a reactance function). Then y_{22} of Eqs. 14.5 represents an LC network which must be developed so that $-y_{12} = 1/q_2(s)$ will have all of its zeros of transmission at infinity.* The ladder developed from the $-y_{12}$ and y_{22} specifications will be of the first Cauer form and synthesis is very simple indeed: (1) develop a ladder network starting from the 2-2' terminals from $-y_{12}$ and y_{22}, (2) connect a 1-ohm resistor to terminals 2-2', and (3) connect a voltage source to terminals 1-1'. The specification function $-Y_{12}$ is realized

---

* Note that if we divide by the even part, the network is not realizable as a grounded structure because the Fialkow-Gerst condition is then violated.

within the same constant multiplier as $-y_{12}$. For example, the 3rd-order Butterworth function is, from Table 13-2,

$$-Y_{12} = \frac{1}{1 + 2s + 2s^2 + s^3} \tag{14.6}$$

from which we make the identifications,

$$-y_{12} = \frac{1}{s^3 + 2s}, \qquad y_{22} = \frac{2s^2 + 1}{s^3 + 2s} \tag{14.7}$$

Expanding y_{22} in a continued fraction gives

$$y_{22} = \cfrac{1}{\frac{1}{2}s + \cfrac{1}{\frac{4}{3}s + \cfrac{1}{\frac{3}{2}s}}} \tag{14.8}$$

The network realization is that shown in Fig. 14-3.

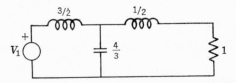

Fig. 14-3. Network realization found from Eq. 14.8 satisfying the specification function, Eq. 14.6.

In the case of resistively terminated RC networks (which are still RC networks), the function $-Y_{12}$ has the same properties as $-y_{12}$ studied in Chapter 11. It is necessary that the zeros of $q_1(s)$ and $q_2(s)$ be interlaced on the negative real axis of the s plane and that the zero of y_{22} nearest to the origin be a zero of $q_1(s)$ in order that $y_{22} = q_1/q_2$ be developable as an RC network. If the zeros of $p(s)$ are also on the negative real axis, then $-Y_{12}$ may be realized as a terminated ladder network. If the zeros of $p(s)$ are complex, however, then a parallel ladder or some equivalent method must be used. In the event that $p(s)$ contains negative coefficients but $p(s)$ does not have zeros on the positive real axis, then both $p(s)$ and $q(s)$ may be augmented by multiplication by factors of the form $(s + a)$ until all coefficients of $p(s)$ are positive.* Our problem then is the choice of suitable functions $q_1(s)$ and $q_2(s)$ from $q(s)$.

* Guillemin, *Synthesis of Passive Networks*, pp. 437–443.

Suppose that $q(s)$ has the factored form,

$$q(s) = (s + \sigma_1)(s + \sigma_2)(s + \sigma_3) \cdots (s + \sigma_n) \qquad (14.9)$$

where
$$0 \leq \sigma_1 < \sigma_2 < \sigma_3 < \cdots < \sigma_n < \infty \qquad (14.10)$$

as required of $-Y_{12}$ for RC networks. We are required to find roots

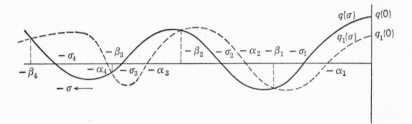

Fig. 14-4. Plot showing how the zeros of $q_2(s)$ are fixed by those of $q(s)$ and $q_1(s)$.

of $q_1(s)$ and $q_2(s)$ which are negative and real and, in addition, interlaced on the negative real axis. We select the roots of $q_1(s)$ to be

$$q_1(s) = (s + \alpha_1)(s + \alpha_2) \cdots (s + \alpha_n) \qquad (14.11)$$

so that $0 \leq \alpha_1 < \sigma_1 < \alpha_2 < \sigma_2 < \cdots < \alpha_n < \sigma_n < \infty \qquad (14.12)$

as shown in Fig. 14-4. Then $q_2(s)$ has its roots fixed by the equation

$$q_2(s) = q(s) - q_1(s) \qquad (14.13)$$

and so the roots are at the intersections of the solid and dashed lines in Fig. 14-4, and

$$q_2(s) = (s + \beta_1)(s + \beta_2) \cdots (s + \beta_n) \qquad (14.14)$$

From the figure we have constructed, observe that

$$\alpha_k < \sigma_k < \beta_k, \qquad k = 1, 2, \cdots, n \qquad (14.15)$$

This insures that the poles and zeros of y_{22} are interlaced. Further, if we require that

$$q_1(0) < q(0) \qquad \text{and} \qquad q_1(\infty)/q(\infty) \leq 1 \qquad (14.16)$$

as we can always do by multiplying either $q_1(s)$ or $q(s)$ by a constant, then we are assured that α_1 is the zero closest to the origin as required for y_{22} to be RC realizable. With y_{22} and $-y_{12}$ so selected, a network terminated in a 1-ohm resistor can always be synthesized.

To illustrate, let it be required to find a network terminated in a 1-ohm resistor to meet the specification

$$-Y_{12}(s) = \frac{p(s)}{q(s)} = \frac{s^2 + s + 1}{2s^2 + 10s + 11} \tag{14.17}$$

The zeros of $q(s)$ are found using the quadratic formula and

$$q(s) = 2(s + 3.366)(s + 1.634) \tag{14.18}$$

as plotted in Fig. 14-5. A suitable choice of $q_1(s)$ is

$$q_1(s) = (s + 1)(s + 3) \tag{14.19}$$

since $q_1(0) = 3 < q(0) = 11$, and also $q_1(\infty) < q(\infty)$. Then $q_2(s)$ is determined graphically as in Fig. 14-5 or algebraically from Eq. 14.13 to be

$$q_2(s) = (s + 2)(s + 4) \tag{14.20}$$

Then from Eqs. 14.5, the short-circuit admittance functions are

$$y_{22} = \frac{(s + 1)(s + 3)}{(s + 2)(s + 4)}, \qquad -y_{12} = \frac{s^2 + s + 1}{(s + 2)(s + 4)} \tag{14.21}$$

These functions are identical with those of Example 4 of Chapter 11. The network satisfying our specifications is then that of Fig. 11-26

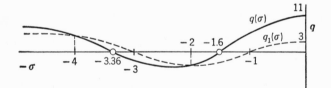

Fig. 14-5. Plot showing zeros of $q(s)$ at -1.634 and -3.366, zeros of $q_1(s)$ chosen at -1 and -3, and zeros of $q_2(s)$ fixed at -2 and -4.

when terminated in a 1-ohm resistor. The freedom in the choice of the roots of $q_1(s)$ illustrated by this example means that there are a large number of network realizations which will meet the given specifications.

14.2   Darlington's driving-point synthesis method

A method for the synthesis of a driving-point impedance function as a two terminal-pair network terminated in a resistive load was described by Sidney Darlington* in 1939.   The method makes use of Eq. 12.55 which, with $R = 1$ ohm, becomes

$$Z(s) = \frac{z_{11}[(1/y_{22}) + 1]}{z_{22} + 1} \qquad (14.22)$$

Writing $Z(s)$ in terms of the even and odd parts of its numerator and denominator polynomials

$$Z(s) = \frac{m_1 + n_1}{m_2 + n_2} \qquad (14.23)$$

we see that two algebraic manipulations of this equation make it of the same form as Eq. 14.22.   These are

$$Z(s) = \frac{m_1}{n_2} \frac{n_1/m_1 + 1}{m_2/n_2 + 1} \qquad \text{(Case A)} \qquad (14.24)$$

$$Z(s) = \frac{n_1}{m_2} \frac{m_1/n_1 + 1}{n_2/m_2 + 1} \qquad \text{(Case B)} \qquad (14.25)$$

For these equations to be the same as Eq. 14.22, we make the identifications

$$z_{11} = m_1/n_2, \quad z_{22} = m_2/n_2, \quad y_{22} = m_1/n_1 \qquad \text{(Case A)} \quad (14.26)$$

or

$$z_{11} = n_1/m_2, \quad z_{22} = n_2/m_2, \quad y_{22} = n_1/m_1 \qquad \text{(Case B)} \quad (14.27)$$

To establish that this equivalence of two equations for impedance $Z(s)$ leads to a synthesis procedure, we will show that

(1) z_{11}, z_{22}, and y_{22} of Eqs. 14.26 and 14.27 are positive real if $Z(s)$ is positive real, and are reactance functions,

(2) a consistent rational z_{12} can always be found, and

(3) the set of functions z_{11}, z_{12}, z_{22} are always compatible in representing a two terminal-pair network.

In addition,

(4) we will examine the consequences of the requirement that $R = 1$ ohm in terms of impedance level scaling.

* "Synthesis of reactance 4-poles which produce prescribed insertion loss characteristics," *Jour. Math. and Phys.*, **18**, 257–353 (1939).   This paper is a summary of Darlington's Ph.D. dissertation at Columbia University.   Darlington also studied at Harvard and MIT and has been with the Bell Telephone Laboratories since 1929.

Completing these steps leads to the formulation of the Darlington method of synthesis of one terminal-pair networks.

Positive real requirement. Assume that $Z(s) = (m_1 + n_1)/(m_2 + n_2)$ is positive real. We wish to show that this implies that the new impedance function $Z_1(s) = (m_1 + n_2)/(m_2 + n_1)$ is also positive real. By the criteria of Section 4.6, for $Z(s) = p(s)/q(s)$ to be positive real, it is necessary that (a) $Z(s)$ be real when s is real, (b) $p + q$ be Hurwitz, and (c) $\mathrm{Re}\, Z(j\omega) \geq 0$ for all ω. Clearly $Z_1(s)$ satisfies conditions (a) and (b) if $Z(s)$ does. To test condition (c), observe that

$$\mathrm{Re}\, Z_1(j\omega) = \frac{m_1 m_2 - n_1 n_2}{m_2{}^2 - n_1{}^2}\bigg|_{s=j\omega} = \frac{m_1 m_2 - n_1 n_2 \big|_{s=j\omega}}{\big|m_2(\omega) \pm j n_1(\omega)\big|^2} \quad (14.28)$$

The numerator of this equation is always positive since it is identical with the numerator of the real part of $Z(j\omega)$. The denominator is the

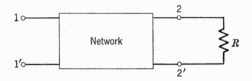

Fig. 14-6. Network structure which is the basis of the Darlington synthesis method.

square of an absolute value and so always positive. Then $Z_1(j\omega) \geq 0$ for all ω and is therefore positive real.*

We know from our studies in Chapters 3 and 4 that the numerator and denominator polynomials of positive real functions are Hurwitz polynomials. Since the impedance functions $Z(s)$ and $Z_1(s)$ of this section are positive real, it follows that the polynomials

$$m_1 + n_1, \quad m_2 + n_2, \quad m_1 + n_2, \quad \text{and} \quad m_2 + n_1 \quad (14.29)$$

are all Hurwitz. Now the quotients of even to odd or odd to even parts of Hurwitz polynomials are reactance functions which are positive real and represent one terminal-pair LC networks. Then

$$(m_1/n_1)^{\pm 1}, \quad (m_2/n_2)^{\pm 1}, \quad (m_1/n_2)^{\pm 1}, \quad \text{and} \quad (m_2/n_1)^{\pm 1} \quad (14.30)$$

are all reactance functions. This means that every function in Eqs. 14.26 and 14.27 is a reactance function and is positive real. If all driving-point functions which describe the network of Fig. 14-6 are

---

* For additional discussion, see Guillemin, *The Mathematics of Circuit Analysis*, pp. 417 ff.

reactance functions, then that network is evidently a lossless (LC) network. We see that the Darlington method of synthesis leads to a network realization in which the only resistor is the terminating element; all other elements are either L or C.

A rational z_{12}. From Eqs. 2.63, we have

$$\frac{z_{11}}{y_{22}} = \Delta_z = z_{11}z_{22} - z_{12}{}^2 \tag{14.31}$$

Solving this equation for z_{12} gives

$$z_{12}{}^2 = z_{11}z_{22} - \frac{z_{11}}{y_{22}} \tag{14.32}$$

If we substitute the values found for these functions in Eqs. 14.26 for Case A, we have

$$z_{12}{}^2 = \frac{m_1}{n_2}\frac{m_2}{n_2} - \frac{m_1}{n_2}\frac{n_1}{m_1} \tag{14.33}$$

so that

$$z_{12} = \frac{1}{n_2}\sqrt{m_1m_2 - n_1n_2} \tag{14.34}$$

Similarly, the substitution of values for Case B from Eqs. 14.27 gives

$$z_{12}{}^2 = \frac{n_1}{m_2}\frac{n_2}{m_2} - \frac{n_1}{m_2}\frac{m_1}{n_1} \tag{14.35}$$

or

$$z_{12} = \frac{1}{m_2}\sqrt{n_1n_2 - m_1m_2} \tag{14.36}$$

To represent a finite network, the impedance function z_{12} *must be a rational function*. What can we do to insure that this will always be the case?

We first observe that the expression within the radical in Eqs. 14.34 and 14.36 is the numerator of the even part of $Z(s)$ or the negative of this quantity. When factored, this even function will have the form

$$m_1m_2 - n_1n_2 = (s^2 + \lambda_1{}^2)^{k_1}(s^2 + \lambda_2{}^2)^{k_1} \cdots \tag{14.37}$$

or, when $s = j\omega$,

$$m_1m_2 - n_1n_2 \Big|_{s=j\omega} = (-1)^{k_1+k_2+\cdots}(\omega^2 + \gamma_1{}^2)^{k_1}(\omega^2 + \gamma_2{}^2)^{k_2} \cdots \tag{14.38}$$

where $-\lambda_j{}^2 = \gamma_j{}^2$. This equation is similar to Eq. 4.76. Now for the impedance function z_{12} to be rational, it is necessary that every exponent, k_1, k_2, $\cdots$, be even. Will this always be the case for positive real functions? The answer to this question is no, as was discussed in Section 4.4. There it was shown that negative real s^2 zeros of Eq. 14.37 occur with even multiplicity for $Z(s)$ positive real so that k_1, k_2, $\cdots$ of Eq. 14.37 are even for such zeros. However, real positive and complex s^2 zeros of this equation need not be of even multiplicity for $Z(s)$ to be positive real, but must be of even multiplicity for z_{12} to be rational. This difficulty is resolved by multiplying $m_1 m_2 - n_1 n_2$ by an auxiliary polynomial

$$W(s) = (m_0 + n_0)(m_0 - n_0) \qquad (14.39)$$

in order that $W(s)(m_1 m_2 - n_1 n_2)$ be a *full square*, assuring that z_{12} is rational. How does this affect the given $Z(s)$? In answering this question, we will pursue an indirect approach. Suppose that $Z(s)$ multiplied in numerator and denominator by $m_0 + n_0$. Then

$$Z(s) = \frac{m_1 + n_1}{m_2 + n_2} \frac{m_0 + n_0}{m_0 + n_0} \qquad (14.40)$$

and $\quad Z(s) = \dfrac{(m_0 m_1 + n_0 n_1) + (m_0 n_1 + n_0 m_1)}{(m_0 m_2 + n_0 n_2) + (n_0 m_2 + m_0 n_2)} = \dfrac{m_1' + n_1'}{m_2' + n_2'} \quad (14.41)$

From this, we see that

$$
\begin{aligned}
m_1' m_2' - n_1' n_2' &= (m_1 m_2 - n_1 n_2)(m_0{}^2 - n_0{}^2) \\
&= (m_1 m_2 - n_1 n_2)\, W(s)
\end{aligned} \qquad (14.42)
$$

Evidently, the answer to our question is that making $m_1 m_2 - n_1 n_2$ into a full square by multiplying by the function $W(s)$ does not affect $Z(s)$. Furthermore, since $W(s)$ must be selected so that its zeros have

TABLE 14-1

---

(1) Form the polynomials:
$\quad m_1' = m_0 m_1 + n_0 n_1 \qquad\qquad\qquad n_1' = m_0 n_1 + n_0 m_1$
$\quad m_2' = m_0 m_2 + n_0 n_2 \qquad\qquad\qquad n_2' = n_0 m_2 + m_0 n_2$

(2) Then:*

Case A	Case B
$z_{11}' = m_1'/n_2'$	$z_{11}' = n_1'/m_2'$
$z_{22}' = m_2'/n_2'$	$z_{22}' = n_2'/m_2'$
$z_{12}' = \dfrac{1}{n_2'} \sqrt{m_1' m_2' - n_1' n_2'}$	$z_{12}' = \dfrac{1}{m_2'} \sqrt{n_1' n_2' - m_1' m_2'}$

---

* In working a given problem, it is not important which case one selects, A or B, so long as the appropriate sign for $W(s)$ is chosen.

symmetry with respect to the imaginary axis, the polynomial $m_0 + n_0$ may be found from $W(s)$ by rejecting its zeros in the right half of the s plane. Thus, the polynomial $m_0 + n_0$ is a Hurwitz polynomial, and is called the auxiliary Hurwitz polynomial in the Darlington method. The revised forms for z_{11}, z_{12}, and z_{22} which insure that z_{12} is rational are summarized in Table 14-1.

Example 1. As an example of the operations just described, consider the driving-point impedance function

$$Z(s) = \frac{s^2 + 2s + 1}{s^2 + s + 1} = \frac{m_1 + n_1}{m_2 + n_2} \tag{14.43}$$

We first form the quantity $m_1 m_2 - n_1 n_2$.

$$m_1 m_2 - n_1 n_2 = (s^2 + 1)^2 - 2s^2 = s^4 + 1$$
$$= (s^2 + \sqrt{2}\, s + 1)(s^2 - \sqrt{2}\, s + 1) \tag{14.44}$$

The simplest form for the auxiliary polynomial is $W(s) = s^4 + 1$ and the auxiliary Hurwitz polynomial is

$$m_0 + n_0 = s^2 + \sqrt{2}\, s + 1 \tag{14.45}$$

If we now multiply the numerator and denominator polynomials of $Z(s)$ by this equation, or use the equations in Table 14-1, we see that

$$m_1' = (s^2 + 1)^2 + 2\sqrt{2}\, s^2 = s^4 + (2 + 2\sqrt{2})s^2 + 1$$
$$n_1' = (s^2 + 1)2s + (s^2 + 1)\sqrt{2}\, s = (2 + \sqrt{2})s(s^2 + 1)$$
$$m_2' = (s^2 + 1)^2 + \sqrt{2}\, s^2 = s^4 + (2 + \sqrt{2})s^2 + 1 \tag{14.46}$$
$$n_2' = (s^2 + 1)\sqrt{2}\, s + s(s^2 + 1) = (1 + \sqrt{2})s(s^2 + 1)$$

For Case A, using the equations of Table 14-1, we have

$$z_{11}' = \frac{s^4 + (2 + 2\sqrt{2})s^2 + 1}{(1 + \sqrt{2})s(s^2 + 1)}$$

$$z_{22}' = \frac{s^4 + (2 + \sqrt{2})s^2 + 1}{(1 + \sqrt{2})s(s^2 + 1)} \tag{14.47}$$

$$z_{12}' = \frac{s^4 + 1}{(1 + \sqrt{2})s(s^2 + 1)}$$

This example will be continued later as Example 2.

The residue condition. We have next to show that the functions z_{11}', z_{12}', and z_{22}' are always compatible in representing a two terminal-pair LC network. This we do by showing that the residue condition is always satisfied for each pole of these functions. For a simple pole located on the imaginary axis of a function of the form $m'(s)/n'(s)$, it was shown in Eq. 4.66 that the residue at pole p_ν is

$$k^{(\nu)} = \frac{m'(p_\nu)}{\dfrac{dn'(p_\nu)}{ds}} \qquad (14.48)$$

The residue condition which applies to all poles of the reactance functions, z_{11}', z_{12}', and z_{22}', is

$$k_{11}^{(\nu)} k_{22}^{(\nu)} - k_{12}^{(\nu)^2} \geq 0 \qquad (14.49)$$

For Case A, we write

$$\frac{m_1'(p_\nu)}{\dfrac{dn_2'(p_\nu)}{ds}} \cdot \frac{m_2'(p_\nu)}{\dfrac{dn_2'(p_\nu)}{ds}} - \frac{m_1'(p_\nu)m_2'(p_\nu) - n_1'(p_\nu)n_2'(p_\nu)}{\left[\dfrac{d}{ds} n_2'(p_\nu)\right]^2} \geq 0 \quad (14.50)$$

which after cancellation reduces to

$$\frac{n_1'(p_\nu)n_2'(p_\nu)}{\left[\dfrac{d}{ds} n_2'(p_\nu)\right]^2} \geq 0 \qquad (14.51)$$

This equation is always satisfied *with the equality sign*, corresponding to the *compact* case, since $n_2'(p_\nu) = 0$ and the other two quantities in the equation are not equal to 0. Thus the residue condition is always fulfilled, and the open-circuit impedance function specifications are compatible. The same conclusion may be reached for Case B.

The network realization. With the residue condition satisfied for all poles of z_{11}', z_{12}', and z_{22}', a network can always be synthesized by the Cauer method outlined in Section 11.4. Since

$$k_{11}^{(\nu)} k_{22}^{(\nu)} = k_{12}^{(\nu)^2} \qquad (14.52)$$

the values permitted for the transformer ratio given by the equation

$$\frac{\left|k_{12}^{(\nu)}\right|}{k_{11}^{(\nu)}} \leq \left|a^{(\nu)}\right| \leq \frac{k_{22}^{(\nu)}}{\left|k_{12}^{(\nu)}\right|} \qquad (14.53)$$

reduce to a single value, namely,

$$\left|a^{(\nu)}\right| = \frac{k_{22}^{(\nu)}}{\left|k_{12}^{(\nu)}\right|} = \frac{\left|k_{12}^{(\nu)}\right|}{k_{11}^{(\nu)}} \qquad (14.54)$$

The elements of the T networks of the Cauer network structure then have the values, from Eqs. 11.77,

$$Z_a = \left[k_{11}^{(\nu)} - \frac{k_{12}^{(\nu)}}{a^{(\nu)}} \right] f_\nu(s) = 0$$

$$Z_b = \left[\frac{k_{22}^{(\nu)}}{{a^{(\nu)}}^2} - \frac{k_{12}^{(\nu)}}{a^{(\nu)}} \right] f_\nu(s) = 0 \qquad (14.55)$$

and
$$Z_c = \frac{k_{12}^{(\nu)}}{a^{(\nu)}} f_\nu(s)$$

where $f_\nu(s)$ has one of the three forms given by Eq. 11.78. The form of network resulting from the Darlington method is that shown in Fig. 14-7.

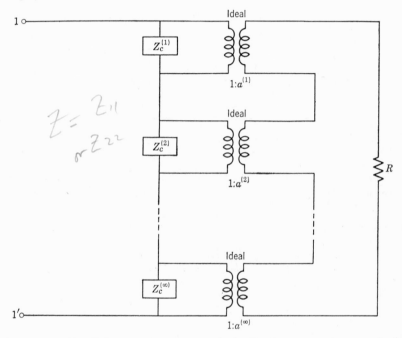

Fig. 14-7. Detailed network structure of the Darlington synthesis method. Compare with Fig. 14-6.

Example 2. The partial fraction expansions for Eqs. 14.47 are

$$z_{11} = \frac{1}{1 + \sqrt{2}} \left(\frac{1}{s} + \frac{2\sqrt{2}\, s}{s^2 + 1} + s \right)$$

$$z_{22} = \frac{1}{1 + \sqrt{2}} \left(\frac{1}{s} + \frac{\sqrt{2}\, s}{s^2 + 1} + s \right) \qquad (14.56)$$

$$z_{12} = \frac{1}{1 + \sqrt{2}} \left(\frac{1}{s} + \frac{-2s}{s^2 + 1} + s \right)$$

From Eq. 14.54,

$$a^{(0)} = 1, \qquad a^{(1)} = -1/\sqrt{2}, \qquad a^{(\infty)} = 1 \tag{14.57}$$

Then, from Eqs. 14.55

$$Z_c^{(0)} = \frac{1}{(1 + \sqrt{2})s}, \qquad Z_c^{(1)} = \frac{2\sqrt{2}s}{(1 + \sqrt{2})(s^2 + 1)}, \qquad Z_c^{(\infty)} = \frac{1}{1 + \sqrt{2}}s$$

$$\tag{14.58}$$

The complete network realization is shown in Fig. 14-8 with the 1:1 ideal transformers removed.

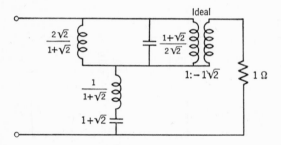

Fig. 14-8. Darlington network for Example 2 with two ideal transformers removed.

Impedance magnitude scaling. The Darlington synthesis method always results in lossless networks terminated in 1-ohm resistors. If we desire to have a different termination, say for a two terminal-pair application, the new element values in the network are

TABLE 14-2
Darlington's Synthesis Procedure

Step	Operation
1	From $Z(s) = \dfrac{m_1 + n_1}{m_2 + n_2}$, evaluate $m_1m_2 - n_1n_2$.
2	Find $W(s)$ which multiplies $m_1m_2 - n_1n_2$ to give a full square making z_{12}' rational.
3	Find the auxiliary Hurwitz polynomial, $m_0 + n_0$, by factoring $W(s)$ and rejecting right half plane zeros.
4	Determine z_{11}', z_{12}', z_{22}' from Table 14-1.
5	Synthesize the required LC network by Cauer's method (or another method) to obtain a network like that of Fig. 14-7.
6	Remove as many ideal transformers as possible.
7	Shift the impedance level if desired.

related to those found with a 1-ohm termination by the scaling relationships given in Chapter 2.

The synthesis procedure described in this section is summarized by the steps given in Table 14-2.

14.3   Properties of Z_{12} for the lossless terminated network

We next study general properties of specification functions that describe lossless networks terminated in a 1-ohm resistor. We will discuss the specification function Z_{12}, noting that our conclusions will apply in each case to G_{12} owing to the similarity of Eqs. 14.1. Synthesis frequently starts with the magnitude squared function, $|Z_{12}(j\omega)|^2$, from which we must determine $Z_{12}(s)$ in proper form to be realized as a lossless terminated network. Our present task is to catalog the properties of these functions preparatory to our study of synthesis procedures in the next section.

(1) The open-circuit impedance functions, z_{12} and z_{22}, are quotients of even to odd or odd to even polynomials. The functions z_{12} and z_{22} refer to the lossless coupling network alone so that z_{22} is a reactance function and z_{12} is an odd function.

(2) Z_{12} for a lossless terminated network has no poles on the imaginary axis. This conclusion stems from the equation

$$Z_{12} = \frac{z_{12}}{1 + z_{22}} \qquad (14.59)$$

Since z_{22} is positive real, $\operatorname{Re} z_{22}(j\omega) \geq 0$ for all ω. Then $z_{22}(j\omega)$ cannot have the value -1 required for there to be a pole on the imaginary axis. This conclusion holds for any network terminated in a resistor. For the case under study, $\operatorname{Re} z_{22}(j\omega) = 0$ since z_{22} is a reactance function.

(3) Zeros of z_{12} are zeros of Z_{12}. Equation 14.59 may be written in the form

$$Z_{12} = \frac{z_{12}}{1 + z_{22}} = \frac{p_{12}/q_{12}}{1 + p_{22}/q_{22}} \qquad (14.60)$$

Now all poles of z_{12} are present in z_{22}, except for some degenerate cases, but there may be poles in z_{22} not in z_{12}. Let the polynomial made up from these poles be $q_0(s)$ so that

$$q_{22}(s) = q_0(s)\, q_{12}(s) \qquad (14.61)$$

Then Z_{12} becomes

$$Z_{12} = \frac{p_{12}q_0}{q_{22} + p_{22}} \tag{14.62}$$

which shows that all zeros of z_{12} are zeros of Z_{12} but that the converse statement is not true because of $q_0(s)$. As a practical matter, we usually start with $Z_{12}(s)$ and then select appropriate forms for z_{12} and z_{22}. Thus we can always select q_{12} and q_{22} to be equal, making $q_0 = 1$ so that the finite zeros of Z_{12} and z_{12} are identical.

(4) Referring to Eq. 14.62, the numerator polynomial of Z_{12} is either even or odd and the denominator polynomial, $q_{22} + p_{22}$, is Hurwitz. This conclusion follows from the properties of z_{12} and z_{22} discussed in item (1). Since both p_{12} and q_0 of Eq. 14.62 are either even or odd, their product is either even or odd. Furthermore, since $z_{22} = p_{22}/q_{22}$ is a reactance function, then the sum $p_{22} + q_{22}$ is a Hurwitz polynomial. To simplify notation, let us rewrite Eq. 14.62 as

$$Z_{12} = \frac{g(s)}{h(s)} = \frac{g(s)}{m_2(s) + n_2(s)} \tag{14.63}$$

where m_2 is an even function and n_2 is odd and $g(s)$ is either even or odd.

(5) The magnitude squared function $\left|Z_{12}(j\omega)\right|^2$ is positive and finite (or bounded) for all ω. The function is positive because it is the square of a real-valued function, and finite or bounded because Z_{12} has no poles on the imaginary axis, $s = j\omega$.

The magnitude squared function is related to $Z_{12}(s)$ by the equation

$$\left|Z_{12}(j\omega)\right|^2 = [Z_{12}(s)\, Z_{12}(-s)]_{s=j\omega} \tag{14.64}$$

In terms of the notation of Eq. 14.63,

$$\left|Z_{12}(j\omega)\right|^2 = \left[\frac{g(s)}{m_2 + n_2}\frac{g(-s)}{m_2 - n_2}\right]_{s=j\omega} = \left[\frac{\pm g^2(s)}{m_2{}^2 - n_2{}^2}\right]_{s=j\omega} \tag{14.65}$$

This equation shows that the numerator of the magnitude squared function is the square of an even or an odd function and is therefore even. The denominator function is derived from the Hurwitz polynomial

$$(m_2 + n_2)(m_2 - n_2) = m_2{}^2 - n_2{}^2 \tag{14.66}$$

which is an even function since even or odd functions squared are even. With $-\omega^2$ substituted for s^2, we have

$$\left|Z_{12}(j\omega)\right|^2 = \frac{A(\omega^2)}{B(\omega^2)} = \frac{A_0 + A_2\omega^2 + \cdots + A_{2n}\omega^{2n}}{B_0 + B_2\omega^2 + \cdots + B_{2m}\omega^{2m}} \tag{14.67}$$

The quotient $A(\omega^2)/B(\omega^2)$ must be positive for all ω [item (5)], but it is not necessary that the A and B coefficients be positive. Further, $B(\omega^2)$ is always positive, being a magnitude squared, and therefore $B(\omega^2) \geq 0$. In summary, we have the following property:

(6) The function $|Z_{12}(j\omega)|^2$ is the quotient of polynomials in ω^2. The coefficients of these polynomials must be real, but need not be positive. Furthermore, $A(\omega^2) \geq 0$ and $B(\omega^2) \geq 0$.

(7) It is necessary that $n \leq m$, where n is the numerator degree of Z_{12} and m is the denominator degree. This requirement for transfer functions follows from stability considerations (proper step-input response) and because Z_{12} may not have a pole at infinity by item (2).

We now turn to a very pertinent question. Suppose that we are given a function $A(\omega^2)/B(\omega^2)$ found from some specifications and fulfilling the last two requirements. How may we determine $Z_{12}(s)$? As a first step we replace ω^2 by $-s^2$ and so form the functions $A(-s^2)$ and $B(-s^2)$ by analytic continuation. The following requirements are made of these functions:

(8) The function $B(-s^2)$ must have quadrantal symmetry, i.e., be symmetrical with respect to both the real and the imaginary axes. When this is the case, the Hurwitz polynomial of the denominator of Z_{12} may be found by separating left-hand and right-half plane zeros,

$$B(-s^2) = h(s)\, h(-s) \qquad (14.68)$$

(9) The function $A(-s^2)$ must have no s^2 zeros which are negative real and of odd multiplicity so that $A(\omega^2)$ is positive for all ω. Furthermore, all zeros must be of even multiplicity in order that $A(-s^2)$ be a full square so that $g(s)$ may be found by extracting the square root. Now $g(s)$ is required to be either even or odd [item (4)]. When even, let $g(s) = m_1$; when odd, let $g(s) = n_1$. Then

$$A(-s^2) = m_1{}^2 \qquad \text{(for g even)} \qquad (14.69)$$

and $\qquad -A(-s^2) = n_1{}^2 \qquad \text{(for g odd)} \qquad (14.70)$

Then Z_{12} is determined for these two possibilities in the forms:

$$Z_{12} = \frac{m_1}{m_2 + n_2} \qquad \text{or} \qquad Z_{12} = \frac{n_1}{m_2 + n_2} \qquad (14.71)$$

A function which is not a full square can be *augmented* in such a way that it becomes a full square by multiplying both numerator and denominator by factors of the form $s^2 + z_j{}^2$. In this manner all numerator factors are made to have even multiplicity.

Example 3. Consider the specification function

$$|Z_{12}(j\omega)|^2 = \frac{A(\omega^2)}{B(\omega^2)} = \frac{1 + \omega^2}{1 + \omega^4} \tag{14.72}$$

which is an even function as required. Now $A(-s^2) = 1 - s^2$ is not a full square so that the function must be augmented. However, $B(-s^2) = 1 + s^4$ is of the proper form and has quadrantal symmetry. Multiplying numerator and denominator by $1 - s^2$ gives

$$|Z_{12}(j\omega)|^2 = \left[\frac{(1 - s^2)^2}{(1 + s^4)(1 - s^2)}\right]_{s=j\omega} = \left[\frac{g^2}{m_2{}^2 - n_2{}^2}\right]_{s=j\omega} \tag{14.73}$$

Here we recognize that $g(s) = 1 - s^2$ and that the left half plane poles of $m_2{}^2 - n_2{}^2$ are

$$m_2 + n_2 = \left(s + \frac{1}{\sqrt{2}} + j\frac{1}{\sqrt{2}}\right)\left(s + \frac{1}{\sqrt{2}} - j\frac{1}{\sqrt{2}}\right)(s + 1) \tag{14.74}$$

Hence the transfer function, which is one function corresponding to Eq. 14.72, is

$$Z_{12}(s) = \frac{1 - s^2}{s^3 + 2.414s^2 + 2.414s + 1} \tag{14.75}$$

(10) The zeros of Z_{12} have symmetry in the s plane with respect to both the real and the imaginary axes. This conclusion follows from the requirement of item (4) that the numerator polynomial of Z_{12} be either even or odd. For an even polynomial, $m(s) = m(-s)$; for an odd polynomial, $n(s) = -n(-s)$. From this it follows that the zeros of $Z_{12}(s)$ and $Z_{12}(-s)$ are the same. These are the double zeros of the product function

$$[Z_{12}(s)\, Z_{12}(-s)]_{s=j\omega} = |Z_{12}(j\omega)|^2 \tag{14.76}$$

that meet the full square requirement of item (9). Now the only way for the zeros of $Z_{12}(s)$ and $Z_{12}(-s)$ to be the same is for these zeros to occur with quadrantal symmetry, or on the real axis or the imaginary axis with symmetry about the origin. These zeros of transmission on the imaginary axis are familiar from our study of the Cauer ladder development of Chapter 10. But zeros of transmission have other s plane locations for some nonladder networks.

(11) Z_{12} is a minimum-phase function if and only if all of its zeros are on the imaginary axis. A minimum-phase network function has all zeros in the left half plane or on the imaginary axis. Zeros of Z_{12} in the left half plane imply corresponding zeros in the right half plane by item (10). Hence the one case that results in a minimum phase Z_{12} is the case with all zeros restricted to the imaginary axis.

The findings of this section are summarized in Table 14-3.

TABLE 14-3
Properties of Functions Describing Lossless Resistively Terminated Networks

Function	Property
z_{12}, z_{22}	1. Both z_{12} and z_{22} are quotients of even to odd or odd to even polynomials. 2. z_{22} is positive real.
$Z_{12}(s)$	1. Zeros of z_{12} are zeros of Z_{12}; zeros of Z_{12} may be chosen to be the zeros of z_{12}. 2. No poles are on the imaginary axis. 3. The numerator polynomial is either even or odd. 4. Zeros have quadrantal symmetry if complex, symmetry with respect to the origin if on either axis. 5. The denominator polynomial is Hurwitz. 6. The function is minimum phase if and only if all zeros are on the imaginary axis. 7. The order of the numerator cannot exceed that of the denominator but may have any smaller value.
$\left\lvert Z_{12}(j\omega) \right\rvert^2 = \dfrac{A(\omega^2)}{B(\omega^2)}$	1. The function is positive and bounded (finite) for all ω. 2. It is a quotient of polynomials in ω^2. 3. The coefficients of $A(\omega^2)$ and $B(\omega^2)$ are real but not necessarily positive. 4. Both $A(\omega^2)$ and $B(\omega^2)$ are positive for all ω. 5. The s^2 roots of $A(-s^2)$ which are negative real must have even multiplicity. 6. $A(-s^2)$ must be a full square (by augmenting if necessary). 7. $B(-s^2)$ has quadrantal symmetry.

14.4   Lossless terminated network synthesis

For the network that has been the object of our study in the preceding section, shown in Fig. 14-9, the power input in the sinusoidal steady state is

$$P_{\text{in}} = \left\lvert I_1 \right\rvert^2 \operatorname{Re} Z_{11} \tag{14.77}$$

while the power output in the terminating resistor R_2 is

$$P_{\text{out}} = \frac{\left\lvert V_2 \right\rvert^2}{R_2} = \left\lvert V_2 \right\rvert^2 \qquad (R_2 = 1) \tag{14.78}$$

Since the network is lossless, the power input and power output must be equal. Then, with a 1-ohm termination,

$$\left|\frac{V_2}{I_1}\right|^2 = |Z_{12}(j\omega)|^2 = \text{Re}\, Z_{11}(j\omega) \qquad (14.79)$$

This equation is the foundation of a synthesis method due to Darlington.* For a given $|Z_{12}|^2$, we know $\text{Re}\, Z_{11}$ from which Z_{11} may be found using the methods of Chapter 8. From Z_{11}, the network may be synthesized by the Darlington driving-point method of Section 14.2.

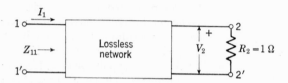

Fig. 14-9. The lossless terminated network for which $\text{Re}\, Z_{11}(j\omega) = |Z_{12}(j\omega)|^2$

Example 4. Suppose that $|Z_{12}(j\omega)|^2$ is required to have the form of a third-order Butterworth response:

$$|Z_{12}(j\omega)|^2 = \frac{1}{1 + \omega^6} \qquad (14.80)$$

Then from Eq. 14.79, this is the real part of the driving-point function $Z_{11}(j\omega)$. This particular example was considered as Eq. 8.17. There Z_{11} was found by the Gewertz method to be

$$Z_{11}(s) = \frac{\frac{2}{3}s^2 + \frac{4}{3}s + 1}{s^3 + 2s^2 + 2s + 1} \qquad (14.81)$$

The reciprocal of this impedance may be expanded as a continued fraction, giving

$$\frac{1}{Z_{11}} = \frac{3}{2}s + \cfrac{1}{\frac{4}{3}s + \cfrac{1}{\frac{1}{2}s + \cfrac{1}{1}}} \qquad (14.82)$$

Hence the ladder network of Fig. 14-10(a) meets the specifications of Eq. 14.80. When driven by a constant-current source, the output voltage magnitude is maximally flat in form. If Z_{11} is realized by the Darlington method, the network of Fig. 14-10(b) is found, which includes one ideal transformer.

---

* One of the results of the paper cited earlier.

A second important synthesis method was studied in Section 14.1. Once again we start with the $|Z_{12}(j\omega)|^2$ specification, but this time we

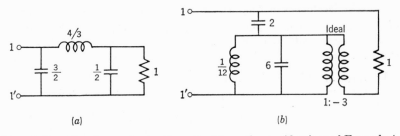

Fig. 14-10. Two forms of network realized from the specifications of Example 4.

determine $Z_{12}(s)$ by the method outlined in the preceding section. In Eq. 14.63, Z_{12} was written in the form

$$Z_{12}(s) = \frac{g(s)}{m_2(s) + n_2(s)} \tag{14.83}$$

where $m_2 + n_2$ is a Hurwitz polynomial and $g(s)$ is either even or odd. This equation may be arranged in the form

$$Z_{12}(s) = \frac{n_1/m_2}{1 + n_2/m_2} \qquad \text{for } g = n_1 \text{ (odd)} \tag{14.84}$$

or $$Z_{12}(s) = \frac{m_1/n_2}{1 + m_2/n_2} \qquad \text{for } g = m_1 \text{ (even)} \tag{14.85}$$

so that each equation is in proper form for comparison with

$$Z_{12} = \frac{z_{12}}{1 + z_{22}} \tag{14.86}$$

Then

$$z_{12} = \frac{n_1}{m_2} \quad \text{and} \quad z_{22} = \frac{n_2}{m_2} \qquad \text{for } g = n_1 \text{ (odd)} \tag{14.87}$$

and $$z_{12} = \frac{m_1}{n_2} \quad \text{and} \quad z_{22} = \frac{m_2}{n_2} \qquad \text{for } g = m_1 \text{ (even)} \tag{14.88}$$

At this point, the path divides. (1) We may synthesize z_{22} as a loss-less ladder network for some cases and do it in such a way that the zeros of z_{12}, the zeros of transmission, are realized. This method was studied in Chapter 10. (2) We may select a z_{11} fulfilling the residue condition and then from the three functions z_{11}, z_{12}, and z_{22} realize a network by the methods of Darlington or Cauer. The first path results in ladder networks which are attractive from a realization point of view. The second requires that a consistent z_{11} be selected so that z_{12} is realized exactly, but this method often requires ideal transformers.

Example 5. It is required to realize

$$Z_{12}(s) = \frac{(s^2 + 1)(s^2 + 4)}{s^4 + s^3 + 34s^2 + 16s + 225} \tag{14.89}$$

by a lossless coupling network terminated in 1 ohm. This function has all of its zeros on the imaginary axis so that the coupling network may be realized as a ladder. Since the numerator is even, we write Z_{12} as

$$Z_{12}(s) = \frac{\dfrac{(s^2 + 1)(s^2 + 4)}{s^3 + 16s}}{1 + \dfrac{s^4 + 34s^2 + 225}{s^3 + 16s}} \tag{14.90}$$

from which z_{22} and z_{12} may be identified. Then

$$z_{22} = \frac{(s^2 + 9)(s^2 + 25)}{s(s^2 + 16)}, \qquad z_{12} = \frac{(s^2 + 1)(s^2 + 4)}{s(s^2 + 16)} \tag{14.91}$$

These specification functions are identical with those of Eqs. 10.36 and 10.37, except that z_{11} has been replaced by z_{22}. The ladder network developed

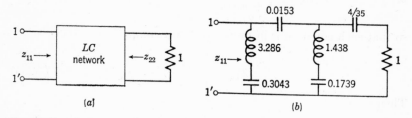

Fig. 14-11. Network realization of Example 5 showing a ladder developed from z_{22} and z_{12} specifications, but with no control over z_{11}.

from these specifications is shown in Fig. 10-16, and when turned end for end it is the network required for this example. The terminated network is shown in Fig. 14-11.

The various methods available for the synthesis of lossless terminated networks are summarized in Table 14-4.

TABLE 14-4

Summary of Synthesis Methods for Lossless Resistively Terminated Networks

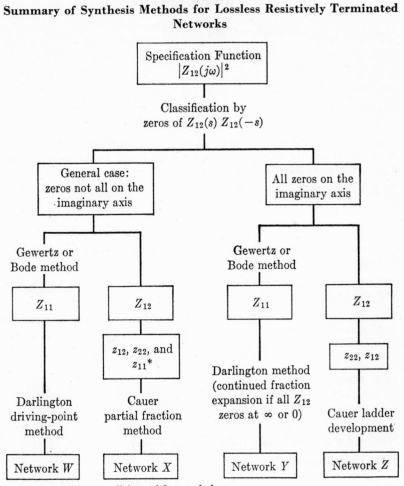

Specification Function
$|Z_{12}(j\omega)|^2$

Classification by
zeros of $Z_{12}(s)\,Z_{12}(-s)$

General case:
zeros not all on the
imaginary axis

All zeros on the
imaginary axis

Gewertz or
Bode method

Gewertz or
Bode method

Z_{11} Z_{12} Z_{11} Z_{12}

z_{12}, z_{22}, and
z_{11}^*

z_{22}, z_{12}

Darlington
driving-point
method

Cauer
partial fraction
method

Darlington method
(continued fraction
expansion if all Z_{12}
zeros at ∞ or 0)

Cauer ladder
development

Network W Network X Network Y Network Z

* From residue condition with equal sign.

FURTHER READING

For additional study on the topics of this chapter, the reader should see Guillemin's *Synthesis of Passive Networks*, pp. 437–443 and Chapter 11, or Balabanian's *Network Synthesis*, Chapters 5 and 6. See also Storer's *Passive Network Synthesis*, Chapters 19, 22, and 23. Many textbooks treat the topics of this and the following chapter together so that the references at the end of Chapter 15 should also be consulted.

PROBLEMS

14-1. Given the following functions:

(a) $Z_{12} = \dfrac{2}{(s+1)(s^2 + 2s + 2)}$

(b) $Z_{12} = \dfrac{10}{(s+1)(s^2 + 2s + 2)(s^2 + 2s + 5)}$

(c) $Z_{12} = \dfrac{100}{(s+1)(s^2 + 2s + 2)(s^2 + 2s + 5)(s^2 + 2s + 10)}$

(1) Draw the pole configurations for these three functions.
(2) Synthesize the three networks terminated in a 1-ohm resistor which satisfies the given Z_{12} specifications.

14-2. For the magnitude response function

$$\frac{1}{(1 + \omega^{2n})^{1/2}}$$

synthesize a network terminated in a 1-ohm resistor which is driven by a voltage source for (a) $n = 4$, (b) $n = 5$.

14-3. Repeat Prob. 14-2 but for a current source and for (a) $n = 3$, (b) $n = 4$, and (c) $n = 5$.

14-4. Synthesize a network terminated in a 1-ohm resistor to meet the specification

$$Z_{12}(s) = \frac{s^2 + 1}{s^3 + s^2 + 3s + 2}$$

14-5. For the specification

$$-Y_{12}(s) = \frac{s^2 + 1}{s^3 + 2s^2 + 2s + 1}$$

synthesize a network terminated in a 1-ohm resistor.

14-6. For the function

$$-Y_{12}(s) = \frac{(s+1)(s+4)}{(s+2)(s+5)}$$

(a) Find two different network realizations.
(b) $-Y_{12}$ is realized within a constant multiplier. What are the values of this constant multiplier for the two networks found in part (a)?

14-7. Repeat Prob. 14-6 for the specification

$$Z_{12}(s) = \frac{s^2}{(s+1)(s+3)}$$

14-8. Starting with Eq. 14.40, carry out the algebraic operations to arrive at Eqs. 14.42.

14-9. For the Darlington method of synthesis of Section 14.2:

(a) Show that for Case A the radical expression in z_{12} must be the square of an even polynomial.

(b) Show that for Case B the radical expression in z_{12} may be the square of an odd polynomial.

(c) Show that for Case B the radical expression in z_{12} may be made even through an appropriate choice of the factors in $W(s) = m_0{}^2 - n_0{}^2$, but only at the expense of yielding a z_{12} of higher order and thereby giving rise to more elements in the network realization.

14-10. Synthesize a network by the Darlington method of this chapter to meet the driving-point impedance specification

$$Z(s) = \frac{5s^2 + 3s + 4}{s^2 + 2s + 2}$$

You may wish to compare your answer with that given by Guillemin in Vol. III of *Advances in Electronics*, p. 293 (Fig. 9).

14-11. Given the impedance function,

$$Z(s) = \frac{s^2 + s + 2}{2s^2 + s + 1}$$

synthesize a network for this $Z(s)$ by the Darlington method. Compare the number of elements of this network with those given by the Brune and Bott and Duffin methods.

14-12. Synthesize a network having the driving-point impedance

$$Z(s) = \frac{5s^2 + 18s + 8}{s^2 + s + 10}$$

by the Darlington method.

14-13. Test the following proposed functions for $|Z_{12}(j\omega)|^2$ to describe a lossless coupling network terminated in a 1-ohm resistor:

(a) $\dfrac{1 + 4\omega^2}{(1 + \omega^2)^2}$ (b) $\dfrac{1}{1 + \omega^8}$ (c) $\dfrac{1 - 4\omega^2}{1 + \omega^4}$

(d) $\dfrac{(1 + \omega^2)^2}{\omega^4 + 4}$ (e) $\dfrac{(1 + \omega^2)^2}{1 - \omega^2 + \omega^6}$

14-14. (a) For the network illustrated in Fig. P14-14, show that the zeros of z_{12} are complex providing $C_2 > 1$.

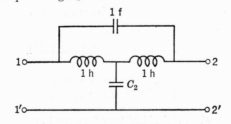

Fig. P14-14

(*b*) How are the zeros of transmission affected if the network is terminated in a 1-ohm resistor (at terminals 2-2')?

14-15. Derive the following general relationship for a lossless terminated network,

$$Z_{12}(s)\, Z_{12}(-s) = \tfrac{1}{2}[Z_{11}(s) + Z_{11}(-s)]$$

and from this equation arrive at Eq. 14.79.

14-16. Synthesize a network by the Darlington method of Section 14.4 for the specification

$$|Z_{12}(j\omega)|^2 = \frac{1}{1 + \omega^4}$$

Is this specification realized exactly or only within a constant multiplier?

14-17. Synthesize a lossless terminated network by the Darlington method to meet the specification

$$|Z_{12}(j\omega)|^2 = \frac{1 + \omega^2}{1 + \omega^4}$$

14-18. Develop a lossless ladder network terminated in a 1-ohm resistor for

$$Z_{12} = H_1 \frac{s^2 + 1}{4s^2 + s + 1}$$

What is the value of H_1 that the network realizes?

14-19. Determine a ladder network terminated in a 1-ohm resistor to realize the specification function

$$Z_{12} = H_2 \frac{(s^2 + 9)(s^2 + 36)}{s(s^2 + 16) + (s^2 + 4)(s^2 + 25)}$$

and find the value of H_2 actually realized by the network.

14-20. The specification function

$$Z_{12} = H_3 \frac{(s^2 + 4)(s^2 + 16)}{(s^2 + 1)(s^2 + 25) + s(s^2 + 9)(s^2 + 36)}$$

describes a lossless ladder network terminated in a 1-ohm resistor. Determine the network and the value of H_3 realized.

14-21. Classify the networks marked W, X, Y, and Z in Table 14-4 as to the following:

(*a*) Is the network function realized minimum phase or not?

(*b*) Is the driving-point impedance at terminals 1-1' a minimum reactance function?

(*c*) Will the network contain ideal transformers, in general?

14-22. Another class of synthesis problems are based on the model with a resistor at the input and an open circuit at the output as shown in Fig. P14-22(c). Show that this class of synthesis problems may be solved using the techniques of this chapter by showing that $G_{12} = V_2/V_1$ for the network of (c) is equal to $Z_{12} = V_2/I_1$ of the network of (a).

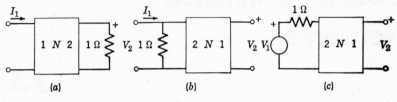

Fig. P14-22

14-23. For the network shown in Fig. P14-23, it is required that

$$\frac{V_2}{V_1} = \frac{s^4}{(s + 1)^4}$$

Find a network realization to satisfy this specification.

14-24. A lossless network is to be driven by a voltage source having an internal resistance of 1 ohm as shown in Fig. P14-23. Synthesize the lossless network such that the voltage ratio transfer function has the following squared magnitude for $s = j\omega$:

$$\left| \frac{V_2}{V_1} \right|^2 = \frac{(1 + \omega^2)^2}{4 + \omega^2}$$

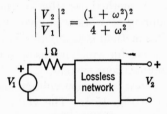

Fig. P14-23

Double-Terminated
Networks

· · · · · · · · · · · · · · *15*

15.1 Properties of double-terminated coupling networks

The synthesis methods described in the preceding chapter apply to the lossless network terminated with resistor R_2 at terminals 2-2'. If there are terminating resistors at both ends of the lossless coupling network which are finite and nonzero, the methods of Chapter 14 are no longer applicable. A method for the synthesis of the double-terminated lossless coupling network was given by Darlington in his classic 1939 paper. This method is practically important both in telephone transmission systems, for which it was originally derived, and in the more general communications system.

Observe first that we now have new voltage and current variables to describe the system in Fig. 15-1. The voltage of the source and the voltage at terminals 1-1' of Fig. 15-1(a) are no longer the same, and so are distinguished as V_s and V_1. Similarly, for Fig. 15-1(b) the current of the source is identified as I_s which is different from the current into the network, I_1. The introduction of new variables requires that we use different specification functions like $\tilde{G}_{12} = V_2/V_s$, $\tilde{Z}_{12} = V_2/I_s$, and, as we shall see, the power loss caused by the insertion of the coupling network.

Referring to Fig. 15-1(a), we see that the impedance of the entire network from the voltage source is

$$\frac{V_s(s)}{I_1(s)} = R_1 + Z_{11} \qquad (15.1)$$

where Z_{11} is the impedance of the network at 1-1' with R_2 connected at 2-2'. Since the ratio V_2/I_1 is the impedance Z_{12} of the last chapter,

424

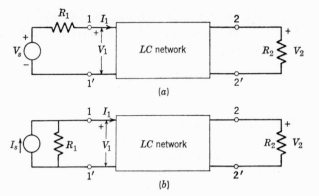

Fig. 15-1. Double-terminated LC networks.

the voltage ratio V_2/V_s may be expressed in the form

$$\frac{V_2}{V_s} = \frac{I_1}{V_s}\frac{V_2}{I_1} = \frac{Z_{12}}{R_1 + Z_{11}} \tag{15.2}$$

An expression for Z_{12} was derived as Eq. 14.79 assuming that $R_2 = 1$ ohm. Without this scaling, the expression is

$$\left| Z_{12}(j\omega) \right|^2 = R_2 \operatorname{Re} Z_{11} \tag{15.3}$$

If we let $s = j\omega$ and then square the magnitude of Eq. 15.2, the resulting equation may be combined with Eq. 15.3 to give

$$\left| \frac{V_2(j\omega)}{V_s(j\omega)} \right|^2 = \frac{R_2 \operatorname{Re} Z_{11}}{\left| R_1 + Z_{11} \right|^2} \tag{15.4}$$

The algebraic operations required to reach our objective are simplified if both sides of this equation are multiplied by $-4R_1/R_2$ and if unity is added to both sides. Then

$$1 - 4\frac{R_1}{R_2}\left| \frac{V_2}{V_s} \right|^2 = \left| \frac{R_1 - Z_{11}}{R_1 + Z_{11}} \right|^2 \tag{15.5}$$

This magnitude squared is familiar from transmission-line theory where it is known as the square of the magnitude of the reflection coefficient at the input or 1-1′ terminals. Let us designate this reflection coefficient as ρ_1 so that

$$\left| \rho_1 \right| = \left| \frac{R_1 - Z_{11}}{R_1 + Z_{11}} \right| = \left| \frac{1 - (Z_{11}/R_1)}{1 + (Z_{11}/R_1)} \right| \tag{15.6}$$

A similar expression may be written for ρ_2, the reflection coefficient at the output or 2-2' terminals. Then Eq. 15.5 may be written in terms of the reflection coefficient* as

$$\frac{4R_1}{R_2} \left| \frac{V_2}{V_s} \right|^2 = 1 - |\rho_1|^2 \tag{15.7}$$

As the next step in our derivation, we will compare the power delivered to the load resistor R_2 to the maximum power that the voltage source is capable of delivering to the load, or the available power. This maximum or reference power is that power delivered to R_2 when the lossless network is an ideal transformer of turns ratio $a^2 = R_2/R_1$ so that $Z_{11} = R_1$. Under this condition, the network is equivalent to one with two resistors of value R_1 in series with the voltage source, and since half of the applied voltage is across either resistor, this maximum power is

$$P_{2\text{max}} = \left| \frac{V_s}{2} \right|^2 \frac{1}{R_1} \tag{15.8}$$

Under any other condition, the power in R_2 is simply

$$P_2 = \frac{|V_2|^2}{R_2} \tag{15.9}$$

The ratio of the power delivered to R_2 to the available or reference power is then

$$\frac{P_2}{P_{2\text{max}}} = \frac{4R_1}{R_2} \left| \frac{V_2}{V_s} \right|^2 \tag{15.10}$$

Combining this equation with Eq. 15.7, we arrive at the important relationship,

$$\frac{P_2}{P_{2\text{max}}} = |t|^2 = 1 - |\rho_1|^2 \tag{15.11}$$

where t is the transmission coefficient. This last equation tells us that

$$|\rho_1(j\omega)|^2 + |t(j\omega)|^2 = 1 \tag{15.12}$$

---

* The reflection coefficient is also called the *scattering coefficient* in network theory since it is related to the scattering matrix which is more familiar in microwave theory. See the review paper by H. J. Carlin, "The scattering matrix in network theory," *IRE Trans.*, **CT-3**, 88–97 (1956).

and that $\left|\rho_1(j\omega)\right|^2 = 1 - \dfrac{\text{power to load}}{\text{power available}}$

$$= \frac{\text{power available} - \text{power to load}}{\text{power available}} \tag{15.13}$$

$$= \frac{\text{``reflected'' power}}{\text{power available}}$$

Indeed, the name reflection coefficient is suggested by the definition of the difference of power available and the power to the load as the power "reflected." Equation 15.12 expresses the equality,

power reflected + power to load = power available

or $\dfrac{\text{power reflected}}{\text{power available}} + \dfrac{\text{power to load}}{\text{power available}} = 1$ (15.14)

Observe from Eq. 15.11 that if $\left|\rho_1\right| = 0$, then $P_2 = P_{2_{\max}}$ and there is no reflection. But when $\left|\rho_1\right| = 1$, there is complete reflection and $P_2 = 0$.

At the beginning of this section, several possible specification functions were suggested. We will next show the relationship of these functions to the transmission coefficient, t. By Eq. 15.10,

$$\left|t(j\omega)\right|^2 = \frac{4R_1}{R_2}\left|\frac{V_2(j\omega)}{V_s(j\omega)}\right|^2 \tag{15.15}$$

and since $V_s = R_1 I_s$, we have

$$\left|t(j\omega)\right|^2 = \frac{4}{R_1 R_2}\left|\frac{V_2(j\omega)}{I_s(j\omega)}\right|^2 = \frac{4}{R_1 R_2}\left|\tilde{Z}_{12}(j\omega)\right|^2 \tag{15.16}$$

The transmission coefficient is also related to $Z_{12} = V_2/I_1$ by Eq. 15.2,

$$\left|t(j\omega)\right|^2 = \frac{4R_1}{R_2\left|R_1 + Z_{11}\right|^2}\left|Z_{12}\right|^2 \tag{15.17}$$

Another important specification we wish to relate to t is the insertion power loss which finds frequent use in communications applications. Suppose that we have a transmission system which is to be compensated for some deficiency by the insertion of a passive network. Before the network is placed in position, the voltage at the receiving end is recorded. This voltage is found to have a smaller value after the insertion of the network. This loss, usually expressed in decibels, is the *insertion loss;* in general, it will vary with frequency.

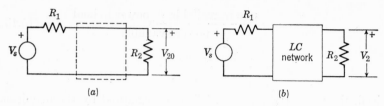

Fig. 15-2. System without (*a*) and with (*b*) the coupling network as used in defining insertion power loss.

Referring to Fig. 15-2(*a*) showing the system without the coupling network, we see that

$$V_{20} = \frac{R_2}{R_1 + R_2} V_s \qquad (15.18)$$

where V_{20} is the voltage across the load without the coupling network. The power delivered to R_2 under the same conditions is

$$P_{20} = \left| \frac{V_s}{R_1 + R_2} \right|^2 R_2 \qquad (15.19)$$

With the network replaced in the system as shown in Fig. 15-2(*b*), the power to the load is

$$P_2 = \frac{|V_2|^2}{R_2} \qquad (15.20)$$

Now the ratio P_{20}/P_2 is defined as the *insertion power ratio.* If measured in logarithmic units, it is equal to $e^{2\alpha}$, where α is the *insertion power loss* in nepers. Then from the last two equations we write

$$\frac{P_{20}}{P_2} = e^{2\alpha} = \left(\frac{R_2}{R_1 + R_2} \right)^2 \left| \frac{V_s}{V_2} \right|^2 \qquad (15.21)$$

and, finally, combining this equation with Eq. 15.15,

$$|t(j\omega)|^2 = \frac{4R_1 R_2}{(R_1 + R_2)^2} e^{-2\alpha} \qquad (15.22)$$

15.2 The Darlington procedure

With this background, we may now outline the steps to be followed in the Darlington method. These are:

(1) From any of the specification functions, $|V_2/V_s|^2$, $|V_2/I_s|^2$, or $e^{2\alpha}$, together with values for R_1 and R_2, determine the squared transmission coefficient, $|t(j\omega)|^2$. Then determine $|\rho_1(j\omega)|^2$.

(2) From $|\rho_1(j\omega)|^2 = [\rho_1(s)\,\rho_1(-s)]_{s=j\omega}$, determine $\rho_1(s)$.

(3) From $\rho_1(s)$ and the value of R_1, determine $Z_{11}(s)$.

(4) From $Z_{11}(s)$, synthesize a network which may or may not contain ideal transformers.

The functions in these steps require further investigation and the steps themselves elaboration. We shall consider these steps in order.

Step 1, the transmission coefficient. The transmission coefficient squared is first found from the specification function using Eq. 15.15, 15.16, 15.17, or 15.22. The range of permitted values for $|t(j\omega)|^2$ and $|\rho_1(j\omega)|^2$ may be found from Eq. 15.12. Equation 15.11 tells us that since P_2 is always less than $P_{2\text{max}}$, it is required that

$$|t(j\omega)|^2 \leq 1 \text{ for all } \omega \tag{15.23}$$

and likewise that

$$|\rho_1(j\omega)|^2 \leq 1 \text{ for all } \omega \tag{15.24}$$

The same conclusion may be reached by a graphical construction with a phasor interpretation of the numerator and denominator magnitudes

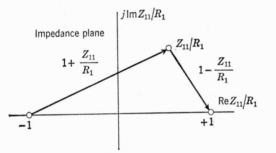

Fig. 15-3. Impedance plane representation of the two phasor quantities that define the reflection coefficient.

of Eq. 15.5. Suppose that we plot the impedance $Z_{11}(j\omega)/R_1$ in the complex impedance plane as shown in Fig. 15-3. Since Z_{11} is a driving-point impedance and therefore positive real, and R_1 is a real, positive constant, Re $Z_{11}(j\omega)/R_1$ will always be in the right half of the impedance plane. Now $1 - Z_{11}/R_1$ is a phasor directed from Z_{11}/R_1 to $+1$, and $1 + Z_{11}/R_1$ is similarly a phasor from -1 to Z_{11}/R_1. So long as Re $Z_{11}(j\omega)/R_1 \geq 0$, we see from the figure that

$$\left|1 - \frac{Z_{11}}{R_1}\right| \leq \left|1 + \frac{Z_{11}}{R_1}\right| \tag{15.25}$$

so that from Eq. 15.5, we see that $|\rho_1|$ is bounded by the limit

$$|\rho_1| \leq 1 \tag{15.26}$$

This conclusion is illustrated by Fig. 15-4, which shows a region of the Z_{11}/R_1 plane and the corresponding region of the ρ_1 plane and illustrates the conclusion that when the real part of Z_{11} is positive, the magnitude of $\rho_1 \leq 1$.*

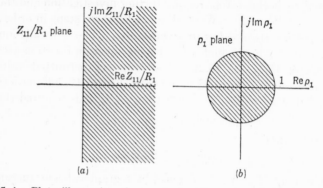

Fig. 15-4. Plots illustrating the conclusion that when Re $Z_{11}/R_1 \geq 0$, then $0 \leq |\rho_1| \leq 1$.

Other important properties of $|t(j\omega)|^2$ are found by generalizing the function (by analytic continuation) as

$$|t(j\omega)|^2 = [t(s)\, t(-s)]_{s=j\omega} \tag{15.27}$$

and similarly

$$|Z_{12}(j\omega)|^2 = [Z_{12}(s)\, Z_{12}(-s)]_{s=j\omega} \tag{15.28}$$

Since, by Eq. 15.17

$$|t(j\omega)|^2 = \frac{4R_1}{R_2\, |R_1 + Z_{11}(j\omega)|^2}\, |Z_{12}(j\omega)|^2 \tag{15.29}$$

then

$$t(s)\, t(-s) = \frac{4R_1}{R_2}\, \frac{Z_{12}(s)\, Z_{12}(-s)}{[R_1 + Z_{11}(s)][R_1 + Z_{11}(-s)]} \tag{15.30}$$

whence

$$t(s) = \sqrt{\frac{4R_1}{R_2}}\, \frac{Z_{12}(s)}{R_1 + Z_{11}(s)} \tag{15.31}$$

This equation gives the relationship of $t(s)$ and Z_{11} and Z_{12}. Another related form of these equations is found from a generalization of the

---

*For further reading on the topic of linear fractional transformations, see R. V. Churchill, *Introduction to Complex Variables and Applications*, McGraw-Hill Book Co., New York, 1948, pp. 57–72, 207.

identity of Eq. 15.3,

$$Z_{12}(s) \, Z_{12}(-s) = R_2 \operatorname{Ev} Z_{11} \tag{15.32}$$

Then Eq. 15.30 becomes

$$t(s) \, t(-s) = 4R_1 \frac{\operatorname{Ev} Z_{11}}{[R_1 + Z_{11}(s)][R_1 + Z_{11}(-s)]} \tag{15.33}$$

An interesting property for $t(s) \, t(-s)$ is found by letting

$$Z_{11}(s) = \frac{m_1 + n_1}{m_2 + n_2} \tag{15.34}$$

Then
$$\operatorname{Ev} Z_{11}(s) = \frac{m_1 m_2 - n_1 n_2}{m_2{}^2 - n_2{}^2} \tag{15.35}$$

The denominator of this equation cancels in the expression for $t(s)$ $t(-s)$ of Eq. 15.33, giving

$$t(s) \, t(-s) = 4R_1 \frac{m_1 m_2 - n_1 n_2}{R_1{}^2(m_2{}^2 - n_2{}^2) + 2R_1(m_1 m_2 - n_1 n_2) + (m_1{}^2 - n_1{}^2)} \tag{15.36}$$

Comparing this equation with Eqs. 15.30 and 15.31, we see that the zeros of the function $t(s) \, t(-s)$ are the zeros of $Z_{12}(s) \, Z_{12}(-s)$ which are the zeros of the numerator of $\operatorname{Ev} Z_{11}$, the solutions of the equation,

$$m_1 m_2 - n_1 n_2 = 0 \tag{15.37}$$

From Eq. 15.31, we see that the poles of $t(s)$ cannot be on the imaginary axis (for the same reasons found in Section 14.3) and that the denominator polynomial of $t(s)$ must be Hurwitz.

This discussion shows us that the properties of $t(s)$ are the same as those of $Z_{12}(s)$ of Section 14.3, as tabulated in Table 14-3. The most important of these properties for $t(s)$ are: (1) no poles on the imaginary axis, (2) the numerator is an even function, and (3) the denominator is Hurwitz. Furthermore, the properties of $|t(j\omega)|^2$ are the same as those of $|Z_{12}(j\omega)|^2$ as tabulated in Table 14-3. Since $|t(j\omega)|^2$ and the other specification functions differ by only a constant multiplier involving R_1 and R_2, these properties also apply to $|V_2/V_s|^2$ and $|V_2/I_s|^2$.

Step 2, the reflection coefficient. The reflection coefficient is to be found from a generalization of Eq. 15.12:

$$\rho_1(s) \, \rho_1(-s) = 1 - t(s) \, t(-s) \tag{15.38}$$

Now $|t(j\omega)|^2$ is an even function which may be expressed as a quotient of polynomials in ω^2,

$$|t(j\omega)|^2 = \frac{A(\omega^2)}{B(\omega^2)} \qquad (15.39)$$

This function is positive, being a magnitude squared, and is limited to values less than unity so that it is required that

$$0 \le \frac{A(\omega^2)}{B(\omega^2)} \le 1 \qquad (15.40)$$

To find the reflection coefficient we substitute Eq. 15.39 into Eq. 15.12, giving

$$|\rho_1(j\omega)|^2 = 1 - \frac{A(\omega^2)}{B(\omega^2)} = \frac{B(\omega^2) - A(\omega^2)}{B(\omega^2)} \equiv \frac{C(\omega^2)}{B(\omega^2)} \qquad (15.41)$$

If we next identify the numerator and denominator of $\rho_1(s)$ as

$$\rho_1(s) = \pm \frac{p_1(s)}{q_1(s)} \qquad (15.42)$$

so that

$$\frac{p_1(j\omega)\, p_1(-j\omega)}{q_1(j\omega)\, q_1(-j\omega)} = \frac{C(\omega^2)}{B(\omega^2)} \qquad (15.43)$$

and if we substitute s for $j\omega$, then

$$\frac{p_1(s)\, p_1(-s)}{q_1(s)\, q_1(-s)} = \frac{C(-s^2)}{B(-s^2)} \qquad (15.44)$$

The problem is to separate $p_1(s)$ from $C(-s^2)$ and $q_1(s)$ from $B(-s^2)$. Now we know from our earlier discussion that $q_1(s)$ is required to be a Hurwitz polynomial, meaning that it is necessary that $B(-s^2)$ be of the form $m_2^2 - n_2^2$ separable into $m_2 + n_2$ and $m_2 - n_2$. Hence to find $q_1(s)$ from $B(-s^2)$, we simply select the zeros of $B(-s^2)$ in the left half of the s plane, rejecting those in the right half plane. Now $C(-s^2)$ is required to have quadrantal symmetry just as $B(-s^2)$ has. What other requirements are made of this function which is the difference of $B(-s^2)$ and $A(-s^2)$? To answer this question, we first generalize Eq. 15.6 to the form,

$$\rho_1 = \frac{1 - [Z_{11}(s)/R_1]}{1 + [Z_{11}(s)/R_1]} \qquad (15.45)$$

The poles of ρ_1 must be in the left half of the s plane since the denominator of this equation is the sum of two positive real functions and is therefore also positive real. The numerator is not necessarily a positive real function, however, being the difference of two positive real functions, so that the zeros of ρ_1 may have any s plane location so long as there is the usual symmetry with respect to the real axis. Then to construct $\rho_1(s)$:

(1) Given $|t(j\omega)|^2 = A(\omega^2)/B(\omega^2)$, or equivalent information, we first form $B(-s^2)$ and $C(-s^2) = B(-s^2) - A(-s^2)$.

(2) From $B(-s^2) = q_1(s)\,q_1(-s)$, we select the zeros of $B(-s^2)$ in the left half plane; these are the poles of $\rho_1(s)$.

(3) From $C(-s^2) = p_1(s)\,p_1(-s)$, we select the zeros of $\rho_1(s)$. These zeros may be in either the left half or right half plane, but must be conjugate if complex.

(4) The constant multiplier of $\rho_1(s)$ is the square root of the constant multiplier of $C(-s^2)/B(-s^2)$ and may be positive or negative.

Step 3, the driving-point impedance function. Solving Eq. 15.45 for Z_{11}/R_1 gives

$$\frac{Z_{11}}{R_1} = \frac{1 - \rho_1}{1 + \rho_1} \tag{15.46}$$

From this equation Z_{11} is found once ρ_1 and R_1 are known. Substituting $\pm p_1(s)/q_1(s)$ for ρ_1 in the last equation gives

$$\frac{Z_{11}}{R_1} = \frac{1 \mp p_1/q_1}{1 \pm p_1/q_1} \tag{15.47}$$

We see that the impedance Z_{11} may have either of two forms,

$$\frac{Z_{11}}{R_1} = \frac{q_1 + p_1}{q_1 - p_1} \text{ or } \frac{q_1 - p_1}{q_1 + p_1} \tag{15.48}$$

depending on which sign of $\rho_1(s)$ is selected. The two associated network realizations are *reciprocal* networks; the impedance of one is the admittance of the other.

Step 4, synthesis of the terminated network. We must first be assured that the Z_{11} just found is positive real so that a network realization exists. For this purpose, we will use the criterion due to Talbot which was outlined in Section 4.6. Starting from Eq. 15.46, which is

$$\frac{Z_{11}}{R_1} = \frac{1 - \rho_1(s)}{1 + \rho_1(s)} \tag{15.49}$$

we recall that Talbot showed that for Z_{11} to be positive real, it is necessary and sufficient that (1) $\rho_1(s)$ have no poles in the right half of the s plane, and (2) that $|\rho_1(j\omega)| \leq 1$. We have fulfilled condition (1) by our selection of left half plane poles for $\rho_1(s)$ and condition (2) is assured since $|t(j\omega)|^2 \leq 1$. Hence Z_{11} is always positive real and a network realization terminated in a 1-ohm resistor may be found by the Darlington method of Chapter 14. This network, however, involves ideal transformers which are not attractive from a practical viewpoint. An important problem is that of determining when it is possible to realize the coupling network in an unbalanced form (common ground) without ideal transformers. The complete answer to

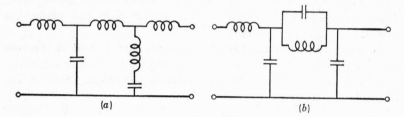

Fig. 15-5. (*a*) Mid-series ladder and (*b*) mid-shunt ladder which may be realized when the Fujisawa conditions are satisfied.

this problem is not yet known. However, the following special cases may be described.

(1) When all of the zeros of transmission are at the origin and/or at infinity, then an LC ladder network may be found by a continued fraction expansion.

(2) When all of the zeros of transmission are on the imaginary axis and a complicated set of conditions due to T. Fujisawa* are satisfied, then low-pass network structures of the form shown in Fig. 15-5 may be realized. For other imaginary axis zero configurations, a ladder realization may or may not exist.†

Table 15-1 summarizes the Darlington procedure of this section.

* "Realizability theorem for mid-series or mid-shunt low-pass ladders without mutual induction," *IRE Trans.*, **CT-2**, 320–325 (1955). See also Balabanian, *Network Synthesis*, Chapter 6. Fujisawa is a member of the faculty at Osaka Prefectural University, Japan.

† An excellent summary of this problem is given by Vitold Belevitch in "Recent developments in filter theory," *IRE Trans.*, **CT-5**, 236–252 (1958). Other papers in this particular issue also relate to this problem.

TABLE 15-1
Darlington's Method for Double-Terminated LC Network Synthesis

Step   Given $|t(j\omega)|^2$ or equivalent, R_1, and R_2:

---

1   Test the requirement, $|t(j\omega)|^2 \le 1$, or an equivalent test such as

$\left|\dfrac{V_2(j\omega)}{V_s(j\omega)}\right|^2 \le \dfrac{R_2}{4R_1}$. If this condition is not satisfied, then it is

necessary to scale t^2. Check the other requirements of $|t(j\omega)|^2$ in
Table 14-3.

2   Find $|\rho_1(j\omega)|^2 = 1 - |t(j\omega)|^2$; form $\rho_1(s)\,\rho_1(-s) = \dfrac{C(-s^2)}{B(-s^2)}$ by letting

$j\omega = s$.

3   Find $\rho_1(s) = \pm p_1(s)/q_1(s)$ by taking the left half plane zeros of
$B(-s^2)$, and either left half plane or right half plane zeros of
$C(-s^2)$.

4   Find $\dfrac{Z_{11}}{R_1} = \dfrac{q_1 + p_1}{q_1 - p_1}$ or $\dfrac{q_1 - p_1}{q_1 + p_1}$.

5   Examine the zeros of $t(s)\,t(-s)$ or from Ev Z_{11}, the roots of
$m_1 m_2 - n_1 n_2 = 0$. If all zeros are at the origin and/or infinity,
develop Z_{11} as a ladder. If all zeros are on the imaginary axis,
test to see if the Fujisawa conditions are satisfied. Otherwise,
synthesize by the Darlington method of Chapter 14 and remove as
many ideal transformers as possible.

6   Shift the impedance level if required.

Example 1. Suppose that it is required to synthesize a network to give a
maximally flat (or Butterworth) response of the form

$$\left|\frac{V_2(j\omega)}{V_s(j\omega)}\right| = \frac{1}{\sqrt{1 + \omega^6}} \tag{15.50}$$

with equal generator and load resistors having normalized values of
$R_1 = R_2 = 1$ ohm. Since this magnitude squared must always be less than
$(R_2/4R_1) = \frac{1}{4}$, it is necessary that the specifications first be scaled to

$$\left|\frac{V_2(j\omega)}{V_s(j\omega)}\right|^2 = \frac{\frac{1}{4}}{1 + \omega^6} \tag{15.51}$$

before the method is applicable. The reflection coefficient magnitude squared
is

$$|\rho_1(j\omega)|^2 = 1 - \frac{1}{1 + \omega^6} = \frac{\omega^6}{1 + \omega^6} \tag{15.52}$$

Replacing ω by s/j gives

$$\rho_1(s)\,\rho_1(-s) = \frac{-s^6}{1 - s^6} \qquad (15.53)$$

Now the poles of this function were shown in Chapter 8 in Fig. 8-4 and the zeros are all at the origin. Assigning the three left half plane poles to $\rho_1(s)$, we have

$$\rho_1(s) = \frac{s^3}{s^3 + 2s^2 + 2s + 1} \qquad (15.54)$$

Then with the positive sign selected and since $R_1 = 1$ ohm,

$$Z_{11} = \frac{2s^2 + 2s + 1}{2s^3 + 2s^2 + 2s + 1} \qquad (15.55)$$

Now the specification function, $t(s)\,t(-s)$, is seen to be an *all-pole* function with all of its zeros at infinity. This being the case, we know that a ladder

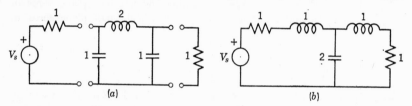

Fig. 15-6. Network realizations of Example 1.

network is possible. This may be found by expanding Z_{11} as a continued fraction:

$$Z_{11} = \cfrac{1}{s + \cfrac{1}{2s + \cfrac{1}{s + \cfrac{1}{1}}}} \qquad (15.56)$$

The network corresponding to this continued fraction expansion is shown in Fig. 15-6(a). If the negative sign is selected in Eq. 15.54, the network is that of Fig. 15-6(b).

Example 2. Consider the specification function

$$|t(j\omega)|^2 = \frac{1 + \omega^4}{1 + \frac{1}{4}\omega^2 + \omega^4} \qquad (15.57)$$

The maximum value of this function occurs at $\omega = 0$, and has a value of unity, meeting the requirement made of the transmission coefficient. The reflection coefficient is next computed:

$$|\rho_1(j\omega)|^2 = 1 - \frac{1 + \omega^4}{1 + \frac{1}{4}\omega^2 + \omega^4} = \frac{\frac{1}{4}\omega^2}{1 + \frac{1}{4}\omega^2 + \omega^4} \qquad (15.58)$$

Then $\quad \rho_1(s)\,\rho_1(-s) = \dfrac{-\frac{1}{4}s^2}{s^4 - \frac{1}{4}s^2 + 1} = \dfrac{(-\frac{1}{2}s)(\frac{1}{2}s)}{(s^2 + \frac{3}{2}s + 1)(s^2 - \frac{3}{2}s + 1)} \qquad (15.59)$

From this equation, we make the selection for $\rho_1(s)$:

$$\rho_1(s) = \frac{-\frac{1}{2}s}{s^2 + \frac{3}{2}s + 1} \tag{15.60}$$

so that the driving-point impedance is, if $R_1 = 1$ ohm,

$$Z_{11}(s) = \frac{s^2 + 2s + 1}{s^2 + s + 1} \tag{15.61}$$

Can this impedance function be developed as a lossless ladder terminated in a 1-ohm resistor? The zeros of $t(s)\,t(-s)$ are the zeros of the equation $s^4 + 1 = 0$. These zeros are complex, indicating that a ladder development is not possible. The impedance function of Eq. 15.61 was considered as

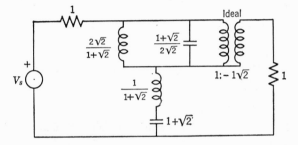

Fig. 15-7.   Network realized by Darlington method in Example 2.

Example 1 of Chapter 14 in our study of the Darlington method. The open-circuit impedance functions that correspond to this Z_{11} were found in Eqs. 14.47 as

$$z_{11} = z_{22} = \frac{s^4 + (2 + 2\sqrt{2})s^2 + 1}{(1 + \sqrt{2})s(s^2 + 1)}$$

$$z_{12} = \frac{s^4 + 1}{(1 + \sqrt{2})s(s^2 + 1)} \tag{15.62}$$

The network synthesized from these functions is shown in Fig. 15-7 and contains one ideal transformer.

15.3 *RC* grounded coupling networks

It was pointed out in Chapter 10 that for many low-frequency applications, networks for electromechanical servomechanisms for example, inductors cannot be used because of their inherent dissipation (and the requirement for high Q) and also because of their size and weight. The Cauer ladder development of Chapter 10 was applied to the model with a voltage driver and no load (open-circuited output terminals). In other applications, there is loading and the voltage source has resistance requiring a double-terminated model with an RC coupling network. While this model is the same as that considered previously in this chapter, most of the properties we have found do not apply because with loss in the coupling network

$$|\rho_1|^2 + |t|^2 < 1 \qquad (15.63)$$

The method we shall study is due to E. S. Kuh* and, as we shall see, it has the advantage that the gain constant of the passive RC network is optimized to the highest possible value.

The model to which the method is applied is shown in Fig. 15-8. It is assumed that one of the input and one of the output terminals

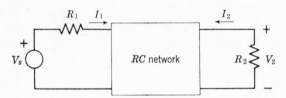

Fig. 15-8.   The model to which the Kuh method is applied.

are connected together (grounded)† and that suitable specification functions are $\tilde{G}_{12} = V_2/V_s$, R_1, and R_2. In factored form, $\tilde{G}_{12}$ may be written

$$\tilde{G}_{12}(s) = K \frac{(s + z_1)(s + z_2) \cdots (s + z_n)}{(s + p_1)(s + p_2) \cdots (s + p_m)} \qquad (15.64)$$

where K is the gain constant which is to be optimized. Although the method may be applied for zeros of transmission with any left half plane location including the imaginary axis, we shall consider the case in which all transmission zeros are on the negative real axis. In addition, we shall assume that there are at least two transmission zeros at infinity. This implies, then, that in the last equation

$$m \geq n + 2 \qquad (15.65)$$

We know that all of the poles of $\tilde{G}_{12}$ for an RC network must be simple and on the negative real axis.

---

* "Synthesis of RC grounded two-ports," *IRE Trans.*, **CT-5**, 55–61 (1958).

† This assumption restricts the zeros of transmission to the left half plane including the imaginary axis. See, for example, S. L. Hakimi and S. Seshu, "Realization of complex zeros of transmission by means of RC networks," *Proc. N.E.C.*, **13**, 1013–1025 (1957).

The consequences of the assumptions made are summarized in Fig. 15-9. The two capacitors, C_1 and C_2, provide the zeros of transmission at infinity. If the short-circuit admittance functions are developed, negative real axis transmission zeros may be realized with a network N' in Fig. 15-9 of the form shown in Fig. 15-10 with series resistors employed for zero shifting and shunt RC networks for zero producing. The Kuh method employs the artifice of incorporating

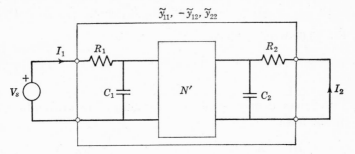

Fig. 15-9. The specific configuration for the case studied. The network N' has the form shown in Fig. 15-10.

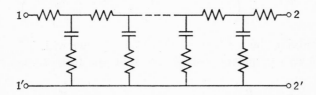

Fig. 15-10. The assumed form of the network N' in Fig. 15-9. The series resistors are used for zero shifting and the shunt RC networks for zero producing.

R_1 and R_2 into the network structure as in Fig. 15-9, which is described for the short-circuit admittance functions, $\tilde{y}_{11}$, $-\tilde{y}_{12}$, and $\tilde{y}_{22}$. Since

$$\tilde{G}_{12} = \frac{V_2}{V_s} = \frac{-I_2 R_2}{V_s} = -\tilde{y}_{12} R_2 \qquad (15.66)$$

we see that $-\tilde{y}_{12}$ is simply related to the specification functions and may be written

$$-\tilde{y}_{12} = \frac{\tilde{G}_{12}}{R_2} = \frac{K}{R_2} \frac{(s + z_1) \cdots (s + z_n)}{(s + p_1) \cdots (s + p_m)} \qquad (15.67)$$

The partial fraction expansion of this function for an RC network is

$$\frac{-\tilde{y}_{12}}{s} = \frac{K}{R_2} \left[\frac{k_{12}^{(0)}}{s} + \frac{k_{12}^{(1)}}{s + p_1} + \cdots + \frac{k_{12}^{(m)}}{s + p_m} \right] \qquad (15.68)$$

Our next problem is to select appropriate forms for the functions $\tilde{y}_{11}$ and $\tilde{y}_{22}$. This we do by assuming that all poles of these functions are compact, i.e., that the residue condition is satisfied at each pole with the equal sign,

$$k_{11}^{(i)} k_{22}^{(i)} = [k_{12}^{(i)}]^2 \tag{15.69}$$

for $i = 0, 1, \cdots, m$. If we let

$$|k_{12}^{(i)}| = \alpha_i \quad \text{and} \quad k_{11}^{(i)} = x_i \tag{15.70}$$

then Eq. 15.69 requires that

$$k_{22}^{(i)} = \frac{\alpha_i^2}{x_i} \tag{15.71}$$

In terms of these defined quantities, $\tilde{y}_{11}$ and $\tilde{y}_{22}$ are written from Eq. 15.68 in the form

$$\frac{\tilde{y}_{11}}{s} = \frac{K}{R_2} \left(\frac{x_0}{s} + \frac{x_1}{s + p_1} + \cdots + \frac{x_m}{s + p_m} \right) \tag{15.72}$$

and

$$\frac{\tilde{y}_{22}}{s} = \frac{K}{R_2} \left(\frac{\alpha_0^2/x_0}{s} + \frac{\alpha_1^2/x_1}{s + p_1} + \cdots + \frac{\alpha_m^2/x_m}{s + p_m} \right) \tag{15.73}$$

By studying the network of Fig. 15-9 together with N' as in Fig. 15-10 at zero frequency, we observe that one further simplification

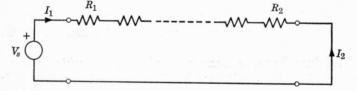

Fig. 15-11. Zero frequency equivalent network to that shown in Fig. 15-9 with N' of Fig. 15-10. For this network, we observe that $\tilde{y}_{11} = -\tilde{y}_{12} = \tilde{y}_{22}$.

may be made in these equations. Since all capacitors are open at this frequency, the equivalent network of the system is that shown in Fig. 15-11. For this network, we observe that

$$\tilde{y}_{11}(0) = \tilde{y}_{22}(0) = -\tilde{y}_{12}(0) \tag{15.74}$$

In terms of Eqs. 15.68, 15.72, and 15.73 for these functions, this implies that

$$k_{12}^{(0)} = \alpha_0 = x_0 \tag{15.75}$$

so that the three specification functions simplify to the form

$$\frac{\tilde{y}_{11}}{s} = \frac{K}{R_2}\left(\frac{\alpha_0}{s} + \frac{x_1}{s + p_1} + \cdots + \frac{x_m}{s + p_m}\right) \qquad (15.76)$$

$$\frac{\tilde{y}_{22}}{s} = \frac{K}{R_2}\left(\frac{\alpha_0}{s} + \frac{\alpha_1^2/x_1}{s + p_1} + \cdots + \frac{\alpha_m^2/x_m}{s + p_m}\right) \qquad (15.77)$$

and $\qquad \dfrac{-\tilde{y}_{12}}{s} = \dfrac{K}{R_2}\left(\dfrac{\alpha_0}{s} + \dfrac{\alpha_1}{s + p_1} + \cdots + \dfrac{\alpha_m}{s + p_m}\right) \qquad (15.78)$

The equivalent network at infinite frequency provides two additional constraints. From Fig. 15-9, we observe that

$$y_{11}(\infty) = \frac{1}{R_1} \qquad \text{and} \qquad y_{22}(\infty) = \frac{1}{R_2} \qquad (15.79)$$

Substituting these "boundary conditions" into Eqs. 15.76 and 15.77 gives

$$\frac{K}{R_2}(\alpha_0 + x_1 + x_2 + \cdots + x_m) = \frac{1}{R_1} \qquad (15.80)$$

and $\qquad \dfrac{K}{R_2}\left(\alpha_0 + \dfrac{\alpha_1^2}{x_1} + \dfrac{\alpha_2^2}{x_1} + \dfrac{\alpha_2^2}{x_2} + \cdots + \dfrac{\alpha_m^2}{x_m}\right) = \dfrac{1}{R_2} \qquad (15.81)$

Once these two equations are solved for all values of x under the condition that the maximum value of K be selected,[*] the specification functions $\tilde{y}_{11}$, $-\tilde{y}_{12}$, and $\tilde{y}_{22}$ are determined, and the network can be synthesized. Before carrying out these steps consider the following example of the procedure we have described.

It is specified that

$$\tilde{G}_{12} = K \frac{1}{(s + 1)(s + 2)} \qquad (15.82)$$

and $R_1 = 1$ ohm, $R_2 = 5$ ohms. This equation satisfies the requirement of Eq. 15.65 so that the method described is applicable. We first determine $-\tilde{y}_{12}$, which is

$$\frac{-\tilde{y}_{12}}{s} = \frac{K}{5} \frac{1}{s(s + 1)(s + 2)} \qquad (15.83)$$

---

[*] This K is maximum for the particular network structure used. A larger value may be found for another network realization. A detailed discussion is given by A. Fialkow, "Two terminal-pair networks containing two kinds of elements only," *Proc. Symposium on Modern Network Synthesis*, Polytechnic Institute of Brooklyn, **1**, pp. 50–65 (1955).

which has the following partial expansion:

$$\frac{-\tilde{y}_{12}}{s} = \frac{K}{5}\left(\frac{\frac{1}{2}}{s} + \frac{-1}{s+1} + \frac{\frac{1}{2}}{s+2}\right) \tag{15.84}$$

From this equation, we may select y_{11} and y_{22} to satisfy the residue condition with the equals sign as in Eq. 15.69, giving

$$\frac{\tilde{y}_{11}}{s} = \frac{K}{5}\left(\frac{\frac{1}{2}}{s} + \frac{x_1}{s+1} + \frac{x_2}{s+2}\right) \tag{15.85}$$

$$\frac{\tilde{y}_{22}}{s} = \frac{K}{5}\left(\frac{\frac{1}{2}}{s} + \frac{1/x_1}{s+1} + \frac{1/4x_2}{s+2}\right) \tag{15.86}$$

At infinite frequency, $y_{11} = 1$ and $y_{22} = \frac{1}{5}$, so that from Eqs. 15.85 and 15.86 we require that

$$\frac{K}{5}\left(\frac{1}{2} + x_1 + x_2\right) = 1 \tag{15.87}$$

and

$$\frac{K}{5}\left(\frac{1}{2} + \frac{1}{x_1} + \frac{1}{4x_2}\right) = \frac{1}{5} \tag{15.88}$$

These two equations must be solved for x_1 and x_2 in such a way that K has its maximum value. This example will be continued after we explain the procedure for this solution.

Kuh has made use of the Lagrange multiplier rule* to find the set of values of x which maximize K under the constraint that none of the values of x may be negative. From this rule, he has shown that

$$\frac{x_1}{\alpha_1} = \frac{x_2}{\alpha_2} = \cdots = \frac{x_m}{\alpha_m} = X \tag{15.89}$$

where X must satisfy the quadratic equation

$$X^2 + \frac{\alpha_0}{A}\left(1 - \frac{R_2}{R_1}\right)X - \frac{R_2}{R_1} = 0 \tag{15.90}$$

where

$$A = \sum_{i=1}^{m} \alpha_i \tag{15.91}$$

---

* See, for example, Guillemin, *The Mathematics of Circuit Analysis*, pp. 143–144, or W. Kaplan, *Advanced Calculus*, Addison-Wesley Publishing Co., Reading, Mass., 1953, p. 129.

Then the maximum value of K is

$$K_{max} = \frac{R_2/R_1}{\alpha_0 + XA} \tag{15.92}$$

and $\tilde{y}_{11}$, $-\tilde{y}_{12}$, and $\tilde{y}_{22}$ are determined.

In terms of the example of Eq. 15.82, Eq. 15.89 gives

$$x_1 = 2x_2 = X \tag{15.93}$$

and Eq. 15.90 becomes

$$X^2 - \tfrac{4}{3}X - 5 = 0 \tag{15.94}$$

The positive value of X satisfying this equation is $X = 3$ so that $x_1 = 3$

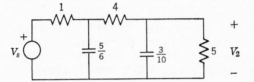

Fig. 15-12.   An example of a network found by the Kuh method.

and $x_2 = \tfrac{3}{2}$. Substituting these values into Eq. 15.92 gives the maximum value to be $K = 1$. Then from Eq. 15.85, $\tilde{y}_{11}$ is determined to be

$$\tilde{y}_{11} = \frac{s^2 + 9s/5 + \tfrac{1}{5}}{s^2 + 3s + 2} \tag{15.95}$$

The continued fraction expansion* of this admittance is

$$\tilde{y}_{11} = \cfrac{1}{1 + \cfrac{1}{\tfrac{5}{6}s + \cfrac{1}{4 + \cfrac{1}{\tfrac{3}{10}s + \tfrac{1}{5}}}}} \tag{15.96}$$

The network realization is seen to be that shown in Fig. 15-12, complete with the proper values of the terminating resistors. The same result is obtained if $\tilde{y}_{22}$ is developed.

---

* In general, a Cauer ladder development with zero-shifting steps will be required.

Variations of the method we have described are available for realizing complex zeros of transmission in the left half plane. The philosophy of these variations is the same as that we have studied, although the details are different. To realize complex zeros, it is necessary to use a bridge or parallel network. For this purpose, a method due to H. M. Lucal* is especially useful.

FURTHER READING

For an advanced study of the topics of this chapter, the reader is referred to Chapter 11 of Guillemin's *Synthesis of Passive Networks*, and also to his review article in *Advances in Electronics*, Vol. III. The use of the Darlington method for the synthesis to equal ripple forms of response is treated by Alex J. Grossman in "Synthesis of Tchebycheff parameter symmetrical filters," *Proc. I.R.E.*, **45**, 457–473 (1957). This article also features a large collection of useful design formulas. Students interested in extensions of the theory of this chapter to the case of nonresistive loads should read George L. Matthaei, "Synthesis of Tchebycheff impedance-matching networks, filters, and interstages," *IRE Trans.*, **CT-3**, 163–172 (1956), and R. M. Fano, "Theoretical limitations on the broadband matching of arbitrary impedances, *Jour. Frank. Inst.*, **249**, 57–83, 139–154 (1950). The use of the Darlington theory in active network synthesis is covered by J. G. Linvill, "The synthesis of active filters," *Proc. Symposium on Modern Network Synthesis*, Polytechnic Institute of Brooklyn, **5**, 453–476 (1955). A summary of the contributions of Giovanni Cocci to insertion loss methods of filter synthesis is given in a technical report by D. J. H. Maclean, Report No. 2, Stanford Electronics Laboratories, June 7, 1956. A general introduction to the field covered by this chapter is given by V. Belevitch, "Recent developments in filter theory," *IRE Trans.*, **CT-5**, 236–252 (1958); this contains a selected bibliography and a description of the work of the German group including Cauer and Piloty. Finally, the source material in the original work of Darlington, referenced in the chapter, makes interesting reading for serious students.

Extensive tables are available for the design of networks of the type discussed in this chapter and in Chapter 14. For an introduction to the use of these tables, see L. Weinberg, "A, B, C, D—network design easy as pie," *Proc. N.E.C.*, **13**, 1057–1066 (1957), which contains a list of references to other tables. Also recommended are the paper by R. Saal and E. Ulbrich, "On the design of filters by synthesis," *IRE Trans.*, **CT-5**, 284–328 (1958), and books by E. Green, *Amplitude-Frequency Characteristics of Ladder Networks*, Marconi's Wireless Telegraph Co., Chelmsford, England, 1954, and H. P. Westman, Editor, *Reference Data for Radio Engineers*, 4th ed., International Telephone and Telegraph Corp., New York, 1956, pp. 164–246.

* "Synthesis of three-terminal *RC* networks," *IRE Trans.*, **CT-2**, 308–316 (1955).

PROBLEMS

15-1. Starting with Eq. 15.4, supply the steps necessary to arrive at Eq. 15.5.

15-2. Given the specifications $R_1 = 1$ ohm, $R_2 = 2$ ohms, and

$$|t(j\omega)|^2 = \frac{1 - \omega^2 + \omega^4}{1 + 2\omega^2 + \omega^4}$$

find the following functions that describe the same network:

$$|\tilde{Z}_{12}(j\omega)|^2, \quad |Z_{12}(j\omega)|^2, \quad \alpha(\omega), \quad \text{and} \quad |\rho_1(j\omega)|^2$$

15-3. Repeat Prob. 15-2 when $R_2 = 2$ ohms, $R_2 = 1$ ohm, and

$$|t(j\omega)|^2 = \frac{1}{1 + \omega^{2n}}$$

15-4. Which of the following functions have acceptable form to be the transmission coefficient squared, $|t(j\omega)|^2$, for a double-terminated LC network? Give a reason for each answer.

(a) $\dfrac{(1 + \omega^2)^2}{2 + \omega^4}$ $\qquad$ (b) $\dfrac{(1 + \omega^2)^3}{16 + \omega^4}$

(c) $\dfrac{\omega^4 - 2\omega^2 + 1}{\omega^4 + 2\omega^2 + 1}$ $\qquad$ (d) $\dfrac{(1 - \omega^2)^2}{-\omega^6 - \omega^4 + \omega^2 + 1}$

(e) $\dfrac{(3 - \omega^2)^2}{\omega^6 + \omega^4 - \omega^2 - 1}$ $\qquad$ (f) $\dfrac{\omega^4 - \omega^2 + 1}{\omega^6 - 3\omega^2 + 2}$

15-5. Synthesize a double-terminated network with $R_1 = 1$ ohm and $R_2 = 1$ ohm to the specification

$$\left| \frac{V_2(j\omega)}{V_s(j\omega)} \right| = \frac{K_4}{\sqrt{1 + \omega^4}}$$

using the Darlington method and realizing the maximum permitted value for K_4. What is this value? For the network that results, how does each element value depend on K_4?

15-6. For the transmission coefficient function

$$|t(j\omega)|^2 = \frac{1}{1 + \omega^8}$$

synthesize a double-terminated coupling network with $R_1 = R_2 = 1$ ohm and determine all element values. Determine element values in the network if both the generator and load resistors are changed from 1 ohm to 72 ohms and if the frequency is scaled upward by a factor of 10^6.

15-7. Find a coupling network to be used with 1-ohm resistors at both ends to satisfy the specification function

$$|t(j\omega)|^2 = \frac{1 - \omega^2 + \omega^4}{1 + 2\omega^2 + \omega^4}$$

15-8. Consider the specification function

$$|t(j\omega)|^2 = K \frac{1 + \omega^2}{1 - \omega^2 + \omega^4}$$

and the requirement that $R_1 = 1$ ohm and $R_2 = 2$ ohms. Choose a convenient value for K, and synthesize a lossless coupling network for this double-terminated system.

15-9. Repeat Prob. 15-5 using one half of the maximum value that may be used for K_4.

15-10. Suppose that for a double-terminated network we set $R_1 = R_2 = 1$ ohm, and then synthesize to meet a given $|t(j\omega)|^2$ specification. If we now change the terminating resistors to the general values of R_1 and R_2 rather than 1 ohm, what changes must be made in the following functions in order that they will describe the new network? Z_{11}, V_2/V_s, V_2/I_s, and Z_{22}.

15-11. It is alleged that the necessary and sufficient condition that $|t(j\omega)|^2 = A(\omega^2)/B(\omega^2)$ represent a double-terminated lossless coupling network is that

$$0 \leq \frac{A(\omega^2)}{B(\omega^2)} \leq 1$$

Is this allegation correct? Support your conclusion.

15-12. Determine the $\tilde{y}_{22}$ which corresponds to the $\tilde{y}_{11}$ given by Eq. 15.95. Expand this $\tilde{y}_{22}$ as a continued fraction and verify that the network given in Fig. 15-12 results.

15-13. Make use of the Kuh method of synthesis to find an RC coupling network (grounded) which is double-terminated to satisfy the specifications

$$\tilde{G}_{12} = \frac{V_2}{V_s} = K \frac{1}{(s + 1)(s + 2)}$$

and $R_1 = 1$, $R_2 = 2$ ohms. The network is to be designed to maximize the value of K.

15-14. Synthesize an RC coupling network for a double-terminated system with $R_1 = 1$ ohm and $R_2 = 2$ ohms to satisfy the specification function

$$\tilde{G}_{12} = K \frac{s + 2}{(s + 1)(s + 3)(s + 4)}$$

and to maximize the value of K.

15-15. Specifications for a double-terminated system require that $R_1 = 2$ ohms and $R_2 = 1$ ohm with

$$\tilde{G}_{12} = K \frac{s + 1}{(s + 2)(s + 3)^2}$$

Synthesize the coupling network that maximizes the value of K.

15-16. The specification function $\tilde{G}_{12}$ has two negative real zeros and a denominator which is of 4th degree. Show that in using Kuh's method the maximum value of K is realized regardless of the order of realizing the zeros of transmission in the ladder development.

The Image Parameter Method

16.1   The image parameters

If in the network of Fig. 16-1 the impedance at side 1 is identical with the source impedance, $Z_{11} = Z_1$, and at the same time for side 2, $Z_{22} = Z_2$, then an *image match* is said to exist in the network. We define $Z_{11} = Z_{I1}$ and $Z_{22} = Z_{I2}$ to be *image impedance* in the sense that both Z_1 and Z_2 see their images as they "look" into the network to which they are connected. This image match condition is similar to the

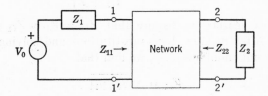

Fig. 16-1.   An image match exists in this system when $Z_{11} = Z_1$ and, with V_0 replaced by a short circuit, $Z_{22} = Z_2$.

constant-resistance condition for the lattice network for which all input impedances are equal to the terminating resistance, R. The image match is the more general case, however, since we deal with impedance instead of resistance and since the two image impedances, Z_{I1} and Z_{I2}, are not necessarily equal.

Networks meeting the image match requirement just described are said to be designed on the *image parameter basis*, following procedures developed by G. A. Campbell, O. J. Zobel, and others in the 1920's.

447

This method is older than but competitive with the Darlington method studied in Chapter 15.

We first find expressions for the set of network functions to be called the image parameters in terms of the familiar open-circuit impedance

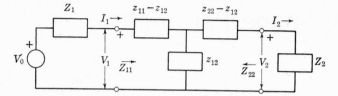

Fig. 16-2. The network of Fig. 16-1 with an equivalent T network in terms of the open-circuit impedance functions.

functions. From the T equivalent of the network of Fig. 16-1 shown in Fig. 16-2, we see that the input impedance at side 1 is

$$Z_{11} = z_{11} - z_{12} + \frac{z_{12}(z_{22} - z_{12} + Z_2)}{z_{22} + Z_2} \tag{16.1}$$

$$= z_{11} - \frac{z_{12}^2}{z_{22} + Z_2} \tag{16.2}$$

Similarly, the impedance at side 2 with the voltage source short-circuited is

$$Z_{22} = z_{22} - \frac{z_{12}^2}{z_{11} + Z_1} \tag{16.3}$$

For an image match, we require that $Z_{11} = Z_1 = Z_{I1}$ and $Z_{22} = Z_2 = Z_{I2}$. After making these substitutions and solving the equations that result simultaneously, we find that

$$Z_{I1} = \sqrt{z_{11}/y_{11}} \tag{16.4}$$

and
$$Z_{I2} = \sqrt{z_{22}/y_{22}} \tag{16.5}$$

These expressions for the image impedances are indeed compact, but they are also irrational, which is new in our study of network functions.

We found in Chapter 2 that three network functions were required to describe reciprocal two terminal-pair networks. We now have two driving-point functions, Z_{I1} and Z_{I2}, and evidently need one transfer function to complete the set. The form of the transfer function which is used is related to the principal application of the theory in the 1920's, transmission lines for the telephone industry. Networks connected in tandem for use with a transmission line are represented in Fig. 16-3.   If these networks are designed in such a way that an image match exists for each pair of connected terminal pairs, i.e., if

$$Z_{I2a} = Z_{I1b} \quad \text{and} \quad Z_{I2b} = Z_{I1c} \tag{16.6}$$

then the input and output voltages, V_1 and V_4, are related by the equation

$$\frac{V_4}{V_1} = \frac{V_2}{V_1} \cdot \frac{V_3}{V_2} \cdot \frac{V_4}{V_3} \tag{16.7}$$

The over-all network function is thus simply related to network functions for the individual networks in cascade.

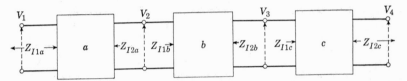

Fig. 16-3.   An image match exists for the three tandemly connected networks when $Z_{I2a} = Z_{I1b}$ and $Z_{I2b} = Z_{I1c}$ and when the input and output ends are also matched.

By analogy to transmission-line theory, we define the *image transfer function* γ by the equation

$$e^{-2\gamma} = \frac{V_2 I_2}{V_1 I_1} \tag{16.8}$$

which is the ratio of output to input voltage-current products.   If the terminations are the image impedances so that $Z_{11} = Z_{I1}$ and $Z_{22} = Z_{I2}$, then

$$V_1 = Z_{I1} I_1 \quad \text{and} \quad V_2 = Z_{I2} I_2 \tag{16.9}$$

Substituting these relationships in Eq. 16.8 gives either the voltage ratio or the current ratio in relationship to γ as

$$\frac{V_2}{V_1} = \sqrt{\frac{Z_{I2}}{Z_{I1}}}\, e^{-\gamma} \tag{16.10}$$

and

$$\frac{I_2}{I_1} = \sqrt{\frac{Z_{I1}}{Z_{I2}}}\, e^{-\gamma} \tag{16.11}$$

For the tandem-connected network of Fig. 16-3, we may write for Eq. 16.7,

$$\frac{V_4}{V_1} = \sqrt{\frac{Z_{I2a}}{Z_{I1a}}}\, e^{-\gamma_a} \sqrt{\frac{Z_{I2b}}{Z_{I1b}}}\, e^{-\gamma_b} \sqrt{\frac{Z_{I2c}}{Z_{I1c}}}\, e^{-\gamma_c} \tag{16.12}$$

With the impedance match required by Eqs. 16.6 satisfied, Eq. 16.12 reduces to

$$\frac{V_4}{V_1} = \sqrt{\frac{Z_{I2c}}{Z_{I1a}}}\, e^{-(\gamma_a + \gamma_b + \gamma_c)} \tag{16.13}$$

This result is readily extended to the case of n image-matched networks connected in tandem. The simplicity of this equation for V_4/V_1 is an important advantage of the image parameter theory which we will examine in greater detail in the sections to follow.

It will be useful in the discussion to follow if z_{11}, z_{12} and z_{22} are expressed in terms of Z_{I1}, Z_{I2}, and γ. Chapter 2 relationships to be used in the derivation are

$$z_{22} = \frac{y_{11}}{\Delta_y}, \qquad y_{22} = \frac{z_{11}}{\Delta_z}, \qquad \text{and} \qquad \Delta_y \Delta_z = 1 \tag{16.14}$$

Substituting the first two into the third, there results

$$\Delta_z \Delta_y = \frac{z_{11}}{y_{22}} \frac{y_{11}}{z_{22}} = 1 \tag{16.15}$$

from which we see that

$$y_{11}z_{11} = y_{22}z_{22} \equiv \psi^2 \tag{16.16}$$

In terms of the defined quantity, ψ, Eqs. 16.4 and 16.5 become

$$z_{11} = \psi Z_{I1} \tag{16.17}$$

and

$$z_{22} = \psi Z_{I2} \tag{16.18}$$

To find z_{12} in terms of the image impedances, observe that

$$Z_{I1}Z_{I2} = \sqrt{\frac{z_{11}z_{22}}{y_{11}y_{22}}} = \Delta_z \tag{16.19}$$

Then

$$z_{12}{}^2 = z_{11}z_{22} - \Delta_z = Z_{I1}Z_{I2}(\psi^2 - 1) \tag{16.20}$$

or

$$z_{12} = \sqrt{Z_{I1}Z_{I2}}\, \sqrt{\psi^2 - 1} \tag{16.21}$$

For the network of Fig. 16-1, V_2/V_1 is expressed in terms of the open-circuit impedance functions by starting from the relationship first derived in Chapter 2, with $Z_L = Z_{I2}$

$$Z_{12} = \frac{z_{12}Z_{I2}}{z_{22} + Z_{I2}} \tag{16.22}$$

Since at end 1, $I_1 = V_1/Z_{I1}$, we have

$$\frac{V_2(s)}{V_1(s)} = \frac{Z_{I2}}{Z_{I1}} \frac{z_{12}}{z_{22} + Z_{I2}} \tag{16.23}$$

Substituting the equations for z_{22} and z_{12} from Eqs. 16.18 and 16.21 into this expression gives

$$\frac{V_2}{V_1} = \sqrt{\frac{Z_{I2}}{Z_{I1}}} \frac{\sqrt{\psi^2 - 1}}{1 + \psi} \tag{16.24}$$

For this equation to be identical with Eq. 16.10, it is necessary that γ be related to ψ by

$$e^{-\gamma} = \frac{\sqrt{\psi^2 - 1}}{1 + \psi} \tag{16.25}$$

Since

$$e^{-\gamma} = \frac{1}{\cosh \gamma + \sinh \gamma} = \frac{\operatorname{csch} \gamma}{1 + \coth \gamma} \tag{16.26}$$

we see that the desired relationship is

$$\psi = \coth \gamma \tag{16.27}$$

Then the image transfer function may be written

$$\gamma = \coth^{-1} \sqrt{y_{11} z_{11}} = \coth^{-1} \sqrt{y_{22} z_{22}} \tag{16.28}$$

The basic relationships for the image parameter theory which have been derived in this section will next be applied to a specific network structure.

16.2   Image parameters for the symmetrical lattice

There are two different approaches to the development of image parameter theory, both stemming from the equations of the preceding section. The Campbell-Zobel theory is developed in terms of component ladder networks. The more recent approach is based on the work of Cauer and Bode and is in terms of the symmetrical lattice structure.

For a symmetrical network, $Z_{I1} = Z_{I2}$ (the symbol Z_I will be used to imply this condition), and the image impedance may be found from the equation, $Z_I = (z_{11}/y_{11})^{1/2}$. For the lattice of Fig. 16-4,

$$z_{11} = \frac{Z_a + Z_b}{2} \quad \text{and} \quad \frac{1}{y_{11}} = \frac{2Z_a Z_b}{Z_a + Z_b} \tag{16.29}$$

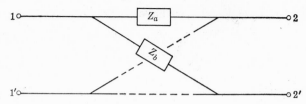

Fig. 16-4. The standard form of the symmetrical lattice.

so that Z_I has the particularly simple form

$$Z_I = \sqrt{Z_a Z_b} \tag{16.30}$$

An expression for the image transfer function in terms of Z_a and Z_b starts from Eq. 16.28:

$$\gamma = \coth^{-1} \sqrt{z_{11} y_{11}} \tag{16.31}$$

Using the identity

$$\coth^{-1} x = \tfrac{1}{2} \ln (x + 1) - \tfrac{1}{2} \ln (x - 1) \tag{16.32}$$

we have

$$\gamma = \tfrac{1}{2} \ln \frac{\sqrt{z_{11} y_{11}} + 1}{\sqrt{z_{11} y_{11}} - 1} \tag{16.33}$$

Since $\sqrt{z_{11} y_{11}} = (Z_a + Z_b)/2(Z_a Z_a)^{\frac{1}{2}}$, Eq. 16.33 becomes

$$\gamma = \tfrac{1}{2} \ln \frac{(\sqrt{Z_a} + \sqrt{Z_b})^2}{(\sqrt{Z_a} - \sqrt{Z_b})^2} \tag{16.34}$$

Depending on the sign we choose for the radical, there are a number of possible equivalent forms to this equation. One of them is

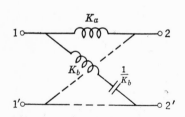

$$\gamma = \ln \frac{1 + \sqrt{Z_b/Z_a}}{1 - \sqrt{Z_b/Z_a}} \tag{16.35}$$

The quantity $(Z_b/Z_a)^{\frac{1}{2}}$ in this equation is given the symbol y_I and is called the *index function.*

Fig. 16-5. Symmetrical lattice network of example.

The important results given by Eqs. 16.30 and 16.35 will next be applied to a simple but very interesting example. Consider the network of Fig. 16-5, for which

$$Z_a = K_a s \quad \text{and} \quad Z_b = K_b \frac{s^2 + 1}{s} \tag{16.36}$$

where $L_b = 1/C_b = K_b$. For this lattice, the image impedance is

$$Z_I(s) = \sqrt{Z_a Z_b} = \sqrt{K_a K_b} \sqrt{1 + s^2} \qquad (16.37)$$

so that $\qquad Z_I(j\omega) = \sqrt{K_a K_b} \sqrt{1 - \omega^2} \qquad (16.38)$

The index function is

$$y_I(s) = \sqrt{\frac{Z_b}{Z_a}} = \sqrt{\frac{K_b}{K_a}} \frac{\sqrt{s^2 + 1}}{s} \qquad (16.39)$$

and $\qquad y_I(j\omega) = -j \sqrt{\frac{K_b}{K_a}} \frac{\sqrt{1 - \omega^2}}{\omega} \qquad (16.40)$

Plots of the two functions, $Z_I(j\omega)$ and $y_I(j\omega)$, are shown in Figs. 16-6 and 16-7 respectively. The image impedance is real for $|\omega| \leq 1$ and

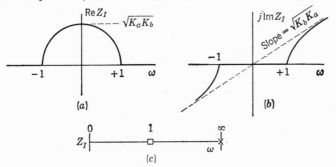

Fig. 16-6. Plots showing the nature of $Z_I(j\omega)$ for the network of Fig. 16-5.

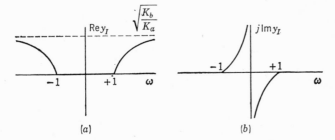

Fig. 16-7. Plots illustrating the behavior of the index function, $y_I(j\omega)$ for the network of Fig. 16-5.

imaginary for all other ω. The transition frequency, $\omega = 1$, is a *branch point* and is denoted on the pole-zero plot by a square, as shown in Fig. 16-6. The index function behaves inversely with the image impedance with respect to being real or imaginary. As shown in Fig. 16-7, $y_I(j\omega)$ is imaginary for $|\omega| \leq 1$ and real for all other ω. For large ω, $y_I(j\omega)$ approaches the value $(K_b/K_a)^{1/2}$.

The index function is related to the image transfer function by the equation,

$$\gamma(j\omega) = \ln \frac{1 + y_I(j\omega)}{1 - y_I(j\omega)} \qquad (16.41)$$

We have just seen that y_I is either real or imaginary, but never complex; either $y_I = a_I$ or $y_I = jb_I$, but $y_I \neq a_I + jb_I$. If y_I is real, then

$$\gamma(j\omega) = \ln \frac{1 + a_I}{1 - a_I} \qquad (16.42)$$

which is real and positive and infinite for Re $y_I = a_I = 1$ at the frequencies shown in Fig. 16-8. If y_I is imaginary, then

$$\gamma(j\omega) = \ln \frac{1 + jb_I}{1 - jb_I} = \ln \left| \frac{1 + jb_I}{1 - jb_I} \right| + j2 \tan^{-1} b_I \qquad (16.43a)$$

or $\qquad \gamma(j\omega) = j2 \tan^{-1} b_I \qquad (16.43b)$

and γ is imaginary. We see that $\gamma(j\omega)$ has a behavior like $Z_I(j\omega)$: it is either real or imaginary but never complex. The real part is

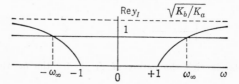

Fig. 16-8. Identification of the frequencies at which Re $y_I(j\omega) = 1$, giving infinite α.

identified as the *attenuation function*, α, and the imaginary part as the *phase function*, β. Then from Eq. 16.10,

$$\frac{V_2(j\omega)}{V_1(j\omega)} = \sqrt{\frac{Z_{12}(j\omega)}{Z_{11}(j\omega)}} \, e^{-\alpha} e^{-j\beta} \qquad (16.44)$$

If we simplify this equation by letting $Z_{12} = Z_{11} = Z_I$ as assumed for the lattice network, then we see that either V_2 is decreased in magnitude with respect to V_1 or shifted in phase with respect to V_1.

We define the band of frequencies for which $\alpha = 0$ as the *pass band*, and that for which $\alpha \neq 0$ as the *stop band*. The frequencies at which transitions from pass to stop bands are made are known as *cutoff frequencies*. For our example, the cutoff frequency is $\omega = 1$ radian/sec, the band of frequencies $|\omega| \leq 1$ is the pass band, and $|\omega| > 1$ is the

stop band.   This particular combination of characteristics describes a
low-pass filter.   Other kinds of filters of interest include high-pass,
band-pass, band-elimination, multiple band-pass, etc.   The following
table summarizes properties of the low-pass filter being studied:

Frequency Range	y_I	Z_I	α	β	Kind of Band
$\lvert\omega\rvert \leq 1$	imaginary	real	zero	nonzero	pass
$\lvert\omega\rvert > 1$	real	imaginary	nonzero	zero or π	stop

The relationship of these properties of the driving-point and transfer
image parameters to the poles, zeros, and branch points for Z_a, Z_b, Z_I,
and y_I is shown in Fig. 16-9.

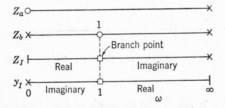

Fig. 16-9.   The relationship of the poles and zeros of various functions illustrated.

The particular form of $\alpha(\omega)$ in the equation

$$\alpha(\omega) = \text{Re } \gamma(j\omega) = \ln \left| \frac{1 + a_I}{1 - a_I} \right| \tag{16.45}$$

depends on the value of K_b/K_a with respect to unity.   Consider the
following three cases: Case 1, $K_b/K_a < 1$; Case 2, $K_b/K_a = 1$; and
Case 3, $K_b/K_a > 1$.   Plots of $\alpha(\omega)$ for these three cases are shown in
Fig. 16-10.   For Case 1, α increases monotonically with α approach-
ing a constant value for infinite ω.   Case 2 differs in that α becomes
infinite for infinite ω.   Case 3 is completely different from the other
two cases in that it has infinite value for a finite frequency, but a
finite limit for infinite frequency.   The phase function in the pass band
is also of interest.   By Eq. 16.43b,

$$\beta = \text{Im } \gamma(j\omega) = 2 \tan^{-1} b_I \tag{16.46}$$

Substituting the value of b_I of Eq. 16.40 gives*

$$\beta = -2 \tan^{-1} \sqrt{\frac{K_b}{K_a}} \frac{\sqrt{1 - \omega^2}}{\omega}, \qquad -1 \leq \omega \leq 1 \qquad (16.47)$$

It was pointed out in Chapter 12 that there are practical reasons for using ladder networks in preference to lattices. The lattice is introduced in the Cauer-Bode procedure we are studying as an artifice leading to, it is hoped, eventual realization of a ladder. Lattice decomposition is often possible, as further study of our example will show.

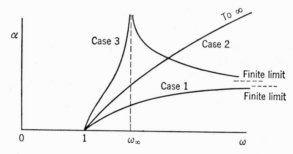

Fig. 16-10. The variation of α with ω is shown for the three cases identified in the text.

For Case 1, $K_a > K_b$ in the network of Fig. 16-11(a). The largest inductor we can remove from the lattice is K_b, which gives the partially decomposed structure of Fig. 16-11(b). Complete decomposition is possible for Case 2. Because $K_a = K_b$, all inductors can be removed and the simple T network of Fig. 16-11(c) results. This network is known as a *constant-k* section in conventional theory because it has the property of a class of networks for which the product of the series arm and shunt arm impedances is a constant. For our network,

$$(K_b s)(K_b/2s) = \tfrac{1}{2}K_b{}^2 \qquad (16.48)$$

It is also interesting to observe that $Z_I(0) = K_b$.

An equivalent ladder structure is also possible for Case 3 and is shown in Fig. 16-11(d). The shunt arm of the equivalent T network contains both an inductor and a capacitor, a combination which produces the infinite attenuation (or zero of transmission!) of Fig. 16-10.

Conventional filter theory makes use of the artifice of relating the parameters of the Case 3 network to those of the network for Case 2

---

* Some authors, for example, Reed in *Electric Network Synthesis*, use an inverse definition for y_I and so obtain results in a different form.

which is known as a *prototype*.   Let the Case 3 K's be distinguished by primes.   We first require that the two structures have identical image impedances in order that they may be used together in filter

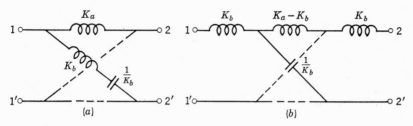

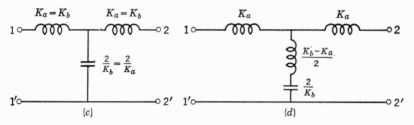

Fig. 16-11.   (a) The general form of the lattice of the example, (b) the Case 1 equivalent network, (c) the Case 2 equivalent T, and (d) the Case 3 equivalent T.

design.   This requires from Eq. 16.38 that

$$\sqrt{K_a K_b} \sqrt{1 - \omega^2} = \sqrt{K_a' K_b'} \sqrt{1 - \omega^2} \qquad (16.49)$$

or $$K_a K_b = K_a' K_b' \qquad (16.50)$$

Next let K_a' and K_a be proportional by the constant m so that

$$K_a' = mK_a, \qquad m < 1 \qquad (16.51)$$

Then from the relationship of Eq. 16.50,

$$K_b' = \frac{1}{m} K_b \qquad (16.52)$$

The elements of the Case 3 network of Fig. 16-11(d) are then seen to be

$$K_a' = mK_a$$

$$\frac{K_b' - K_a'}{2} = \frac{1 - m^2}{2m} K_a \qquad (16.53)$$

and $$\frac{2}{K_b'} = \frac{2m}{K_b}$$

The resulting equivalent network as shown in Fig. 16-12(b) is known as the *m-derived* section, derived from the prototype of Fig. 16-12(a) in such a way that the two networks have the same image imped-

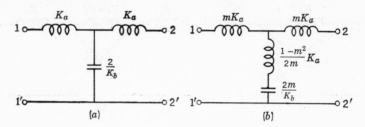

Fig. 16-12. (a) A Case 2 prototype section, and (b) the corresponding Case 3 *m*-derived section.

ances. The frequency at which there is infinite attenuation is the resonant frequency of the shunt LC combination,

$$\omega_\infty = \frac{1}{\sqrt{LC}} = \frac{1}{\sqrt{\dfrac{1-m^2}{2m}K_a\dfrac{2m}{K_b}}} = \frac{1}{\sqrt{1-m^2}} \qquad (16.54)$$

since the constants, K_a and K_b, relate to the Case 2 network for which $K_a = K_b$.

The cutoff frequency of the example we have studied occurred at 1 radian/sec. Networks having any other cutoff frequency, ω_0, may be found by frequency scaling.

16.3 More complicated lattices

If we restrict our study to LC lattice networks of the symmetrical variety, then $Z_a(j\omega) = \pm jX_a$ and $Z_b(j\omega) = \pm jX_b$, and Eq. 16.30 becomes

$$Z_I(j\omega) = \sqrt{Z_a Z_b} = \sqrt{(\pm jX_a)(\pm jX_b)} \qquad (16.55)$$

The analysis of the preceding section showed that in the pass band Z_I is real and y_I is imaginary whereas the opposite identification characterizes the stop band. Evidently, the same sign for $\pm jX_a$ and $\pm jX_b$ identifies a stop band and the opposite sign for these functions implies a pass band. This sign rule makes it convenient to identify stop and pass bands from a comparison of plots of $\pm X_a(\omega)$ and $\pm X_b(\omega)$ of the form shown in Fig. 16-13.

From Fig. 16-13(a), we see that the reactance functions $X_a(\omega)$ and $X_b(\omega)$ are opposite in sign over a band of frequencies only if the poles of Z_a coincide with the zeros of Z_b and vice versa over the band of frequencies. Similarly, the two reactance functions have the same sign over a band of frequencies only when the poles and zeros of Z_a and Z_b coincide over that band of frequencies, the situation shown in Fig. 16-13(b). A pole or a zero in Z_a or Z_b but not in both defines a frequency at which a transition is made from pass to stop or stop to

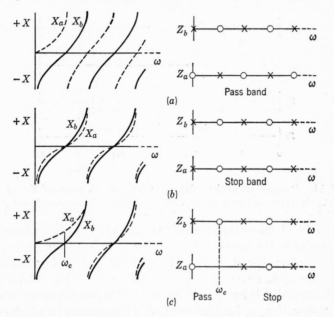

Fig. 16-13. Three plots showing that the relationship of the poles and zeros of the arm impedances Z_a and Z_b determines the pass bands, stop bands, and cutoff frequencies.

pass and is therefore a cutoff frequency. One cutoff frequency is shown in Fig. 16-13(c). From the three parts of this figure, we see that the characteristics with respect to pass and stop bands are determined for the lattice by a comparison of the poles and zeros of the two driving-point impedance functions, Z_a and Z_b.

How do the poles and zeros of Z_a and Z_b relate to the functions Z_I and y_I? First, a cutoff frequency evidently corresponds to a branch point in both Z_I and y_I, for it is at the cutoff frequencies that Z_I and y_I change from real to imaginary. From the equation $Z_I = (Z_a Z_b)^{1/2}$, we see that when Z_a and Z_b have the same poles and zeros, these are poles and zeros of Z_I. Similarly, the relationship $y_I = (Z_b/Z_a)^{1/2}$ may be used to show that when Z_b has a pole at the same frequency that Z_a has a zero, then y_I contains this pole. Dual statements may be made for zeros of y_I. These statements are illustrated in Fig. 16-14. Observe from the figure that Z_I has poles and zeros only when it is imaginary, and that y_I has poles and zeros only under the same imaginary value condition. When Z_I is imaginary, its poles and zeros coincide with those of Z_b and Z_a; when y_I is imaginary, its poles and zeros are those of Z_b.

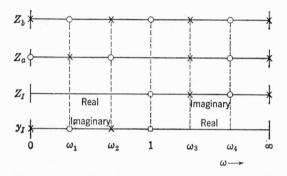

Fig. 16-14. Comparison of the poles, zeros, and branch points of Z_I and y_I with respect to the poles and zeros of the lattice impedance functions, Z_b and Z_a.

Figure 16-14 shows that for the low-pass filter the index function y_I is of interest in the interval, $1 \leq \omega \leq \infty$. It is helpful to transform this large interval to $0 \leq \omega \leq 1$ by plotting y_I as a function of $1/\omega$ rather than ω, as shown in the left-hand parts of Fig. 16-15. Now the index function is but a means to the end of determining the nature of the attenuation, α, for a given filter. The manner in which control of y_I leads to control of α is shown by Fig. 16-15. When y_I is real,

$$\alpha = \ln \left| \frac{1 + y_I}{1 - y_I} \right| \qquad (16.56)$$

showing that the attenuation is infinite when $y_I = 1$. Consider the variation of y_I in Fig. 16-15(a) in which $y_I = 1$ only at $1/\omega = 0$ or $\omega = \infty$. The figure shows the corresponding attenuation plot with α increasing monotonically with frequency.

A different y_I characteristic is shown in Fig. 16-15(b). The index function is unity at frequency ω_2, giving infinite attenuation as shown. The attenuation at infinite frequency is

$$\alpha_1 = \ln \left| \frac{1 + (1 + \epsilon_y)}{1 - (1 + \epsilon_y)} \right| = \ln \frac{2 + \epsilon_y}{\epsilon_y} \qquad (16.57)$$

and at ω_1 it has the same value since

$$\ln \left| \frac{1 + \dfrac{1}{1 + \epsilon_y}}{1 - \dfrac{1}{1 + \epsilon_y}} \right| = \ln \frac{2 + \epsilon_y}{\epsilon_y} = \alpha_1 \qquad (16.58)$$

The figure shows that the attenuation is equal to or greater than α_1 in the interval $\omega_1 \leq \omega \leq \infty$.

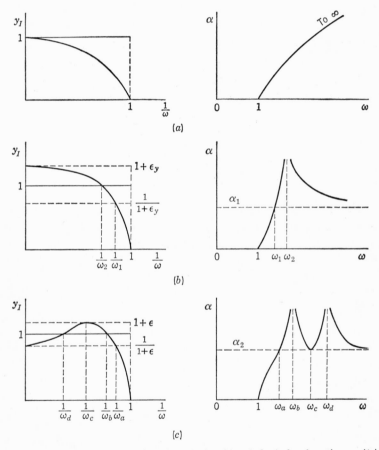

Fig. 16-15. Three plots showing the relationship of the index function, $y_I(1/\omega)$, and the attenuation function, $\alpha(\omega)$.

The possibility of two intersections of the $y_I(1/\omega)$ curve with the line at $+1$ is shown in Fig. 16-15(c). The characteristic may be adjusted to give equal ripple (Chebyshev-like) behavior for y_I in the

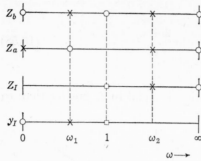

stop band, resulting in the same attenuation α_2 at ω_a, ω_c, and at infinite frequency, and at the same time infinite attenuation at ω_b and ω_d. More complicated variations of $y_I(1/\omega)$ are possible, especially with more poles and zeros in Z_a and Z_b, but the three of Fig. 16-15 illustrate the philosophy of our approach.

Fig. 16-16. Properties of Z_a, Z_b, Z_I, and y_I for the illustrative example.

We will next illustrate by means of an example the shaping of the $y_I(1/\omega)$ characteristic

to give a Chebyshev-like form. For the pole-zero configuration shown in Fig. 16-16,

$$Z_b(j\omega) = \frac{K_b j\omega(1 - \omega^2)}{(\omega_1{}^2 - \omega^2)(\omega_2{}^2 - \omega^2)}$$

and

$$Z_a(j\omega) = \frac{K_a(\omega_1{}^2 - \omega^2)}{j\omega(\omega_2{}^2 - \omega^2)}$$

(16.59)

Then the index function is

$$y_I(j\omega) = \sqrt{\frac{Z_b(j\omega)}{Z_a(j\omega)}} = \left[\frac{K_b}{K_a} \frac{(j\omega)^2(1 - \omega^2)(\omega_2{}^2 - \omega^2)}{(\omega_1{}^2 - \omega^2)^2(\omega_2{}^2 - \omega^2)}\right]^{\frac{1}{2}}$$

(16.60)

After some algebraic reduction, there results

$$y_I(j\omega) = \sqrt{\frac{K_b}{K_a}} \frac{\sqrt{1 - \dfrac{1}{\omega^2}}}{\omega_1{}^2\left(\dfrac{1}{\omega_1{}^2} - \dfrac{1}{\omega^2}\right)}$$

(16.61)

This equation is arbitrarily broken into two parts which are plotted in Fig. 16-17. One is the radical quantity,

$$\sqrt{\frac{K_b}{K_a}} \sqrt{1 - \frac{1}{\omega^2}}$$

(16.62)

and the other is a reactance function

$$\frac{1}{\omega_1{}^2\left(\dfrac{1}{\omega_1{}^2} - \dfrac{1}{\omega^2}\right)}$$

(16.63)

which has a pole at $\omega = \omega_1$. By adjusting the constant $(K_b/K_a)^{1/2}$ and the frequency ω_1, the shape of the $y_I(1/\omega)$ may be controlled to some degree, at least to the extent of giving the three kinds of characteristics of Fig. 16-15.

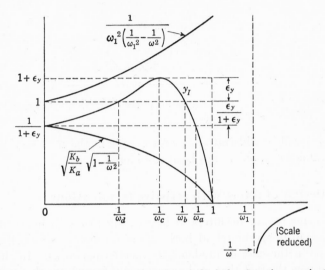

Fig. 16-17. Plot showing the construction of the index function, y_I, in terms of two other factors. The adjustment of the constant $(K_b/K_a)^{\frac{1}{2}}$ and ω_1 gives an equal ripple form to $y_I(1/\omega)$.

Suppose that we set as our objective the realization of y_I and α functions of the form of Fig. 16-15(c). This may be accomplished by requiring that

$$\sqrt{\frac{K_b}{K_a}} = \frac{1}{1 + \epsilon_y} \qquad (16.64)$$

and then adjusting ω_1 to give the attenuation at ω_c which is the same as that at infinite frequency. In making this choice, we have no control over the frequencies of infinite attenuation, ω_b and ω_d. Alternatively, we may set desired values for ω_b and ω_d and then accept any values for $y_{I\min}$ and $y_{I\max}$.

Once the proper adjustment of $(K_b/K_a)^{1/2}$ and ω_1 is made and the desired form of $\alpha(\omega)$ is realized, the lattice network may be synthesized by the realization of the driving-point functions, Z_a and Z_b. For the example of Fig. 16-16, the lattice network is that shown in Fig. 16-18. When the element values are known, the lattice may be decomposed into an equivalent ladder in some cases. The complete realization

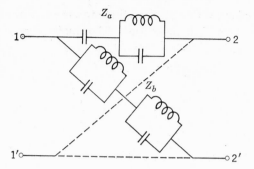

Fig. 16-18. A lattice network realization of the characteristic of Fig. 16-17 from the poles and zeros of Fig. 16-16.

procedure will be illustrated by an example in the next section after the termination problem has been considered.

16.4 Design of filters with resistive terminations

The image parameter filters we have studied thus far in the chapter have had an image match at both sets of terminals—or at all sets of terminals in the case of tandemly connected networks. In this section, we face the fact that we have no image impedance devices available for the source and the load; the closest approximation is a resistor

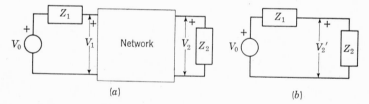

Fig. 16-19. The two networks used in the derivation of the relationship for the voltage insertion ratio, V_2'/V_2.

which is invariant with frequency. Since the assumption of image match of our analysis does not apply to resistively terminated networks, our results are invalid or at best an approximation. Actually, of course, the picture is not nearly this dark. We "patch up" the theory by a correction factor. This correction factor will allow us to compute, and to some degree to control, the loss in the pass band and to find the actual loss in the stop band. We find the desired correction factor by the indirect route of considering the two networks shown in Fig. 16-19 from which we compute the ratio of a voltage in one network to a voltage in the other.

The network shown in Fig. 16-19(a) was studied in Chapter 2 (see Prob. 2-20). From the equivalent T representation of the network, the equation

$$\frac{V_2}{V_0} = \frac{z_{12}Z_2}{\Delta_z + z_{22}Z_1 + z_{11}Z_2 + Z_1Z_2} \tag{16.65}$$

was derived (with the Chapter 2 notation changed to match that of this chapter). We first normalize the resistive terminations to 1-ohm values, both 1 ohm because we are considering symmetrical networks, making $Z_1 = Z_2 = 1$. The open-circuit impedance functions are next expressed in terms of the image parameters. Letting $Z_{I1} = Z_{I2} = Z_I$ and substituting Eq. 16.27 into Eqs. 16.17, 18, and 21, we have*

$$z_{11} = z_{22} = Z_I \coth \gamma \quad \text{and} \quad z_{12} = Z_I \operatorname{csch} \gamma \tag{16.66}$$

Also, by Eq. 16.19 we have $\Delta_z = Z_I{}^2$, so the inverse of Eq. 16.65 becomes

$$\frac{V_0}{V_2} = \frac{Z_I{}^2 + 2Z_I \coth \gamma + 1}{Z_I \operatorname{csch} \gamma} \tag{16.67}$$

In terms of exponential quantities, this equation is written

$$\frac{V_0}{V_2} = \frac{Z_I{}^2 + 2Z_I \left(\dfrac{e^\gamma + e^{-\gamma}}{e^\gamma - e^{-\gamma}}\right) + 1}{Z_I \dfrac{2}{e^\gamma - e^{-\gamma}}} \tag{16.68}$$

By routine algebraic manipulation, this equation becomes

$$\frac{V_0}{V_2} = e^\gamma \frac{(Z_I + 1)^2}{2Z_I} \left[1 - \left(\frac{Z_I - 1}{Z_I + 1}\right)^2 e^{-2\gamma}\right] \tag{16.69}$$

The network of Fig. 16-19(b) is derived from that shown in (a) by simply removing the coupling network. The voltage at the load is related to the voltage at the source by the equation

$$\frac{V_0}{V_2{}'} = 2 \tag{16.70}$$

Then the ratio of Eq. 16.69 to 16.70 becomes

$$\frac{V_2{}'}{V_2} = e^\gamma \frac{(Z_I + 1)^2}{4Z_I} \left[1 - \left(\frac{Z_I - 1}{Z_I + 1}\right)^2 e^{-2\gamma}\right] \tag{16.71}$$

* For a general derivation, applicable to nonsymmetrical networks, see Reed, *loc. cit.*, Sec. 7.2.

This ratio is known as the voltage *insertion ratio*. The *insertion loss function* is defined by the relationship

$$\ln \frac{V_2'}{V_2} = \text{insertion loss} + j \text{ insertion angle} = A + jB \quad (16.72)$$

The insertion loss was studied in Chapter 15; it is a measure of the loss caused by inserting a coupling network into a system, e.g., a compensating or equalizing network into a transmission line. Combining Eqs. 16.71 and 16.72 gives

$$A + jB = \gamma + \ln \left[\frac{(Z_I + 1)^2}{4Z_I} \right] + \ln \left[1 - \left(\frac{Z_I - 1}{Z_I + 1} \right)^2 e^{-2\gamma} \right] \quad (16.73)$$

and the insertion loss is

$$A = \alpha + \ln \left| \frac{(Z_I + 1)^2}{4Z_I} \right| + \ln \left| 1 - \left(\frac{Z_I - 1}{Z_I + 1} \right)^2 e^{-2\gamma} \right| \quad \text{nepers} \quad (16.74)$$

The three parts of this equation are given identifying names. The first is the now familiar attenuation loss. The second is given the name *reflection loss*, and the third *interaction loss*. In equation form,

insertion loss = attenuation loss
$$+ \text{ reflection loss} + \text{ interaction loss} \quad (16.75)$$

We now have an equation involving the insertion loss owing to the network coupling the resistive source impedance to the resistive load and the attenuation function of the image parameter theory. The difference between these two quantities is the reflection loss and the interaction loss. Once these quantities are known, they may be added to the attenuation loss found for an image-matched network to given the actual insertion loss for the resistively terminated case.

A comparison of the three kinds of losses which add to give the insertion loss are shown in the following chart for a typical case. (There are exceptions to this case, to be sure.)

Band	Attenuation Loss	Reflection Loss	Interaction Loss
pass	zero	**small**	very small
stop	**large**	small	very small

We see from the chart that in the pass band the important loss is the reflection loss, whereas in the stop band attenuation loss is of paramount importance. In the last section we studied the control of the attenuation loss by the control of the index function, y_I. We will next study the control of the reflection loss in the pass band.

Since Z_I is real in the pass band, the second term in Eq. 16.74 becomes simply

$$\alpha_R = \ln \frac{(Z_I + 1)^2}{4Z_I} \quad \text{nepers} \quad \text{or} \quad 20 \log_{10} \frac{(Z_I + 1)^2}{4Z_I} \quad \text{db} \quad (16.76)$$

Observe from the equation that when $Z_I = 1$ the reflection loss is 0! This result reminds us that the reflection loss is indeed 0 with an image match. Other values of α_R may be found from a plot of $Z_I(\omega)$ in the pass band in exactly the same way that $\alpha(\omega)$ was studied from the plot of $y_I(1/\omega)$ in the stop band in the last section. Thus in Fig. 16-20,

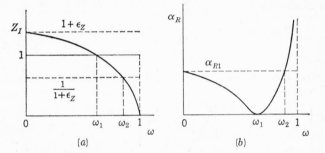

Fig. 16-20. Plots illustrating the relationship of the reflection loss, α_R, to the image impedance in the pass band.

we see that the maximum value of the reflection loss corresponds to the maximum deviation of $Z_I(\omega)$ from unity. If the maximum deviation over a band of frequencies is ϵ_Z, then for that frequency band,

$$\alpha_{R\text{max}} = \ln \frac{(2 + \epsilon_Z)^2}{4(1 + \epsilon_Z)} \quad \text{nepers} \quad (16.77)$$

Suppose that the image impedance-frequency curve is bounded by the upper limit $1 + \epsilon_Z$ and/or the lower limit $1/(1 + \epsilon_Z)$ in the frequency interval, $0 \leq \omega \leq \omega_Z$, as shown in Fig. 16-21(a). The ratio of the frequency ω_Z to the cutoff frequency ω_0,

$$k_Z = \frac{\omega_Z}{\omega_0} \quad (16.78)$$

is defined as the *coverage* relating to reflection loss. Similarly, for the $y_I(1/\omega)$ characteristic of Fig. 16-21(b), the ratio

$$k_y = \frac{1/\omega_y}{1/\omega_0} = \frac{\omega_0}{\omega_y} \quad (16.79)$$

is the *coverage* relating to attenuation.   Both coverages have values less than unity.   A large value for each is desirable.

To illustrate the use of the relationships found thus far, let it be required to find the network to satisfy the specifications for a low-pass filter shown in Fig. 16-22.   It is required that the reflection loss be less than 0.2 db in the pass band from 0 to 0.75 radians/sec, and that

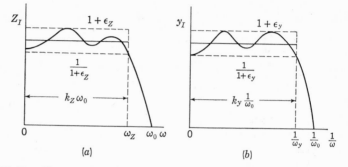

Fig. 16-21.   Plots of Z_I and y_I which are used to define the coverage figures, k_y and k_z.

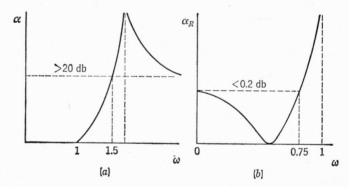

Fig. 16-22.   Specifications pertaining to the attenuation and reflection loss for the example.

the attenuation be at least 20 db at $\omega = 1.5$ and infinite frequencies. Our solution may be found in the following steps:

(1) From the shapes of the required α and α_R characteristics of Fig. 16-22, we will first assume that the network of Fig. 16-5 having the characteristics shown in Fig. 16-9 will be of adequate complexity.   If this assumption proves to be incorrect, we will then assume a more complicated network.

(2) We next determine appropriate values for the tolerances.   Using Eq. 16.57, the choice $\epsilon_y = 0.15$ gives $\alpha_1 = 23.1$ db, which is greater

than 20 db as required. By Eq. 16.77, $\alpha_{R_{max}} = 0.172$ db when $\epsilon_Z = 0.3$, which is less than 0.2 of the specifications.

(3) To find the coverages corresponding to the tolerances selected in the last step, we first determine Z_I and y_I. For the network selected in step (1), Z_I is given by Eq. 16.38 and y_I by Eq. 16.40. We evaluate K_a and K_b in these equations from the requirement at zero frequency that

$$\sqrt{\frac{K_b}{K_a}} = 1 + \epsilon_y = 1.15 \qquad \text{and} \qquad \sqrt{K_a K_b} = 1 + \epsilon_Z = 1.30 \quad (16.80)$$

Solving these equations gives the values $K_a = 1.13$ and $K_b = 1.49$ so that

$$y_I(j\omega) = -j1.15 \sqrt{(1/\omega)^2 - 1}$$

and
$$Z_I(\omega) = 1.30 \sqrt{1 - \omega^2} \qquad\qquad (16.81)$$

Referring to the plots of these two equations in Fig. 16-23, we see that the coverages may be found by determining the frequency at which

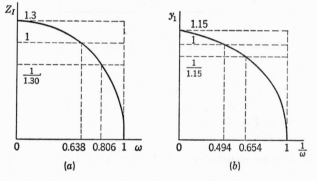

Fig. 16-23. The Z_I and y_I functions determined from the specifications given in Fig. 16-22.

y_I has the value $1/(1 + \epsilon_y) = 1/1.15$, and Z_I similarly has the value $1/1.30$. Solving these equations gives $k_y = 0.654$ and $k_Z = 0.806$.

(4) Knowing the coverages, we next determine the frequencies for comparison with the specification frequencies of $\omega = 1.5$ and $\omega = 0.75$ of Fig. 16-22. From Eqs. 16.78 and 16.79, we have

$$\omega_Z = \omega_0 k_Z = 0.806 \qquad \text{and} \qquad \omega_y = \frac{\omega_0}{k_y} = 1.53 \qquad (16.82)$$

and both values are better than the specification figures.

(5) The frequencies of zero reflection loss and infinite attenuation in Fig. 16-22 are found by setting y_I and Z_I to 1.0. These values are found to be 0.638 and 2.02 as shown in Fig. 16-23.

(6) The complete characteristics of the filter are now fixed and are found to be within the specifications set. The network may next be

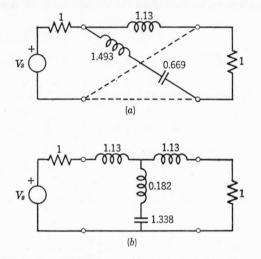

Fig. 16-24. Network realizations in lattice and ladder form satisfying the specifications given by Fig. 16-22.

found from the lattice impedance functions, $Z_a = 1.13s$, and $Z_b = 1.49s + 1/0.67s$. The network in both lattice and equivalent ladder form is shown in Fig. 16-24.

16.5 The ladder equivalent of the lattice filter

Because many applications require a filter with a common ground (the so-called unbalanced structure), an important part of filter synthesis is the reduction of a lattice to an equivalent ladder. We know from Chapter 12 that such an equivalent ladder composed of passive elements alone does not always exist. When it does, a method may be used in which the frequencies of infinite attenuation (the zeros of transmission) are realized by successive steps of lattice decomposition. This method bears remarkable similarity to the Cauer ladder development of Chapter 10 by which z_{11} or z_{22} is developed in such a way that the zeros of z_{12} are realized.

The method will be explained by means of an example. Consider Z_a and Z_b functions having the reactance plots shown in Fig. 16-25(a).

The impedance Z_b has an internal pole and zero but Z_a has only an internal zero. Observe that there are two frequencies at which the reactance plots intersect and $Z_a = Z_b$. At these frequencies, $y_I = 1$ and a frequency of infinite attenuation is identified. The steps in this ladder development involve *these* frequencies.

Suppose that we first consider frequency ω_1. The removal of an inductor from the arms of the lattice of value

$$L_1 = \frac{X_b(\omega_1)}{\omega_1} = \frac{X_a(\omega_1)}{\omega_1} \quad (16.83)$$

will cause the intersection to occur at a zero of each of the functions

$$Z_{b1} = Z_b - L_1 s$$

and

$$Z_{a1} = Z_a - L_1 s \quad (16.84)$$

at the frequency ω_1 as shown in Fig. 16-25(b). The removal of a pole from the two functions Y_{a1} and Y_{b1}, the reciprocals of the impedances of Eq. 16.84, causes the lattice to decompose as shown in Fig. 16-26(c) with a shunt-connected LC network which resonates at ω_1 producing the required frequency of infinite attenuation. The func-tions remaining after this pole-removal step have reactance plots shown in Fig. 16-25(d).

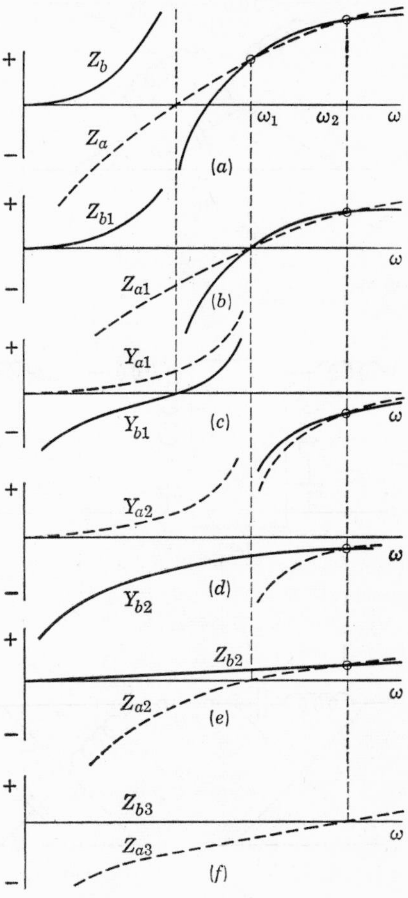

Fig. 16-25. Record of the reduction of a lattice to an equivalent ladder.

Our interest next shifts to the frequency ω_2 at which the two func-tions Z_{b2} and Z_{a2} of Fig. 16-25(e) intersect. Repeating the first step of our previous development gives $Z_{b3} = 0$ and the Z_{a3} curve shown in Fig. 16-25(f) and the development is complete as shown in Fig. 16-26(d) short of our objective of an unbalanced network. However, when phase is not important, we may make use of an artifice shown in Figs. 16-26(e) and (f). These two networks are seen to have identical z_{11}

and z_{22} descriptions, but z_{12} of the first is the negative of the second. So except for a 180° phase shift, the network of Fig. 16-26(g) is equivalent to that of (d) and the ladder development is complete. The

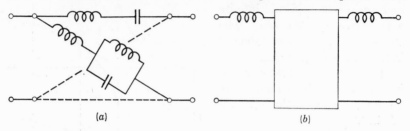

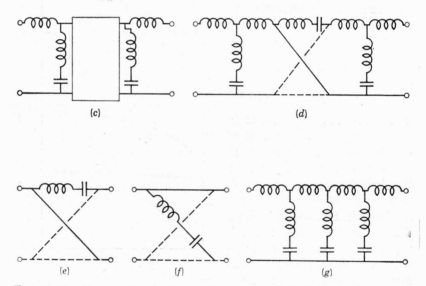

Fig. 16-26. Various steps in the development of the ladder network from the lattice by the procedure of Fig. 16-25.

student will better understand these steps through the medium of homework problems!

16.6 The design of composite filters

The method of lattice filter design described in Sections 16.4 and 16.5 has made use of one lattice. For simple problems, the arms of the lattice have been simple; problems of greater complexity have resulted in more complicated networks in the arms of the lattice.   In Section 16.1, we found that for networks connected in tandem so that an image match existed for each network, as in Fig. 16.3, the attenuation for the composite network was the summation of the attenuation of the component networks.   (The same statements apply to the phase.)   A method of design that exploits this characteristic is due to Zobel, Campbell, Wagner, and others.   In this method, the component networks are selected to be of especially simple form which are readily

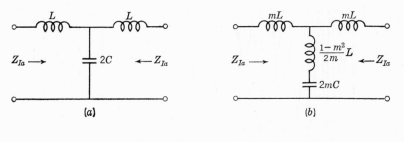

(a)   (b)

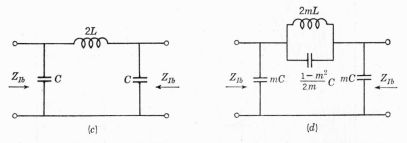

(c)   (d)

Fig. 16-27.   The four standard sections used in the design of composite filters; (a) and (c) are *constant-k* and (b) and (d) *m-derived* sections.

designed.   The method has the disadvantages that it often requires more elements than the lattice method, and often involves cut and try in satisfying specifications.

The standard low-pass sections of the Zobel-Campbell method were derived in Section 16.2 from the lattice.   These sections are shown in Fig. 16-27.   The sections shown in (a) and (c) of the figure are *constant-k* sections, and those of (b) and (d) are *m-derived* sections.   The four sections have only two different image impedances.   For the network of (a), Z_{Ia} is given by Eq. 16.38 which, when normalized so that $\sqrt{K_a K_b} = 1$, is

$$Z_{Ia}(\omega) = \sqrt{1 - \omega^2}, \qquad \omega \le 1 \qquad (16.85)$$

It is assumed that the reader is familiar with the network of (c) from Problem 16-4.   There it was shown, again normalizing $\sqrt{K_a K_b} = 1$, that

$$Z_{Ib}(\omega) = \frac{1}{\sqrt{1 - \omega^2}}, \qquad \omega \leq 1 \qquad (16.86)$$

The attenuation characteristics of these two kinds of filters were described in Section 16.2 and are plotted in Fig. 16-28 as a function of

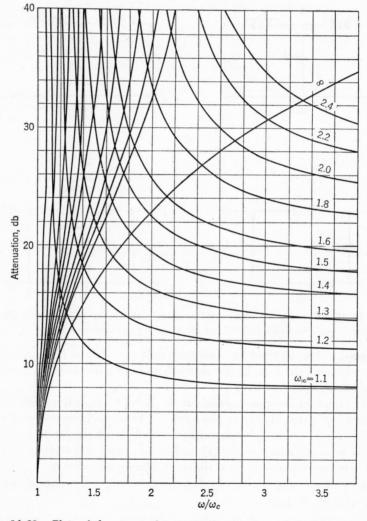

Fig. 16-28.   Plots of the attenuation per section for the m-derived low-pass case with $\omega_\infty = 1/\sqrt{1 - m^2}$ as parameter.   The case $\omega_\infty = \infty$ describes the attenuation per section of a constant-k low-pass filter.

the frequency of infinite attenuation which is related to m by $\omega_\infty = 1/\sqrt{1 - m^2}$. Observe that in this figure the curve marked $\omega_\infty = \infty$ corresponds to the *constant-k* case.

The Zobel-Campbell theory makes use of half-sections which are derived from the standard sections of Fig. 16-27. Observe that these sections have geometrical symmetry; if they are bisected (in the Bartlett bisection theorem sense), then the three standard half-sections shown in Fig. 16-29 result. When incorporated in a composite filter, these half-sections provide half the attenuation of a full section. The motivation for using the half-sections comes from an examination of their impedance properties. Routine analysis of the three networks*

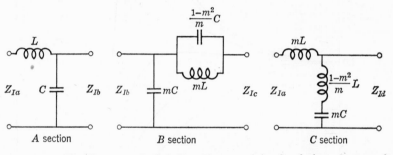

Fig. 16-29. The three standard half-sections used in the design of composite filters.

shows that the image impedance has four forms: Z_{Ia} and Z_{Ib} as given in Eqs. 16.85 and 16.86, and two new forms, identified as Z_{Ic} and Z_{Id}, which are

$$Z_{Ic} = \frac{\sqrt{1 - \omega^2}}{1 - (1 - m^2)\omega^2} \tag{16.87}$$

and

$$Z_{Id} = \frac{1 - (1 - m^2)\omega^2}{\sqrt{1 - \omega^2}} \tag{16.88}$$

The image impedances for the three standard half-sections are identified in Fig. 16-29.

If we plot the variation of Z_{Ic} and Z_{Id} with frequency with m as a parameter, then the characteristics shown in Figs. 16-30 and 16-31 are found. Compared to the variations for Z_{Ia} and Z_{Ib}, the values of Z_{Ic} and Z_{Id} are better approximations to 1, which is the normalized value of the load and source resistors, in the pass band from $\omega = 0$ to $\omega = 1$. The best value of m is approximately 0.6. This constant image impedance makes it possible to minimize the mismatch between

---

* See Van Valkenburg, *Network Analysis*, Chapter 13.

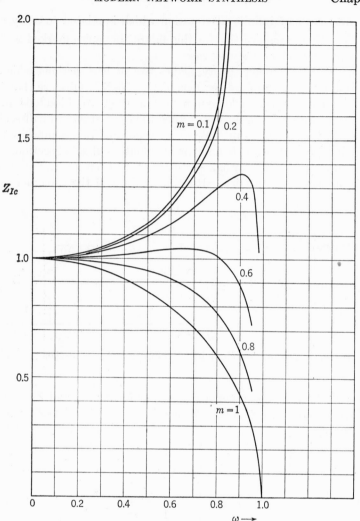

Fig. 16-30. Plot showing the variation of Z_{Ic} with frequency, with m as a parameter, for $0 \leqq \omega \leqq 1$.

the image impedance and the load and source resistors and so minimizes the reflection loss α_R in the pass band. In summary, we see that the m-derived sections provide the zeros of transmission (frequencies of infinite attenuation) at finite frequencies, making it possible to adjust the attenuation in the stop band. The constant-k sections provide the zeros of transmission at infinity. The m-derived half-sections afford a better match to the source and load.

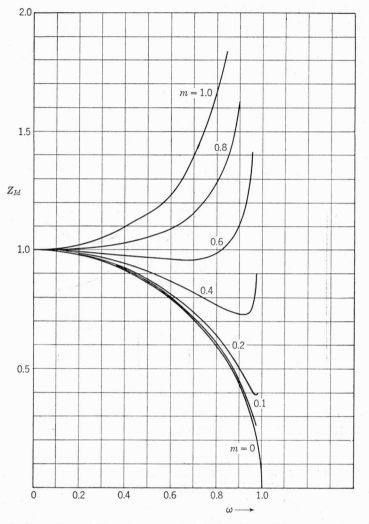

Fig. 16-31. The variation of the image impedance Z_{Id}, with m as a parameter, in the pass band.

An example will illustrate the method. Let the specifications for a low-pass filter be as follows: (1) The insertion loss in the pass band is to be minimized. (2) The insertion loss is to be at least 20 db at $f = 2100$ cycles/sec and 40 db for all frequencies higher than 2400 cycles/sec. (3) The load is a 600-ohm resistor and the generator has internal resistance equal to 600 ohms. In solving this problem to find a suitable filter, we make the assumption that the attenuation is equal to the insertion loss. We also observe that, in minimizing the pass-band insertion loss, the image impedance should be as nearly equal to the load resistance over a band of frequencies as possible.

Let us assume that the cutoff frequency is 2000 cycles/sec. Then frequencies may be normalized in terms of this f_0. The impedance level is also normalized so that the resistive terminations are equal to 1 ohm. From the curves of Fig. 16-28, we see that if $\omega_\infty = 1.1$, we approximately satisfy the requirement that the attenuation be 20 db at $\omega = 1.05$. However, additional sections will be required to insure that the attenuation is greater than 40 db for frequencies higher than 1.2. Suppose that we select $\omega_\infty = 1.25$ $(m = 0.6)$ for the second

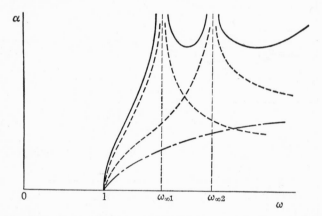

Fig. 16-32. The attenuation characteristics of a composite filter made up of two m-derived sections and one constant-k section.

m-derived section (which will also be used for matching terminations) and also make use of one half-section of constant-k filter to provide the high-frequency attenuation. From these choices, a plot like that of Fig. 16-32 is made. If the specifications are not met within satisfactory margins, the values of ω_∞ may be adjusted or additional sections added. This cut-and-try aspect of the method is one of its disadvantages, but not a serious disadvantage since the plotting is simple and routine.

Next, the half-sections are arranged in such a way that there is an image impedance match for each half-section and also that Z_{Ic} or Z_{Id} with $m = 0.6$ appears at both the input and output terminals of the filter for approximate match with the resistive terminations. One of several possible arrangements is that shown in Fig. 16-33(a), which may be simplified to the form of (*b*) by combining redundant elements. The design is completed by inverse scaling of the frequency and the impedance level, and all element values in the network are determined.

From the network realization, the insertion loss may be computed for comparison with the specifications. Alternatively, an experimental filter may be built and the insertion loss measured.

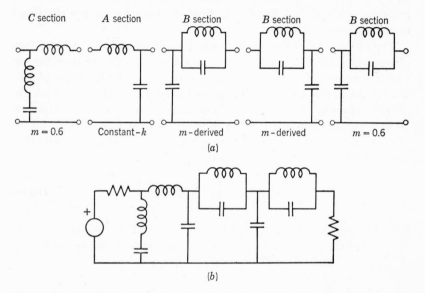

Fig. 16-33. (*a*) A composite filter having an image match for each half-section, and (*b*) the simplified composite filter with redundant elements combined.

16.7   Frequency transformations

The approximation studies of Chapter 13 were restricted to the low-pass (or brick wall) case, and similarly in this chapter only low-pass filters have been considered. We will next show that the results for the low-pass case can readily be adapted to other cases (high-pass, band-pass, etc.) by a transformation of the frequency variable.*

An elementary form of frequency transformation is already familiar from our study of frequency scaling in Chapter 2. If we now distinguish between frequency and normalized frequency by letting normalized frequency be $\text{Im } S = \Omega$ and frequency be $\text{Im } s = \omega$ as

---

* General references to this subject are Cauer, *Synthesis of Linear Communication Networks*, pp. 299–332, and Bode, *Network Analysis and Feedback Amplifier Design*, pp. 208–211.

usual, then the transformation of frequency scaling is

$$S = \frac{s}{\omega_1} \quad \text{or} \quad \Omega = \frac{\omega}{\omega_1} \qquad (16.89)$$

By this transformation, element values are adjusted in such a way that network function behavior at 1 radian/sec takes place instead at ω_1 radian/sec. The frequency scale is either magnified or reduced as suits our convenience, but the scale of the function we are plotting is not necessarily affected.

The philosophy of frequency scaling applies to a more general form of frequency transformation. As a specific example, suppose that we wish to accomplish an inversion in the frequency scale for an LC network. Now the reactance of an inductor varies directly with frequency whereas that of a capacitor varies inversely with frequency. Now if the frequency variation of each element is inverted, the frequency variation of the new network will be inverted in comparison with the original network. The transformation we seek is evidently

$$S = \frac{1}{s} \quad \text{or} \quad \Omega = \frac{-1}{\omega} \qquad (16.90)$$

By this transformation, LS becomes L/s and $1/CS$ becomes s/C. Inductors are replaced by capacitors and capacitors by inductors.

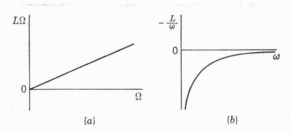

Fig. 16-34. Two plots illustrating the consequences of the frequency transformation, $\Omega = -1/\omega$.

The variation of reactance of an inductor with frequency shown in Fig. 16-34(a) is transformed to the form of the variation of reactance of a capacitor as in Fig. 16-34(b) by this transformation.

A specific example in terms of the low-pass filter will further illustrate the properties of the transformation of Eq. 16.90. We start with the low-pass filter of Fig. 16-35(a). For this lattice, $Z_a = S$ and $Z_b = S + 1/S$. After the frequency transformation, $Z_a = 1/s$ and $Z_b = 1/s + s$, and the lattice realization is that of (b) in Fig. 16-35.

By routine analysis in terms of Z_a and Z_b, we see that the pass and stop bands have been interchanged and that the attenuation characteristic in the frequency range from 1 to ∞ in (a) is now inversely in the range

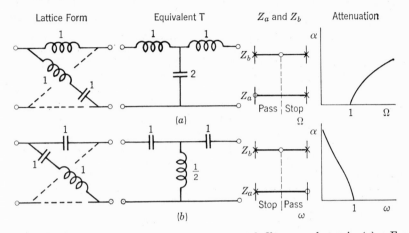

Fig. 16-35. Properties of the low-pass constant-k filter are shown in (a). For comparison, the network and its characteristics resulting from the transformation $S = 1/s$ are shown in (b).

0 to 1 in (b). The transformation of Eq. 16.90 is the *low-pass to high-pass* transformation. A more general transformation that transforms from low-pass to high-pass and at the same time scales the frequency is

$$S = \frac{\omega_0}{s} \quad \text{or} \quad \Omega = \frac{-\omega_0}{\omega} \tag{16.91}$$

How might we write the most general form of the frequency transformation of which Eqs. 16.89 and 16.91 are special cases? Let us write this transformation as

$$S = \phi(s) \tag{16.92}$$

where $\phi(s)$ is a quotient of polynomials. Now the special case in which $\phi(s)$ is a positive real function finds some use,[*] but the most important special case of Eq. 16.92 by far is the case in which $\phi(s)$ is a reactance function.[†] In this case, inductors and capacitors are replaced by networks of inductors and capacitors but not resistors.

[*] J. L. Stewart, "Graphical interpretations for frequency transformations," *1958 IRE WESCON Convention Record*, Pt. 2, 42–45.

[†] A. Papoulis, "Frequency transformations in filter design," *IRE Trans.*, **CT-3**, 140–144 (1956). Papoulis shows that $X(\omega)$ is a special case of a general frequency transformation, $\omega^2 = F(\Omega^2)$.

We distinguish this special case by the notation

$$S = A(s) \quad \text{or} \quad \Omega = X(\omega) \tag{16.93}$$

The problem in making use of this transformation, as we shall see, is to find values of ω corresponding to specified values of Ω or to determine

$$s = A^{-1}(S) \quad \text{or} \quad \omega = X^{-1}(\Omega) \tag{16.94}$$

Figure 16-36(a) shows the attenuation characteristic for the low-pass, constant-k filter with a cutoff frequency at 1 radian/sec. We seek a

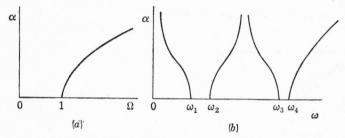

(a)   (b)

Fig. 16-36. (a) The attenuation for the low-pass constant-k filter. (b) The attenuation property desired to be accomplished by a frequency transformation such that $\Omega = 1$ transforms to ω_1, ω_2, ω_3, and ω_4.

transformation such that the attenuation at $\Omega = 1$ transforms to the attenuation at ω_1, ω_2, ω_3, and ω_4, Fig. 16-36(b); this transformation will have the form of Eq. 16.94.

As an example of a reactance function transformation, consider

$$S = k_1 \left(\frac{s}{\omega_0} + \frac{\omega_0}{s} \right) \tag{16.95}$$

and the low-pass attenuation characteristic of Fig. 16-37. What value of s corresponds to the cutoff frequencies, $S = \pm j1$? This question

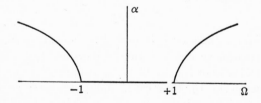

Fig. 16-37. The low-pass attenuation characteristic which is to be transformed by $\Omega = X(\omega)$.

turns out to be an important one in studying reactance transformations; such frequencies are referred to as the $\pm j$-points by Cauer. We are interested in values of ω corresponding to each value of Ω, but we are especially interested in values of ω for $S = \pm j1$ because these are the cutoff frequencies. Substituting $S = \pm j1$ and $s = j\omega$ in Eq. 16.95, we find that this equation reduces to

$$\omega^2 \pm \frac{\omega_0}{k_1} \omega - \omega_0^2 = 0 \qquad (16.96)$$

The solutions of this equation are

$$\omega_1, \omega_2, \omega_3, \omega_4 = \omega_0 \left[\pm \frac{1}{2k_1} \pm \sqrt{\left(\frac{1}{2k_1}\right)^2 + 1} \right] \qquad (16.97)$$

From this result, we observe that

$$\omega_1\omega_2 = \omega_3\omega_4 = \omega_0^2 \qquad (16.98)$$

and also that

$$\omega_2 - \omega_1 = \omega_4 - \omega_3 = \frac{\omega_0}{k_1} \equiv B \qquad (16.99)$$

where B is the bandwidth of the transformed pass band. Then k_1 of Eq. 16.95 may be expressed in terms of ω_0 and B, where ω_0 is the geometrical mean frequency and B the bandwidth. In terms of these factors, Eq. 16.95 becomes

$$S = \frac{\omega_0}{B} \left(\frac{s}{\omega_0} + \frac{\omega_0}{s} \right) \qquad (16.100)$$

If we let Ω have other values than ± 1, then we can find the corresponding values of ω by the same procedure as used for this computation. Alternatively, we may make use of a graphical solution of the equation $\omega = X^{-1}(\Omega)$ as illustrated in Fig. 16-38. The low-pass characteristic of Fig. 16-37 is shown at the top of Fig. 16-38. The solution of the equation $\omega = X^{-1}(\Omega)$ is accomplished by projecting values of Ω to the $45°$ line [avoiding the necessity of plotting $\alpha(\Omega)$ on edge] and thence to the $X(\omega)$ curve. The values of ω so determined at the bottom of the figure are associated with the α of the corresponding Ω. The attenuation α_1 in Fig. 16-38 illustrates this identification.

What effect does the transformation have on the network elements? The impedance of the inductor LS is replaced by

$$L \frac{\omega_0}{B} \left(\frac{s}{\omega_0} + \frac{\omega_0}{s} \right) = \frac{Ls}{B} + \frac{L\omega_0^2}{Bs} \qquad (16.101)$$

which represents the impedance of a series LC combination with the inductor of value L/B and the capacitor of value $B/L\omega_0^2$ as shown in

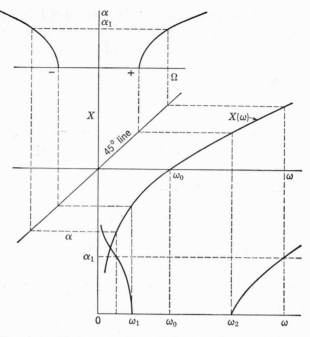

Fig. 16-38. A graphical construction which solves the equation $\omega = X^{-1}(\Omega)$.

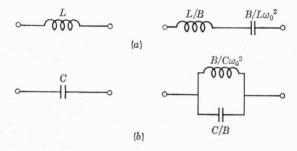

Fig. 16-39. In the low-pass to band-pass transformation, L becomes series LC and C becomes parallel LC. Here B is the bandwidth and ω_0 is the geometrical mean frequency.

Fig. 16-39(a). Similarly, $1/CS$ is replaced by

$$\frac{1}{C\dfrac{\omega_0}{B}\left(\dfrac{s}{\omega_0} + \dfrac{\omega_0}{s}\right)} = \frac{1}{\dfrac{C}{B}s + \dfrac{C\omega_0{}^2}{Bs}} \tag{16.102}$$

which represents a parallel LC combination with an inductor of value

$B/C\omega_0{}^2$ and a capacitor of value C/B as in Fig. 16-39(b).   In summary, the low-pass to band-pass transformation is accomplished by replacing every inductor for a series LC combination and every capacitor by a parallel LC network.   The simplicity of this transformation is shown by the example of Fig. 16-40 for which it is desired that $\omega_1 = 2$ and

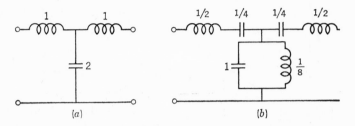

(a)   (b)

Fig. 16-40. An example of the low-pass to band-pass transformation for $B = 2$ and $\omega_0 = \sqrt{8}$.

$\omega_2 = 4$.   Since $B = 2$ and $\omega_0 = \sqrt{8}$, we make direct use of Fig. 16-39 in drawing the band-pass filter of Fig. 16-40(b) complete with element values.

A summary of the elementary transformations described or easily derived from the discussion is given in Table 16-1.

TABLE 16-1
Elementary Frequency Transformations

Description: low-pass to	Transformation
high-pass	$S = \dfrac{\omega_0}{s}$
band-pass	$S = \dfrac{\omega_0}{B}\left(\dfrac{s}{\omega_0} + \dfrac{\omega_0}{s}\right)$
band-elimination	$S = \dfrac{1}{\dfrac{\omega_0}{B}\left(\dfrac{s}{\omega_0} + \dfrac{\omega_0}{s}\right)}$
general (for the LC case)	$S = A(s)$, a reactance function

If a reactance transformation more complicated than the transformations given in Table 16-1 is required, it may be found by a $\pm j$-point analysis, which is illustrated in Fig. 16-41.   It is required to find a transformation from a low-pass filter to one having two pass bands and two stop bands with the three cutoff frequencies identified as ω_a, ω_b, and ω_c in the figure. Since cutoff frequencies are identified by the condition $X(\omega) = \pm 1$, straight lines having these two values are drawn. To realize the required number of cutoff frequencies, we

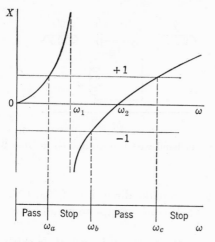

see that $X(\omega)$ must have the form shown in Fig. 16-41, which is described by

$$X(\omega) = K\omega \frac{\omega_2^2 - \omega^2}{\omega_1^2 - \omega^2} \quad (16.103)$$

(Drawing a few reactance curves quickly leads to this conclusion.) From the three prescribed cutoff frequencies, ω_a, ω_b, and ω_c, we may solve for the three unknowns of the last equation: ω_1, ω_2, and K, and $X(\omega)$ is determined. The remainder of the problem is solved by steps analogous to those given to illustrate the low-pass to band-pass case: L is replaced by a reactance function $LA(s)$ and C is replaced by a susceptance function $CA(s)$ and both functions may then be scaled in magnitude.

Fig. 16-41. An illustration of the method by which suitable $X(\omega)$ transformations may be determined to satisfy prescribed j-point (cutoff frequency) specifications.

FURTHER READING

An excellent reference for the method of lattice design described in this chapter is Guillemin's *Communication Networks*, Vol. II, Chapter 10 (and Chapter 9 for the constant-k and m-derived filters). Also recommended are Reed's *Electric Network Synthesis*, which is devoted exclusively to the topics of this chapter; Cauer's *Synthesis of Linear Communication Networks*, Chapters 6 and 7; and Bode's *Network Analysis and Feedback Amplifier Design*, Chapter 11. A more detailed treatment of the design of composite filters is given in the author's *Network Analysis*, Chapter 13. In addition to the references cited in Section 16.7 on frequency transformations, the reader should see the concise summary given by Storer, *Passive Network Synthesis*, Chapter 14, and also the paper by P. R. Aigrain, B. R. Tearer, Jr., and E. M. Williams, "Generalized theory of the band-pass low-pass analogy," *Proc. I.R.E.*, **37,** 1152–1155 (1949).

PROBLEMS

16-1. Complete the algebraic operations in detail in arriving at Eqs. 16.4 and 16.5.

16-2. Starting with Eq. 16.22, derive Eq. 16.28 supplying the detailed steps.

16-3. Simplify Eq. 16.19 to obtain Eq. 16.21.

16-4.* Substitute the following two equations in place of Eqs. 16.36:

$$Y_a = K_a \frac{s^2 + 1}{s} \quad \text{and} \quad Y_b = K_b s$$

(a) Draw a schematic of the lattice network derived from the given Y_a and Y_b.

(b) Starting with these equations in place of Eqs. 16.36, carry out a development paralleling that in Section 16.2, including a detailed consideration of the three cases identified after Eq. 16.45.

16-5. The arms of a lattice are described by

$$Z_a = K_a \frac{s(s^2 + 4)}{s^2 + 1} \quad \text{and} \quad Z_b = K_b \frac{s^2 + 9}{s}$$

(a) Plot the poles, zeros, and branch points of the corresponding Z_I and y_I in a form similar to Fig. 16-14.

(b) Identify the pass bands and stop bands.

(c) Determine the frequencies of infinite loss (the zeros of transmission) if $K_a = K_b = 1$.

16-6. Repeat the three parts of Prob. 16-5 for

$$Z_a = \frac{s^2 + 1}{s(s^2 + 4)} \quad \text{and} \quad Z_b = \frac{s^2 + 9}{s}$$

16-7. Consider a lattice network of the form shown in Fig. 16-11(a). For this network, the following tolerances are specified:

$$\epsilon_Z = 0.50 \quad \text{and} \quad \epsilon_y = 0.25$$

(a) Find the corresponding coverages, k_Z and k_y.

(b) Plot $Z_I(\omega)$, $y_I(1/\omega)$, α_R in the pass band, and α in the stop band.

(c) Find Z_a and Z_b for these specifications.

(d) Reduce the lattice to an equivalent ladder doubly terminated in 1-ohm resistors.

16-8. Repeat the four parts of Prob. 16-7 for

$$\epsilon_Z = 0.30 \quad \text{and} \quad \epsilon_y = 0.15$$

16-9. Derive Eq. 16.69 starting from Eq. 16.67.

16-10. Consider the constant-k, low-pass filter of Fig. 16-5 with $K_a = K_b = 1$. For this network doubly terminated in 1-ohm resistors:

* This problem should be worked by all students since the results are used in Section 16.6.

(a) Plot the reflection loss and the insertion loss in the pass band.

(b) Plot the attenuation, the reflection loss, and the insertion loss in the stop band. Comment on the relative size of the quantities plotted in the two bands.

16-11. For the symmetric lattice, show that the insertion ratio is

$$\text{insertion ratio} = \frac{Z_a + Z_b + Z_a Z_b + 1}{Z_b - Z_a}$$

16-12. Starting with Z_a and Z_b given in Prob. 16-5 with $K_a = K_b = 1$, decompose the lattice to find an equivalent ladder network. Give element values.

16-13. From the impedance functions describing the arms of a lattice as given in Prob. 16-6, determine an equivalent ladder network if one exists.

16-14. Design a low-pass lattice filter to meet the following specifications: The filter is to be terminated at both ends in 1 ohm. The cutoff frequency has the normalized value of 1 radian/sec. The loss in the pass band must be less than 0.5 db from 0 to $\omega = 0.75$ at least. The loss in the stop band must be 25 db or more for all ω greater than 1.1.

(a) Describe completely the reflection loss in the pass band and the attenuation in the stop band. Do so by giving the frequencies of infinite attenuation, minimum attenuation, etc.

(b) Realize the network as a lattice.

(c) Reduce the lattice to an equivalent ladder.

(d) Using the equation given in Prob. 16-11, compute the actual insertion loss for a number of frequencies to plot the insertion loss as a function of frequency. Compare this result with a plot of the attenuation.

16-15. Repeat the four parts of Prob. 16-14 with the specifications identical except that the insertion loss in the stop band is to be 40 db or greater for all ω greater than 1.2.

16-16. Show that the maximum magnitude of the reflection loss in the stop band is 6 db. Using this result, show that α will never be greater than the corresponding insertion loss A by more than 6 db.

16-17. For the lattice shown in Fig. P16-17, find a grounded network in the form of a bridged-T which is equivalent.

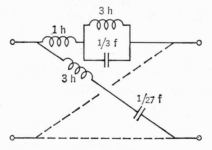

Fig. P16-17

16-18. For the arm impedances of a lattice given with Prob. 16-5, let $K_a = 1$ and $K_b = \frac{1}{3}$. Decompose the corresponding lattice in the form of a bridged-T (grounded structure).

16-19. Derive Eqs. 16.87 and 16.88.

16-20. A composite filter is to be made using two A sections (see Fig. 16-29) and two sections which may be either B or C or one of each. Draw schematics showing all possible ways these four half-sections can be connected together so that the image impedances match. (Solving this problem may remind you of playing dominos.)

16-21. A composite filter is to be composed of two A sections (identified in Fig. 16-29) and four B or C sections. It is required that m-derived half-sections be used on either end with $m = 0.6$. Draw schematic diagrams showing at least three ways the six sections can be combined with the image impedances matching.

16-22. Design a low-pass composite filter to satisfy the following specifications: The insertion loss is to be 30 db at 25 kc/sec, and 60 db for all frequencies higher than 30 kc/sec. The insertion loss in the pass band is to be minimized. The terminating resistor is to have a value of 72 ohms and the voltage driver has an internal resistance of 72 ohms. Draw a schematic of the filter together with all element values. If the voltage source which is connected to the input of the filter has an internal resistance of 100 ohms, how is the design changed?

16-23. The following specifications are given for a low-pass filter: The insertion loss is to be 70 db at 50 kc/sec and is to have a minimum value at 40 kc/sec. Both terminating resistors have the value 100 ohms. Design a filter to satisfy these specifications, at the same time attempting to minimize the number of elements used in the filter.

16-24. A low-pass filter is to have a cutoff frequency of 1 radian/sec, and at 1.05 radians/sec it is required that the output be not more than 5% of the input. How many A sections (of the type shown in Fig. 16-29) are required to meet this specification?

16-25. Starting with the characteristics given in Fig. 16-35(a), use the frequency transformation $S = s + 1/s$ to determine the resulting networks or characteristics like those given in Fig. 16-35(b).

16-26. Starting with the low-pass attenuation characteristics of Fig. 16-37, use a construction like that of Fig. 16-38 to find the $\alpha(\omega)$ characteristic that results from the low-pass to band-elimination transformation.

16-27. Find element transformations like those of Fig. 16-39 for the low-pass to band-elimination transformation.

16-28. Given the low-pass network in Fig. P16-28, draw schematics of the networks derived from this one by appropriate frequency transformations which are described as (a) high pass, (b) band pass, (c) band elimination.

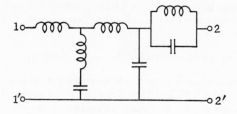

Fig. P16-28

16-29. We seek a transformation $\Omega = X(\omega)$ which will transform the characteristics of a low-pass, constant-k filter to a multiple band-pass filter as shown in Fig. P16-29.

(a) Sketch the $X(\omega)$ that must be used.

(b) Write an equation for $X(\omega)$.

Fig. P16-29

16-30. Figure P16-30 specifies a multiple band-pass filter and its cutoff frequencies. Find an appropriate $X(\omega)$ with all parameters evaluated that will transform the low-pass characteristic of Fig. 16-37 to the required attenuation characteristic. Construct a table showing the network that results in applying this transformation to an inductor and a capacitor in the low-pass filter.

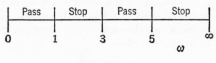

Fig. P16-30

Selected Bibliography

The following references are cited frequently in the Further Reading sections at the end of each of the chapters. For an exhaustive bibliography on modern network synthesis, the reader is referred to that contained in the textbook by Tuttle.

Aseltine, John A., *Transform Method in Linear System Analysis*, McGraw-Hill Book Co., New York, 1958.

Balabanian, Norman, *Network Synthesis*, Prentice-Hall, Englewood Cliffs, N. J., 1958.

Bayard, Marcel, *Théorie des réseaux de Kirchhoff: régime sinusoidal et synthèses*, La Revue d'Optique, Paris, 1954.

Belevitch, V., *Théorie des circuits de telecommunication*, Librairie universitaire, Louvain, Belgium, 1957.

Bode, H. W., *Network Analysis and Feedback Amplifier Design*, D. Van Nostrand Co., Princeton, N. J., 1945.

Brenner, Egon, and Mansour Javid, *Analysis of Electric Circuits*, McGraw-Hill Book Co., New York, 1959.

Cauer, Wilhelm, *Synthesis of Linear Communication Networks*, McGraw-Hill Book Co., New York, 1958. (Translated from the German second edition by G. E. Knausenberger and J. N. Warfield.)

Cheng, David K., *Analysis of Linear Systems*, Addison-Wesley Publishing Co., Reading, Mass., 1959.

Gardner, M. F., and J. L. Barnes, *Transients in Linear Systems*, Vol. I, John Wiley & Sons, New York, 1942.

Guillemin, E. A., "A Summary of Modern Methods of Network Synthesis," in *Advances in Electronics*, Vol. III, pp. 261–303, Academic Press, New York, 1951.

Guillemin, E. A., *Communication Networks*, Vol. II, John Wiley & Sons, New York, 1935.

Guillemin, E. A., *Introductory Circuit Theory*, John Wiley & Sons, New York, 1953.

Guillemin, E. A., *The Mathematics of Circuit Analysis*, John Wiley & Sons, New York, 1949.

Guillemin, E. A., *Synthesis of Passive Networks*, John Wiley & Sons, New York, 1957.

Kuh, E. S., and D. O. Pederson, *Principles of Circuit Synthesis*, McGraw-Hill Book Co., New York, 1959.

Reed, M. B., *Electric Network Synthesis—Image Parameter Method*, Prentice-Hall, Englewood Cliffs, N. J., 1955.

Reza, F. M., and S. Seely, *Modern Network Analysis*, McGraw-Hill Book Co., New York, 1959.

Seshu, Sundaram, and N. Balabanian, *Linear Network Analysis*, John Wiley & Sons, New York, 1959.

Skilling, H. H., *Electrical Engineering Circuits*, John Wiley & Sons, New York, 1957.

Stewart, J. L., *Circuit Theory and Design*, John Wiley & Sons, New York, 1956.

Storer, J. E., *Passive Network Synthesis*, McGraw-Hill Book Co., New York, 1957.

Truxal, J. G., *Automatic Feedback Control System Synthesis*, McGraw-Hill Book Co., New York, 1955.

Tuttle, D. F., Jr., *Network Synthesis*, Vol. I, John Wiley & Sons, New York, 1958.

Van Valkenburg, M. E., *Network Analysis*, Prentice-Hall, Englewood Cliffs, N. J., 1955.

Weber, Ernst, *Linear Transient Analysis*, Vols. I and II, John Wiley & Sons, New York, 1954 and 1956.

Index